Statistical Theory and Methodology in Science and Engineering

A WILEY PUBLICATION IN APPLIED STATISTICS

Statistical Theory and Methodology in Science and Engineering

K. A. BROWNLEE

Associate Professor of Statistics
The University of Chicago

New York · London
John Wiley & Sons, Inc.

Library of Congress Catalog Card Number: 60–11719
PRINTED IN THE UNITED STATES OF AMERICA

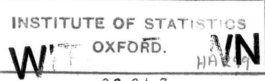

Preface

The appearance of yet another elementary textbook on statistical methods calls for a word of explanation, if not of apology. The present book has grown out of a three-quarter sequence using very slight mathematics, roughly college algebra, partly for students in the experimental sciences and partly for statistics majors, the main objective being to give both groups some facility and self-confidence in the actual use of statistical methods.

For these purposes it would be unsatisfactory to provide nothing but recipes for the standard statistical methods: conversely, one could dwell on theory to the serious detriment, in fact, exclusion, of instruction in the use of the methods. In choosing a middle ground between these two extremes, I have leaned towards attempting to convey understanding of principles rather than practice, a choice rationalized on the ground that at this mathematical level the market is better provided with textbooks for the latter than the former. In making a choice of topics, those that are interesting and useful clearly belong, and those that are uninteresting and of little use clearly do not, but there is a continual struggle between the interesting but useless and the uninteresting but useful. The length of this book was determined by the amount that can be covered in three quarters of three hours per week, and this is responsible for the exclusion of some topics which in themselves are attractive.

It is my hope and belief that the mathematical techniques necessary for reading this book profitably are quite slight. The book is not appropriate for anyone not familiar with the simplest parts of college algebra: for example, the ideas of exponents and logarithms and simple algebraic manipulation. On the other hand, though use is made of elementary differential and integral calculus at quite a number of points, I feel that a reader without this equipment should be able to skip to the end results without being confused.

K. A. Brownlee

Chicago, Illinois
June, 1960

Acknowledgments

The body of statistical theory and techniques expounded in this book is largely due to Professors R. A. Fisher and J. Neyman and their associates. I am deeply conscious of how feeble and anemic present-day statistical theory and practice would be without their work.

My thanks are due R. R. Blough, W. H. Kruskal, H. V. Roberts, and several anonymous reviewers who commented on parts of an earlier draft of this textbook. I am particularly indebted to D. L. Wallace, who made very many valuable comments and suggestions. The foregoing obviously have no responsibility for any inadequacies of the present form.

My thanks for permission to reproduce data are due the editors of *Analytical Chemistry,* the *Astrophysical Journal,* the *Australian Journal of Applied Science, Chemical Engineering Progress, Food Research, Industrial & Engineering Chemistry,* the *Journal of the American Chemical Society,* the *Journal of the Chemical Society,* the *Journal of Hygiene,* the *Journal of the Institute of Actuaries,* the *New York State Journal of Medicine,* the *Philosophical Transactions of the Royal Society,* and the *Proceedings of the Berkeley Symposium on Mathematical Statistics and Probability.* My thanks are also due Chapman & Hall, for permission to reproduce data from *Principles of Biological Assay,* by C. W. Emmens; the Chemical Publishing Company, for data from *Industrial Experimentation,* by K. A. Brownlee; the London Transport Executive for data from *Statistical Design of Experiments,* by F. A. Menzler; and the *New York World-Telegram & Sun* for data from the *World Almanac and Book of Facts.*

I am indebted to Professor Sir Ronald A. Fisher, Cambridge; to Dr. Frank Yates, Rothamsted; and to Messrs. Oliver & Boyd, Edinburgh, for permission to reprint parts of Tables III and V from their book *Statistical Tables for Biological, Agricultural and Medical Research.* I am also indebted to Professor E. S. Pearson and the Biometrika Trustees for permission to quote extensively from some of the tables in *Biometrika Tables for Statisticians,* volume I, edited by E. S. Pearson and H. O. Hartley, and to Dr. A. Hald and John Wiley & Sons for permission to quote extensively from some of the tables in *Statistical Tables and Formulas.*

My work on the book was partly supported during the summer of 1958 by the Office of Naval Research. The typing of the manuscript also was partly supported by the Office of Naval Research.

K. A. B.

Contents

CHAPTER 1

Mathematical Ideas

1.1. Introduction

This is primarily a textbook on *statistics*, not on *probability*, and we will deal with the latter only as much as is necessary. The two disciplines are, however, closely related, and in fact are often confused. In *probability*, a branch of mathematics, we specify the structure of a problem, construct a mathematical model to correspond, specify the values of the parameters (the numerical constants of the system), and then deduce the behavior of the system, e.g., the distribution of the relative number of times each possible outcome will occur. In *statistics*, we assume the structure of the system and the corresponding model, but not numerical values for the parameters, and from the observed outcomes we attempt to infer the values of the parameters.

The above characterizations will be clearer from a simple example; a sample of size n is taken from a lot of N electric light bulbs containing a proportion θ of defectives. What is the distribution of the number of defectives x in repeated samples? Specifically, suppose $n = 100$, $N = 10{,}000$, and $\theta = 0.1$. We will not get exactly $100 \times 0.1 = 10$ defectives in every sample. Often we will get 10, in fact more often than any other outcome, but we will also often get 9, and 11, and 8, etc. What proportions of the time in repeated samples will x equal . . . , 6, 7, 8, . . . , etc.? This is a question in *probability*. Conversely, suppose that we take a sample of size n and actually observe x defectives. What can we say about θ? For example, what is the most likely value of θ, and in what range is θ likely to lie? These are questions in *statistics*.

Modern statistics is the product of many diverse influences, and some potentially important contributions got lost in the mists of indifference of their time. A conscientious historian would have to disinter these and give due credit, even though he may be almost the first man to read them since the date of their publication. However, some of the main landmarks are generally agreed upon. Studies of gambling problems by the French mathematicians Pascal and Fermat in the year 1654 were important in the start of probability. Over the next two centuries, astronomers were interested in the theory of observational errors; in the early nineteenth century Laplace and Gauss made important contributions. For a general account up to the middle of the nineteenth century see Todhunter [1]. By the start of the twentieth century a school under the leadership of Karl Pearson [2] in London had become interested in statistics initially from the point of view of its application to biological measurements. An associate of this group, W. S. Gosset, published in 1908 under the pseudonym "Student" a solution to the problem of the comparison of the means of two small samples [3].

Modern statistics may be said to have begun with the appointment in 1919 of R. A. Fisher to the staff of the Rothamsted Experiment Station in England. Fisher's contributions [4], [5], [6] are threefold: first, a broad attack on the fundamental principles of estimation and inference, second, the solution of a large number of problems in distribution theory that were roadblocks to further progress, and third, the creation of the science of the design of experiments, involving three main principles, namely, the essentialness of replication and randomization, and the desirability of the reduction of error when possible by appropriate organization of the experiment.

In the thirties J. Neyman, at that time in London, developed with E. S. Pearson [7] the theory of hypothesis testing and confidence intervals. In the forties, A. Wald and his associates of the Statistical Research Group at Columbia University created the ideas and techniques of sequential analysis [8]. In more recent years the volume of publication has become relatively enormous, much of it inspired, sometimes rather remotely, by the wide variety of practical problems to which statistics is now being applied. It is now difficult to be expert in more than one or two subdivisions of the field.

1.2. Concept of Sample Space

The concept of *sample space* is a convenient method of representing the outcome of an experiment. By *experiment* we mean some procedure upon which we embark and at whose completion we observe certain results.

For example, we may feed a vitamin supplement to a group of hogs and observe their weights after a certain number of weeks, or we may toss a coin a certain number of times and observe how many times it falls with the head uppermost, or we may drop a given number of light bulbs from a certain height and observe the respective numbers which are undamaged, have the filament broken, or have the glass envelope broken.

The set of all possible outcomes of an experiment is represented by the sample space. Each possible outcome is represented by a sample point. For example, if our experiment is to drop two light bulbs in sequence, with possible outcomes $U =$ undamaged, $F =$ filament broken, and $G =$ glass envelope broken, then the possible outcomes are as represented in Table 1.1 where the ordering of the symbols within the parentheses ( ) corresponds to the time sequence. Here the sample space contains nine sample points.

Table 1.1

(U, U)	(F, U)	(G, U)
(U, F)	(F, F)	(G, F)
(U, G)	(F, G)	(G, G)

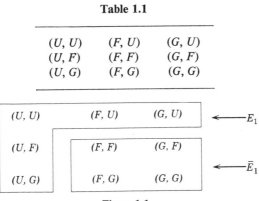

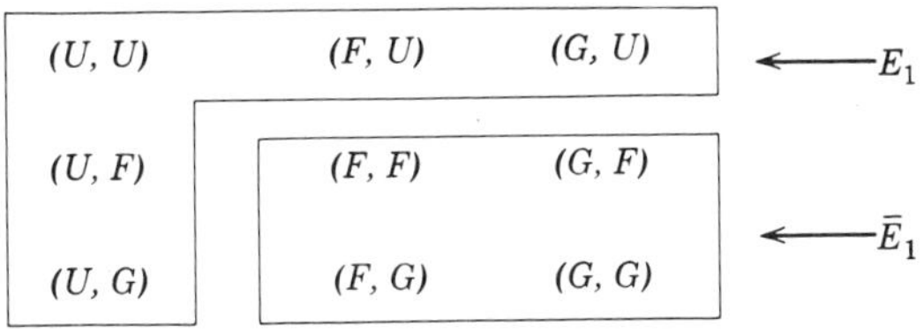

Figure 1.1

An *event* is the sum of sample points with some specified property. Thus the outcome (U, U) is the event "both undamaged." In this case the event consists of only one sample point: Such an event may be called a *simple event*. The event "one or more glass envelopes broken" is made up of the sample points (U, G), (F, G), (G, U), (G, F), and (G, G); such an event, which can be decomposed further into a set of simple events, may be called a *compound event*.

Suppose now that we consider a particular experiment. This will give rise to a fixed sample space. Consider an event E defined as a particular set of the sample points. Then all the sample points not in this set form the complementary event "not E," denoted by $\bar{E}$.

Consider the foregoing experiment of dropping two light bulbs. Define the event E_1 as "one or more undamaged." Then E_1 and $\bar{E}_1$ are as in Figure 1.1.

Also, events E_1, E_2 may be defined such that an outcome may belong in more than one of them. The event (E_1E_2) is made up of those sample points belonging to both E_1 and E_2. For example, if the event E_1 as before is "one or more undamaged" and the event E_2 is "one or more filaments broken," then E_1 and E_2 are as in Figure 1.2, and (E_1E_2) is made up of the points (U, F) and (F, U).

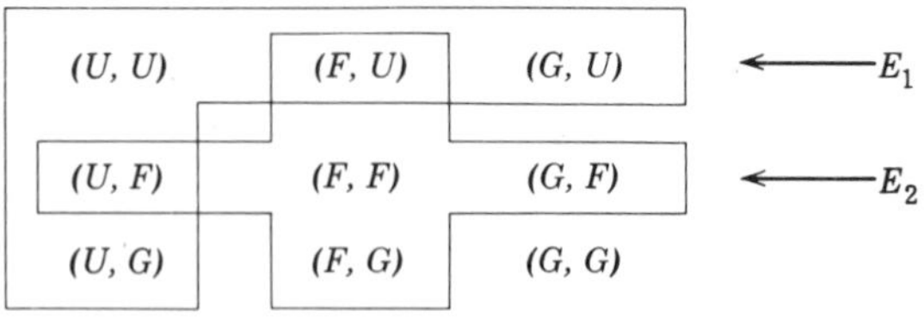

Figure 1.2

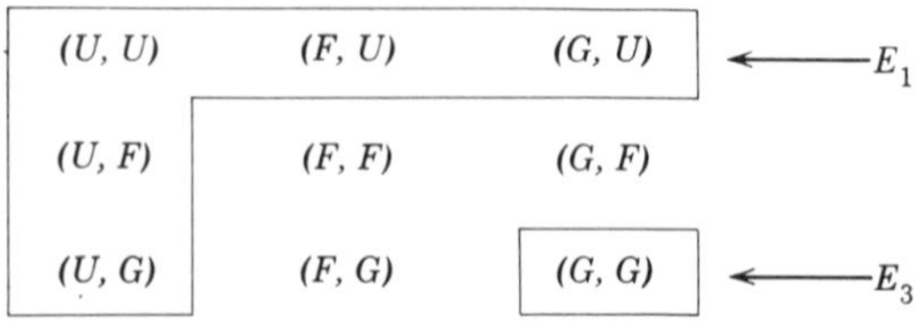

Figure 1.3

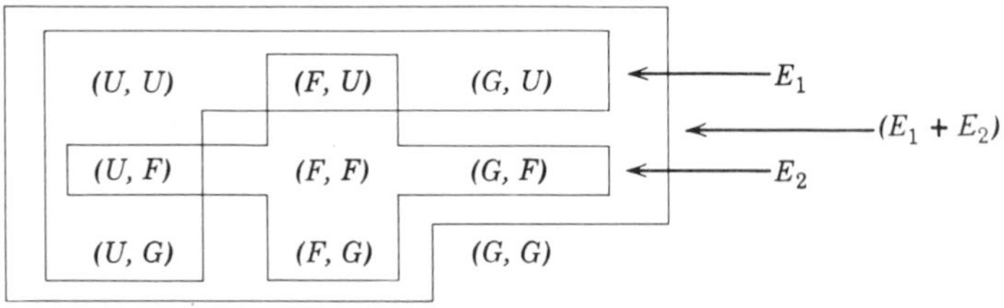

Figure 1.4

It is possible for the two events E_1 and E_2 to be so defined that (E_1E_2) is empty of sample points; in other words, the event (E_1E_2) is impossible. We then say that E_1, E_2 are *mutually exclusive* events. For example, if we define E_1 as before as "one or more undamaged" and E_3 as "both glass envelopes broken," then Figure 1.3 shows that (E_1E_3) is empty of sample points.

A further piece of symbolism is useful. By $(E_1 + E_2)$ we mean the event "at least one of the two events, i.e., either E_1 but not E_2, or E_2 but not E_1, or E_1 and E_2 together." For the previous definitions of E_1 and E_2, $(E_1 + E_2)$ is shown in Figure 1.4.

1.3. Probability

As an axiom we associate with every point A_i in the sample space a number, called the probability of A_i, denoted by $\Pr\{A_i\}$. These probabilities must be nonnegative and comply with the condition that

$$\Pr\{A_1\} + \Pr\{A_2\} + \cdots = 1, \tag{3.1}$$

where the summation is over the entire sample space. We further suppose that the probability of an event E, $\Pr\{E\}$, is the sum of all the probabilities of the sample points A_i in E.

These axioms lead to some useful rules. In (3.1), if a certain set of the points A_i correspond to an event E, the complementary set will correspond to the complementary event $\bar{E}$, so E and $\bar{E}$ will have associated with them the entire set of points, and therefore

$$\Pr\{E\} + \Pr\{\bar{E}\} = 1. \tag{3.2}$$

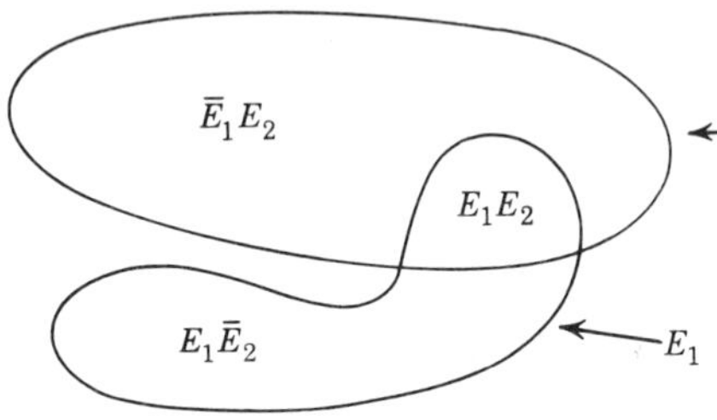

Figure 1.5

Also, if the events E_1 and E_2 are mutually exclusive, then $\Pr\{E_1\}$ is the sum of the probabilities of the sample points A_i corresponding to E_1, and $\Pr\{E_2\}$ is the sum of the probabilities of the sample points corresponding to E_2, and $\Pr\{E_1 + E_2\}$ is the sum of the probabilities of both sets of sample points; i.e.,

$$\Pr\{E_1 + E_2\} = \Pr\{E_1\} + \Pr\{E_2\}. \tag{3.3}$$

This holds only when E_1 and E_2 are mutually exclusive.

Consider the case where E_1, E_2 are not mutually exclusive, so that the event (E_1E_2) is not empty of sample points. In Figure 1.5 we see that the region E_1 can be split into two parts, $E_1\bar{E}_2$ and E_1E_2, and the region E_2 can likewise be split into two parts, E_1E_2 and $\bar{E}_1E_2$, the part E_1E_2 being common to both E_1 and E_2. It therefore follows that the event $(E_1 + E_2)$

can be regarded as made up of three mutually exclusive events, and so

$$\Pr\{E_1 + E_2\} = \Pr\{\bar{E}_1E_2\} + \Pr\{E_1E_2\} + \Pr\{E_1\bar{E}_2\}.$$

We can simultaneously add and subtract $\Pr\{E_1E_2\}$ to the right-hand side leaving the equation unchanged:

$$\Pr\{E_1 + E_2\} = \Pr\{\bar{E}_1E_2\} + \Pr\{E_1E_2\} + \Pr\{E_1\bar{E}_2\} + \Pr\{E_1E_2\} - \Pr\{E_1E_2\}.$$

Now $\{\bar{E}_1E_2\}$ and $\{E_1E_2\}$ are mutually exclusive events; so by (3.3)

$$\Pr\{\bar{E}_1E_2\} + \Pr\{E_1E_2\} = \Pr\{\bar{E}_1E_2 + E_1E_2\} = \Pr\{E_2\}.$$

Likewise

$$\Pr\{E_1\bar{E}_2\} + \Pr\{E_1E_2\} = \Pr\{E_1\bar{E}_2 + E_1E_2\} = \Pr\{E_1\}.$$

So

$$\Pr\{E_1 + E_2\} = \Pr\{E_1\} + \Pr\{E_2\} - \Pr\{E_1E_2\}. \tag{3.4}$$

As an illustration of these ideas, consider the experiment of drawing a single card from a well-shuffled deck. The sample space will consist of 52 sample points corresponding to the 52 possible cards that might be drawn. Intuitively, if the deck is well shuffled, this implies that the probability of any one card being drawn is the same as that for all the other cards, i.e.,

$$\Pr\{A_1\} = \Pr\{A_2\} = \cdots = \Pr\{A_{52}\}.$$

But these 52 outcomes are the entire sample space; so by (3.1) $\Pr\{A_i\} = 1/52$ for $i = 1, 2, \ldots, 52$. Now define the event E_1 as the occurrence of a heart. E_1 will contain 13 sample points, all of probability 1/52, so

$$\Pr\{E_1\} = \Pr\{\text{heart}\} = 13 \times \frac{1}{52} = \frac{1}{4}.$$

Also define the event E_2 as the occurrence of an honor card (ace, king, queen, jack, or ten). There are $4 \times 5 = 20$ honor cards in the deck; so

$$\Pr\{E_2\} = \Pr\{\text{honor}\} = 20 \times \frac{1}{52} = \frac{5}{13}.$$

We can now use (3.4) to give us

$$\Pr\{\text{a heart or an honor or a heart honor}\}$$
$$= \Pr\{E_1\} + \Pr\{E_2\} - \Pr\{E_1E_2\} = \frac{13}{52} + \frac{20}{52} - \frac{5}{52} = \frac{28}{52}.$$

This we can readily check as there are 13 hearts, including the 5 heart honors, plus 3×5 other honors, making a total of 28 cards which are either hearts or honors or heart honors.

1.4. Conditional Probability

Suppose that the events E_1, E_2 are among the possible outcomes of an experiment, and that we are interested in $\Pr\{E_1\}$. Suppose that we are now informed that E_2 has occurred. What can we now say about the probability of E_1?

Referring to Figure 1.5, we know that

$$\Pr\{E_1\} = \frac{\text{sum of probabilities of sample points in } E_1}{\text{sum of probabilities of all points in entire sample space}}$$

However, if we know that E_2 has occurred, we know that the outcome of the experiment must be in a more restricted region than the entire sample space; in fact, it must be in the region E_2. It is thus reasonable to define the probability of E_1, given that E_2 has occurred, as

$$\begin{aligned}\Pr\{E_1|E_2\} &= \frac{\text{sum of probabilities of points in } (E_1E_2)}{\text{sum of probabilities of points in } E_2} \\ &= \frac{\left\{\dfrac{\text{sum of probabilities of points in } (E_1E_2)}{\text{sum of probabilities of all points in entire sample space}}\right\}}{\left\{\dfrac{\text{sum of probabilities of points in } E_2}{\text{sum of probabilities of all points in entire sample space}}\right\}} \\ &= \frac{\Pr\{E_1E_2\}}{\Pr\{E_2\}}. \qquad (4.1)\end{aligned}$$

This implies

$$\Pr\{E_1E_2\} = \Pr\{E_2\}\Pr\{E_1|E_2\}. \qquad (4.2)$$

Clearly an analogous argument will give

$$\Pr\{E_2|E_1\} = \frac{\Pr\{E_2E_1\}}{\Pr\{E_1\}} \qquad (4.3)$$

and

$$\Pr\{E_2E_1\} = \Pr\{E_1\}\Pr\{E_2|E_1\}. \qquad (4.4)$$

For example, suppose that we have a deck of cards from which the five diamond honors have been removed. Let the experiment be to draw one card at random from the $52 - 5 = 47$ cards in the abbreviated deck. Let the event E_1 be that the chosen card is an honor and the event E_2 be that the chosen card is a heart. Then the event E_1 consists of 15 sample points each with probability 1/47; so

$$\Pr\{\text{honor}\} = \Pr\{E_1\} = \frac{15}{47} = 0.319.$$

The event (E_1E_2) is the appearance of an honor heart. The number of sample points in (E_1E_2) is 5, each with probability 1/47. The number of sample points in E_2 is 13, each with probability 1/47. Thus, if we catch a glimpse of the card and know that it is a heart, we can then say that the probability that it is an honor is, by (4.1),

$$\Pr\{\text{honor}|\text{heart}\} = \Pr\{E_1|E_2\} = \frac{\Pr\{E_1E_2\}}{\Pr\{E_2\}} = \frac{5/47}{13/47} = \frac{5}{13} = 0.385.$$

This is a mild illustration of the bridge proverb; "one peep is worth two finesses."

Considering this situation from another viewpoint, we can calculate the probability of getting a heart honor in two ways, using (4.2) and (4.4):

$$\begin{aligned}\Pr\{\text{honor heart}\} &= \Pr\{\text{honor}\}\Pr\{\text{heart}|\text{honor}\}\\ &= \Pr\{E_1\}\Pr\{E_2|E_1\} = \frac{15}{47}\times\frac{5}{15} = \frac{5}{47},\end{aligned}$$

or

$$\begin{aligned}\Pr\{\text{heart honor}\} &= \Pr\{\text{heart}\}\Pr\{\text{honor}|\text{heart}\}\\ &= \Pr\{E_2\}\Pr\{E_1|E_2\} = \frac{13}{47}\times\frac{5}{13} = \frac{5}{47}.\end{aligned}$$

1.5. Independence

Suppose that the probability of the event E_1 is the same whether or not the event E_2 occurs; i.e.,

$$\Pr\{E_1|E_2\} = \Pr\{E_1|\bar{E}_2\}. \tag{5.1}$$

We then say that E_1 is *independent* of E_2. Equation (5.1) constitutes a satisfactorily intuitive definition of independence, but we will now show that it implies

$$\Pr\{E_1E_2\} = \Pr\{E_1\}\Pr\{E_2\}, \tag{5.2}$$

as this latter form is more convenient and in fact is usually given as the definition of independence. From (4.1) we have

$$\Pr\{E_1|E_2\} = \frac{\Pr\{E_1E_2\}}{\Pr\{E_2\}}. \tag{5.3}$$

We can substitute $\bar{E}_2$ for E_2, to get

$$\Pr\{E_1|\bar{E}_2\} = \frac{\Pr\{E_1\bar{E}_2\}}{\Pr\{\bar{E}_2\}}. \tag{5.4}$$

Now, if our definition of independence (5.1) is satisfied, the left-hand sides of (5.3) and (5.4) are equal, and hence

$$\frac{\Pr\{E_1E_2\}}{\Pr\{E_2\}} = \frac{\Pr\{E_1\bar{E}_2\}}{\Pr\{\bar{E}_2\}}.$$

Multiplying out gives

$$\Pr\{E_1E_2\}\Pr\{\bar{E}_2\} = \Pr\{E_1\bar{E}_2\}\Pr\{E_2\}.$$

But $\Pr\{\bar{E}_2\} = 1 - \Pr\{E_2\}$, by (3.2), and so

$$\Pr\{E_1E_2\}\,(1 - \Pr\{E_2\}) = \Pr\{E_1\bar{E}_2\}\Pr\{E_2\},$$

and hence $$\begin{aligned}\Pr\{E_1E_2\} &= \Pr\{E_1E_2\}\Pr\{E_2\} + \Pr\{E_1\bar{E}_2\}\Pr\{E_2\}\\ &= (\Pr\{E_1E_2\} + \Pr\{E_1\bar{E}_2\})\Pr\{E_2\}.\end{aligned}$$

But $\Pr\{E_1E_2\} + \Pr\{E_1\bar{E}_2\} = \Pr\{E_1\}$; so

$$\Pr\{E_1E_2\} = \Pr\{E_1\}\Pr\{E_2\}. \tag{5.5}$$

We note also, substituting this in (5.3), that, in the case of independence,

$$\Pr\{E_1|E_2\} = \Pr\{E_1\}. \tag{5.6}$$

Thus we have shown that our definition of independence (5.1) implies the usual definition (5.2). The arguments can be used in reverse to show that (5.2) implies (5.1); these two definitions are therefore equivalent.

Equation (3.4), or the lack of it, is the basis of a common probabilistic fallacy. Suppose that two missiles are fired at a target independently and that each has a probability of 0.2 of destroying the target. The popular misconception is that the probability of the target's being destroyed is $0.2 + 0.2 = 0.4$. The fallaciousness of this argument is evident if the probability of either missile destroying the target were 0.6; then this argument would give as the probability of the target's being destroyed $0.6 + 0.6 = 1.2$, an obviously impossible result. The correct answer is obtained as follows: Let E_1 be the event "target destroyed by first missile" and E_2 the event "target destroyed by second missile." By (3.4)

$$\begin{aligned}&\Pr\{\text{target destroyed}\}\\ &\quad= \Pr\{\text{target destroyed by first missile, or second missile, or both}\}\\ &\quad= \Pr\{E_1 + E_2\} = \Pr\{E_1\} + \Pr\{E_2\} - \Pr\{E_1E_2\}.\end{aligned}$$

Here $\Pr\{E_1E_2\}$ is the probability of the target's being destroyed by both missiles. By (5.2), when the events are independent,

$$\Pr\{E_1E_2\} = \Pr\{E_1\}\Pr\{E_2\},$$

and so

$$\Pr\{\text{target destroyed}\} = 0.2 + 0.2 - 0.2 \times 0.2 = 0.36.$$

As a similar example, consider an experiment consisting of drawing one card from a deck, replacing it, and drawing another. Let E_1 be the event of getting a spade on the first draw and E_2 be the event of getting a spade on the second draw. Then $\Pr\{E_1\} = 13/52 = 1/4$ and $\Pr\{E_2\} = 13/52 = 1/4$. Then

$$\Pr\{\text{both cards are spades}\} = \Pr\{E_1E_2\} = \Pr\{E_1\}\Pr\{E_2\} = \frac{1}{4} \times \frac{1}{4} = \frac{1}{16},$$

since the two draws are independent. We might note in passing that

$$\begin{aligned}\Pr\{\text{at least one card is a spade}\} &= \Pr\{E_1 + E_2\}\\ &= \Pr\{E_1\} + \Pr\{E_2\} - \Pr\{E_1E_2\}\\ &= \frac{1}{4} + \frac{1}{4} - \frac{1}{16} = \frac{7}{16},\end{aligned}$$

or, alternatively,

$$\begin{aligned}\Pr\{\text{at least one card is a spade}\} &= 1 - \Pr\{\text{neither card is a spade}\}\\ &= 1 - \Pr\{\bar{E}_1\bar{E}_2\} = 1 - \Pr\{\bar{E}_1\}\Pr\{\bar{E}_2\}\\ &= 1 - \frac{3}{4} \times \frac{3}{4} = \frac{7}{16}.\end{aligned}$$

We might also note that

$$\begin{aligned}\Pr\{\text{exactly one card is a spade}\} &= \Pr\{E_1\bar{E}_2 + \bar{E}_1E_2\}\\ &= \Pr\{E_1\bar{E}_2\} + \Pr\{\bar{E}_1E_2\}\\ &= \Pr\{E_1\}\Pr\{\bar{E}_2\} + \Pr\{\bar{E}_1\}\Pr\{E_2\}\\ &= \frac{1}{4} \times \frac{3}{4} + \frac{3}{4} \times \frac{1}{4} = \frac{6}{16}.\end{aligned}$$

To illustrate the difference that dependence may make, consider the related experiment in which first one card and then another are withdrawn from the deck, this time without replacement. Here

$$\begin{aligned}\Pr\{\text{both cards are spades}\} = \Pr\{E_1E_2\} &= \Pr\{E_1\}\Pr\{E_2|E_1\}\\ &= \frac{13}{52} \times \frac{12}{51} = \frac{1}{17},\end{aligned}$$

since on the second draw, if a spade had already been withdrawn from the deck on the first draw, then there are only 12 spades in the remaining 51 cards. Here, without replacement, the result of the second drawing is dependent on the result of the first drawing.

1.6. The Concepts of Random Variable, Probability Function, and Cumulative Distribution Function

A *random variable* is a function which takes a defined value for every point in the sample space. For example, consider the sample space for the experiment consisting of the independent tossing of two fair coins. We can define a random variable x' as the total number of heads observed. The values that x' can take are represented by x. The sample space consists of the four points (0, 0), (0, 1), (1, 0), and (1, 1), and at these points x takes the values 0, 1, 1, and 2. Let A_1 be the occurrence of a head with the first coin and A_2 the occurrence of a head with the second coin. The coins are assumed to be fair, and hence $\Pr\{A_i\} = 1/2$, and the two throws are assumed to be independent; so

$$\Pr\{A_1A_2\} = \Pr\{A_1\}\Pr\{A_2\} = \frac{1}{2} \times \frac{1}{2} = \frac{1}{4}.$$

Likewise $$\Pr\{\bar{A}_1A_2\} = \Pr\{\bar{A}_1\}\Pr\{A_2\} = \left(1 - \frac{1}{2}\right) \times \frac{1}{2} = \frac{1}{4},$$

etc. Thus the probability attached to each point in the sample space is 1/4. The probabilities of the events x' taking the values 0, 1, and 2 are therefore 1/4, 1/4 + 1/4 = 1/2, and 1/4, respectively. This can be expressed in tabular form (Table 1.2). The probability that the random variable x' takes the value x, $\Pr\{x' = x\}$ is known as the *probability function* of x and is represented by $p_{x'}\{x\}$. The sum over all possible values of x of the terms $p_{x'}\{x\}$, must equal one.

Table 1.2

x	0	1	2
$p_{x'}\{x\}$	1/4	1/2	1/4

As another example, consider the sample space corresponding to the experiment of rolling onto a table a pair of fair four-sided dice (i.e., regular tetrahedra with sides made up of equilateral triangles). Let the four faces of each die be numbered 1, 2, 3, and 4. If the dice are fair, the probability of a given face of one of the dice being in contact with the table is 1/4, and, if the throws are independent, the probability of obtaining the result (1,1) is $(1/4)\times(1/4) = 1/16$, and likewise for all the other possible outcomes. Thus each of the 16 points in the sample space has a probability 1/16. We can define a random variable y' as the sum of the numbers in contact with the surface of the table. The points in the sample space and the corresponding values of y are as follows:

(1, 1) = 2	(2, 1) = 3	(3, 1) = 4	(4, 1) = 5
(1, 2) = 3	(2, 2) = 4	(3, 2) = 5	(4, 2) = 6
(1, 3) = 4	(2, 3) = 5	(3, 3) = 6	(4, 3) = 7
(1, 4) = 5	(2, 4) = 6	(3, 4) = 7	(4, 4) = 8

From this we can construct the probability function of the random variable y' (Table 1.3).

Table 1.3

y	2	3	4	5	6	7	8
$p_{y'}\{y\}$	1/16	2/16	3/16	4/16	3/16	2/16	1/16

Note that we could define another random variable z' on the same sample space, for example, the ratio of the larger to the smaller number. The sample space, the same as before, and the corresponding values of z are:

(1, 1) = 1	(2, 1) = 2	(3, 1) = 3	(4, 1) = 4
(1, 2) = 2	(2, 2) = 1	(3, 2) = 3/2	(4, 2) = 2
(1, 3) = 3	(2, 3) = 3/2	(3, 3) = 1	(4, 3) = 4/3
(1, 4) = 4	(2, 4) = 2	(3, 4) = 4/3	(4, 4) = 1

From this we can construct the probability function of the random variable z' (Table 1.4).

Table 1.4

z	1	4/3	3/2	2	3	4
$p_{z'}\{z\}$	4/16	2/16	2/16	4/16	2/16	2/16

The two sample spaces which we have just discussed contain only a finite number of points, actually 4 and 16, respectively. Such sample spaces are known as *discrete*. In addition, if the points in a sample space are infinite in number but can be arranged in a simple countable sequence, then that sample space is also regarded as discrete. We will encounter an example of this latter type in Section 4.4, the Poisson distribution. A random variable which is defined on a discrete sample space is known as a discrete random variable, and its probability function is known as a discrete probability function.

It is often convenient to represent discrete probability functions graphically, by raising a line on the x axis with height equal to the corresponding probability at each value of x. Tables 1.2, 1.3, and 1.4 thus give rise to Figures 1.6, 1.7, and 1.8.

Suppose that the values of x, ordered by increasing magnitude, are x_i, $i = 0, 1, \ldots, N$ (it is possible in some cases, for example, the Poisson distribution, for N to go to infinity).

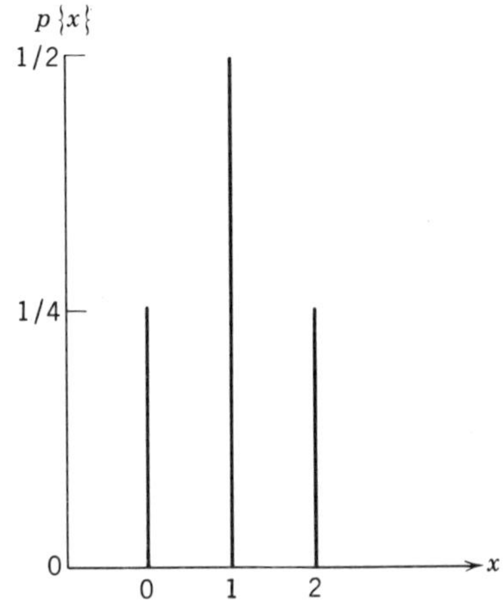

Figure 1.6

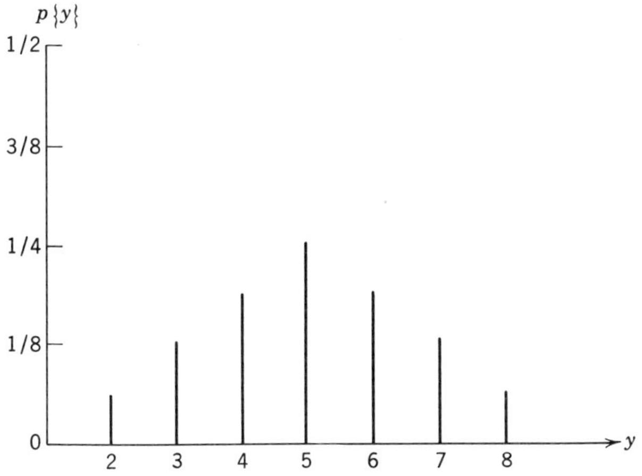

Figure 1.7

Then define the *cumulative distribution function*, sometimes abbreviated as cdf, as

$$P\{x_n\} = \Pr\{x' \leq x_n\} = \sum_{i=0}^{n} p\{x_i\} = p\{x_0\} + p\{x_1\} + \cdots + p\{x_n\}. \quad (6.1)$$

$P\{x_n\}$ is the probability that x' is less than or equal to x_n. Tables 1.2, 1.3, 1.4 of probability functions give rise to corresponding cumulative distribution functions, Tables 1.5, 1.6, and 1.7.

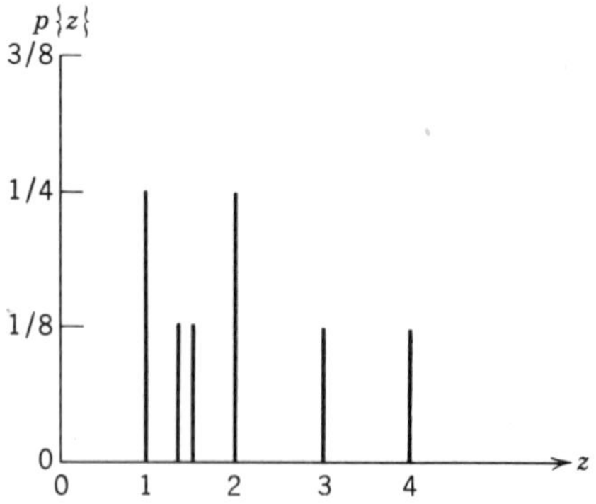

Figure 1.8

Table 1.5

x	0	1	2
$P_{x'}\{x\}$	1/4	3/4	1

Table 1.6

y	2	3	4	5	6	7	8
$P_{y'}\{y\}$	1/16	3/16	6/16	10/16	13/16	15/16	16/16

Table 1.7

z	1	4/3	3/2	2	3	4
$P_{z'}\{z\}$	4/16	6/16	8/16	12/16	14/16	16/16

These cumulative distribution functions can be represented graphically (Figures 1.9, 1.10, and 1.11).

It follows from (6.1) that $P\{x_N\} = 1$, and that

$$p\{x_n\} = P\{x_n\} - P\{x_{n-1}\}. \tag{6.2}$$

So far we have considered only three rather artificial probability functions, but, before proceeding to a more general and important example of a discrete probability function, the binomial distribution, we shall review the topic of permutations and combinations.

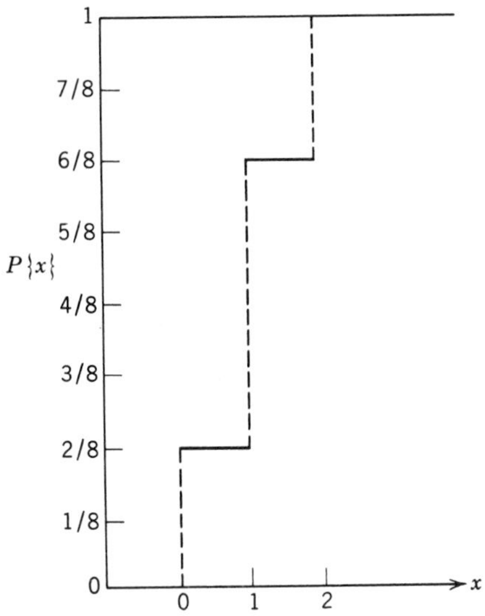

Figure 1.9

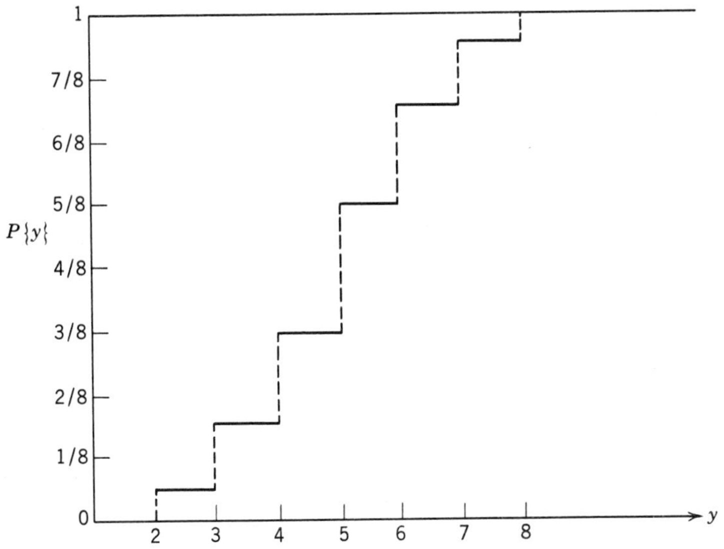

Figure 1.10

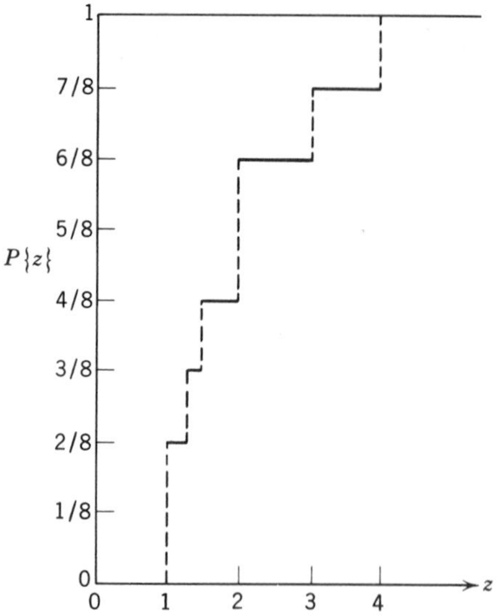

Figure 1.11

1.7. Permutations and Combinations

Assume that we have n distinguishable objects and a row of cells numbered 1, 2, . . . , r, where $r \leq n$. We wish to know the number of different ways in which a selection of r of the n objects can be placed in the r cells, one object to a cell.

For filling the first cell we have a choice of n objects. For filling the second cell we now have a choice of only $(n - 1)$ objects, since one object has already been allocated. Continuing down the row of cells, when we come to fill the rth cell, $(r - 1)$ objects have been used up in filling the previous $(r - 1)$ cells, leaving only $n - (r - 1)$ objects available from which to make our final choice. The standard symbol for the number of ways in which r cells can be filled from n objects is P_r^n, and it is apparent that

$$P_r^n = n(n-1)(n-2)\cdots(n-r+1). \tag{7.1}$$

The factorial symbol ! is convenient; for example, $n!$ is defined as $n! = n(n-1)\cdots 3 \times 2 \times 1$. We can thus write

$$P_r^n = n(n-1)\cdots(n-r+1)\frac{(n-r)(n-r-1)\cdots 2\times 1}{(n-r)(n-r-1)\cdots 2\times 1} = \frac{n!}{(n-r)!}. \tag{7.2}$$

Incidentally, we note that $1! = 1$. Also, in general, $n! = n(n-1)!$; so $(n-1)! = n!/n$. To have this formula hold for the case of $n = 1$, we define $0! = 1$.

In the special case where we are placing n objects in n cells, i.e., we are using all the objects, the number of possible arrangements, or permutations, is given by putting $r = n$ in (7.1); so

$$P_n^n = n(n-1)\cdots 2 \times 1 = n!. \tag{7.3}$$

Equation (7.2) with the convention $0! = 1$ also gives the same result:

$$P_n^n = \frac{n!}{(n-n)!} = \frac{n!}{0!} = n!.$$

Now consider that our n objects are not completely distinguishable, as supposed so far, but instead fall into k different groups; the different groups are distinguishable one from another, but within a group the objects cannot be distinguished from other objects of the same group. Let there be n_1 objects of the first kind, n_2 objects of the second kind, and let $\sum_i^k n_i = n$. For example, we might have n_1 red balls, n_2 yellow balls, etc. If all the n objects were distinguishable, and we were to arrange all of them in a row, the total number of permutations would be $P_n^n = n!$. Now temporarily label n_1 indistinguishable objects of the first kind, a_1, $a_2, \ldots, a_{n_1}$. A certain subset of the whole set of $n!$ permutations will have these a's in certain cells. For example, one such permutation will be

	a_1			a_2	a_3			a_4				

But, if the a's are actually indistinguishable, this permutation will be indistinguishable from

	a_7			a_4	a_1			a_6				

in which the same cells are occupied by a's, but the a's are permuted around among these particular cells. In both these cases the cells left blank are assumed to be occupied by exactly the same objects other than a's. The number of ways in which we can permute the a's around is

$P_{n_1}^{n_1} = n_1!$. Similar results hold for the other groups of objects. Now we have the identity:

$$\begin{pmatrix}\text{Total number of permutations, assuming} \\ \text{the objects are completely distinguishable}\end{pmatrix}$$
$$= \begin{pmatrix}\text{number of distinguishable permutations of } n \text{ objects made} \\ \text{up of } k \text{ groups of objects indistinguishable within each group}\end{pmatrix}$$
$$\times \begin{pmatrix}\text{number of permutations of objects within the first} \\ \text{group, assuming that they are distinguishable}\end{pmatrix}$$
$$\times \text{ (same for second group)}$$
$$\times \cdots \times \text{ (same for } k\text{th group).}$$

The left-hand side of this identity is $n!$. The second, third, etc. terms on the right-hand side are $n_1!\ n_2! \cdots n_k!$, since the permutation of the objects of the first group among themselves can be made independently of the permutation of the objects of the second group among themselves, etc. Thus we have

$$\begin{pmatrix}\text{Number of distinguishable permutations of} \\ n_1 \text{ objects of type } a,\ n_2 \text{ objects of type } b, \text{ etc.}\end{pmatrix} = \frac{n!}{n_1!n_2! \cdots n_k!}. \tag{7.4}$$

In the special, but important, case where there are only two types of objects, say n of one kind and $(N - n)$ of the other, then (7.4) becomes

$$\frac{N!}{n!(N-n)!}. \tag{7.5}$$

We now turn to the problem of determining the number of ways of choosing x out of a set of n distinguishable objects. This is known as the number of *combinations* and is represented by the symbol $\binom{n}{x}$. Other symbols sometimes encountered for this number are C_x^n, ${}_nC_x$, etc. Imagine that the n objects are lined up in a row beside n cells. Suppose that we have x disks labeled "choose" and $(n - x)$ disks labeled "do not choose." The number of different ways in which we can permute these x disks of one kind and $(n - x)$ disks of the other kind is, by (7.5), $n!/[x!(n - x)!]$. But each different arrangement of the disks determines a different choice of the objects lined up beside the cells into which the disks are placed. Thus the number of different choices of the n objects x at a time is equal to the number of permutations of the disks, i.e.,

$$\binom{n}{x} = \frac{n!}{x!(n-x)!}. \tag{7.6}$$

These formulas will be illustrated by a few examples. Suppose that we have four different letters *a*, *b*, *c*, and *d*. The possible permutations of these taken two at a time are

$$ab \quad ba \quad ac \quad ca \quad ad \quad da \quad bc \quad cb \quad bd \quad db \quad cd \quad dc.$$

The number of such permutations, by (7.2), is $P_2^4 = 4!/(4-2)! = 12$. The possible combinations of these four letters taken two at a time are

$$ab \quad ac \quad ad \quad bc \quad bd \quad cd.$$

The number of such combinations, by (7.6), is $4!/[2!(4-2)!] = 6$. The difference between the permutations and the combinations is that in the former the order of the letters is relevant, so that *ab* is a different permutation from *ba*, whereas regarded as combinations *ab* represents exactly the same choice as *ba*.

Now suppose that we have two *a*'s, two *b*'s, and one *c*; *a*, *a*, *b*, *b*, *c*. The possible permutations of all five letters is

aabbc	*aabcb*	*aacbb*	*ababc*	*abacb*	*abbac*	*abbca*
abcab	*abcba*	*acabb*	*acbab*	*acbba*	*baabc*	*baacb*
babac	*babca*	*bacab*	*bacba*	*bbaac*	*bbaca*	*bbcaa*
bcaab	*bcaba*	*bcbaa*	*caabb*	*cabab*	*cabba*	*cbaab*
cbaba	*cbbaa*					

The number of such permutations, by (7.4), is $5!/(2!2!1!) = 30$.

1.8. The Binomial Distribution

Suppose that we make a series of independent trials, and that the outcome of each trial is either A with probability $\Pr\{A\} = \theta$ or $\bar{A}$ with probability $\Pr\{\bar{A}\} = 1 - \theta$. We suppose that θ is constant for all trials and that successive trials are independent. Call the occurrence of an A a "success." We wish to calculate the probability of exactly x successes in n trials.

Let us consider the case where only two trials are made. There are several possible outcomes. First, A may occur on both; the trials are supposedly independent; so, using (5.5),

$$\Pr\{AA\} = \Pr\{A\}\Pr\{A\} = \theta\theta = \theta^2.$$

Second, A may occur on one trial but not on the other; this can happen in two ways, namely, $A\bar{A}$ and $\bar{A}A$. We have, using (3.3) and (5.5),

$$\begin{aligned}\Pr\{A\bar{A} + \bar{A}A\} &= \Pr\{A\bar{A}\} + \Pr\{\bar{A}A\} = \Pr\{A\}\Pr\{\bar{A}\} + \Pr\{\bar{A}\}\Pr\{A\} \\ &= \theta(1-\theta) + (1-\theta)\theta = 2\theta(1-\theta).\end{aligned}$$

Last, A may occur on neither:

$$\Pr\{\bar{A}\bar{A}\} = \Pr\{\bar{A}\}\Pr\{\bar{A}\} = (1-\theta)^2.$$

Let $p_n\{x\}$ denote the probability that there are x successes in n trials. Then we note, as a check,

$$\begin{aligned}\sum_{x=0}^{2} p_2\{x\} &= p_2\{0\} + p_2\{1\} + p_2\{2\} \\ &= (1-\theta)^2 + 2(1-\theta)\theta + \theta^2 = [(1-\theta)+\theta]^2 = 1.\end{aligned}$$

Proceeding in the same way for three trials, we see that the probabilities of the possible outcomes are

$$p_3\{0\} = \Pr\{\bar{A}\bar{A}\bar{A}\} = \Pr\{\bar{A}\}\Pr\{\bar{A}\}\Pr\{\bar{A}\} = (1-\theta)^3,$$

$$p_3\{1\} = \Pr\{A\bar{A}\bar{A} + \bar{A}A\bar{A} + \bar{A}\bar{A}A\} = 3\Pr\{A\}\Pr\{\bar{A}\}\Pr\{\bar{A}\} = 3\theta(1-\theta)^2,$$

$$\begin{aligned}p_3\{2\} &= \Pr\{AA\bar{A}\} + \Pr\{A\bar{A}A\} + \Pr\{\bar{A}AA\} \\ &= 3\Pr\{A\}\Pr\{A\}\Pr\{\bar{A}\} = 3\theta^2(1-\theta),\end{aligned}$$

$$p_3\{3\} = \Pr\{AAA\} = \Pr\{A\}\Pr\{A\}\Pr\{A\} = \theta^3.$$

Again, as a check,

$$\sum_{x=0}^{3} p_3\{x\} = (1-\theta)^3 + 3(1-\theta)^2\theta + 3(1-\theta)\theta^2 + \theta^3 = [(1-\theta)+\theta]^3 = 1.$$

We will now generalize to the case of n trials. The probability of x successes is

$$p_n\{x\} = \Pr\left\{\underbrace{A\cdots A}_{x\ times}\ \underbrace{\bar{A}\ \cdots\ \bar{A}}_{(n-x)\ times} + \begin{array}{l}\text{same written in all}\\ \text{possible permutations}\end{array}\right\}$$

The number of possible permutations of x A's and $(n-x)$ $\bar{A}$'s is given by (7.5) as $n!/x!(n-x)!$ which by (7.6) is equal to $\binom{n}{x}$. The probability of any one particular arrangement is $\theta^x(1-\theta)^{n-x}$. Thus

$$p_n\{x\} = \binom{n}{x}\theta^x(1-\theta)^{n-x}. \tag{8.1}$$

The binomial theorem asserts that

$$(P+Q)^N = \sum_{x=0}^{N}\binom{N}{x}P^xQ^{N-x};$$

so, inserting θ for P, $(1-\theta)$ for Q, n for N, we have

$$[\theta + (1-\theta)]^n = \sum_{x=0}^{n}\binom{n}{x}\theta^x(1-\theta)^{n-x} \tag{8.2}$$

and we see that $p_n\{x\}$, see (8.1), equals the $(x + 1)$th term in this binomial expansion, which is why the probability function (8.1) is known as the *binomial probability distribution function.* The left-hand side of (8.2) is automatically equal to 1, since $\theta + (1 - \theta) = 1$, and so $\sum_{x=0}^{n} p_n\{x\} = 1$, as it must. In (8.1) every choice of n and θ gives a different distribution; the constants n, θ are known as the *parameters* of the distribution. Two binomial probability distributions are shown graphically in Figures 1.12 and 1.13: $n = 9$ for both; $\theta = 0.1$ for the first and 0.5 for the second.

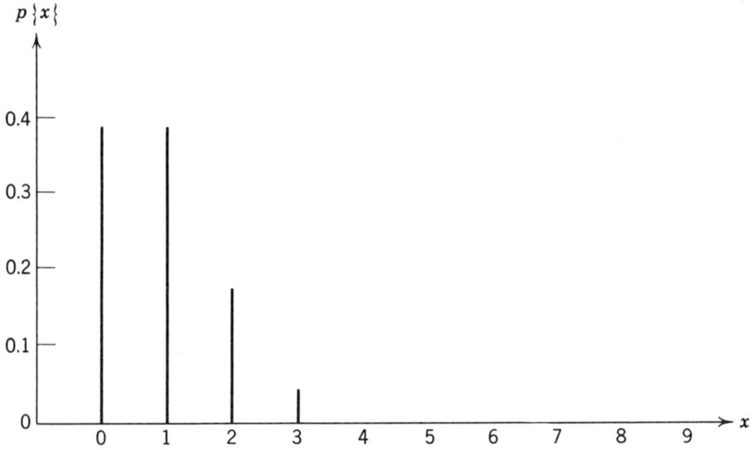

Figure 1.12

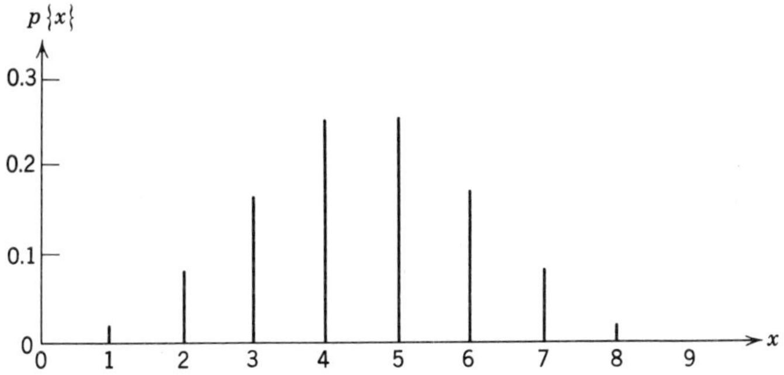

Figure 1.13

1.9. Continuous Frequency Functions

So far we have only considered discrete probability functions in which the probability is zero except for a discrete set of points on the line. We will now consider the case where x can vary continuously along the line. We will approach this question empirically.

Consider a very large population of some item, say cucumbers, from which we take a sample of 100 and measure the lengths to the nearest 4 cm, in such a way that anything between 22 and 26 is recorded as 24, etc. We can regard this as a discrete distribution, in which the cucumbers have lengths confined to nominal values 24, 28, 32, etc., and represent it by a line graph (Figure 1.14) similar to Figures 1.6, 1.7, and 1.8, in which the

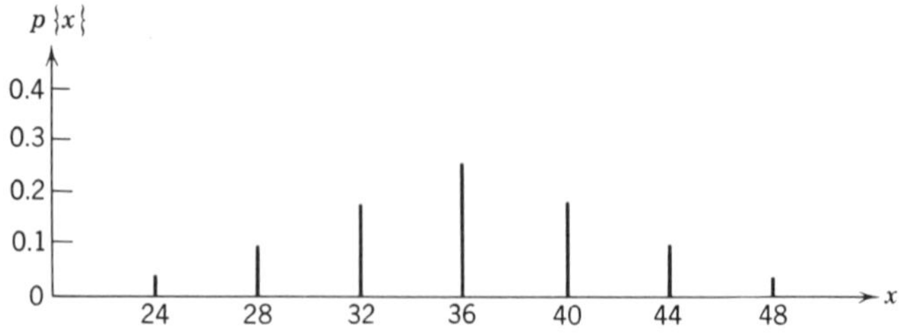

Figure 1.14

height of the line at each nominal length of cucumbers is equal to the fraction of the sample with that nominal length. For the hypothetical data in Table 1.8, since the sample size is 100, the observed numbers must be divided by 100 to give the estimated values of $p\{x\}$, the fourth line in the table. Alternatively, we can replace the line graph by a *histogram*, a figure in which rectangles replace the lines, with the area of each rectangle equal to the fraction of the sample with each nominal size. The vertical scale must be adjusted so that the total area is 1. Since the base of each rectangle is 4 cm, the heights of the rectangles have to be one quarter of the corresponding lines (fifth line in Table 1.8). This is given in Figure 1.15.

Now suppose that we take a sample of twice the initial size, and measure the cucumbers to the nearest 2 cm, so that anything between 22 and 24 is recorded as 23 cm, etc. The observed numbers might be as in the eighth row of Table 1.8. We again construct a histogram in which the area of each rectangle is equal to the fraction of the sample with each nominal size. The base of each rectangle is 2 cm; so the $p\{x\}$ for a line graph, ninth row, have to be divided by 2 to make each area correct and to make the total area equal to one. This gives us Figure 1.16.

Now suppose that the process is repeated indefinitely, larger and larger

Table 1.8

Nominal length	24	28	32	36	40	44	48
Actually the interval	22–26	26–30	30–34	34–38	38–42	42–46	46–50
Number in sample	4	10	18	36	18	10	4
$p\{x\}$ for line graph	0.04	0.10	0.18	0.36	0.18	0.10	0.04
$p\{x\}$ for histogram	0.010	0.025	0.045	0.090	0.045	0.025	0.010

Nominal length	23	25	27	29	31	33	35	37	39	41	43	45	47	49
Actually the interval	22–4	24–6	26–8	28–30	30–2	32–4	34–6	36–8	38–40	40–2	42–4	44–6	46–8	48–50
Number in sample	2	6	8	12	16	20	36	36	20	6	12	8	6	2
$p\{x\}$ for line graph	0.01	0.03	0.04	0.06	0.08	0.10	0.18	0.18	0.10	0.08	0.06	0.04	0.03	0.01
$p\{x\}$ for histogram	0.005	0.015	0.020	0.030	0.040	0.050	0.090	0.090	0.050	0.040	0.030	0.020	0.015	0.005

samples being taken and measured to finer and finer intervals. Then in the limit we will obtain a smooth curve for the histogram, as indicated in Figure 1.16. Such a curve is known as a *continuous probability density*

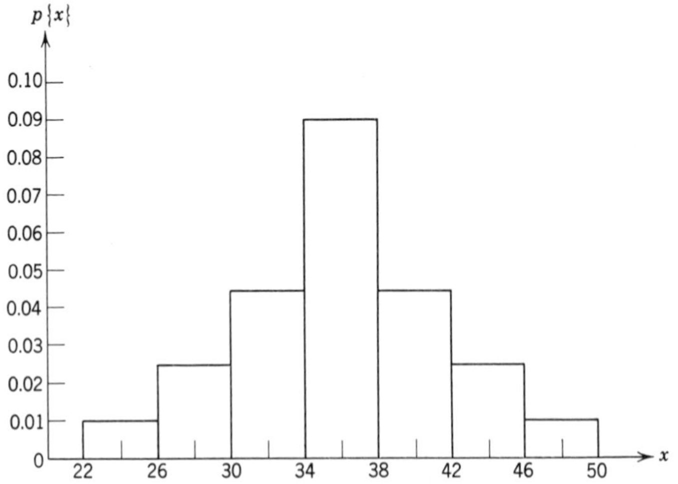

Figure 1.15

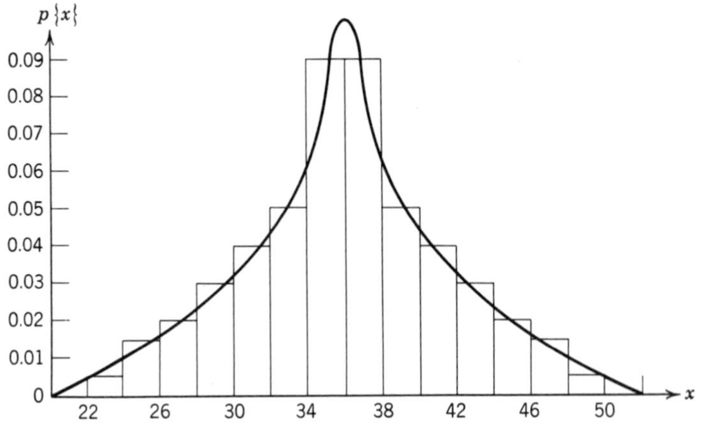

Figure 1.16

distribution, and the function $p\{x\}$ defining the curve is known as the *probability density* function. The probability that an observation taken at random from a population with density function $p\{x\}$ lies between x_a and x_b is given by the area under the curve between x_a and x_b (Figure 1.17).

The operation of finding such an area is handled mathematically by the technique of integration, denoted by the symbol $\int_{x_a}^{x_b} p\{x\}\, dx$. In this symbolic representation, $\int$ represents the operation of finding the area, the x of dx represents the variable which is being varied (in the present case, there is only one variable which could be varied, and so the dx part is somewhat redundant, but in general with a function of several variables we need to specify which variable is being varied), the function following the $\int$ sign is the function in question, and the lower and upper limits of integration, here x_a and x_b, are the limits between which we are finding

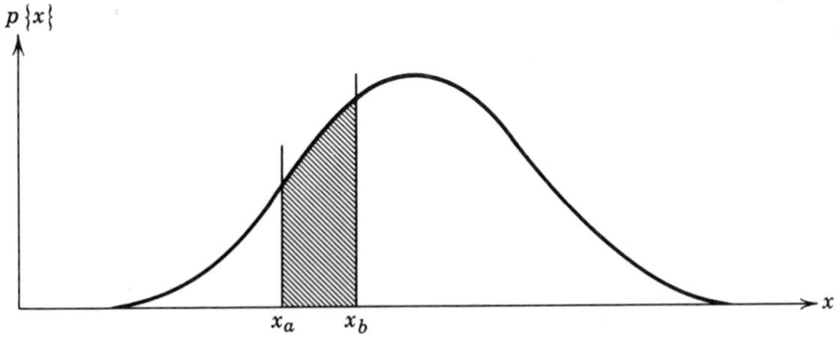

Figure 1.17

the area. The mathematics of the operation of integration are of slight or great difficulty depending on the analytical form of the function being integrated. In this textbook we will never demand that the reader be able to perform the integrations himself, but it is important that he understand the simple physical meaning of the symbol and the corresponding operation, namely, finding the area under the curve between specified limits.

It follows that for $p\{x\}$ to be a probability density it must satisfy the condition that $p\{x\} \geq 0$ for all x and that

$$\int_{-\infty}^{\infty} p\{x\}\, dx = 1. \tag{9.1}$$

Also, we see that

$$\Pr\{x_a < x < x_b\} = \int_{x_a}^{x_b} p\{x\}\, dx. \tag{9.2}$$

$$\Pr\{x < x_a\} = \int_{-\infty}^{x_a} p\{x\}\, dx. \tag{9.3}$$

$$\Pr\{x > x_b\} = \int_{x_b}^{\infty} p\{x\}\, dx. \tag{9.4}$$

Equation (9.2) is represented by the shaded area in Figure 1.17. Equations (9.3) and (9.4) are represented by the left-hand and right-hand shaded areas, respectively, in Figure 1.18.

In dealing with continuous distributions, we replace the summation operation that sufficed for discrete distributions by the integration operation. Thus the *cumulative distribution function* in the continuous case, analogous to (6.1) in the discrete case, is

$$P\{x\} = \int_{-\infty}^{x} p\{t\}\, dt. \tag{9.5}$$

From a given probability density function $p\{x\}$ we can compute $P\{x\}$ for every x, and construct its graphical form. $P\{x\}$ must start at zero on the

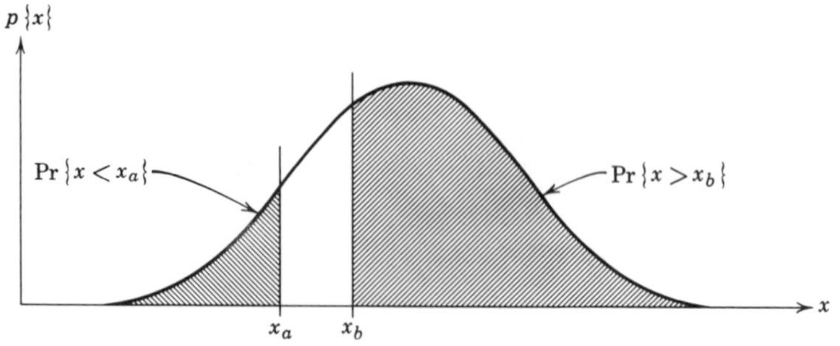

Figure 1.18

left-hand end, since $\int_{-\infty}^{-\infty} p\{x\}\, dx = 0$, and must reach 1 on the right-hand side, since $\int_{-\infty}^{\infty} p\{x\}\, dx = 1$ by (9.1). The upper part of Figure 1.19 gives the cumulative distribution $P\{x\}$ corresponding to the density function $p\{x\}$ in the lower part of the figure. A cumulative distribution function graph has the property that its slope can never be negative, since the probability density function from which it is derived can never be negative.

By the elementary rules of calculus, the derivative of a function $f(x)$, denoted by the symbol $df(x)/dx$, is equal to the slope of the function at the point x. Furthermore, the derivative of an indefinite integral of a function is the function itself; i.e., the derivative of (9.5) with respect to x is

$$\frac{d\,P\{x\}}{dx} = p\{x\}, \tag{9.6}$$

so the slope of the cumulative distribution function is equal to the probability density at that point.

To see this graphically, consider in Figure 1.19 the cdf over the region x to $(x + dx)$, where dx is a small increment in x. The cdf will in general be slightly curved over this region, but, by making dx very small, we can approximate the curve by a straight line. For a change in x of dx, $P\{x\}$ increases by an amount $d\,P\{x\} = p\{x\}\,dx$, since the vertical side of the triangle equals the slope times the horizontal base. If we look at the probability density curve (lower part of Figure 1.19), we get the complementary picture. The increase in area on going from x to $(x + dx)$ is the

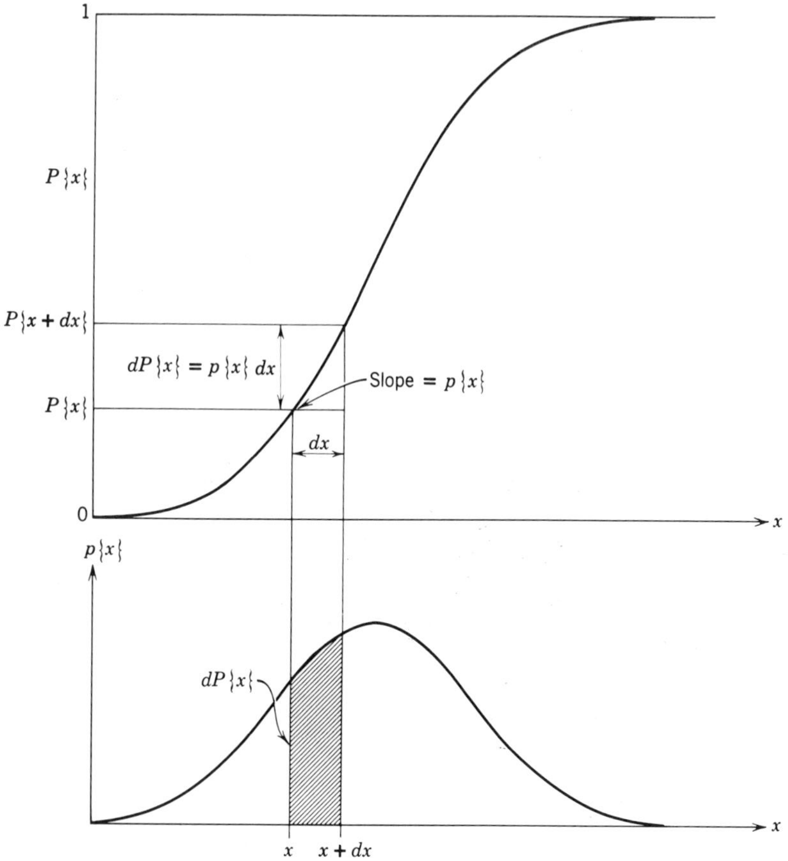

Figure 1.19

shaded part. For a small increment dx this area can be approximated by a rectangle of height $p\{x\}$ and base dx and hence an area $p\{x\}\,dx$. But this increase in area is the change in $P\{x\}$ on going from x to $(x + dx)$, i.e., $d\,P\{x\}$; so again $d\,P\{x\} = p\{x\}\,dx$ or

$$\frac{d\,P\{x\}}{dx} = p\{x\} \tag{9.7}$$

which is a rough justification of (9.6).

1.10. Examples of Continuous Distributions

Any continuous function which is never negative and for which $\int_{-\infty}^{\infty} f(x)\,dx = 1$ can be regarded as a probability density function.

The simplest *rectangular* or *uniform* distribution, graphed in the upper part of Figure 1.20, has the density function

$$\begin{aligned} p\{x\} &= \frac{1}{a}, \qquad -\frac{a}{2} < x < \frac{a}{2}, \\ &= 0, \qquad \text{otherwise.} \end{aligned} \tag{10.1}$$

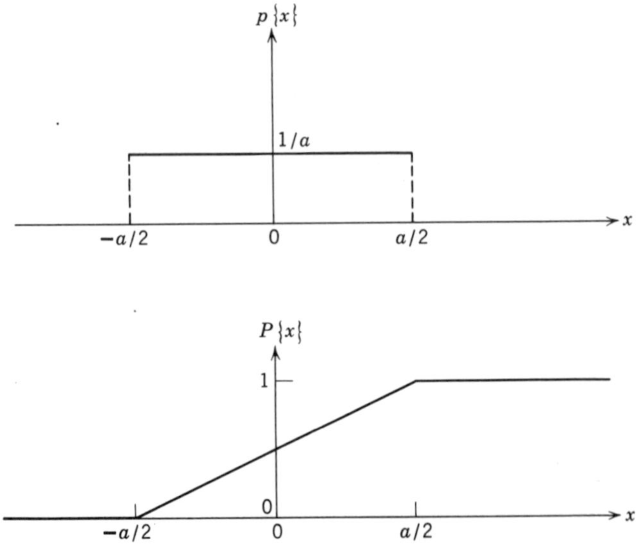

Figure 1.20

The parameter a must be greater than zero. Varying a will generate a family of such distributions. Also any distribution can be shifted up or down the x axis. The cumulative distribution function is

$$\begin{aligned} P\{x\} &= \int_{-\infty}^{x} p\{t\}\,dt = \frac{1}{a}\int_{-a/2}^{x} dt = \frac{t}{a}\Big|_{-a/2}^{x} \\ &= \frac{1}{a}\left[x - \left(-\frac{a}{2}\right)\right] = \frac{x}{a} + \frac{1}{2} \end{aligned} \tag{10.2}$$

for x satisfying the inequality $-a/2 < x < a/2$. For $x = -a/2, P\{x\} = 0$; for $x = 0$, $P\{x\} = 1/2$; and, for $x = a/2$, $P\{x\} = 1$. The cumulative distribution function is thus zero up to $-a/2$, a straight line with slope $1/a$ from $(-a/2, 0)$ to $(a/2, 1)$, and 1 for $x > a/2$, as shown in the lower part of Figure 1.20.

Another simple family of continuous probability density functions is the negative exponential:

$$\begin{aligned} p\{x\} &= \theta e^{-\theta x}, \qquad 0 < x < \infty, \\ &= 0, \qquad \text{otherwise,} \end{aligned} \tag{10.3}$$

where θ is a fixed parameter greater than zero, and e is the base of natural logarithms. The cumulative distribution function is

$$\begin{aligned} P\{x\} &= \theta \int_0^x e^{-\theta t}\, dt = \theta\left(-\frac{1}{\theta} e^{-\theta t}\right)\Bigg|_0^x = -e^{-\theta t}\Bigg|_0^x \\ &= -\frac{1}{e^{\theta x}} - \left(-\frac{1}{e^0}\right) = 1 - \frac{1}{e^{\theta x}}. \end{aligned} \tag{10.4}$$

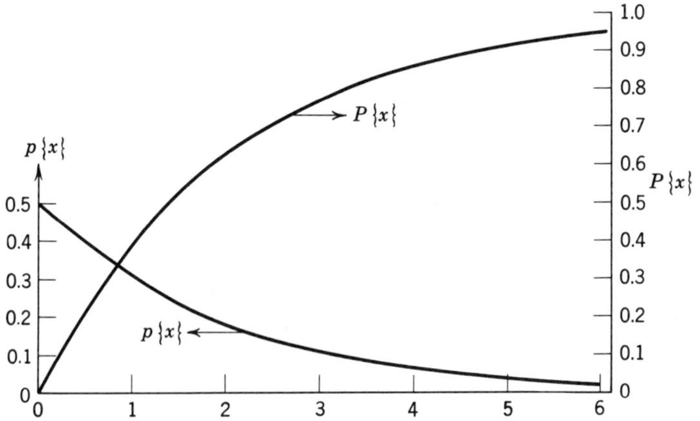

Figure 1.21

The probability density function (10.3) and the cumulative distribution function (10.4) are graphed in Figure 1.21 for the case $\theta = 0.5$. Each value of θ will give a different but similar distribution.

A particularly important family of continuous probability density functions is the so-called normal or gaussian:

$$p\{x\} = \frac{1}{\sqrt{2\pi}\,\sigma} e^{-(x-\xi)^2/2\sigma^2}, \tag{10.5}$$

where ξ and σ are fixed parameters, π has its traditional meaning, and e is the base of natural logarithms. The cumulative distribution function is

$$P\{x\} = \frac{1}{\sqrt{2\pi}\,\sigma}\int_{-\infty}^{x} e^{-(t-\xi)^2/2\sigma^2}\,dt, \tag{10.6}$$

involving an integration that does not lead to a standard explicit form, and the integration has to be performed numerically. The normal distribution is discussed further in Sections 1.12 and 1.15.

1.11. Transformations of Distribution Functions

We are often faced with the problem of finding the distribution of a function $y = f(x)$ of a random variable x, already knowing the distribution of x itself. For example, suppose that the distribution of diameters d of a certain population of ball bearings is normal, (10.5). The volume of a

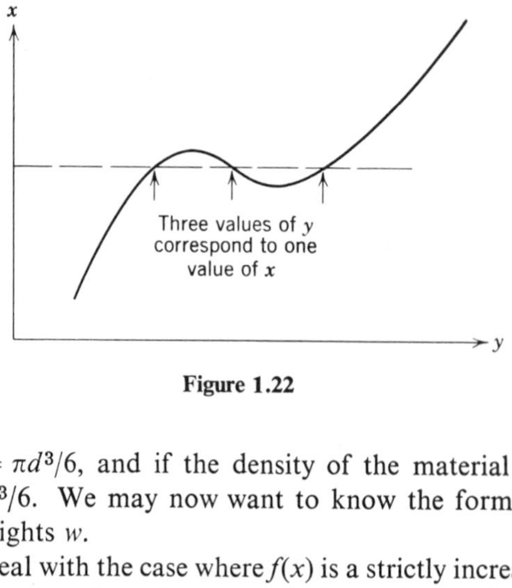

Figure 1.22

sphere is $\frac{4}{3}\pi r^3 = \pi d^3/6$, and if the density of the material is ρ then the weight $w = \rho\pi d^3/6$. We may now want to know the form of the distribution of the weights w.

We will only deal with the case where $f(x)$ is a strictly increasing function of x, so that to every value of x corresponds a unique value of $y = f(x)$, and vice versa. For example, the function sketched in Figure 1.22 is inadmissible, but that in Figure 1.24 is admissible.

In the discrete case things are simple. Whenever x takes a particular value x_i, then simultaneously y takes a uniquely defined value $y_i = f(x_i)$. The original variable x is a random variable, since to every point in the sample space is attached a value x. Likewise, to the point to which was attached the value x_i will also be attached the value $y_i = f(x_i)$;

so y is also a random variable with the probability function $q(y)$ such that

$$q\{y\} = q\{f(x)\} = p\{x\}. \tag{11.1}$$

The continuous case is more troublesome. Consider two points close together on the y axis, P_1 at y and P_2 at $(y + dy)$ (Figure 1.23). Let y be a function of $x, f(x)$, and let x be a function of y, $g(y)$ (Figure 1.24). Then corresponding to the points P_1, P_2 with coordinates y, $y + dy$ will be points P_1', P_2' with coordinates $g(y)$, $g(y + dy)$ on the x axis. Now, whenever y falls in the interval (P_1, P_2), x will simultaneously fall in the interval (P_1', P_2') (Figure 1.25). The probability of the former is approximately (see Figure 1.23)

(Probability density of y at P_1) $\times$ (length of interval P_1, P_2) $= q\{y\}\, dy$

where $q(y)$ is the probability density of y, and likewise the probability of the latter is approximately $p\{x\}\, dx$ (see Figure 1.25); so

$$q\{y\}\, dy = p\{x\}\, dx. \tag{11.2}$$

An examination of the relevant part of Figure 1.24 shows that $dx = (dg/dy)\, dy$. More formally, the length of the interval (P_1', P_2') on the x axis is $dx = g(y + dy) - g(y)$. By Taylor's theorem in elementary calculus,

$$g(y + dy) = g(y) + \frac{dg}{dy}\, dy + \text{higher-order terms.}$$

Neglecting the higher-order terms, this gives

$$dx = g(y + dy) - g(y) \simeq \frac{dg}{dy}\, dy.$$

Substituting for dx in (11.2), we get

$$q\{y\}\, dy \simeq p\{x\} \frac{dg}{dy}\, dy = p\{g(y)\} \frac{dg}{dy}\, dy$$

or

$$q\{y\} \simeq p\{g(y)\} \frac{dg}{dy}. \tag{11.3}$$

In words, the probability density function for y equals the formula for the probability density for x, with $g(y) = x$ substituted for x, times the derivative of $g(y)$ with respect to y. The foregoing discussion assumed that y was a strictly increasing function of x everywhere. The same result is readily obtained if y is a strictly decreasing function of x everywhere, the

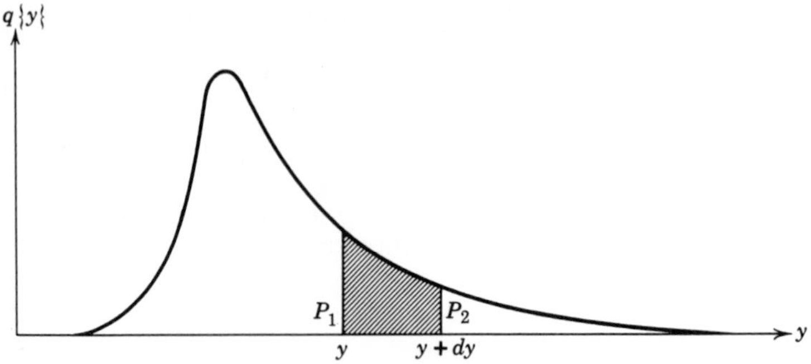

Figure 1.23

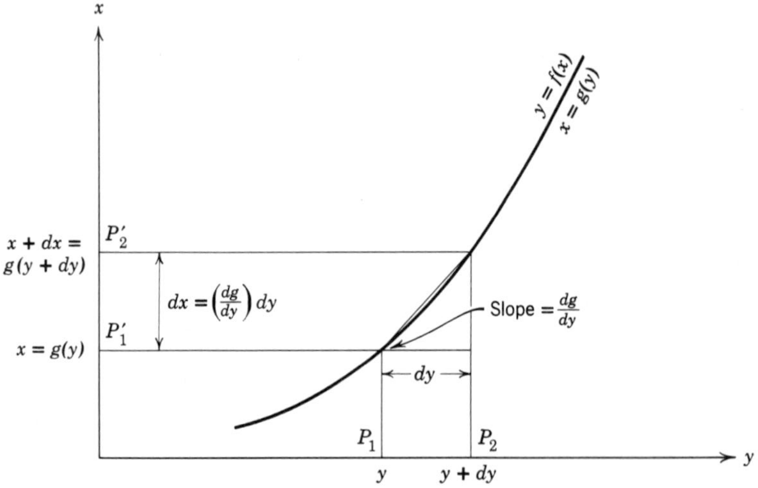

Figure 1.24

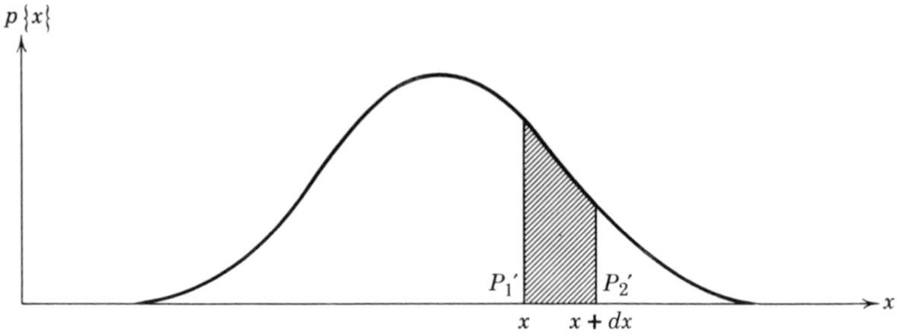

Figure 1.25

only difference being that in (11.3) in place of dg/dy the absolute value of dg/dy, namely $|dg/dy|$, appears.

The next section is an illustration of a transformation of a density function.

1.12. The Standardized Normal Distribution

The probability density function for the normal distribution is

$$p\{x\} = \frac{1}{\sqrt{2\pi}\,\sigma}\, e^{-(x-\xi)^2/2\sigma^2}. \tag{12.1}$$

This involves the familiar constant π and two parameters ξ, σ (whose significance will be evaluated later). As equation (12.1) stands, it is a different function for every pair of values ξ, σ and it is obviously impossible to tabulate an infinity of normal distributions. However, all these normal distributions can be reduced to a common form, the standardized normal distribution, by a simple transformation. Define

$$y = f(x) = \frac{x-\xi}{\sigma} = \frac{x}{\sigma} - \frac{\xi}{\sigma}. \tag{12.2}$$

The inverse function $x = g(y)$ is obtained by solving (12.2) for x:

$$x = g(y) = \sigma y + \xi. \tag{12.3}$$

The derivative of $g(y)$ with respect to y is $dg(y)/dy = \sigma$. We now substitute in (11.3):

$$q(y) = \frac{1}{\sqrt{2\pi}\,\sigma}\, e^{-y^2/2} \cdot \sigma = \frac{1}{\sqrt{2\pi}}\, e^{-y^2/2}.$$

This is the standardized normal distribution, for which we reserve the symbol $\phi(u)$:

$$\phi(u) = \frac{1}{\sqrt{2\pi}}\, e^{-u^2/2}. \tag{12.4}$$

The cumulative form, for which we will use the symbol $\Phi(u)$, is

$$\Phi(u) = \int_{-\infty}^{u} \frac{1}{\sqrt{2\pi}}\, e^{-t^2/2}\, dt. \tag{12.5}$$

A random variable with the probability density (12.4) is often referred to as a *unit or standardized normal deviate*. The properties of $\phi(u)$ and of $\Phi(u)$ are discussed in Section 1.15.

1.13. The Concept of Expectation

Two of the most useful properties of a random variable are its *expectation* (or *expected value* or *mean*) and its *variance*. In this section we will discuss expectation, defined as

$$E[x] = \sum_i x_i\, p\{x_i\}, \qquad \text{in the discrete case,} \tag{13.1}$$

$$= \int_{-\infty}^{\infty} x\, p\{x\}\, dx, \qquad \text{in the continuous case.} \tag{13.2}$$

The usefulness of the concept of expectation is that it corresponds to our intuitive idea of average. Consider the binomial distribution of Figure 1.12 with $n = 9$, $\theta = 0.1$. The random variable x could be the number of defective electronic tubes found in random samples of nine from a population of tubes whose fraction defective is 0.1. The numerical values of $p\{x\}$, calculated with (8.1), are given in the first column of Table 1.9.

Table 1.9

x	$p\{x\}$	$1{,}000{,}000p\{x\}$	$x \times 1{,}000{,}000p\{x\}$
0	0.387420	387,420	0
1	0.387420	387,420	387,420
2	0.172187	172,187	344,374
3	0.044641	44,641	133,923
4	0.007440	7,440	29,760
5	0.000827	827	4,135
6	0.000061	61	366
7	0.000003	3	21
8	0.000000	0	0
9	0.000000	0	0

If we imagine drawing 1,000,000 samples, we would expect to find 0 defectives in the sample $1{,}000{,}000 \times 0.387420 = 387{,}420$ times, etc. Thus the total number of defectives found in the 1,000,000 samples would be

$$0 \times 387{,}420 + 1 \times 387{,}420 + 2 \times 172{,}187 + \cdots = 899{,}999;$$

so the average number of defectives per sample is $899{,}999/1{,}000{,}000 = 0.9$. This calculation is exactly that of the expected value (13.1). The expected value is not necessarily the most frequent value (which is known as the *mode* of the distribution). In fact, for a discrete distribution the expected value may never occur at all. For example, the binomial distribution is confined to the integers 0, 1, 2, . . . , n, and there is no reason in general why its expectation, which we shall show is $n\theta$, should be an integer. In the present example, for instance, there are actually two most frequent values, 0 and 1, and the expected value 0.9 is equal to neither of them.

If we visualize a distribution plotted on stiff card and cut out, and then balanced on a knife edge parallel to the $p\{x\}$ axis, it will balance at the expected value of x. The expected value is equal to the center of gravity of the distribution along the x axis.

From our definitions the expectation of a constant is the constant itself. For example, if x is a continuous random variable and a and b are constants, then the expectation of the linear function $(a + bx)$ is

$$E[a + bx] = \int_{-\infty}^{\infty}(a + bx)\, p\{x\}\, dx = a\int_{-\infty}^{\infty} p\{x\}\, dx + b\int_{-\infty}^{\infty} x\, p\{x\}\, dx$$
$$= a + b\, E[x]. \tag{13.3}$$

Here, if we put $b = 0$, we see that $E[a] = a$; so the expectation of a constant is that constant, and, if we put $a = 0$, then $E[bx] = b\, E[x]$. Also, since the operation of finding the expected value of a random variable x yields a constant $E[x]$, the expectation of an expectation is the expectation itself; i.e., $E[E[x]] = E[x]$.

Further, the expected value of the deviation of a random variable from its expectation is

$$E[x - E[x]] = E[x] - E[E[x]] = E[x] - E[x] = 0;$$

i.e., the expected value has the property that the expected value of the deviations about it is zero.

We also need to be able to determine the expected value of a function of x, say, $y = f(x)$, given the distribution function of x: by the definition (13.2),

$$E[y] = \int_{-\infty}^{\infty} y\, p\{y\}\, dy. \tag{13.4}$$

For functions with the properties specified in Section 1.11 on the transformation of distributions, so that $y = f(x)$ is a single-valued function of x and $x = g(y)$ is a single-valued function of y, we can substitute $f(x)$ for y and $p\{g(y)\}\, dg/dy$ for $p\{y\}$, from (11.3), in (13.4). We also need to change the variable of integration from y to x. The rule for change of variable, when $v = \phi(u)$, $u = \psi(v)$ is

$$\int_a^b h(v)\, dv = \int_{\psi(a)}^{\psi(b)} h(\phi(u))\, \phi'(u)\, du. \tag{13.5}$$

To apply this formula, replace v by y, u by x, $\phi(u)$ by $f(x)$, $\psi(v)$ by $g(y)$, and $h(v)$ by $y\,p\{y\}$. Changing the variable in $y\,p\{y\}$ to x

gives $f(x)\,p\{g(y)\}\,dx/dy$, corresponding to $h(\phi(u))$. Corresponding to $\phi'(u) = dy/du$, we have dy/dx. Also when $y = \infty$, $x = g(\infty) = \infty$, and, when $y = -\infty$, $x = -\infty$. Therefore

$$E[f(x)] = \int_{-\infty}^{\infty} y\,p\{y\}\,dy = \int_{-\infty}^{\infty} f(x)\,p\{x\}\,\frac{dx}{dy}\frac{dy}{dx}\,dx$$
$$= \int_{-\infty}^{\infty} f(x)\,p\{x\}\,dx. \tag{13.6}$$

In other words, we can obtain $E[f(x)]$ directly from $p\{x\}$ and we do not need to determine $p\{f(x)\}$. The analogous formula holds for discrete distributions:

$$E[f(x)] = \sum_i f(x_i)\,p\{x_i\}. \tag{13.7}$$

Although we have indicated the proof of (13.6) only for the case where the transformation of x to y and vice versa is one to one, actually (13.6) is completely general and may be used to derive the expectation of any transformation of a random variable.

To consider a simple example of the expected value of a distribution, Table 1.10 details the calculation of the expectation of the random variable y equal to the sum of two four-sided dice whose frequency distribution was given in Table 1.3.

Table 1.10

y_i	$p\{y_i\}$	$y_i\,p\{y_i\}$
2	1/16	2/16
3	2/16	6/16
4	3/16	12/16
5	4/16	20/16
6	3/16	18/16
7	2/16	14/16
8	1/16	8/16

$$E[y] = \sum_i y_i\,p\{y_i\} = 80/16 = 5$$

A more interesting example is the expectation of the binomial distribution (8.1). By the definition of expectation (13.1),

$$E[x] = \sum_{x=0}^{n} x\binom{n}{x}\theta^x(1-\theta)^{n-x}. \tag{13.8}$$

We note that

$$x\binom{n}{x} = \frac{xn!}{x!(n-x)!} = \frac{(n-1)!}{(x-1)!(n-x)!}\,n = \binom{n-1}{x-1}n;$$

so (13.8) can be written as

$$E[x] = n\theta \sum_{x=1}^{n} \binom{n-1}{x-1} \theta^{x-1}(1-\theta)^{n-x} \tag{13.9}$$

We have changed the lower limit of the summation from 0 in (13.8) to 1 in (13.9), for when $x = 0$ the corresponding term in the summation is zero and adds nothing to the summation and hence can be omitted. Equation (13.9) will appear in a more satisfactory form if we write $x = y + 1$, so $x - 1 = y$, and $n = m + 1$, so $n - 1 = m$. In (13.9) x ranges over 1 to n, or 1 to $(m + 1)$, so y ranges over 0 to m; then

$$E[x] = n\theta \sum_{y=0}^{m} \binom{m}{y} \theta^{y}(1-\theta)^{m-y}.$$

The summation following $n\theta$ is the sum of all the terms of a binomial distribution for samples of size m, and the sum of any frequency distribution must equal one. Hence

$$E[x] = n\theta. \tag{13.10}$$

To turn to continuous distributions, the rectangular distribution (10.1) has the expectation, using the definition (13.2),

$$E[x] = \int_{-a/2}^{a/2} x \cdot \frac{1}{a}\,dx = \frac{1}{a}\frac{x^2}{2}\Big|_{-a/2}^{a/2} = 0. \tag{13.11}$$

The expectation of the exponential distribution (10.3) is

$$E[x] = \int_0^\infty x\theta\, e^{-\theta x}\,dx.$$

If we use the rule for integration by parts,

$$\int f(x)\,g'(x)\,dx = f(x)\,g(x) - \int g(x)\,f'(x)\,dx \tag{13.12}$$

and identify $f(x)$ with x, so that $f'(x) = 1$, and $g'(x)$ with $\theta\, e^{-\theta x}$, so that $g(x) = -e^{-\theta x}$, we get

$$\int_0^\infty x\theta\, e^{-\theta x}\,dx = x(-e^{-\theta x})\Big|_0^\infty - \int_0^\infty (-e^{-\theta x}) \cdot 1 \cdot dx$$

$$= 0 - \left(\frac{1}{\theta}\,e^{-\theta x}\right)\Big|_0^\infty = \frac{1}{\theta}. \tag{13.13}$$

For the normal distribution (10.5),

$$E[x] = \int_{-\infty}^{\infty} x\, p\{x\}\, dx = \int_{-\infty}^{\infty} [\xi + (x - \xi)]\, p\{x\}\, dx$$
$$= \xi \int_{-\infty}^{\infty} p\{x\}\, dx + \int_{-\infty}^{\infty} (x - \xi) \frac{1}{\sqrt{2\pi}\,\sigma} e^{-(x-\xi)^2/2\sigma^2}\, dx. \qquad (13.14)$$

Since the integral over the whole line of any probability density function is 1, the first term on the right-hand side is ξ. To evaluate the second term, we write $y = x - \xi$ and obtain

$$\frac{1}{\sqrt{2\pi}\,\sigma} \int_{-\infty}^{\infty} y e^{-y^2/2\sigma^2}\, dy = -\frac{\sigma}{\sqrt{2\pi}} e^{-y^2/2\sigma^2} \Big|_{-\infty}^{\infty} = 0. \qquad (13.15)$$

Thus for the normal distribution

$$E[x] = \xi. \qquad (13.16)$$

For the standardized normal distribution, given by the substitution $u = (x - \xi)/\sigma$, we have, using (13.3),

$$E[u] = E\left[\frac{x - \xi}{\sigma}\right] = \frac{E[x] - \xi}{\sigma} = \frac{\xi - \xi}{\sigma} = 0; \qquad (13.17)$$

i.e., the standardized normal distribution has expectation zero.

We have defined two of the classical so-called measures of central tendency, the expected value or the mean and the mode. The third, the *median*, say x_m, is that value of x which has half the mass of the distribution below it and half the mass above it. Thus if we pick an x at random it is equally likely to lie above as below the median x_m.. For symmetric distributions, for example, the rectangular or the normal, the median coincides with the expectation, but, for asymmetric distributions, this will not usually be the case. For example, for the exponential distribution (10.3) we find the median x_m by requiring that x_m satisfy the condition that $\Pr\{x < x_m\} = 1/2$. But from (10.4) we have

$$\Pr\{x < x_m\} = P\{x_m\} = 1 - \frac{1}{e^{\theta x_m}}.$$

Equating these and solving for x_m, we get

$$x_m = \frac{1}{\theta} \log_e 2 = \frac{0.69315}{\theta}. \qquad (13.18)$$

Incidentally, we recall from (13.13) that the expectation of the exponential distribution is $1/\theta$; so the median is $0.693E[x]$, and Figure 1.21 shows that the mode of the exponential distribution is zero.

1.14. The Concept of Variance

As a measure of the spread of a distribution the *variance*, defined as the expected value of the square of the deviation of the random variable x from its expectation, has many mathematical and statistical advantages:

$$V[x] = E[(x - E[x])^2]. \tag{14.1}$$

The units of measurement of variance are squared units on the original scale. The square root of the variance, commonly represented by the symbol σ, is known as the *standard deviation*. For purposes of computing variances, it is often convenient to use the following identity:

$$\begin{aligned} V[x] &= E[x^2 + (E[x])^2 - 2x\,E[x]] = E[x^2] + E[(E[x])^2] - 2E[x\,E[x]] \\ &= E[x^2] + (E[x])^2 - 2(E[x])^2 = E[x^2] - (E[x])^2; \end{aligned} \tag{14.2}$$

i.e., the variance of the random variable x is equal to the expectation of the square of x minus the square of the expectation of x.

An alternative identity is sometimes useful for computing variances:

$$\begin{aligned} V[x] = E[x^2] - (E[x])^2 &= E[x^2] - E[x] - (E[x])^2 + E[x] \\ &= E[x(x-1)] - E[x]\{E[x] - 1\}. \end{aligned} \tag{14.3}$$

If a and b are constants, then the variance of a linear function of x, say $(a + bx)$, is

$$\begin{aligned} V[a + bx] &= E[(a + bx)^2] - (E[a + bx])^2 \\ &= E[a^2 + 2abx + b^2x^2] - (a + b\,E[x])^2 \\ &= E[a^2] + 2ab\,E[x] + b^2\,E[x^2] - a^2 - 2ab\,E[x] - b^2(E[x])^2 \\ &= b^2\{E[x^2] - (E[x])^2\} = b^2\,V[x]. \end{aligned} \tag{14.4}$$

Thus the effect of adding a constant a to a random variable leaves the variance unchanged, but the variance of bx is b^2 times the variance of x.

To use (14.2) to compute the variance of the random variable y with the distribution given in Table 1.3, we need to find $E[y^2]$, y^2 being a function of y. Using (13.7), $E[y^2] = \sum_i y_i^2\, p\{y_i\}$. This summation is performed in the third column of Table 1.11. In Table 1.10 we found $E[y] = 5$. Substituting in (14.2), we get $V[y] = 27.5 - (5)^2 = 2.5$.

To calculate the variance of the binomial distribution (8.1), we will use the alternative computing formula for variance (14.3). In computing $E[x(x-1)]$, $x(x-1)$ is a function of x, and by (13.7)

$$E[x(x-1)] = \sum_i x_i(x_i - 1)\, p\{x_i\} = \sum_{x=0}^{n} x(x-1) \binom{n}{x} \theta^x (1-\theta)^{n-x}. \tag{14.5}$$

We note that

$$x(x-1)\binom{n}{x} = x(x-1)\cdot\frac{n!}{x!(n-x)!} = n(n-1)\cdot\frac{(n-2)!}{(x-2)!(n-x)!}$$
$$= n(n-1)\binom{n-2}{x-2}.$$

Substituting in (14.5),

$$E[x(x-1)] = n(n-1)\theta^2\sum_{x=2}^{n}\binom{n-2}{x-2}\theta^{x-2}(1-\theta)^{n-x}. \qquad (14.6)$$

We have changed the lower limit of summation from 0 in (14.5) to 2 in (14.6), for clearly when $x = 0$ or 1 the corresponding terms in the summation are zero and add nothing to the summation and hence can be

Table 1.11

y_i	$p\{y_i\}$	$y_i^2\,p\{y_i\}$
2	1/16	4/16
3	2/16	18/16
4	3/16	48/16
5	4/16	100/16
6	3/16	108/16
7	2/16	98/16
8	1/16	64/16

$E[y^2] = \sum_i y_i^2\,p\{y_i\} = 440/16 = 27.5$

omitted. Equation (14.6) will appear in a more satisfactory form if we write $x = y + 2$, so $x - 2 = y$, and $n = m + 2$, so $n - 2 = m$. In (14.6) x ranges over 2 to n; so y ranges over 0 to m; then

$$E[x(x-1)] = n(n-1)\theta^2\sum_{y=0}^{m}\binom{m}{y}\theta^{y}(1-\theta)^{m-y}.$$

The summation is just the sum of all the terms of a binomial distribution, and the sum of any frequency distribution must equal one. Hence $E[x(x-1)] = n(n-1)\theta^2$. From (13.10), for the binomial distribution $E[x] = n\theta$. Making these substitutions in (14.3), we obtain for the variance of the binomial distribution

$$V[x] = n(n-1)\theta^2 - n\theta(n\theta - 1) = n\theta(1-\theta). \qquad (14.7)$$

If instead of considering the number of "successes" x in the binomial distribution, we consider the proportion of successes $h = x/n$, then by (14.4) the variance of h is

$$V[h] = V\left[\frac{x}{n}\right] = \frac{1}{n^2} V[x] = \frac{\theta(1-\theta)}{n}. \tag{14.8}$$

To consider some examples of the calculation of variances of continuous distributions, for the rectangular distribution, (10.1), we first obtain $E[x^2]$ by substituting $p\{x\}$ in (13.6):

$$\begin{aligned} E[x^2] &= \int_{-\infty}^{\infty} x^2\, p\{x\}\, dx = \int_{-a/2}^{a/2} x^2 \left(\frac{1}{a}\right) dx \\ &= \frac{1}{a} \cdot \frac{x^3}{3}\Bigg|_{-a/2}^{a/2} = \frac{a^2}{12}. \end{aligned} \tag{14.9}$$

Since we found in (13.11) that for (10.1) $E[x] = 0$, $V[x] = E[x^2] = a^2/12$.

For the exponential distribution, substituting $p\{x\} = \theta e^{-\theta x}$ from (10.3) in (13.6).

$$E[x^2] = \int_0^{\infty} x^2\, \theta e^{-\theta x}\, dx.$$

Using the formula for integration by parts (13.12), and identifying $f(x)$ with x^2, so that $f'(x) = 2x$, and $g'(x)$ with $\theta e^{-\theta x}$, so that $g(x) = -e^{-\theta x}$, we have

$$\begin{aligned} E[x^2] &= x^2(-e^{-\theta x})\Big|_0^{\infty} - \int_0^{\infty} (-e^{-\theta x})\, 2x\, dx \\ &= 0 + 2\int_0^{\infty} x\, e^{-\theta x}\, dx. \end{aligned} \tag{14.10}$$

In (13.13) we found

$$E[x] = \theta \int_0^{\infty} x e^{-\theta x}\, dx = \frac{1}{\theta},$$

and so the integral in (14.10) equals $1/\theta^2$, and we get

$$E[x^2] = \frac{2}{\theta^2}. \tag{14.11}$$

Substituting in (14.2), we get for the variance of the exponential distribution,

$$V[x] = \frac{2}{\theta^2} - \left(\frac{1}{\theta}\right)^2 = \frac{1}{\theta^2}. \tag{14.12}$$

The variance of the normal distribution (10.5) is important. We will first find the variance of the standardized form (12.4). From (13.17), $E[u] = 0$; so

$$V[u] = E[(u - E[u])^2] = E[u^2] = \int_{-\infty}^{\infty} u^2 \, p\{u\} \, du$$

$$= \int_{-\infty}^{\infty} u^2 \cdot \frac{1}{\sqrt{2\pi}} e^{-u^2/2} \, du. \tag{14.13}$$

This integral can be handled by using the formula for integration by parts (13.12), identifying $f(x)$ with u, so that $f'(x) = 1$, and $g'(x)$ with $ue^{-u^2/2}$, so that $g(x) = -e^{-u^2/2}$;

$$\int_{-\infty}^{\infty} u^2 e^{-u^2/2} \, du = u(-e^{-u^2/2}) \Big|_{-\infty}^{\infty} - \int_{-\infty}^{\infty} (-e^{-u^2/2}) \cdot 1 \cdot du$$

$$= 0 + \sqrt{2\pi} \int_{-\infty}^{\infty} \frac{1}{\sqrt{2\pi}} e^{-u^2/2} \, du = \sqrt{2\pi}, \tag{14.14}$$

since the latter integral is just that of the standardized normal distribution (12.5) over the entire line which must equal 1. Substituting in (14.13), the variance of the standardized normal distribution (12.4) is

$$V[u] = 1. \tag{14.15}$$

If we now consider a random variable x defined as $x = \sigma u + \xi$, where u has the standardized normal distribution, then x will have the normal distribution with parameters ξ, σ^2. We saw in (13.16) that $E[x] = \xi$, and from (14.4)

$$V[x] = V[u\sigma + \xi] = \sigma^2 \, V[u] = \sigma^2. \tag{14.16}$$

We thus see that the parameters, ξ, σ^2 of the normal distribution, first introduced without explanation in (10.5), are actually its expectation and variance, respectively. We often refer to the normal distribution with mean ξ and variance σ^2 as the distribution $N(\xi, \sigma^2)$; with this notation the standardized normal distribution is $N(0, 1)$.

For any random variable x, the standardized form is defined as

$$\frac{x - E[x]}{\sqrt{V[x]}} = w, \qquad \text{say.} \tag{14.17}$$

Then

$$E[w] = \frac{E[x] - E[E[x]]}{\sqrt{V[x]}} = 0, \tag{14.18}$$

and

$$V[w] = E[(w - E[w])^2] = E[w^2]$$

$$= \frac{E[(x - E[x])^2]}{V[x]} = \frac{V[x]}{V[x]} = 1. \tag{14.19}$$

Thus any random variable when put in standardized form using (14.17) has a zero expectation and a unit variance.

1.15. The Properties of the Standardized Normal Distribution

We saw in Section 1.12, that the substitution $u = (x - \xi)/\sigma$ transforms the general normal distribution (12.1) into the standardized normal distribution $\phi(u)$ (12.4). We saw in (13.17) that the standardized normal distribution has expectation zero, and in (14.15) that it has unit variance. We now examine in more detail the properties of

$$\phi(u) = \frac{1}{\sqrt{2\pi}} e^{-u^2/2} \tag{15.1}$$

and

$$\Phi(u) = \int_{-\infty}^{u} \frac{1}{\sqrt{2\pi}} e^{-t^2/2}\, dt. \tag{15.2}$$

In the first place, $\phi(u)$ is symmetrical about $u = 0$, as $-(-u)^2 = -(u)^2$; so

$$\phi(-u) = \phi(u). \tag{15.3}$$

Second, the larger the absolute value of u, $|u|$, the smaller is $\phi(u)$; i.e., $\phi(u)$ tends to zero as u tends to $\pm\infty$, and conversely $\phi(u)$ takes its maximum at $u = 0$, when $\phi(u) = 1/\sqrt{2\pi} = 0.3989$. More formally,

$$\frac{d\phi(u)}{du} = \frac{1}{\sqrt{2\pi}} e^{-u^2/2} \left(-\frac{1}{2}\right) \cdot 2u = -u\phi(u),$$

and

$$\frac{d^2\phi(u)}{du^2} = -\phi(u) + (-u)(-u\phi(u)) = (u^2 - 1)\,\phi(u),$$

which by the usual rules imply that $\phi(u)$ has a maximum at $u = 0$ and points of inflection at $u = \pm 1$. The function $\phi(u)$ is graphed in the upper part of Figure 1.26. Certain properties of $\Phi(u)$ can be immediately inferred. From the symmetry about zero of $\phi(u)$, the area in the lower tail below $-u$ must equal the area in the upper tail above $+u$:

$$\int_{-\infty}^{-u} \phi(t)\, dt = \int_{u}^{\infty} \phi(t)\, dt = 1 - \int_{-\infty}^{u} \phi(t)\, dt;$$

so

$$\Phi(-u) = 1 - \Phi(u), \tag{15.4}$$

and

$$\Phi(-u) + \Phi(u) = 1. \tag{15.5}$$

The table of $\Phi(u)$ gives immediately the probability that an observation taken at random from a standardized normal distribution is less than any specified number. For example, from Table I in the appendix we get

$$\Pr\{u < -1.96\} = \Phi(-1.96) = 0.025,$$

$$\Pr\{u < 1.96\} = \Phi(1.96) = 0.975.$$

Conversely, we can enter the body of Table I with a specified probability and read off the corresponding unit normal deviate. For example, the value of u that 95 per cent of all observations are less than is found by solving the equation

$$P\{u < u_P\} = \Phi(u_P) = P \tag{15.6}$$

for $P = 0.95$. Entering the body of the table with $\Phi(u_P) = 0.95$, we see that $u_{0.95} = 1.645$.

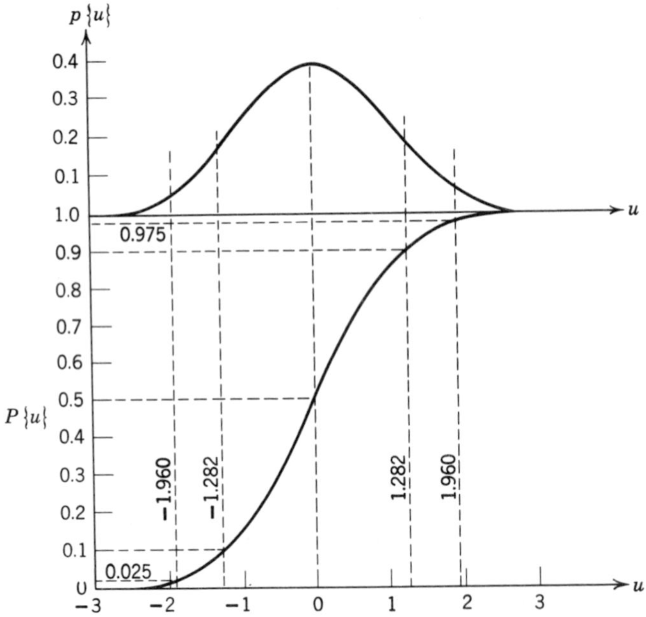

Figure 1.26

These two operations, namely, given u_P to find P and given P to find u_P, can also be performed readily for any normal distribution if we know its mean ξ and its variance σ^2. In the equation for the cumulative distribution function of the normal distribution,

$$P\{x\} = \frac{1}{\sqrt{2\pi}\,\sigma}\int_{-\infty}^{x} e^{-(t-\xi)^2/2\sigma^2}\,dt, \tag{15.7}$$

change the variable from t to $u = (t - \xi)/\sigma$. Then

$$P\{x\} = \frac{1}{\sqrt{2\pi}\,\sigma}\int_{-\infty}^{(x-\xi)/\sigma} e^{-u^2/2}\sigma\,du = \Phi\left(\frac{x-\xi}{\sigma}\right). \tag{15.8}$$

For example, suppose that we are given that $\xi = 100$, $\sigma = 10$, and we want the probability that an observation taken at random from this distribution is less than 120. We have

$$\Pr\{x < 120\} = P\{120\} = \Phi\left(\frac{120 - 100}{10}\right) = \Phi(2) = 0.97725.$$

Conversely, given the same distribution, what is the value of x_P that a fraction P of all observations are less than? We solve the equation

$$\Phi\left(\frac{x_P - \xi}{\sigma}\right) = P. \tag{15.9}$$

For example, if P is specified as 0.95, we know that the solution of $u_{0.95}$ in $\Phi(u_{0.95}) = 0.95$ is $u_{0.95} = 1.645$; so

$$\Phi(1.645) = 0.95 = \Phi\left(\frac{x_{0.95} - \xi}{\sigma}\right).$$

Thus $1.645 = (x_{0.95} - \xi)/\sigma = (x_{0.95} = 100)/10$, or $x_{0.95} = 116.45$.

An immediate application of (15.8) is to the question: What is the probability that an observation will lie k or more times the standard deviation below the mean?

$$\Pr\{x < \xi - k\sigma\} = \Phi\left(\frac{(\xi - k\sigma) - \xi}{\sigma}\right) = \Phi(-k). \tag{15.10}$$

The probability that an observation will lie below k times the standard deviation above the mean is $\Phi(k)$. The probability that an observation will lie above k times the standard deviation above the mean is

$$\Pr\{x > \xi + k\sigma\} = 1 - \Pr\{x < \xi + k\sigma\} = 1 - \Phi(k) = \Phi(-k). \tag{15.11}$$

We can also ask: What is the probability that an observation deviates from the mean by more than k times the standard deviation in either direction, i.e., that x lies outside the interval $(\xi \pm k\sigma)$? This is

$$\begin{aligned}\Pr\{x < \xi - k\sigma\} + \Pr\{x > \xi + k\sigma\} &= \Phi(-k) + \Phi(-k)\\ &= 2\Phi(-k) = 2[1 - \Phi(k)].\end{aligned} \tag{15.12}$$

For example, for $k = 1.96$, $2\Phi(-1.96) = 2 \times 0.025 = 0.05$, or alternatively $2[1 - \Phi(1.96)] = 2[1 - 0.975] = 0.05$.

1.16. Joint Frequency Functions: the Discrete Case

Consider the experiment consisting of dropping three light bulbs in sequence with possible outcomes U = undamaged, F = filament broken, and G = glass envelope broken. The sample space contains 27 sample points. If the successive drops are independent, then for example

$$\Pr\{UUU\} = \Pr\{U\}\Pr\{U\}\Pr\{U\}.$$

Define two random variables,

$$x = \text{number of } U\text{'s}, \qquad y = \text{number of } F\text{'s},$$

and let

$$\Pr\{U\} = \frac{1}{2}, \qquad \Pr\{F\} = \frac{1}{3}, \qquad \Pr\{G\} = \frac{1}{6}.$$

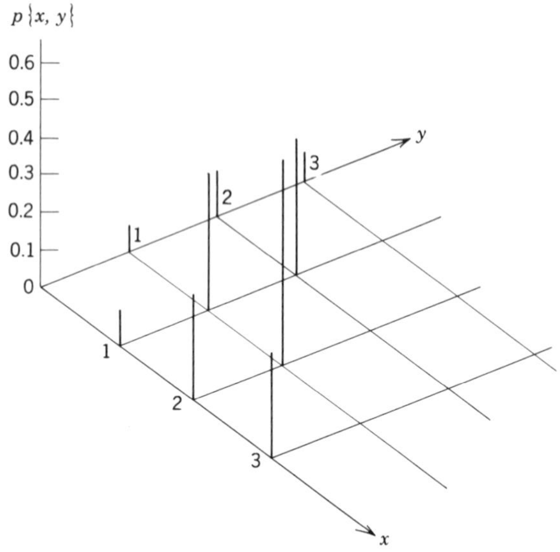

Figure 1.27

For each of the 27 points in the sample space we can tabulate the values taken by x and y and also the probability of that point occurring (see Table 1.12). For example, for the sample point (U, U, U) we have $x = 3$, $y = 0$, and $\Pr\{UUU\} = (1/2)(1/2)(1/2) = 1/8 = 27/216$. This sample point is therefore labeled $(U, U, U)(3, 0)$ 27, the denominator 216 being omitted for conciseness.

From Table 1.12 we can construct Table 1.13 showing the probability of obtaining any pair of values of x and y.

It is natural to express Table 1.13 in a two-way form (Table 1.14) and also to represent it graphically (Figure 1.27).

Table 1.12

$(U, U, U)(3, 0)$	27	$(U, F, U)(2, 1)$	18	$(U, G, U)(2, 0)$	9
$(U, U, F)(2, 1)$	18	$(U, F, F)(1, 2)$	12	$(U, G, F)(1, 1)$	6
$(U, U, G)(2, 0)$	9	$(U, F, G)(1, 1)$	6	$(U, G, G)(1, 0)$	3
$(F, U, U)(2, 1)$	18	$(F, F, U)(1, 2)$	12	$(F, G, U)(1, 1)$	6
$(F, U, F)(1, 2)$	12	$(F, F, F)(0, 3)$	8	$(F, G, F)(0, 2)$	4
$(F, U, G)(1, 1)$	6	$(F, F, G)(0, 2)$	4	$(F, G, G)(0, 1)$	2
$(G, U, U)(2, 0)$	9	$(G, F, U)(1, 1)$	6	$(G, G, U)(1, 0)$	3
$(G, U, F)(1, 1)$	6	$(G, F, F)(0, 2)$	4	$(G, G, F)(0, 1)$	2
$(G, U, G)(1, 0)$	3	$(G, F, G)(0, 1)$	2	$(G, G, G)(0, 0)$	1

Table 1.13

(x, y)	$(216) \times p\{x, y\}$
(0, 0)	1
(1, 0)	$3 + 3 + 3 = 9$
(2, 0)	$9 + 9 + 9 = 27$
(3, 0)	27
(0, 1)	$2 + 2 + 2 = 6$
(1, 1)	$6 + 6 + 6 + 6 + 6 + 6 = 36$
(2, 1)	$18 + 18 + 18 = 54$
(0, 2)	$4 + 4 + 4 = 12$
(1, 2)	$12 + 12 + 12 = 36$
(0, 3)	8

Table 1.14

$216 \times p\{x, y\}$

		y = 0	1	2	3
	0	1	6	12	8
	1	9	36	36	0
x	2	27	54	0	0
	3	27	0	0	0

In general, a discrete bivariate distribution will appear as in Table 1.15, where it is supposed that x and y are confined to the discrete values $x_1, \ldots, x_n$ and $y_1, \ldots, y_m$. The probability of any particular pair of values, x_i, y_j, is $p\{x_i, y_j\}$. The marginal probabilities for x can be obtained by summing over y, and vice versa, viz.:

$$p\{x_i\} = \sum_j^m p\{x_i, y_j\}, \tag{16.1}$$

$$p\{y_j\} = \sum_i^n p\{x_i, y_j\}. \tag{16.2}$$

In (16.1) and (16.2) $p\{x_i\}$ and $p\{y_j\}$ are the probability functions of x and y, respectively, and in general are different functions, and therefore a notation should be used which makes it clear that they are different

Table 1.15

	y_1	$\cdots$	y_j	$\cdots$	y_m	$\sum_j^m p\{x_i, y_j\}$
x_1	$p\{x_1, y_1\}$	$\cdots$	$p\{x_1, y_j\}$	$\cdots$	$p\{x_1, y_m\}$	$p\{x_1\}$
$\vdots$	$\vdots$					
x_i	$p\{x_i, y_1\}$		$p\{x_i, y_j\}$		$p\{x_i, y_m\}$	$p\{x_i\}$
$\vdots$	$\vdots$					
x_n	$p\{x_n, y_1\}$		$p\{x_n, y_j\}$		$p\{x_n, y_m\}$	$p\{x_n\}$
$\sum_i^n p\{x_i, y_j\}$	$p\{y_1\}$		$p\{y_j\}$		$p\{y_m\}$	

functions. For example, one could be $p\{\ \}$ and the other $q\{\ \}$, or one could be $p_x\{\ \}$ and the other $p_y\{\ \}$. In situations where there is no risk of confusion we will omit the distinguishing subscripts. For example, for Table 1.14,

$$p\{y_2\} = \frac{12 + 36 + 0 + 0}{216} = \frac{48}{216} = \frac{2}{9}.$$

This result can be checked by regarding y as a binomially distributed variable with $n = 3$, $\theta = 1/3$, and using (8.1):

$$p_3\{y = 2\} = \binom{3}{2}\left(\frac{1}{3}\right)^2\left(1 - \frac{1}{3}\right)^{3-2} = \frac{2}{9}.$$

The conditional probability that $x = x_i$, given that $y = y_j$, can be found by using (4.1):

$$\Pr\{x = x_i | y = y_j\} = \frac{\Pr\{x = x_i \text{ and } y = y_j\}}{\Pr\{y = y_j\}} = \frac{p\{x_i, y_j\}}{p\{y_j\}}. \quad (16.3)$$

It is convenient to call this the conditional frequency function and use the symbol $p\{x|y\}$. Also, if x and y are independent, using (5.6), namely, $\Pr\{E_1|E_2\} = \Pr\{E_1\}$, gives

$$\Pr\{x = x_i | y = y_j\} = \Pr\{x = x_i\}.$$

Substituting from (16.3) and writing $\Pr\{x = x_i\} = p\{x_i\}$, we get that, in the case of x, y independent,

$$p\{x_i, y_j\} = p\{x_i\}\, p\{y_j\}; \quad (16.4)$$

i.e., the joint frequency function is the product of the two marginal frequency functions. In the case of the bivariate distribution of Table 1.14, for example, we have just seen that $p\{y = 2\} = 2/9$, whereas from the table, for example, $p\{y = 2 | x = 0\} = 12/216 = 1/18$, so for this distribution $p\{y|x\} \neq p\{y\}$, and hence x and y are not independent. Similarly, $p\{x = 3\} = 27/216$; so $p\{x = 3\}p\{y = 2\} = (27/216) \times (2/9)$ which is not equal to $p\{x = 3, y = 2\}$ which is 0.

1.17. Joint Frequency Functions: the Continuous Case

Consider a function $p\{x, y\} \geq 0$ for all x, y such that

$$\int_{-\infty}^{\infty}\int_{-\infty}^{\infty} p\{x, y\}\, dy\, dx = 1. \quad (17.1)$$

This function $p\{x, y\}$ can be regarded as a two-dimensional, or bivariate, probability density function and is the analog of the univariate probability density functions we have been considering hitherto. Also, analogously to (9.5) in the univariate case, we can define a cumulative distribution function

$$P\{x_i, y_j\} = \Pr\{x \leq x_i, y \leq y_j\} = \int_{-\infty}^{x_i}\int_{-\infty}^{y_j} p\{x, y\}\, dy\, dx. \quad (17.2)$$

Graphically, we can use the two horizontal dimensions to represent x, y and the vertical dimension to represent $p\{x, y\}$. Thus $p\{x, y\}$ generates a surface above the plane $p\{x, y\} = 0$. The total volume enclosed between this surface and this plane, by (17.1), is 1. $P\{x_i, y_j\}$ is the volume under the surface measured over the shaded area only (Figure 1.28).

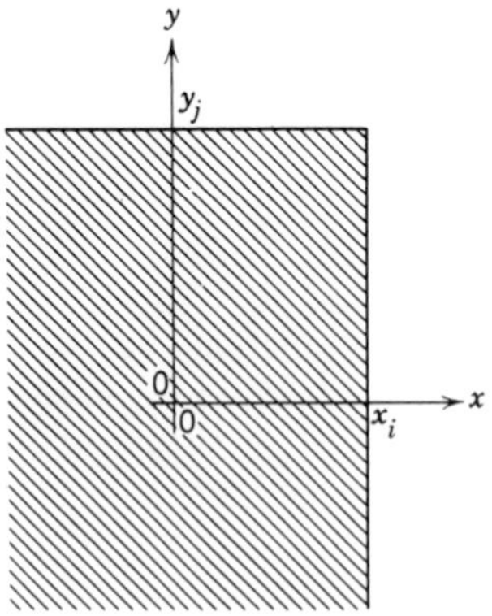

Figure 1.28

In manipulating bivariate probability density functions we will often find it convenient to reverse the order of integration, i.e., to assume

$$\int_{x_a}^{x_b}\int_{y_c}^{y_d} p\{x, y\}\, dy\, dx = \int_{y_c}^{y_d}\int_{x_a}^{x_b} p\{x, y\}\, dx\, dy. \tag{17.3}$$

This is always legitimate in the situations in which we are involved. Technically, it is permissible if the integral is absolutely convergent. The requirement that $p\{x, y\} \geq 0$ implies that if the integrals converge then they are absolutely convergent, and the requirement (17.1) implies that they are convergent; hence they are absolutely convergent.

The only example of a continuous bivariate distribution we will encounter in this book is the bivariate normal:

$$p\{x, y\} = \frac{1}{2\pi\sigma_x\sigma_y\sqrt{1-\rho^2}} \exp\left\{-\frac{1}{2(1-\rho^2)}\left[\left(\frac{x-\xi}{\sigma_x}\right)^2 - 2\rho\left(\frac{x-\xi}{\sigma_x}\right)\left(\frac{y-\eta}{\sigma_y}\right) + \left(\frac{y-\eta}{\sigma_y}\right)^2\right]\right\}. \tag{17.4}$$

This will be discussed in detail in Chapter 12.

We may wish to find the marginal probability density function of x alone, given $p\{x, y\}$. Intuitively, we would expect to get this by integrating $p\{x, y\}$ over y. More formally, we can proceed as follows:

$$\Pr\{-\infty < x < x_1\} = \Pr\{-\infty < x < x_1, -\infty < y < \infty\}$$
$$= \int_{-\infty}^{x_1}\int_{-\infty}^{\infty} p\{x, y\}\, dy\, dx = \int_{-\infty}^{x_1} Q(x)\, dx \tag{17.5}$$

if we define $Q(x)$ as

$$Q(x) = \int_{-\infty}^{\infty} p\{x, y\}\, dy. \tag{17.6}$$

Also, considering x alone,

$$\Pr\{-\infty < x < x_1\} = \int_{-\infty}^{x_1} p\{x\}\, dx. \tag{17.7}$$

The left-hand sides of (17.5) and (17.7) are identical, and so the right-hand sides are equal:

$$\int_{-\infty}^{x_1} p\{x\}\, dx = \int_{-\infty}^{x_1} Q(x)\, dx. \tag{17.8}$$

Intuitively, if we regard x_1 as a variable we have here two functions of x_1 which are equal for all values of x_1, and this implies that the functions must be identical. More formally, we can use a standard rule of calculus (see, for example, Courant, *Differential and Integral Calculus*, vol. I, p. 111),

$$\frac{d}{dx}\int_a^x f(u)\, du = f(x).$$

Differentiating both sides of (17.8) with respect to the variable x_1, and substituting from (17.6) for Q gives

$$p\{x_1\} = Q(x_1) = \int_{-\infty}^{\infty} p\{x_1, y\}\, dy.$$

But this is true for any x, not only x_1, and so

$$p\{x\} = \int_{-\infty}^{\infty} p\{x, y\}\, dy, \tag{17.9}$$

as we had guessed would be the case.

1.18. Conditional Distributions in the Continuous Case

We want a function $p\{x|y\}$ which will be the probability density function of x when y is known; i.e.,

$$\Pr\{x_a < x < x_b|y\} = \int_{x_a}^{x_b} p\{x|y\}\, dx. \tag{18.1}$$

We start from our definition of conditional probability (4.1), $\Pr\{E_1|E_2\} = \Pr\{E_1E_2\}/\Pr\{E_2\}$, and identify E_1 with the event $x_a < x < x_b$ and E_2 with the event $y_0 - c < y < y_0 + c$. Thus

$$\Pr\{x_a < x < x_b|y_0 - c < y < y_0 + c\} = \frac{\Pr\{x_a < x < x_b,\, y_0 - c < y < y_0 + c\}}{\Pr\{y_0 - c < y < y_0 + c\}} = \frac{\int_{x_a}^{x_b}\int_{y_0-c}^{y_0+c} p\{x, y\}\, dy\, dx}{\int_{y_0-c}^{y_0+c} p\{y\}\, dy}. \tag{18.2}$$

Figure 1.29 shows that the area under the curve $p\{y\}$ bounded by the lines $y = y_0 - c$, $y = y_0 + c$ can be approximated by a rectangle with the base of length $2c$ and the height $p\{y_{0'}\}$, where $y_{0'}$ is some value of y in the interval $(y_0 - c,\ y_0 + c)$. In other words, we can choose $y_{0'}$, so that

$$\int_{y_0 - c}^{y_0 + c} p\{y\}\, dy = 2c\, p\{y_{0'}\}.$$

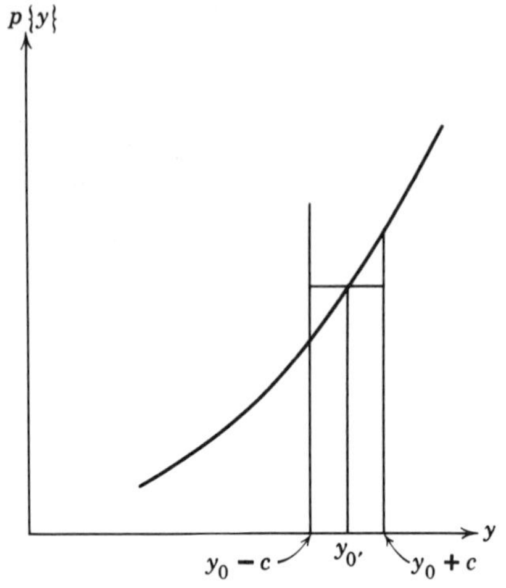

Figure 1.29

The numerator of (18.2) is graphically represented in Figures 1.30 and 1.31. If we suppose that the x and y axes are in the plane of the paper and the $p\{x, y\}$ axis is vertical to the paper, the shaded area in Figure 1.30 is the base of the volume represented by the numerator of (18.2). Figure 1.31 is a three-dimensional sketch of this volume element, resting on this base. The volume

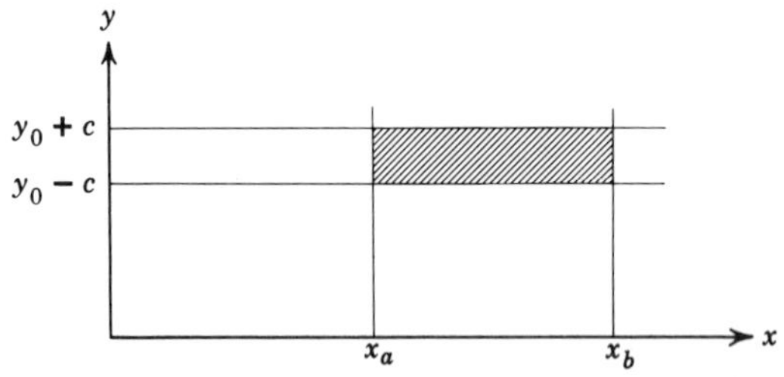

Figure 1.30

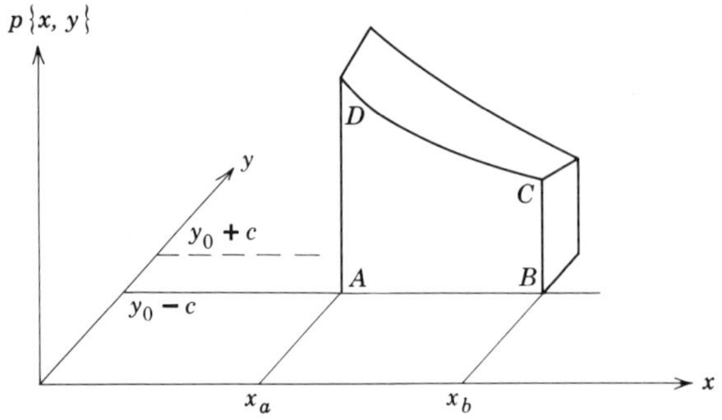

Figure 1.31

of this element could be approximated as the area of the face marked $ABCD$ times the thickness, which is $[(y_0 + c) - (y_0 - c)] = 2c$. A better approximation would be given by using instead of $ABCD$ a similar area, say, $A'B'C'D'$, not actually shown, lying between the two faces, say, at $y_{0''}$, where $y_{0''}$, not actually shown, lies in the interval $(y_0 - c, y_0 + c)$. The upper edge $C'D'$, analogous to CD but moved from $y = y_0 - c$ to $y = y_{0''}$, has the functional form $p\{x, y_{0''}\}$, and so the area $A'B'C'D'$ will be given by integrating this from x_a to x_b, viz. $\int_{x_a}^{x_b} p\{x, y_{0''}\}\,dx$. Hence the volume of this element is given by multiplying this area by the thickness $2c$, giving

$$2c\int_{x_a}^{x_b} p\{x, y_{0''}\}\,dx.$$

We can now substitute for the numerator and denominator of (18.2):

$$\Pr\{x_a < x < x_b | y_0 - c < y < y_0 + c\} = \frac{2c\int_{x_b}^{x_a} p\{x, y_{0''}\}\,dx}{2c\,p\{y_{0'}\}} = \frac{\int_{x_a}^{x_b} p\{x, y_{0''}\}\,dx}{p\{y_{0'}\}}.$$

We now let c tend to 0, when both $y_{0'}$ and $y_{0''}$ will tend to y_0; thus in the limit

$$\Pr\{x_a < x < x_b | y = y_0\} = \frac{\int_{x_a}^{x_b} p\{x, y_0\}\,dx}{p\{y_0\}}.$$

This holds good for any x_a, x_b. In particular, we can let $x_a = -\infty$, when the left-hand side is the cumulative form $P\{x_b | y = y_0\}$ of the probability density function $p\{x|y\}$. On differentiating a cumulative form we get the density form (9.6); so we have

$$p\{x|y\} = \frac{p\{x, y\}}{p\{y\}}. \tag{18.3}$$

1.19. Independent Random Variables: the Continuous Case

Our definition of independence (5.1), $\Pr\{E_1|E_2\} = \Pr\{E_1|\bar{E}_2\}$, was shown to be equivalent to (5.6), $\Pr\{E_1|E_2\} = \Pr\{E_1\}$. We now identify E_2 with the event $y_c < y < y_d$ and E_1 with the event $x_a < x < x_b$; so, when x and y are independent,

$$\Pr\{y_c < y < y_d | x_a < x < x_b\} = \Pr\{y_c < y < y_d\}. \tag{19.1}$$

Using (4.3), $\Pr\{E_2|E_1\} = \Pr\{E_1E_2\} / \Pr\{E_1\}$, the left-hand side of (19.1) is

$$\Pr\{y_c < y < y_d|x_a < d < x_b\} = \frac{\Pr\{y_c < y < y_d, x_a < x < x_b\}}{\Pr\{x_a < x < x_b\}}$$
$$= \frac{\int_{y_c}^{y_d}\int_{x_a}^{x_b} p\{x, y\}\,dx\,dy}{\int_{x_a}^{x_b} p\{x\}\,dx}. \tag{19.2}$$

The right-hand side of (19.1) is of course $\int_{y_c}^{y_d} p\{y\}\,dy$. [Of course $p\{x\}$ and $p\{y\}$, being the density functions of x and y, in general are different functions and in principle need distinguishing suffices, e.g., $p_x\{x\}$ and $p_y\{y\}$. However, where there is no danger of the functions being confused we will omit the suffices.] We therefore have, for x and y independent,

$$\frac{\int_{y_c}^{y_d}\int_{x_a}^{x_b} p\{x, y\}\,dx\,dy}{\int_{x_a}^{x_b} p\{x\}\,dx} = \int_{y_c}^{y_d} p\{y\}\,dy,$$

whence

$$\int_{y_c}^{y_d}\int_{x_a}^{x_d} p\{x, y\}\,dx\,dy = \int_{x_a}^{x_b} p\{x\}\,dx \int_{y_c}^{y_d} p\{y\}\,dy$$
$$= \int_{x_a}^{x_b}\int_{y_c}^{y_d} p\{x\}\,p\{y\}\,dy\,dx. \tag{19.3}$$

This identity must hold for all x_a, x_b, y_c, y_d. Intuitively, this must imply that the functions being integrated are identical, and in fact this is the case; so, when x and y are independent,

$$p\{x, y\} = p\{x\}\,p\{y\}. \tag{19.4}$$

1.20. Expectation in the Multivariate Case

We have seen, (13.6), that, if x is a random variable with probability density function $p\{x\}$, and $f(x)$ is a function of x, then the expectation of $f(x)$ is

$$E[f(x)] = \int_{-\infty}^{\infty} f(x)\,p\{x\}\,dx.$$

Now consider the case of a function $h(x_1, \ldots, x_k)$ of several random variables $x_1, \ldots, x_k$ with joint probability density function $p\{x_1, \ldots, x_k\}$. It is natural to define the expectation of $h(x_1, \ldots, x_k)$ as

$$E[h(x_1,\ldots,x_k)] = \int_{-\infty}^{\infty}\cdots\int_{-\infty}^{\infty} h(x_1,\ldots,x_k)\,p\{x_1,\ldots,x_k\}\,dx_1\ldots dx_k. \tag{20.1}$$

We can use this to find the expectation of the sum of two random variables x, y:

$$\begin{aligned} E[x+y] &= \int_{-\infty}^{\infty}\int_{-\infty}^{\infty}(x+y)\,p\{x,y\}\,dx\,dy \\ &= \int_{-\infty}^{\infty}\int_{-\infty}^{\infty}x\,p\{x,y\}\,dy\,dx + \int_{-\infty}^{\infty}\int_{-\infty}^{\infty}y\,p\{x,y\}\,dx\,dy \\ &= \int_{-\infty}^{\infty}x\left[\int_{-\infty}^{\infty}p\{x,y\}\,dy\right]dx + \int_{-\infty}^{\infty}y\left[\int_{-\infty}^{\infty}p\{x,y\}\,dx\right]dy. \end{aligned}$$

We now use (17.9) for the two expressions in [ ] and obtain

$$E[x+y] = \int_{-\infty}^{\infty}x\,p\{x\}\,dx + \int_{-\infty}^{\infty}y\,p\{y\}\,dy = E[x] + E[y]. \quad (20.2)$$

Thus the expectation of the sum of two random variables is equal to the sum of their expectations. Incidentally, if x and y are separate observations, say, z_1 and z_2, from the same distribution with expectation ζ, then $E[z_1 + z_2] = E[z_1] + E[z_2] = 2\zeta$.

This generalizes to the case of n observations:

$$E\left[\sum_i^n z_i\right] = \sum_i^n E[z_i] = n\zeta \quad (20.3)$$

and

$$E\left[\frac{1}{n}\sum_i^n z_i\right] = \zeta; \quad (20.4)$$

i.e., the expected value of the mean of n observations from a distribution is the expectation of that distribution.

1.21. Covariance and the Correlation Coefficient

The *covariance* of two random variables x and y is defined as the expected value of the product of the deviations of x and y from their expected values:

$$\text{Cov}[x, y] = E[(x - E[x])(y - E[y])]. \quad (21.1)$$

For actually computing a covariance, an equivalent form is often more convenient:

$$\begin{aligned} \text{Cov}[x, y] &= E[xy - yE[x] - xE[y] + E[x]\,E[y]] \\ &= E[xy] - E[x]\,E[y]. \end{aligned} \quad (21.2)$$

If large positive deviations of x are associated with large positive deviations of y, and likewise large negative deviations of the two variables occur together, then the covariance will be positive. Furthermore, if positive deviations of x are associated with negative deviations of y, and vice versa, then the covariance will be negative. On the other hand, if positive and negative deviations of x occur equally frequently with positive and negative deviations of y, then the covariance will tend to zero. Thus the covariance is a measure of a particular kind of association between two random variables.

It will be noted that the variance is the special case of the covariance of a random variable with itself:

$$\begin{aligned}\text{Cov}[x, x] &= E[(x - E[x])(x - E[x])] \\ &= E[(x - E[x])^2] = V[x]. \end{aligned} \tag{21.3}$$

If v, w are two random variables, and $x = a + bv$, $y = c + dw$ are two linear functions of them, a, b, c, and d being constants, then $E[x] = a + b\,E[v]$ and $E[y] = c + d\,E[w]$, and so

$$\begin{aligned}\text{Cov}[x, y] &= E[(a + bv - a - b\,E[v])(c + dw - c - d\,E[w])] \\ &= bd\,E[(v - E[v])(w - E[w])] = bd\,\text{Cov}[v, w]. \end{aligned} \tag{21.4}$$

Equation (14.4) was a special case of this.

Suppose that x, y are two random variables with a joint distribution. The covariance of their standardized forms is known as their *correlation coefficient*:

$$\rho_{xy} = \text{Cov}\left[\frac{x - E[x]}{\sqrt{V[x]}}, \frac{y - E[y]}{\sqrt{V[y]}}\right]. \tag{21.5}$$

Using the definition of covariance (21.1), this readily reduces to

$$\rho_{xy} = \frac{\text{Cov}[x, y]}{\sqrt{V[x]\,V[y]}}. \tag{21.6}$$

If $\rho_{xy} = 0$, we say that x and y are uncorrelated, and this implies $\text{Cov}[x, y] = 0$.

Now consider the covariance of independent variables. We know from (19.4) that, if x and y are independent, $p\{x, y\} = p\{x\}\,p\{y\}$. The definition of covariance (21.1) involves $E[xy]$; using the definition of expectation in the multivariate case (20.1), we have

$$E[xy] = \int_{-\infty}^{\infty}\int_{-\infty}^{\infty} xy\; p\{x, y\}\; dx\, dy;$$

so, for the case of x, y independent,

$$\begin{aligned}E[xy] &= \int_{-\infty}^{\infty}\int_{-\infty}^{\infty} xy\; p\{x\}\; p\{y\}\; dx\, dy \\ &= \int_{-\infty}^{\infty} x\, p\{x\}\, dx \int_{-\infty}^{\infty} y\, p\{y\}\, dy = E[x]\,E[y]. \end{aligned} \tag{21.7}$$

Substituting this in (21.2), we see that $\text{Cov}[x, y] = 0$ and by (21.6) also $\rho_{xy} = 0$. Thus independent variables are uncorrelated. The converse, however, is generally not true. Two random variables can be uncorrelated but not independent. A simple example of this is to let $p\{x, y\} = 1/4$ at the points $(-1, 0)$, $(0, 1)$, $(0, -1)$, and $(1, 0)$; see Figure 1.32. Then, by the discrete analogy of (20.1),

$$E[xy] = \sum_i \sum_j (x_i y_j)\, p\{x_i, y_j\}$$
$$= (-1) \times 0 \times \frac{1}{4} + 0 \times 1 \times \frac{1}{4} + 0 \times (-1) \times \frac{1}{4} + 1 \times 0 \times \frac{1}{4} = 0.$$

Also $$E[x] = \sum_i x_i\, p\{x_i\} = (-1) \times \frac{1}{4} + 0 \times \frac{1}{2} + 1 \times \frac{1}{4} = 0,$$

and likewise $E[y] = 0$. The covariance of x and y is thus

$$\text{Cov}[x, y] = E[xy] - E[x]\, E[y] = 0 - 0 \times 0 = 0.$$

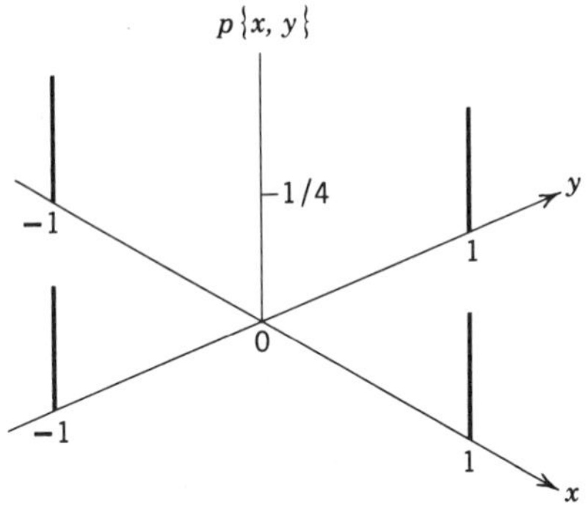

Figure 1.32

Thus x, y have zero covariance, but are obviously not independent. For example, at $x = -1$, $y = 0$, we have $p\{x, y\} = 1/4$, and $p\{x\} = 1/4$. $p\{y\} = 1/2$; so the relationship (16.4), $p\{x, y\} = p\{x\}\,p\{y\}$, which is necessary for the independence of x and y, is not satisfied.

1.22. The Variance of a Mean

We saw in (20.4) that the expectation of the mean of n observations from a distribution was the expectation of that distribution. We now want to consider the variance of a sample mean. Let us start with the sum of two random variables, $z = x + y$; its variance will be

$$V[z] = E[z^2] - (E[z])^2 = E[(x + y)^2] - (E[x + y])^2$$
$$= E[x^2] + 2E[xy] + E[y^2] - (E[x])^2 - 2E[x]\, E[y] - (E[y])^2$$
$$= V[x] + V[y] + 2\,\text{Cov}[x, y] \tag{22.1}$$
$$= V[x] + V[y] + 2\rho\sqrt{V[x]\, V[y]} \tag{22.2}$$

the last line being an alternative form given by using (21.6).

This result generalizes easily. Let $x_1, \ldots, x_n$ be random variables, and consider any linear combination

$$z = a_0 + a_1 x_1 + \cdots + a_n x_n, \tag{22.3}$$

where the a_i are fixed constants. Then

$$E[z] = a_0 + a_1\, E[x_1] + \cdots + a_n\, E[x_n] \tag{22.4}$$

and

$$\begin{aligned} V[z] &= E[(z - E[z])^2] \\ &= E[(a_0 + a_1 x_1 + \cdots + a_n x_n - a_0 - a_1\, E[x_1] - \cdots - a_n\, E[x_n])^2] \\ &= E[\{a_1(x_1 - E[x_1]) + \cdots + a_n(x_n - E[x_n])\}^2] \\ &= E[\sum_i^n a_i^2(x_i - E[x_i])^2 + \sum_{\substack{i \\ i \neq j}}^n \sum_j^n a_i a_j (x_i - E[x_i])(x_j - E[x_j])] \\ &= \sum_i^n a_i^2\, E[(x_i - E[x_i])^2] + \sum_{\substack{i \\ i \neq j}}^n \sum_j^n a_i a_j\, E[(x_i - E[x_i])(x_j - E[x_j])] \\ &= \sum_i^n a_i^2\, V[x_i] + \sum_{\substack{i \\ i \neq j}}^n \sum_j^n a_i a_j \operatorname{Cov}[x_i, x_j]. \end{aligned} \tag{22.5}$$

An alternative form for (22.5), using (21.3), is

$$V[z] = \sum_i^n \sum_j^n a_i a_j \operatorname{Cov}[x_i, x_j]: \tag{22.6}$$

in this form the double summation includes the cases $i = j$ which give the variance terms in (22.5). Also, the covariance term in (22.5) involves every combination of i with j, excluding $i = j$, and may be written as

$$2 \sum_{\substack{i=1 \\ i<j}}^{n-1} \sum_{j=2}^{n} a_i a_j \operatorname{Cov}[x_i, x_j]. \tag{22.7}$$

If in (22.3) we put $a_0 = 0$, $a_1 = a_2 = \cdots = 1$, then z is just the simple sum, and

$$V[z] = \sum_i^n V[x_i] + \sum_{\substack{i \\ i \neq j}}^n \sum_j^n \operatorname{Cov}[x_i, x_j]. \tag{22.8}$$

If the variables are uncorrelated, then their covariances are zero and

$$V[z] = \sum_i^n V[x_i]. \tag{22.9}$$

Often we are in the case where the variables x_i are independent, and since independence implies zero covariance (22.9) will hold here also.

To consider the special, but important, case of the mean of n independent observations from the same distribution, the distribution having mean ξ and variance σ^2, in (22.3) put $a_0 = 0$ and $a_i = 1/n$, $i = 1, \ldots, n$. Then

$$z = \frac{x_1}{n} + \cdots + \frac{x_n}{n} = \frac{1}{n}\sum_i^n x_i = \bar{x};$$

i.e., with these values for the coefficients, a_i, z is the mean, say $\bar{x}$. Using (22.4) and (22.5), we have

$$E[\bar{x}] = \frac{1}{n}E[x_1] + \cdots + \frac{1}{n}E[x_n] = \frac{\xi}{n} + \cdots + \frac{\xi}{n} = \xi, \tag{22.10}$$

and

$$V[\bar{x}] = \frac{1}{n^2}V[x_1] + \cdots + \frac{1}{n^2}V[x_n] = \frac{\sigma^2}{n^2}\cdot n = \frac{\sigma^2}{n}. \tag{22.11}$$

1.23. The Addition Theorem for the Normal Distribution

In the preceding section we have proved that, if z is a linear combination of random variables x_i (22.3), then it has expectation (22.4) and variance (22.5). It is possible, but lengthy with the techniques so far at our disposal, to prove further that any linear combination z of normally distributed random variables x_i is itself normally distributed. A proof will be given at the end of Section 12.4. In particular this applies to the mean of n independent identically normally distributed variables x_i from a population $N(\xi, \sigma^2)$: the mean will be normally distributed $N(\xi, \sigma^2/n)$.

REFERENCES

1. Todhunter, I., *A History of the Mathematical Theory of Probability.* London: Macmillan & Co., 1865. New York: Chelsea Publishing Co., 1949.
2. Pearson, E. S., *Karl Pearson.* London: Cambridge University Press, 1938.
3. ——— and J. Wishart (eds.), *"Student's" Collected Papers.* London: Biometrika Office, 1942.
4. Fisher, R. A., *Statistical Methods for Research Workers.* 1st ed.; Edinburgh: Oliver & Boyd, 1925.
5. ——— *The Design of Experiments.* 1st ed.; Edinburgh: Oliver & Boyd, 1935.
6. ——— *Contributions to Mathematical Statistics*, W. A. Shewhart (ed.). New York: John Wiley & Sons, 1950.

7. Neyman, J., and E. S. Pearson, "On the problem of the most efficient tests of statistical hypotheses," *Philosophical Transactions of the Royal Society*, A, 231(1933), 289–337.
8. Wald, A., *Sequential Analysis*. New York: John Wiley & Sons, 1947.

EXERCISES

1.1. From a panel of 10 judges we are to select a committee of 3. How many ways can this be done:

(*a*) If the committee is to have a chairman, a vice-chairman, and a secretary, and these are to be specified?

(*b*) If the committee is to function with all three members on an equal footing?

1.2. A panel of 10 judges, 7 from one party and 3 from another, are to sit on a rostrum facing an audience. Assuming that differences between individuals from the same party are indistinguishable, how many ways can the rostrum be arranged?

1.3. An investment advisor draws up a list of 12 stocks.

(*a*) In how many ways can a client form a portfolio of 5 stocks from this list?

(*b*) If the list of 12 stocks contains 4 steels, 5 oils, and 3 office equipments, in how many ways can a client pick a portfolio containing 2 steels, 2 oils, and 1 office equipment?

1.4. There are 10 starters in a horse race. Assuming there are no ties;

(*a*) In how many ways can the horses cross the finishing line?

(*b*) In how many ways can the first three places be filled?

1.5. Suppose the probability that a certain piece of airborne electronic equipment will not be in working order on completion of its first flight is 0.6, and the probability of failure drops to half its previous value on each succeeding flight; e.g., if the equipment survived its first flight, the probability of failure on the second flight is 0.3, etc. What is the probability that the equipment will be in working order:

(*a*) After three flights?

(*b*) After five flights, given that it has survived the first two flights?

1.6. On third down and a few yards to go for a touchdown, a coach decides to run two pass plays. His quarterbacks B and K have probabilities 0.9 and 0.8 of getting the pass off satisfactorily. His favorite pass receivers Z and M have probabilities 0.7 and 0.6 of taking the pass if it is satisfactory, and making the touchdown. In the two forthcoming plays the coach can send in B and Z for one play and K and M for the other, or B and M for one play and K and Z for the other. Find the probabilities of a touchdown under these two strategies.

1.7. A professor of psychology writes the following:

Let us now consider whether estimates of the probability of success in a given task obey rules similar to those of mathematical probability or are subject to different, psychological rules. One rule of mathematical probability convenient for such a test is the additive theorem, namely, that small, independent probabilities of a particular event add up to a larger probability. Thus, if you are drawing for a lucky ticket in a pool, your chances of success will increase in proportion to the number of tickets you take. In one of our experiments we confronted our subjects with a choice between taking a single large probability or a set of smaller probabilities; e.g., they were allowed to draw either one ticket from a box of 10 or 10 tickets from 100, in the latter case putting back the ticket drawn each time before making the next draw. Mathematically, of course, the chance of drawing the prize ticket was exactly the same in both cases. But most of the subjects proved to be guided mainly by psychological rather than mathematical considerations.

If the 10 draws had to be made from 100 tickets in one box, about four-fifths of the subjects preferred to make a single draw from a box of 10.

Comment.

1.8. An aircraft has four engines, two on the left wing and two on the right wing. Suppose that the probability of any one engine failing on a certain trans-ocean flight is 0.1, and that the probability of any one engine failing is independent of the behavior of the others. What is the probability of the crew getting wet:

(*a*) If the plane will fly on any two engines?

(*b*) If the plane requires at least one (i.e., one or more) engines operating on both sides in order to fly?

1.9. In an experiment, six mice are to be divided into two groups of three mice each, one group to be the control and the other group to receive the experimental treatment. Assuming that all ways of dividing the mice up into two groups are equiprobable, what is the probability that the control group will contain the three heaviest mice?

1.10. In four experiments, 12 mice are to be divided into (*a*) two groups of 6, (*b*) three groups of 4, (*c*) four groups of 3, (*d*) six groups of 2. Assuming that all ways are equiprobable:

(i) What is the probability of any particular grouping in each of these four experiments?

(ii) If one of the groups is a control group, what is the probability that this group contains the heaviest mice in each of these four experiments?

1.11. If A is independent of B, show that B is independent of A, assuming that (5.1) is our definition of independence.

1.12. If A is independent of B, show that $\bar{A}$ is independent of $\bar{B}$.

1.13. The Chevalier de Méré (1654) wanted to know the following probabilities:

(*a*) Probability of seeing one or more sixes in four throws of a six-sided die.

(*b*) Probability of seeing one or more double sixes in 24 throws with a pair of dice.

The Chevalier thought that these two probabilities should be the same, but he threw dice so assiduously he convinced himself they were different. Evaluate these two probabilities.

1.14. A piggy bank contains seven nickels, eight dimes, six quarters, and four half dollars. You are permitted to withdraw one coin at random and then another. The random variable x is your gain in cents. What is (*a*) the distribution of x? (*b*) the probability that your gain will be more than 35 cents? (*c*) the expectation of x? (*d*) the variance of x?

1.15. In an eight-floor apartment house the elevator takes 10 seconds to get from one floor to the adjoining floor. Individuals leave and arrive with equal frequency, and the traffic arising from any floor is the same as for any other floor. The traffic density is low, so that the probability of the elevator called by one individual while it is in use by another individual is to be regarded as zero.

For a tenant (*a*) on the second floor, (*b*) on the eighth floor, what are (i) the distributions of waiting times? (ii) the expected values of the waiting times? (iii) the variances of the waiting times?

1.16. A soap company distributes entry blanks to a lottery requiring nothing but the filling in of one's name and the mailing of the blank. The prize schedule is

1st prize, $25,000	Next	5 prizes,	$1,000 each
2nd prize, $10,000	Next	10 prizes,	$500 each
3rd prize, $5,000	Next	50 prizes,	$250 each
	Next	100 prizes,	$100 each
	Next	1100 prizes,	$25 each

Assume that 10 million entry blanks are returned. Let the random variable x be your gain from participation. (*a*) What is the distribution of x? (*b*) What is its expected value? (*c*) Supposing that the only cost of entry is the four-cent stamp for mailing in the entry, does it make sense to participate?

1.17. The word "love" in the title of "For Love or Money" is meant to be a synonym for prizes. The show is unusual among daytime programs in that it offers cash as an alternative to love. The money is hard to come by in any serious amount. A kind of electronic roulette ball . . . darts from side to side of a stated number, such as 01400 and determines the payoff as it comes to rest: $.01, $.14, $1.40, $14, $140, or $1400. As any bookmaker's infant child could tell you, the chances of winning a respectable bundle are only two in six. The odds, therefore, are two to one against the player who goes for the cash instead of for a prize that is worth . . . $140. I'll detain you no longer with the laws of Pascal.—JOHN LARDNER in *The New Yorker*, July 19, 1958.

Comment. By "odds of n to 1 against" is meant a probability of $1/(1 + n)$. Assume each outcome equally likely.

1.18. $x_1, x_2, \ldots, x_n$ are independent random variables with expectations $\xi_1, \xi_2, \ldots, \xi_n$ and variances σ^2. The constants $a_{11}, a_{12}, \ldots, a_{1n}$ and $a_{21}, a_{22}, \ldots, a_{2n}$ define the linear combinations

$$y_1 = a_{11}x_1 + a_{12}x_2 + \cdots + a_{1n}x_n$$
$$y_2 = a_{21}x_1 + a_{22}x_2 + \cdots + a_{2n}x_n$$

(*a*) What is the condition that y_1 and y_2 should be uncorrelated? (*b*) Using the result from (*a*), show that the arithmetic mean $\bar{x}$ is uncorrelated with each deviation from the mean $(x_i - \bar{x})$.

1.19. We have a joint density function $p\{x, y\} = 1$ for $0 < x < 1, 0 < y < 1$, and $p\{x, y\} = 0$ otherwise. Find the probabilities that (*a*) $x > 0.5$ and $y > 0.7$, (*b*) $x > 0.5$, (*c*) $x > y$, (*d*) $x > 0.5$, given that $y = 0.5$, (*e*) $x > y$, given that $y < 0.5$, (*f*) $x + y < 1$.

1.20. A small plane will take four passengers in addition to the pilot. The pilot knows that the safe payload for the four passengers is 720 lb. Assuming that the passengers are selected at random from a normal population with mean weight 150 lb and standard deviation 32 lb, how often will four passengers overload the plane?

1.21. You are packing by machine 16 cookies to a box. The label states that the box contains 1 lb of cookies. The weight of the individual cookies is normally distributed with a mean of 1 oz and a standard deviation of 0.1 oz. If a customer buys a box at random, what are the probabilities that he receives (*a*) less than 1 lb, (*b*) less than 15 oz, (*c*) more than 16.5 oz? If you wish to change your manufacturing process so that the mean weight of the cookies is such that only one customer in a hundred will receive less than 1 lb, what should the new mean weight of the cookies be, assuming that the standard deviation remain unchanged? Further, if you could also reduce the standard deviation to 0.05 oz, what mean weight would satisfy the condition specified in the previous sentence?

1.22. Suppose that you drive from New York to San Francisco, 3040 miles by a certain route, starting with new spark plugs in your eight-cylinder engine. Suppose that the satisfactory life of a plug is normally distributed with a mean of 5000 miles and a standard deviation of 1000 miles. What is the probability that you will roll over the Bay Bridge with your motor still purring (with the original plugs) on all eight cylinders?

1.23. Pipes (for tobacco) are being packed in fancy plastic boxes. The length of the pipes is normally distributed with a mean of 5 in. and a standard deviation of 0.04 in. The internal length of the boxes is normally distributed with a mean of 5.1 in. and a standard deviation of 0.03 in. What proportion of the time will the box be too small for the pipe?

CHAPTER 2

Statistical Ideas

2.1. Statistical Inference

Statistics is frequently defined as the science of making wise decisions in the presence of uncertainty. To cite Savage's example in his review [1] of Wald's book [2], the decision to be made may be whether to take an umbrella on one's trip to the office. This approach requires a knowledge of the relative costs of carrying an umbrella when the day turns out to be fine and of getting wet through failing to carry an umbrella when the day turns out to be wet. The practical usefulness of this approach has been severely hindered by the rareness with which one can actually estimate with any confidence the cost functions. Whether this obstacle can be circumvented sufficiently to bring this decision-theory approach into common use remains to be seen. For an elementary account, see Chernoff and Moses [3].

Classical statistical inference operates one stage further back from the decision-making process: Very roughly speaking, it confines itself to establishing what can be said about the facts of the situation, and it leaves the decision as to what to actually do, if anything, to the common sense of the experimenter.

Two broad categories that have received particular attention are the problems of *estimation* and of the *testing of (statistical) hypotheses*. The first problem is subdivided into *point estimation* and *interval estimation* of the parameters of a distribution. For example, given a sample of n observations from a distribution assumed normal, we may wish to obtain point estimates of the mean ξ, or the variance σ^2, or both the mean and variance, or conceivably some function such as e^ξ or $\xi + k\sigma$. We may, on the other hand, wish to obtain an interval which we are confident will include the actual value of the parameter or parameters: This is the problem of interval estimation.

The second problem, hypothesis testing, consists of making an assumption about the distribution function of a random variable, very often about the numerical values of one or more of the parameters of the distribution function, and deciding whether those values of the parameters are consistent in some sense with our sample of observations on that random variable. For example, in the case of the normal distribution, the hypothesis might be that $\xi = 0$, or that $\sigma^2 = 1$. Of course, if we could take infinitely large samples of observations, we would be able, in an ordinary case, to determine the parameters of the distribution in question exactly, and there would be no statistical problem. The problems of statistical inference are to do the best we can with limited samples of observations.

Implicit in the treatment of the problems of statistical inference is the assumption that we are able to obtain random samples of observations. A *random sample* can be defined as consisting of statistically independent identically distributed random variables, i.e., random variables with the same distribution function.

As an example of how we may generate a random sample, consider a sample space with all n points equiprobable. Let x be a random variable, so that associated with every point in the sample space is a characteristic x_i. Let $n(x_i)$ be the number of points with characteristic x_i. Now sample N points from the sample space, replacing each point obtained before taking the next sample. Then we will observe x_i with probability $n(x_i)/n$. Since the drawings are with replacement, they are independent. Since all observations come from the same sample space, they will have the same distribution function. Thus our observations will satisfy our definition of a random sample.

Suppose we take a random sample of two observations on a random variable with distribution function $p\{x\}$. The pair of observations, x_1, x_2 will have a bivariate distribution function $p\{x_1, x_2\}$. But, if the sample was random, as supposed, the observations will be independent, and by (19.4)

$$p\{x_1, x_2\} = p\{x_1\}\, p\{x_2\}.$$

Clearly this will generalize to n observations; so

$$p\{x_1, \ldots, x_n\} = p\{x_1\} \cdots p\{x_n\}. \tag{1.1}$$

2.2. Some Principles of Point Estimation

Suppose that we have a random sample of n observations $x_1, \ldots, x_n$ from a population with distribution function of known form $p\{x : \theta_1, \ldots, \theta_k\}$, involving k parameters θ_j, $j = 1, \ldots, k$. For example, $p\{\ \}$ could be the normal distribution which has the two parameters ξ and σ. We may wish to estimate ξ, or we may wish to estimate σ^2 either in the case where ξ is known or in the case where ξ is unknown. The general problem is to estimate one (or more) of the θ_j, the remaining θ_j being either known or unknown. The function of the observations we choose, $\hat{\theta}(x_1, \ldots, x_n)$ is known as the *estimator*, and, when we insert a particular sample of numerical values for the x_i, we obtain a numerical value of the function which is known as an *estimate*. Often there will be several functions which naturally suggest themselves as estimators: For example, as estimators of the mean of a normal distribution we might use the arithmetic mean, the median, the mode, the midrange (the arithmetic mean of the largest and smallest observations in the sample), etc.

What criteria should we use for choosing our estimator? Obviously, in principle the answer may depend on the particular purpose for which we want it. However, conventional statistics attempts to answer this question in general terms, in order to generate estimators of general utility, since it would be impractical to have to consider every separate problem completely from first principles. In practice, our choice is sometimes influenced by economic considerations; one estimator may be somewhat better than another, but, if it requires \$500.00 of computation whereas the alternative requires only \$5.00, we may well decide that the margin of superiority of the former does not justify the additional expenditure and that the latter is adequate for our needs.

Confining our discussion to the one-parameter case, intuitively we want our estimator $\hat{\theta}$ to yield estimates whose distribution is close in some sense to θ. This broad criterion is not sufficient to resolve ambiguities, however. In Figure 2.1, showing the distribution of three alternative estimators $\hat{\theta}_a$, $\hat{\theta}_b$, and $\hat{\theta}_c$, the first two have the advantage that their expected values are equal to θ. This property, namely, that

$$E[\hat{\theta}] = \theta, \tag{2.1}$$

is known as *unbiasedness*. The bias of an estimator θ is defined as

$$(E[\hat{\theta}] - \theta). \tag{2.2}$$

The estimator $\hat{\theta}_a$ is preferable to $\hat{\theta}_b$ in that medium-sized deviations occur less frequently; on the other hand, extreme deviations are more frequent with $\hat{\theta}_a$ than with $\hat{\theta}_b$. Using the variance, $V[\hat{\theta}] = E[(\hat{\theta} - E[\hat{\theta}])^2]$, as a measure of spread, the third estimator $\hat{\theta}_c$ is the best of the three, but, since its expected value is not equal to θ, it is a biased estimator.

Unbiased estimators have the following desirable property: If we have a series of independent unbiased estimates, then their average will also be unbiased. On the other hand, the average of biased estimates will be biased, no matter how large the number being averaged.

For comparing estimators, including biased estimators, a useful criterion is the *mean-square error*, defined as the expected value of the square of the deviation of the estimate from the parameter, $E[(\hat{\theta} - \theta)^2]$. This quantity is equal to the variance plus the square of the bias, as can be shown as follows:

$$\begin{aligned} E[(\hat{\theta} - \theta)^2] &= E[\{(\hat{\theta} - E[\hat{\theta}]) + (E[\hat{\theta}] - \theta)\}^2] \\ &= E[(\hat{\theta} - E[\hat{\theta}])^2] + E[(E[\hat{\theta}] - \theta)^2] + 2(E[\hat{\theta}] - \theta)\, E[\hat{\theta} - E[\hat{\theta}]] \\ &= V[\hat{\theta}] + (\text{bias})^2 \end{aligned} \tag{2.3}$$

since

$$E[\hat{\theta} - E[\hat{\theta}]] = E[\hat{\theta}] - E[E[\hat{\theta}]] = E[\hat{\theta}] - E[\hat{\theta}] = 0.$$

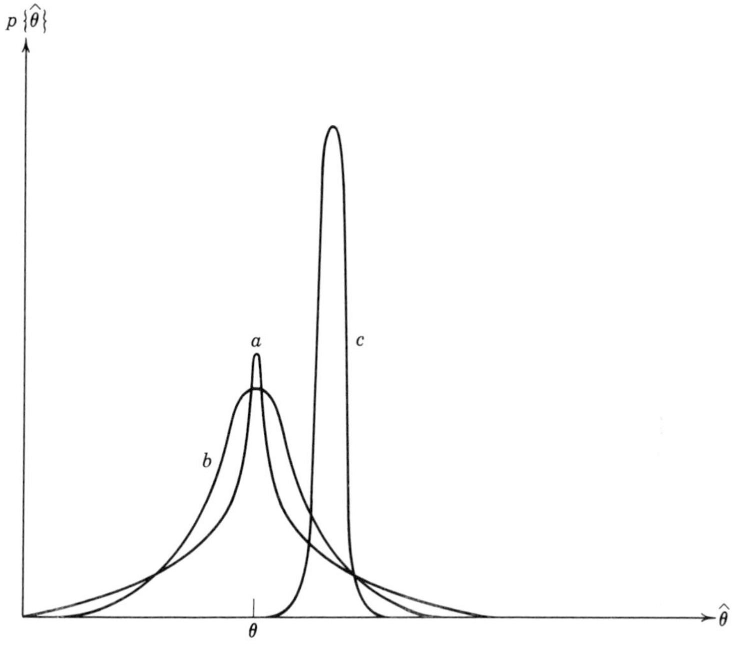

Figure 2.1

A further criterion, consistency, involves the behavior of an estimator as the sample size increases indefinitely. Specifically, if for any small quantity ϵ, the probability that the absolute value of the deviation of $\hat{\theta}$ from θ is less than ϵ tends to 1 as n tends to infinity; i.e., if

$$\Pr\{|\hat{\theta} - \theta| < \epsilon\} \to 1 \qquad \text{as } n \to \infty, \tag{2.4}$$

then we say that the estimator θ is *consistent*.

Among the class of consistent estimators, there will be one or more with minimum variance: This (or these) is (or are) the *efficient* estimator(s). The *efficiency* of any other estimator is defined as the ratio of the variance of the efficient estimator(s) to the variance of the other estimator.

2.3. The Method of Maximum Likelihood

A rather satisfactory general method of estimation is the method of maximum likelihood [4]; this is to choose that value of θ which maximizes the likelihood function defined as

$$L = p\{x_1 : \theta\} \cdots p\{x_n : \theta\} \tag{3.1}$$

where $p\{x : \theta\}$ is the distribution function of x, of known form, but containing the unknown parameter θ. In the likelihood function L, the observed x's are considered as constants and the parameter θ as a variable. Maximum-likelihood estimators are often biased, but have the advantages of being consistent and asymptotically normal and asymptotically efficient under general conditions.

As one example of maximum-likelihood estimation, suppose that we take a sample of size n from a binomial population with parameter θ and find x defectives in the sample. We wish to estimate θ, the proportion of defectives in the population. The likelihood function is

$$L = p\{x : n, \theta\} = \binom{n}{x} \theta^x (1 - \theta)^{n-x}. \tag{3.2}$$

In maximizing this, it is more convenient to maximize its logarithm, which amounts to the same thing; those values of the parameters which maximize $\log L$ will maximize L. The logarithm of (3.2) is

$$\log L = \log\binom{n}{x} + x \log \theta + (n - x) \log(1 - \theta).$$

The usual device for maximization with respect to a parameter is to differentiate with respect to the parameter and equate to zero:

$$\frac{d \log L}{d\theta} = \frac{x}{\theta} + (n - x)\frac{-1}{1 - \theta}$$

which yields $\hat{\theta} = x/n$ on equating to zero. The symbol ^ is conventionally used over a symbol to denote the maximum-likelihood estimator. Thus $\hat{\theta}$ is the maximum-likelihood estimator of θ.

When the distribution function has several parameters, we can usually find the values of the parameters that maximize $\log L$ by differentiating with respect to the parameters and equating to zero; i.e., we put

$$\frac{\partial \log L}{\partial \theta_1} = \frac{\partial \log L}{\partial \theta_2} = \cdots = 0.$$

Frequently the value of, say, θ_1, that maximizes $\log L$ depends on the value of θ_2; so to estimate θ_1 we have also to estimate θ_2. This is not always the case.

As an example, consider the estimation of the parameter ξ of a normal distribution from a sample $x_1, \ldots, x_n$. The likelihood function is obtained by substituting the normal density function in (3.1):

$$\begin{aligned} L &= \frac{1}{\sqrt{2\pi}\,\sigma} \exp\left[-\frac{(x_1-\xi)^2}{2\sigma^2}\right] \cdots \frac{1}{\sqrt{2\pi}\,\sigma} \exp\left[-\frac{(x_n-\xi)^2}{2\sigma^2}\right] \\ &= \left(\frac{1}{2\pi\sigma^2}\right)^{n/2} \exp\left[-\frac{1}{2\sigma^2}\sum_i^n (x_i-\xi)^2\right]. \end{aligned} \tag{3.3}$$

Thus the logarithm of the likelihood is

$$\log L = -\frac{n}{2}\log(2\pi\sigma^2) - \frac{1}{2\sigma^2}\sum_i^n (x_i - \xi)^2 . \tag{3.4}$$

Differentiating with respect to ξ gives

$$\frac{\partial \log L}{\partial \xi} = -\frac{1}{2\sigma^2}\sum_i^n 2(x_i-\xi)(-1). \tag{3.5}$$

Equating to zero and solving for $\hat{\xi}$, the maximum-likelihood estimator of ξ, gives

$$\sum_i^n (x_i - \hat{\xi}) = 0 = \left(\sum_i^n x_i\right) - n\hat{\xi},$$

whence

$$\hat{\xi} = \frac{\sum_i^n x_i}{n} \tag{3.6}$$

which of course is the sample mean, usually denoted by $\bar{x}$. Note that we obtained $\hat{\xi}$ without having to estimate σ^2.

To obtain the maximum-likelihood estimator of σ^2 we differentiate (3.4) with respect to σ^2:

$$\frac{\partial \log L}{\partial \sigma^2} = -\frac{n}{2}\frac{1}{\sigma^2} + \frac{1}{2(\sigma^2)^2}\sum_i^n (x_i-\xi)^2. \tag{3.7}$$

If ξ is known we equate this to zero and solve for $\widehat{\sigma^2}$:

$$\widehat{\sigma^2} = \sum_i^n \frac{(x_i - \xi)^2}{n}. \tag{3.8}$$

If ξ is unknown, we put the two partial derivatives (3.5) and (3.7) equal to zero, giving $\hat{\xi} = \bar{x}$ as before and $\widehat{\sigma^2} = \sum_i^n (x_i - \hat{\xi})^2/n$ Substituting for $\hat{\xi}$ from the former into the latter gives

$$\widehat{\sigma^2} = \sum_i^n \frac{(x_i - \bar{x})^2}{n}. \tag{3.9}$$

In this case, therefore, we had to obtain $\hat{\xi}$ in order to obtain $\widehat{\sigma^2}$.

In the foregoing we obtained the maximum-likelihood estimator of σ^2, i.e., $\widehat{\sigma^2}$. We might have chosen instead to obtain the maximum-likelihood estimator of σ, i.e., $\hat{\sigma}$. We would then have differentiated (3.4) with respect to σ:

$$\frac{\partial \log L}{\partial \sigma} = -\frac{n}{\sigma} + \frac{1}{\sigma^3} \sum_i^n (x_i - \xi)^2.$$

We equate to zero and solve for $\hat{\sigma}$:

$$\hat{\sigma} = \sqrt{\sum_i^n (x_i - \hat{\xi})^2/n} = \sqrt{\sum_i^n (x_i - \bar{x})^2/n}. \tag{3.10}$$

We thus see that

$$(\hat{\sigma})^2 = (\widehat{\sigma^2}). \tag{3.11}$$

This illustrates a general property of maximum-likelihood estimators, and one which is highly desirable, namely, *invariance*. Generally, if $f(\theta)$ is a single-valued function of θ, and $\hat{\theta}$ is the maximum-likelihood estimator of θ, then $f(\hat{\theta})$ is the maximum-likelihood estimator of $\widehat{f(\theta)}$, i.e., $f(\theta)$. In the foregoing example, $\sigma = \sqrt{\sigma^2}$ is a single-valued function of σ^2, and $\hat{\sigma} = \sqrt{\widehat{\sigma^2}}$.

Let us now check on the expected value of $\hat{\sigma}^2$ to see if it is a biased estimator. We have

$$\begin{aligned} n\hat{\sigma}^2 &= \sum_i^n (x_i - \bar{x})^2 = \sum_i^n [(x_i - \xi) - (\bar{x} - \xi)]^2 \\ &= \sum_i^n (x_i - \xi)^2 + n(\bar{x} - \xi)^2 - 2(\bar{x} - \xi) \sum_i^n (x_i - \xi) \\ &= \sum_i^n (x_i - \xi)^2 - n(\bar{x} - \xi)^2, \end{aligned} \tag{3.12}$$

since

$$2(\bar{x} - \xi) \sum_i^n (x_i - \xi) = 2(\bar{x} - \xi) \left(\sum_i^n x_i - n\xi \right)$$
$$= 2(\bar{x} - \xi)(n\bar{x} - n\xi) = 2n(\bar{x} - \xi)^2.$$

Thus $$E[n\hat{\sigma}^2] = \sum_i^n E[(x_i - \xi)^2] - n\, E[(\bar{x} - \xi)^2]. \tag{3.13}$$

Now $E[(x_i - \xi)^2]$ is just the definition of $V[x_i] = \sigma^2$, and similarly $E[(\bar{x} - \xi)^2]$ is the variance of $\bar{x}$, $V[\bar{x}] = \sigma^2/n$, since $E[\bar{x}] = \xi$. Hence

$$n\, E[\hat{\sigma}^2] = n\sigma^2 - n\frac{\sigma^2}{n} = \sigma^2(n - 1);$$

so $$E[\hat{\sigma}^2] = \sigma^2\left(\frac{n-1}{n}\right). \tag{3.14}$$

Thus the maximum-likelihood estimator (3.9) of the variance of a normal distribution is biased. If we choose to define s^2 as

$$s^2 = \sum_i^n \frac{(x_i - \bar{x})^2}{n - 1} \tag{3.15}$$

it will have an expected value

$$E[s^2] = E\left[\sum_i^n \frac{(x_i - \bar{x})^2}{n-1}\right] = E\left[\frac{n}{n-1} \frac{\sum_i^n (x_i - \bar{x})^2}{n}\right]$$
$$= \frac{n}{n-1} E[\hat{\sigma}^2] = \frac{n}{n-1} \sigma^2 \frac{(n-1)}{n} = \sigma^2, \tag{3.16}$$

and hence be unbiased.

For a technical presentation of the properties of maximum-likelihood estimators, see Sections 33.2 and 33.3 of [5].

The general subject of estimation is clearly large, and also rather controversial because it is possible to give different weights to the various criteria, and to make up criteria of one's own, depending on one's view as to what the estimate is to be used for. In this book we will not explore this topic further, except in Chapter 11 where we introduce another method, the method of least squares, which in the case where the underlying distribution is normal gives results identical with those of the method of maximum likelihood. In the remainder of this book we will be dealing only with situations in which simple common sense does not lead us astray.

2.4. Choice of Weights to Give a Weighted Mean of Minimum Variance

Suppose that we have k observations x_i, all with the same expectation ξ, but with variances σ_i^2. We wish to choose values for the coefficients a_i so that a linear combination of the x_i, defined as

$$\bar{x} = \sum_i^k a_i x_i , \tag{4.1}$$

will be unbiased and of minimum variance. For $\bar{x}$ to be unbiased, its expected value,

$$E[\bar{x}] = E\left[\sum_i^k a_i x_i\right] = \sum_i^k a_i\, E[x_i] = \xi \sum_i^k a_i , \tag{4.2}$$

must equal ξ, so we require that

$$\sum_i^k a_i = 1. \tag{4.3}$$

The variance of $\bar{x}$ is

$$V[\bar{x}] = V\left[\sum_i^k a_i x_i\right] = \sum_i^k a_i^2\, V[x_i] = \sum_i^k a_i^2 \sigma_i^2. \tag{4.4}$$

We wish to determine the values of a_i which will make the variance of $\bar{x}$ a minimum, subject to the earlier condition of unbiasedness (4.3). From this condition we can write

$$a_k + \sum_i^{k-1} a_i = \sum_i^k a_i = 1;$$

so

$$a_k = 1 - \sum_i^{k-1} a_i . \tag{4.5}$$

Thus the variance of $\bar{x}$ can be written in terms of $a_1, \ldots, a_{k-1}$:

$$\begin{aligned} V[\bar{x}] &= \sum_i^{k-1} a_i^2 \sigma_i^2 + \left(1 - \sum_i^{k-1} a_i\right)^2 \sigma_k^2 \\ &= \sum_i^{k-1} a_i^2 \sigma_i^2 + \left[1 - 2\sum_i^{k-1} a_i + \left(\sum_i^{k-1} a_i\right)^2\right] \sigma_k^2 . \end{aligned}$$

To find the values of a_i which make this a minimum we differentiate with respect to a_j and equate to zero:

$$\begin{aligned} \frac{\partial V[\bar{x}]}{\partial a_j} &= 2a_j\sigma_j^2 - 2\sigma_k^2 + 2\left(\sum_i^{k-1} a_i\right)\sigma_k^2 \\ &= 2\left[a_j\sigma_j^2 - \left(1 - \sum_i^{k-1} a_i\right)\sigma_k^2\right] = 0. \end{aligned}$$

Substituting (4.5) in this, we get

$$a_j = a_k\left(\frac{\sigma_k^2}{\sigma_j^2}\right), \qquad j = 1, \ldots, k-1. \tag{4.6}$$

However, this relationship is obviously true for $j = k$ also. We can therefore sum over $j = 1, \ldots, k$ to get

$$\sum_j^k a_j = a_k \sigma_k^2 \sum_j^k \frac{1}{\sigma_j^2}.$$

But, from (4.3), $\sum_i^k a_i = 1$; so

$$a_k = \frac{1}{\sigma_k^2 \sum_i^k \frac{1}{\sigma_i^2}}. \tag{4.7}$$

Substituting (4.7) into (4.6) gives, for any j,

$$a_j = \frac{1}{\sigma_j^2 \sum_i^k \frac{1}{\sigma_i^2}}. \tag{4.8}$$

These a_i, then, are the values which make $\bar{x} = \sum_i^k a_i x_i$ unbiased and of minimum variance. If we use these coefficients, the variance of $\bar{x}$, using (4.4), is

$$V[\bar{x}] = \sum_i^k a_i^2 \sigma_i^2 = \sum_i^k \left(\frac{1}{\sigma_i^2 \sum_i^k \frac{1}{\sigma_i^2}}\right)^2 \sigma_i^2 = \frac{1}{\left(\sum_i^k \frac{1}{\sigma_i^2}\right)^2} \sum_i^k \frac{\sigma_i^2}{\sigma_i^4} = \frac{1}{\sum_i^k \frac{1}{\sigma_i^2}}. \tag{4.9}$$

Sometimes for convenience in notation we use weights $w_i = 1/\sigma_i^2$,

$$w_i = \frac{1}{\sigma_i^2} = a_i \sum_i^k \frac{1}{\sigma_i^2} = a_i \sum_i^k w_i,$$

so that

$$a_i = \frac{w_i}{\sum_i^k w_i} \tag{4.10}$$

and

$$\bar{x} = \frac{\sum_i^k w_i x_i}{\sum_i^k w_i} \tag{4.11}$$

with variance

$$V[\bar{x}] = \frac{1}{\sum_{i}^{k} w_i}. \tag{4.12}$$

2.5 Some Principles of Hypothesis Testing

The simplest situation is the test of a hypothesis against a single alternative. We suppose that under the *null hypothesis* H_0 the frequency function is $p\{x:\theta_0\}$ and under the *alternative hypothesis* the frequency function is $p\{x:\theta_1\}$. The two hypotheses in question supposedly completely define the two distributions; i.e., θ_0 and θ_1 are both specified, and if there are further parameters in the distribution functions they are assumed known. Hypotheses of this type are known as *simple hypotheses.* If any parameters are not specified completely the hypothesis is called a *composite hypothesis.* For example, if the distribution is the normal and the parameter in which we are interested is ξ, but the variance is unknown, then we would be concerned with a composite hypothesis. Again, if the alternative distribution is the normal with known variance but it is merely specified that $\xi_1 > \xi_0$, or that $\xi_1 \neq \xi_0$, then ξ_1 is not specified completely and so we are dealing with a composite alternative hypothesis. In this and the two following sections we will be dealing with simple hypotheses.

We are going to take an observation x, and we want a criterion for accepting the null hypothesis (and rejecting the alternative) or accepting the alternative hypothesis (and rejecting the null hypothesis).

We start by defining a region on the line such that if the observation falls in this region then we accept the null hypothesis; this is the *region of acceptance.* The complementary region, where we reject the null hypothesis, is known as the *region of rejection* or the *critical region.*

On what basis shall we choose these regions? The first criterion is that only in a small fraction α of the time shall we reject the null hypothesis as false when in fact it is true. To reject the null hypothesis as false when in fact it is true is to commit a *type I error* or an *error of the first kind.* Clearly we wish to commit such an error only rarely: Common choices for α are 0.05 or 0.01. The numerical value selected for α is known as the *level of significance* of the test.

To be a little more specific, suppose that under the alternative hypothesis the distribution is shifted without change of shape to the right so that the expected value of x under the alternative hypothesis $E_{\theta_1}[x]$ is greater than $E_{\theta_0}[x]$, the expected value under the null hypothesis. Then it is reasonable to determine the critical region as that part of the line to the right of some value x_c, where x_c is chosen (see Figure 2.2) so that, if the null hypothesis is true so that x has the distribution $p\{x:\theta_0\}$, the probability of a random observation falling in the critical region is α, i.e.

$$\int_{x_c}^{\infty} p\{x:\theta_0\}\,dx = \alpha. \tag{5.1}$$

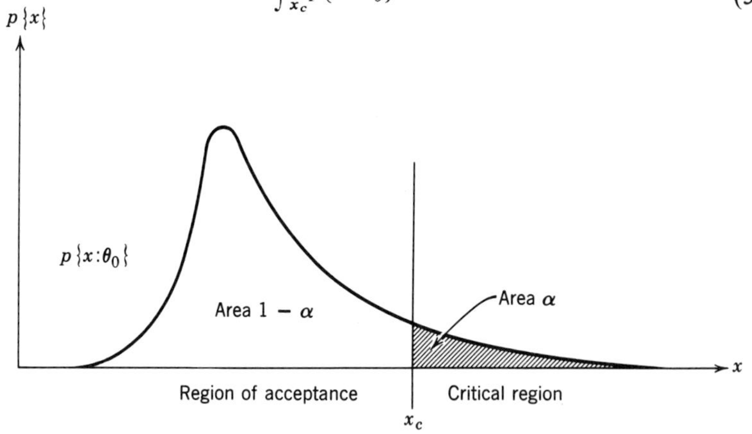

Figure 2.2

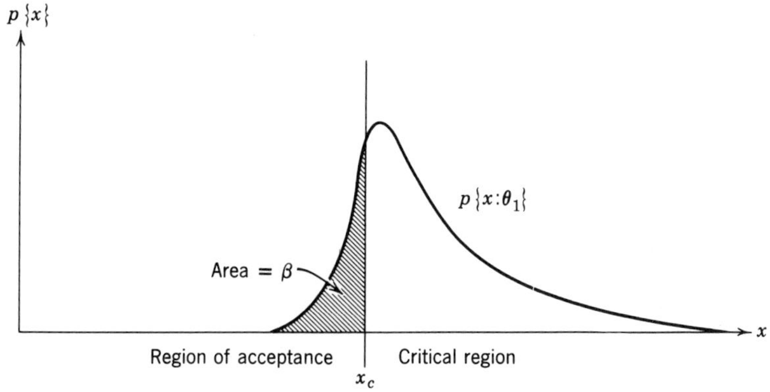

Figure 2.3

We now consider what will happen if actually H_1 is true and x has the frequency function $p\{x:\theta_1\}$. Since we supposed earlier that the difference between $p\{x:\theta_0\}$ and $p\{x:\theta_1\}$ was that the distribution was shifted to the right, the situation is as in Figure 2.3.

Even under H_1, our observation x may fall in the region of acceptance $x < x_c$. The probability of this happening is the shaded area in Figure 2.3, and the symbol β is used for this probability:

$$\int_{-\infty}^{x_c} p\{x:\theta_1\}\,dx = \beta. \tag{5.2}$$

Obviously, to accept H_0 when in fact it is false is an error, known as an *error of the second kind*, or a *type II* error. The probability of the complementary event, namely, of x falling in the region of rejection when it does come from $p\{x:\theta_1\}$ so that H_1 is true and H_0 is false, is known as *the power of the test*. Clearly we would like to have $(1-\beta)$, the power, large, say 0.90 or 0.99, but in practice restrictions of time and money mean we have often to settle for substantially less. It will be convenient to use the symbol π for the power:

$$\pi = 1 - \beta = \int_{x_c}^{\infty} p\{x:\theta_1\}\, dx. \tag{5.3}$$

The end result of a statistical test can be summarized in Table 2.1.

Table 2.1

	True situation	
Conclusion of experimenter	H_0 true H_1 false	H_0 false H_1 true
H_0 true H_1 false	Conclusion correct	Conclusion false Type II error committed
H_0 false H_1 true	Conclusion false Type I error committed	Conclusion correct

The usual procedure is to choose α small, say 0.05 or 0.01. For specified θ_0 and θ_1, and a given $p\{x:\theta\}$, then β will be determined, and often it will be substantially larger than what we would regard as a satisfactorily small value, say, 0.1. We will then be chary of actually rejecting H_1; while we accept H_0, we do not completely rule out the possibility that H_1 is true. Such a situation is illustrated by Figure 2.4. Here, if x falls at the point indicated, it is clearly in the region of acceptance, and so we accept H_0. However, such a value of x could very easily arise in sampling from the alternative distribution $p\{x:\theta_1\}$; the probability $\int_{-\infty}^{x_c} p\{x:\theta_1\}\, dx$ is by no means small, being about 3/16, and it would be hazardous to rule out the possibility that H_1 is true. Nevertheless, the customary procedure is to accept H_0 until we are forced by further data to revise our opinion.

The above procedure is standard but clearly open to a variety of criticisms. For example, the conventional policy of choosing α and leaving β to fend for itself often appears as an arbitrary asymmetry. Further, no cognizance is taken of the possibility that the economic or social consequences of an error of one kind may be quite different from those of an error of the other kind. Also, the insistence on a decision may be unreasonable; it may make more sense to render an undecided verdict, with a demand for more data if possible, and this again really depends on the cost of obtaining more data and the known or unknown costs of delay.

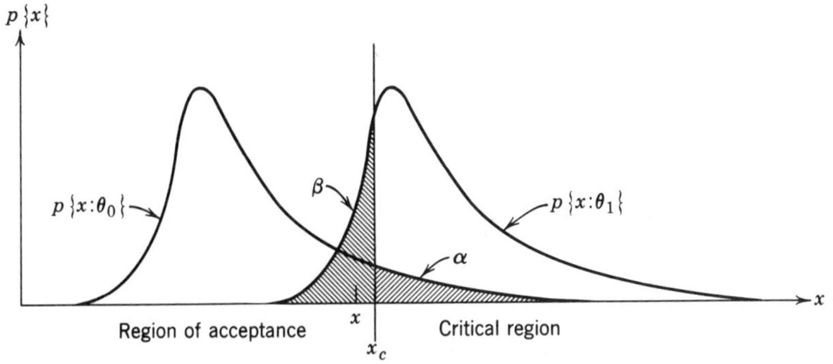

Figure 2.4

However, statisticians have found themselves able in practice to function satisfactorily within the foregoing standard framework, and we will not explore any of the proposed developments for they have not yet proved themselves sufficiently satisfactory to gain even partial acceptance.

2.6. A Criterion for Choosing between Alternative Tests

We have seen that we construct a test by dividing the x axis into two regions, the region of acceptance and the critical region, and so far the only restriction we have imposed on this choice is that the probability of an error of the first kind should be

$$\int_R p\{x:\theta_0\}\,dx = \alpha, \tag{6.1}$$

where R is the region of rejection. In the preceding section we stated that in the case in question a reasonable choice for the critical region was the upper tail of the distribution $p\{x:\theta_0\}$ without discussing whether this was the best choice. We now examine this question.

Consider an alternative critical region, for example, that defined by $x_d < x < x_e$ in Figure 2.5, where x_d and x_e satisfy the condition that the probability of an error of the first kind continues to be α:

$$\int_{x_d}^{x_e} p\{x:\theta_0\}\,dx = \alpha.$$

The obvious basis for comparing the two tests, since they have the same probability of a type I error, is the relative magnitudes of the probabilities of their type II errors.

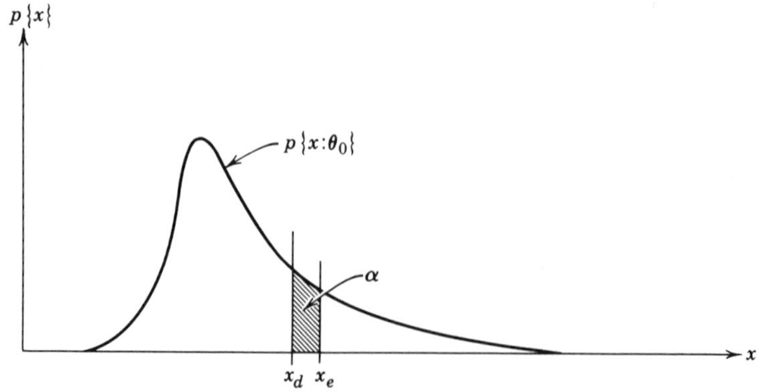

Figure 2.5

Figure 2.6 shows the relation to the alternative distribution $p\{x:\theta_1\}$ of the two alternative critical regions. If β_1 and β_2 are the probabilities of error of the second kind of the two tests, then

$$\beta_1 = \int_{-\infty}^{x_c} p\{x:\theta_1\}\, dx,$$

$$\beta_2 = \int_{-\infty}^{x_d} p\{x:\theta_1\}\, dx + \int_{x_e}^{\infty} p\{x:\theta_1\}\, dx.$$

In Figure 2.6, it is clear that β_2 is much greater than β_1; so the first test is much to be preferred.

To proceed on a more rigorous basis, we use the so-called Neyman–Pearson lemma, which states that the critical region should include those values of x for which $p\{x:\theta_1\}$ is as large as possible relative to $p\{x:\theta_0\}$. We choose those x's for which

$$\frac{p\{x:\theta_1\}}{p\{x:\theta_0\}} > K \tag{6.2}$$

where K has to be adjusted so that the level of significance of the test is a preselected value α. In other words, (6.2) will define a critical region of x, say R, and we must adjust K so that

$$\int_R p\{x:\theta_0\}\, dx = \alpha.$$

The Neyman–Pearson lemma asserts that a test constructed in accordance with the above rule will have maximum possible power (and minimum possible probability of error of the second kind).

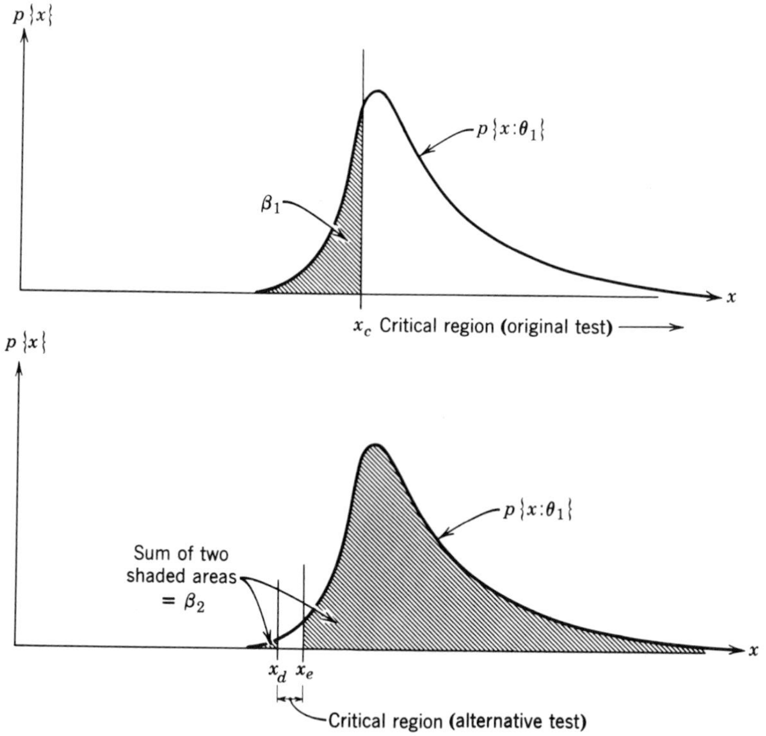

Figure 2.6

A proof is as follows. Suppose that our choice of tests following the Neyman–Pearson lemma, leads to a critical region R containing a small interval $\delta x'$ about a point x'. Consider whether we can do better, i.e., get a test with greater power, by replacing this small interval $\delta x'$ by an alternative interval $\delta x''$ about a point x'' not in the original critical region R. For the alternative test to have the same level of significance as the original test the amount of probability in the new interval added to R must equal that in the old interval which has been deleted from R:

$$p\{x':\theta_0\}\delta x' = p\{x'':\theta_0\}\delta x''. \tag{6.3}$$

Multiplying both sides by K gives

$$Kp\{x':\theta_0\}\delta x' = Kp\{x'':\theta_0\}\delta x''. \tag{6.4}$$

The power of the original test was (5.3) $\int_R p\{x:\theta_1\}\,dx$. With the proposed change, we remove from this integral an amount $p\{x':\theta_1\}\delta x'$ and substitute an amount $p\{x'':\theta_1\}\delta x''$. The increase in power is thus

$$p\{x'':\theta_1\}\delta x'' - p\{x':\theta_1\}\delta x'. \tag{6.5}$$

Now we know that x' lay in the original critical region R, and so from (6.2)

$$\frac{p\{x':\theta_1\}}{p\{x':\theta_0\}} > K,$$

whence

$$Kp\{x':\theta_0\}\delta x' < p\{x':\theta_1\}\delta x'. \tag{6.6}$$

Also we know that x'' lies in the region of acceptance of the original test; so

$$\frac{p\{x'':\theta_1\}}{p\{x'':\theta_0\}} < K,$$

whence

$$p\{x'':\theta_1\}\delta x'' < Kp\{x'':\theta_0\}\delta x''. \tag{6.7}$$

Now, by (6.4), the right-hand side of (6.7) is equal to the left-hand side of (6.6); so

$$p\{x'':\theta_1\}\delta x'' < p\{x':\theta_1\}\delta x',$$

and hence

$$p\{x'':\theta_1\}\delta x'' - p\{x':\theta_1\}\delta x' < 0. \tag{6.8}$$

The left-hand side of this inequality is identical with (6.5), the increase in power of the test given by the proposed substitution. Thus we have proved that the increase in power is negative; i.e., the change produces a decrease in the power of the test. Therefore the original test must have been optimum.

In the case where we have not a single observation x but instead a random sample $x_1, \ldots, x_n$, then in (6.2) in place of $p\{x:\theta_1\}$ we use $p\{x_1, \ldots, x_n:\theta_1\}$, which from (1.1), since the sample is supposedly random, equals $p\{x_1:\theta_1\}\cdots p\{x_n:\theta_1\}$. The denominator of (6.2) is treated similarly. Thus the criterion (6.2) becomes

$$\frac{p\{x_1:\theta_1\}\cdots p\{x_n:\theta_1\}}{p\{x_1:\theta_0\}\cdots p\{x_n:\theta_0\}} > K. \tag{6.9}$$

The foregoing ideas are due to Neyman and Pearson, [6], [7], and [8].

2.7. A One-Sided Test of an Observation from a Normal Population with Known Variance

In Section 2.5 we discussed the construction of tests of a null hypothesis against a simple alternative, and in Section 2.6 we saw that for this situation the Neyman–Pearson lemma (6.2) gave a method of constructing the most powerful test at a specified level of significance α. When the alternative hypothesis is not a simple hypothesis, e.g., $\theta = \theta_1$, but rather a composite hypothesis, e.g., $\theta > \theta_0$ or $\theta \neq \theta_0$, then usually there is no test which is more powerful than any other test for all possible alternative values of θ; i.e., usually a *uniformly most powerful test* does not exist.

There are instances, however, where a uniformly most powerful test does exist, one being the problem of testing the null hypothesis that a normal population has expectation $\xi = \xi_0$ against the alternative that $\xi > \xi_0$. Consider a particular value $\xi_1 > \xi_0$ for the alternative hypothesis: For this value, by the Neyman–Pearson lemma (6.2) the best test is that for which the range of x determining the critical region satisfies the inequality

$$\frac{p\{x:\xi_1, \sigma^2\}}{p\{x:\xi_0, \sigma^2\}} > K. \tag{7.1}$$

Now
$$\frac{p\{x:\xi_1, \sigma^2\}}{p\{x:\xi_0, \sigma^2\}} = \frac{\dfrac{1}{\sqrt{2\pi}\,\sigma} e^{-(x-\xi_1)^2/2\sigma^2}}{\dfrac{1}{\sqrt{2\pi}\,\sigma} e^{-(x-\xi_0)^2/2\sigma^2}} = e^{-[(x-\xi_1)^2-(x-\xi_0)^2]/2\sigma^2}$$

$$= e^{x(\xi_1-\xi_0)/\sigma^2} \cdot e^{-(\xi_1^2-\xi_0^2)/2\sigma^2} \tag{7.2}$$

The second exponential here is some known positive constant, say c, since ξ_1 and ξ_0 are specified and σ^2 is known. The first exponential is of the form e^{ax} where $a = (\xi_1 - \xi_0)/\sigma^2$ is a positive constant since $(\xi_1 - \xi_0) > 0$. Thus $p\{x : \xi_1, \sigma^2\}/p\{x: \xi_0, \sigma^2\}$ has the form ce^{ax} with both a and c positive: Therefore it increases with increasing x. Thus, to select all x for which this function is greater than K, we start with x at $+\infty$ and allow it to decrease until we have taken in an amount of the null distribution $p\{x : \xi_0, \sigma^2\}$ equal to the required level of significance α. The largest x which lies in the region of acceptance, say x_c, is given by substituting an equality sign for the inequality in (7.1), i.e., by putting (7.2) equal to K. Taking logarithms,

$$x_c\frac{\xi_1 - \xi_0}{\sigma^2} - \frac{\xi_1^2 - \xi_0^2}{2\sigma^2} = \log K, \tag{7.3}$$

and solving for x_c:

$$x_c = \frac{2\sigma^2 \log K + (\xi_1^2 - \xi_0^2)}{2(\xi_1 - \xi_0)}. \tag{7.4}$$

The critical region for the test is all values of x larger than x_c. In (7.4), ξ_1, ξ_0, and σ^2 are constants, and K has to be adjusted so that

$$\int_{x_c}^{\infty} \frac{1}{\sqrt{2\pi}\,\sigma} e^{-(x-\xi_0)^2/2\sigma^2}\,dx = \alpha. \tag{7.5}$$

This equation determines the value of x_c and hence the critical region $x > x_c$. In this instance, therefore, the problem of finding the critical region is solved without having actually to evaluate K.

Equation (7.5) implies

$$P\{x_c\} = \int_{-\infty}^{x_c} \frac{1}{\sqrt{2\pi}\,\sigma} e^{-(t-\xi_0)^2/2\sigma^2}\,dt = 1 - \alpha.$$

In (1.15.8) we had $P\{x\} = \Phi[(x - \xi)/\sigma]$; so we have

$$\Phi\left(\frac{x_c - \xi_0}{\sigma}\right) = 1 - \alpha,$$

or

$$\frac{x_c - \xi_0}{\sigma} = u_{1-\alpha},$$

whence

$$x_c = \xi_0 + \sigma u_{1-\alpha}. \tag{7.6}$$

Thus, for example, if we choose a level of significance $\alpha = 0.05$, Table I of the appendix gives $u_{0.95} = 1.645$, and $x_c = \xi_0 + 1.645\sigma$; i.e., the bottom edge of the critical region is 1.645 times the standard deviation above the expectation under the null hypothesis.

We have found that $x_c = \xi_0 + u_{1-\alpha}\sigma$ is the value of x for which (7.1) with the inequality replaced by an equality sign is true. Inserting this value x_c for x will determine K, and inserting the solution obtained for K in (7.3) will show that x_c is actually independent of ξ_1, even though ξ_1 does appear in (7.4) in the form that it is given there. Of course, since (7.6) already shows that x_c is independent of ξ_1, these steps are somewhat unnecessary, but it will directly demonstrate the consistency of our calculations. From (7.2) we have

$$K = e^{-[(x_c-\xi_1)^2-(x_c-\xi_0)^2]/2\sigma^2};$$

so

$$\log K = -\frac{(\xi_0 + u_{1-\alpha}\sigma - \xi_1)^2 - (\xi_0 + u_{1-\alpha}\sigma - \xi_0)^2}{2\sigma^2}$$

and

$$2\sigma^2 \log K = -(\xi_1 - \xi_0)^2 + 2(\xi_1 - \xi_0)u_{1-\alpha}\sigma.$$

Substituting this in (7.4), we obtain $x_c = \xi_0 + u_{1-\alpha}\sigma$ as before. It is particularly important to note that in this instance the equation determining the critical region (7.4) does not actually involve ξ_1; so the critical region is going to be the same no matter what the particular value of ξ_1 is, so long as it is greater than ξ_0. In this example of a composite alternative hypothesis, therefore, a uniformly most powerful test does exist.

The power of the foregoing test is by definition the probability that we reject the null hypothesis $\xi = \xi_0$ when ξ is equal to the alternative ξ_1, i.e., the probability that the observation x lies in the critical region, greater than x_c. Thus the power when ξ has the value ξ_1 is

$$\begin{aligned}\pi(\xi_1) = \Pr\{x > x_c | \xi = \xi_1\} &= \int_{x_c}^{\infty} \frac{1}{\sqrt{2\pi}\,\sigma} e^{-(x-\xi_1)^2/2\sigma^2}\,dx \\ &= 1 - \Phi\left(\frac{x_c - \xi_1}{\sigma}\right). \qquad (7.7)\end{aligned}$$

This form of the power function involves first calculating x_c from (7.6); substituting this value of x_c in (7.7) gives us an expression involving ξ_1 and ξ_0, and σ and α, as follows,

$$\begin{aligned}\pi(\xi_1) &= 1 - \Phi\left(\frac{\xi_0 + \sigma u_{1-\alpha} - \xi_1}{\sigma}\right) = 1 - \Phi\left(u_{1-\alpha} + \frac{\xi_0 - \xi_1}{\sigma}\right) \\ &= \Phi\left(-u_{1-\alpha} - \frac{\xi_0 - \xi_1}{\sigma}\right) = \Phi\left(u_\alpha + \frac{\xi_1 - \xi_0}{\sigma}\right) \qquad (7.8)\end{aligned}$$

using the facts that $1 - \Phi(u) = \Phi(-u)$ (1.15.4), and that $-u_{1-\alpha} = u_\alpha$ by the property of symmetry of the normal distribution.

We have so far considered tests based on a single observation. For n observations we use (6.9). Consider the case where we take a sample of n independent observations x_i from a normal distribution of known variance σ^2 and unknown mean ξ. We wish to test the null hypothesis $H_0:\xi = \xi_0$ against the alternative $\xi > \xi_0$ at the level of significance α. Substituting for $p\{x_i\}$ in (6.9),

$$\begin{aligned}&\frac{p\{x_1:\xi_1, \sigma^2\}\cdots p\{x_n:\xi_1, \sigma^2\}}{p\{x_1:\xi_0, \sigma^2\}\cdots p\{x_n:\xi_0, \sigma^2\}} \\ &= \frac{\dfrac{1}{\sqrt{2\pi}\,\sigma}\exp\left[-\dfrac{(x_1-\xi_1)^2}{2\sigma^2}\right]\cdots\dfrac{1}{\sqrt{2\pi}\,\sigma}\exp\left[-\dfrac{(x_n-\xi_1)^2}{2\sigma^2}\right]}{\dfrac{1}{\sqrt{2\pi}\,\sigma}\exp\left[-\dfrac{(x_1-\xi_0)^2}{2\sigma^2}\right]\cdots\dfrac{1}{\sqrt{2\pi}\,\sigma}\exp\left[-\dfrac{(x_n-\xi_0)^2}{2\sigma^2}\right]} \\ &= \frac{\exp\left[-\dfrac{1}{2\sigma^2}\sum_i^n (x_i-\xi_1)^2\right]}{\exp\left[-\dfrac{1}{2\sigma^2}\sum_i^n (x_i-\xi_0)^2\right]} = \exp\left[\bar{x}\frac{(\xi_1-\xi_0)}{\sigma^2/n}\right]\exp\left(-\frac{\xi_1^2-\xi_0^2}{2\sigma^2/n}\right). \qquad (7.9)\end{aligned}$$

This is similar to (7.2) except that it is a function of $\bar{x}$ instead of x and of σ^2/n instead of σ^2. With these changes the argument proceeds as before. The critical region, analogous to (7.6), will be

$$\bar{x} > \xi_0 + \frac{u_{1-\alpha}\sigma}{\sqrt{n}}, \tag{7.10}$$

and the power function, analogous to (7.8), will be

$$\pi(\xi_1) = \Phi\left(u_\alpha + \frac{\xi_1 - \xi_0}{\sigma/\sqrt{n}}\right) = \Phi(u_\alpha + \delta) \tag{7.11}$$

if we define $\delta = (\xi_1 - \xi_0)/(\sigma/\sqrt{n})$. For example, for a test at the level of significance $\alpha = 0.05$, $u_\alpha = -1.645$, and when $\delta = 1$,

$$\pi(\xi_1) = \Phi(-1.645 + 1) = \Phi(-0.645) = 0.2594.$$

In this way Table 2.2 is prepared, and the power function is plotted in Figure 2.7.

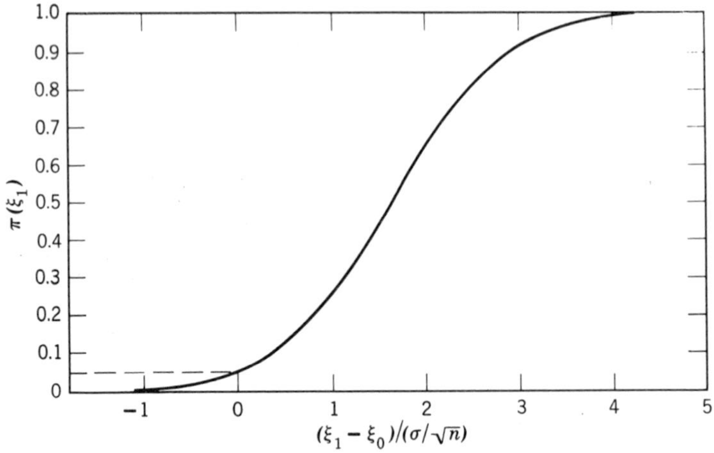

Figure 2.7

Table 2.2. Power of One-Tailed Test at Level of Significance 0.05 of Mean of *n* Observations from a Normal Distribution

$\frac{\xi_1 - \xi_0}{\sigma/\sqrt{n}}$	−1.0	−0.5	0	0.5	1	1.5	2	2.5	3	3.5	4
$\pi(\xi_1)$	.004	.016	.050	.126	.259	.442	.639	.804	.912	.968	.999

Table 2.2 and Figure 2.7 show that, when $\xi_1 = \xi_0$, the power coincides with the level of significance. Also, when $\xi_1 < \xi_0$, there is some probability, but very slight, of rejecting $H_0: \xi = \xi_0$ in favor of the alternative $\xi = \xi_1 > \xi_0$.

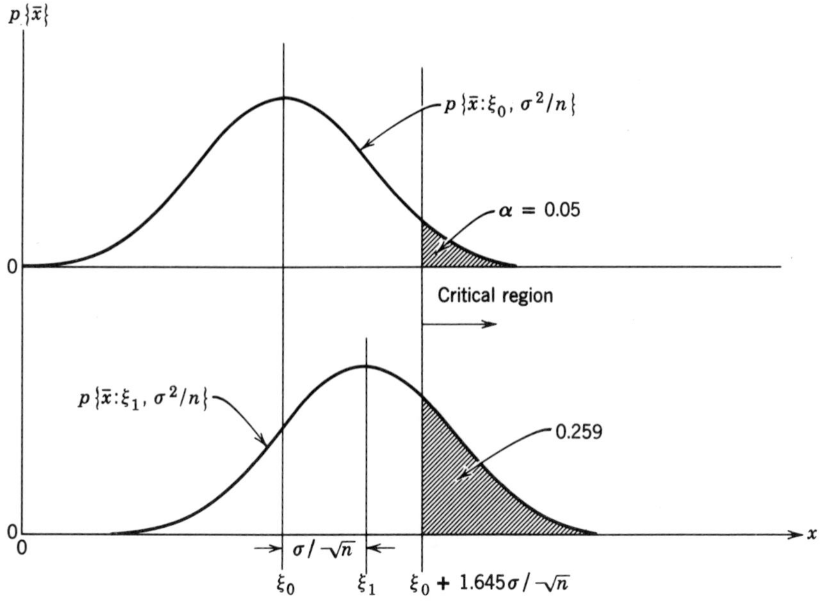

Figure 2.8

Figure 2.8 shows graphically the basis of the power calculation for $\delta = 1$ with $\alpha = 0.05$. The mean of the alternative distribution ξ_1 is at a distance $1 \times \sigma/\sqrt{n}$ above the mean of the null distribution σ_0. The probability density curves are represented in different parts of the figure to avoid confusing overlap. The critical region defined as an area $\alpha = 0.05$ in the upper tail of the null distribution $p\{\bar{x}:\xi_0, \sigma^2/n\}$ is marked in the upper curve $1.645 \times \sigma/\sqrt{n}$ above ξ_0. If $\bar{x}$ actually has the alternative distribution $p\{\bar{x}:\xi_1, \sigma^2/n\}$, it will be distributed as in the lower part of the figure, and the probability that $\bar{x}$ will fall in the critical region is

$$\int_{\xi_0+1.645\sigma/\sqrt{n}}^{\infty} p\left\{\bar{x}:\xi_1, \frac{\sigma^2}{n}\right\} d\bar{x} = \int_{\xi_1+0.645\sigma/\sqrt{n}}^{\infty} p\left\{\bar{x}:\xi_1, \frac{\sigma^2}{n}\right\} d\bar{x}$$

$$= 1 - \int_{-\infty}^{\xi_1+0.645\sigma/\sqrt{n}} p\left\{\bar{x}:\xi_1, \frac{\sigma^2}{n}\right\} d\bar{x} = 1 - \Phi\left(\frac{\xi_1 + 0.645\sigma/\sqrt{n} - \xi_1}{\sigma/\sqrt{n}}\right)$$

$$= 1 - \Phi(0.645) = 0.259.$$

We have been discussing the test with the alternative hypothesis $H_1: \xi > \xi_0$. When H_1 is $\xi < \xi_0$, the critical region becomes $x < x_c = \xi_0 + \sigma u_\alpha$ for a single observation, or $\bar{x} < \bar{x}_c = \xi_0 + \sigma u_\alpha/\sqrt{n}$ for the mean of n observations, and in this latter case the power is

$$\pi(\xi_1) = \Phi\left(u_\alpha + \frac{\xi_0 - \xi_1}{\sigma/\sqrt{n}}\right).$$

Thus for a test at the level of significance $\alpha = 0.05$, $u_\alpha = -1.645$, and for $(\xi_0 - \xi_1)/(\sigma/\sqrt{n}) = 1$, $\pi(\xi_1) = \Phi(-1.645 + 1) = 0.2594$. Therefore, we can use Table 2.2, as it stands, for the power of this other alternative hypothesis, $H_1: \xi = \xi_1 < \xi_0$, if we replace $(\xi_1 - \xi_0)/(\sigma/\sqrt{n})$ in the table by $(\xi_0 - \xi_1)/(\sigma/\sqrt{n})$.

We can use (7.11) to calculate the number of observations necessary to give a specified power $(1 - \beta)$, assuming that σ is known. Putting (7.11) equal to $(1 - \beta)$,

$$\Phi\left(u_\alpha + \frac{\xi_1 - \xi_0}{\sigma/\sqrt{n}}\right) = 1 - \beta.$$

But, in general, $\Phi(u_P) = P$, and so $\Phi(u_{1-\beta}) = 1 - \beta$, whence

$$u_\alpha + \left(\frac{\xi_1 - \xi_0}{\sigma/\sqrt{n}}\right) = u_{1-\beta}.$$

Solving for n, and writing $u_{1-\alpha}$ for $-u_\alpha$,

$$n = (u_{1-\beta} + u_{1-\alpha})^2\left(\frac{\sigma}{\xi_1 - \xi_0}\right)^2. \tag{7.12}$$

This equation often gives surprisingly large values of n for powers that we might consider desirable. Suppose $\sigma = 0.12$, and we wish to test at the level of significance $\alpha = 0.01$, so that $u_{1-\alpha} = u_{0.99} = 2.326$. Suppose that, if $\xi_1 - \xi_0 = 0.02$, i.e., one-sixth of the standard deviation, we want to have a probability of 0.95 of rejecting the null hypothesis; so $u_{1-\beta} = u_{0.95} = 1.645$. These values give $n = 568$.

2.8. The Testing of Composite Hypotheses

In Section 2.6 we considered the criterion (6.9) for the construction of the best test of a simple null hypothesis against a simple alternative. In the case of multiparameter distributions, (6.9) would become

$$\frac{p\{x_1, \ldots, x_n : \theta_{1,a}, \theta_2, \ldots, \theta_k\}}{p\{x_1, \ldots, x_n : \theta_{1,0}, \theta_2, \ldots, \theta_k\}} > K, \tag{8.1}$$

where the θ's are the parameters: $\theta_2, \ldots, \theta_k$ are completely specified and θ_1 takes the value $\theta_{1,0}$ under the null hypothesis and $\theta_{1,a}$ under the alternative hypothesis.

For example, in Section 2.7 we tested the null hypothesis that the mean of a normal distribution was ξ_0 against the alternative that it was ξ_1, in both cases the variance being assumed known.

We can regard the parameters $\theta_1, \ldots, \theta_k$ as being represented in a k-dimensional space, the coordinates corresponding to the parameters. For a simple hypothesis, all the coordinates are specified, and we have a single point in the parameter space. For a composite hypothesis, a certain region in the parameter space is specified. For example, with a normal distribution

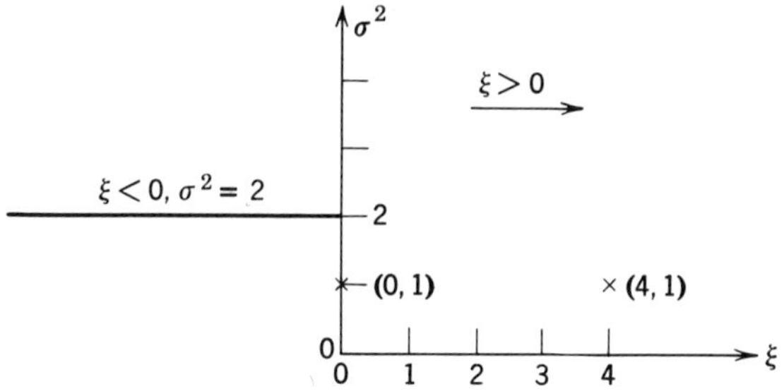

Figure 2.9

there are two parameters, ξ and σ^2 (Figure 2.9). Specifying $\xi = 0$, $\sigma^2 = 1$ and $\xi = 4$, $\sigma^2 = 1$ gives two simple hypotheses, represented by the points (0, 1) and (4, 1). $\xi < 0$, $\sigma^2 = 2$ is the line at $\sigma^2 = 2$ to the left of the ξ axis and is a composite hypothesis. $\xi > 0$ is the entire right-hand quadrant and is also a composite hypothesis. The entire admissible space of the null hypothesis plus the alternative hypothesis is represented by the symbol Ω. In this example, the region below the ξ axis is always inadmissible since σ^2 can never be negative. The region corresponding to a particular composite hypothesis, the null hypothesis, is represented by ω.

Suppose that now the null hypothesis is composite, the parameters being allowed to vary within a region ω. The function

$$p\{x_1, \ldots, x_n:\theta_1, \ldots, \theta_k\} = \prod_i^n p\{x_i:\theta_1, \ldots, \theta_k\} \tag{8.2}$$

by (1.1) is the likelihood as defined in (3.1). By the method of maximum likelihood we can find the maximum-likelihood estimators of the θ's, and by definition these will maximize the likelihood; call this value of the likelihood $L(\omega)$. Now suppose that the parameters are permitted to vary over the space permitted under both the null and the alternative hypotheses Ω; again find the maximum-likelihood estimators, and insert them in (8.2) to obtain the maximum value of the likelihood under both hypotheses. Call this $L(\Omega)$. Then the natural extension of (6.9), which is for simple hypotheses, to the case of composite hypotheses is the ratio $L(\Omega)/L(\omega)$. It is, however, more usual to use the reciprocal, denoted by λ,

$$\lambda = \frac{L(\omega)}{L(\Omega)}, \tag{8.3}$$

and call it the *likelihood ratio*. Clearly λ is positive since it is a ratio of products of probability functions which must always be positive. Also λ cannot be greater than 1 since the maximum value for L varying the parameters in a region ω cannot exceed the maximum value for L varying the parameters in a region Ω, where ω is a subset of Ω. Thus λ must lie in the interval 0 to 1. A small value of λ indicates that the likelihood computed using ω, corresponding to the null hypothesis, is relatively unlikely, and so we should reject the null hypothesis. Conversely, a value of λ close to 1 indicates that the null hypothesis is very plausible and should be accepted. We therefore define a critical region as

$$0 < \lambda < C \tag{8.4}$$

where C is a constant chosen so that the level of significance of the test is at the desired level α.

2.9. A Two-Sided Test of an Observation from a Normal Population with Known Variance

To apply the procedure of the previous section to testing that a group of n observations came from a normal population with mean ξ_0 and known variance σ^2 against the alternative that the mean is $\xi_1 \neq \xi_0$, we write down the likelihood function (3.3):

$$L = \left(\frac{1}{2\pi\sigma^2}\right)^{n/2} \exp\left[-\frac{1}{2\sigma^2}\sum_i^n (x_i - \xi)^2\right].$$

In Section 2.3 we saw that, allowing ξ to vary, L was maximized by putting $\xi = \sum_i^n \frac{x_i}{n} = \bar{x}$ (3.6). Thus

$$L(\Omega) = \left(\frac{1}{2\pi\sigma^2}\right)^{n/2} \exp\left[-\frac{1}{2\sigma^2}\sum_i^n (x_i - \bar{x})^2\right].$$

Under the null hypothesis H_0, there are no parameters which are allowed to vary, since we are assuming σ^2 to be fixed and known, and ξ is fixed at ξ_0; thus

$$L(\omega) = \left(\frac{1}{2\pi\sigma^2}\right)^{n/2} \exp\left[-\frac{1}{2\sigma^2}\sum_i^n (x_i - \xi_0)^2\right].$$

Substituting these values for $L(\omega)$ and $L(\Omega)$ in the definition of the likelihood ratio (8.3), and canceling out common factors gives

$$\lambda = \frac{\exp\left[-\frac{1}{2\sigma^2}\sum_i^n (x_i - \xi_0)^2\right]}{\exp\left[-\frac{1}{2\sigma^2}\sum_i^n (x_i - \bar{x})^2\right]}.$$

But $\sum_i^n (x_i - \xi_0)^2 = \sum_i^n [(x_i - \bar{x}) + (\bar{x} - \xi_0)]^2 = \sum_i^n (x_i - \bar{x})^2 + n(\bar{x} - \xi_0)^2$, since $2\sum_i^n (x_i - \bar{x})(\bar{x} - \xi_0) = 2(\bar{x} - \xi_0)\sum_i^n (x_i - \bar{x}) = 2(\bar{x} - \xi_0)\cdot 0 = 0$. Thus the likelihood ratio is

$$\lambda = \exp\left[-\frac{n}{2\sigma^2}(\bar{x} - \xi_0)^2\right]. \tag{9.1}$$

The edge of the critical region $\bar{x}_c$ is determined by

$$\exp\left[-\frac{n}{2\sigma^2}(\bar{x}_c - \xi_0)^2\right] = C$$

or, solving for $\bar{x}_c$,

$$\bar{x}_c = \xi_0 - \sqrt{-\log C}\sqrt{2}\frac{\sigma}{\sqrt{n}} \quad \text{and} \quad \xi_0 + \sqrt{-\log C}\sqrt{2}\frac{\sigma}{\sqrt{n}}. \tag{9.2}$$

Since C is less than 1, $\log C$ is negative, and so $\bar{x}_c$ is of the form

$$\bar{x}_c = \xi_0 \pm k\frac{\sigma}{\sqrt{n}} \tag{9.3}$$

where $k = \sqrt{-2\log C}$. Referring to (9.1) we see that, if $\bar{x}$ is far from ξ_0, in either direction, then $(\bar{x} - \xi_0)^2$ will be large, and hence λ small. Thus large values of $|\bar{x} - \xi_0|$ call for rejection of the null hypothesis. The critical region is that part of the line below $\xi_0 - k\sigma/\sqrt{n}$ plus that part of the line above $\xi_0 + k\sigma/\sqrt{n}$ (see Figure 2.10). The total area of the curve in the critical region has to equal α: Since the normal distribution is symmetrical about its mean, this implies that the area of each tail is $\alpha/2$. The critical region will be

$$\bar{x} < \xi_0 + u_{\alpha/2}\frac{\sigma}{\sqrt{n}} \qquad \text{and} \qquad \bar{x} > \xi_0 + u_{1-\alpha/2}\frac{\sigma}{\sqrt{n}}. \tag{9.4}$$

Since $u_{\alpha/2} = -u_{1-\alpha/2}$, the left-hand term can be written $\bar{x} < \xi_0 - u_{1-\alpha/2}\sigma/\sqrt{n}$, and (9.4) is equivalent to saying: Reject if $(\bar{x} - \xi_0)/(\sigma/\sqrt{n})$ is less than $-u_{1-\alpha/2}$ or greater than $+u_{1-\alpha/2}$. This is equivalent to saying: Reject if

$$\left|\frac{\bar{x} - \xi_0}{\sigma/\sqrt{n}}\right| > u_{1-\alpha/2}\,. \tag{9.5}$$

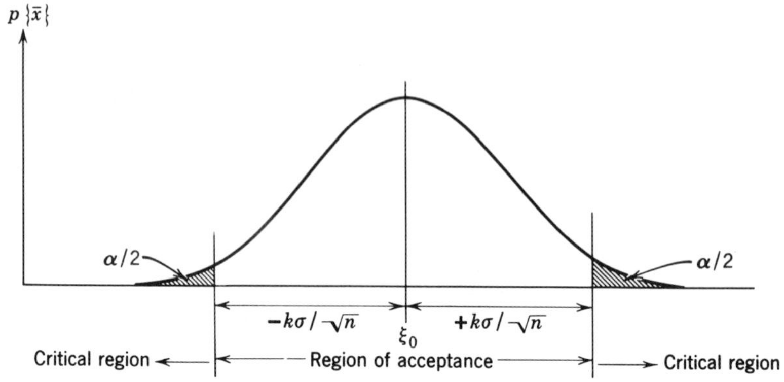

Figure 2.10

The power of this test is, it being understood that $\xi = \xi_1$,

$$\begin{aligned}\pi(\xi_1) &= \Pr\left\{\frac{\bar{x} - \xi_0}{\sigma/\sqrt{n}} < -u_{1-\alpha/2}\right\} + \Pr\left\{\frac{\bar{x} - \xi_0}{\sigma/\sqrt{n}} > u_{1-\alpha/2}\right\} \\ &= \Pr\left\{\frac{\bar{x} - \xi_1}{\sigma/\sqrt{n}} + \frac{\xi_1 - \xi_0}{\sigma/\sqrt{n}} < -u_{1-\alpha/2}\right\} + \Pr\left\{\frac{\bar{x} - \xi_1}{\sigma/\sqrt{n}} + \frac{\xi_1 - \xi_0}{\sigma/\sqrt{n}} > u_{1-\alpha/2}\right\} \\ &= \Pr\left\{\frac{\bar{x} - \xi_1}{\sigma/\sqrt{n}} < u_{\alpha/2} - \frac{\xi_1 - \xi_0}{\sigma/\sqrt{n}}\right\} + 1 - \Pr\left\{\frac{\bar{x} - \xi_1}{\sigma/\sqrt{n}} < -u_{\alpha/2} - \frac{\xi_1 - \xi_0}{\sigma/\sqrt{n}}\right\}.\end{aligned} \tag{9.6}$$

Now under the alternative hypothesis $\xi = \xi_1$, the random variable $(\bar{x} - \xi_1)/(\sigma/\sqrt{n})$ is a unit normal deviate. Each of these two probability statements is therefore of the form $\Pr\{u < k\} = \Phi(k)$. We therefore have, defining $(\xi_1 - \xi_0)/(\sigma/\sqrt{n}) = \delta$,

$$\begin{aligned}\pi(\xi_1) &= \Phi(u_{\alpha/2} - \delta) + 1 - \Phi(-u_{\alpha/2} - \delta) \\ &= \Phi(u_{\alpha/2} - \delta) + \Phi(u_{\alpha/2} + \delta)\end{aligned} \tag{9.7}$$

since $1 - \Phi(-u) = \Phi(u)$. For example, for $\alpha = 0.05$, $u_{0.05/2} = -1.96$ and, for $\delta = 1$,

$$\pi(\xi_1) = \Phi(-1.96 - 1) + \Phi(-1.96 + 1) = \Phi(-2.96) + \Phi(-0.96)$$
$$= 0.0015 + 0.1685 = 0.1700.$$

In this way, Table 2.3 is prepared, and the function is plotted in Figure 2.11. The function is symmetrical about 0, and so only the first two negative values are tabulated.

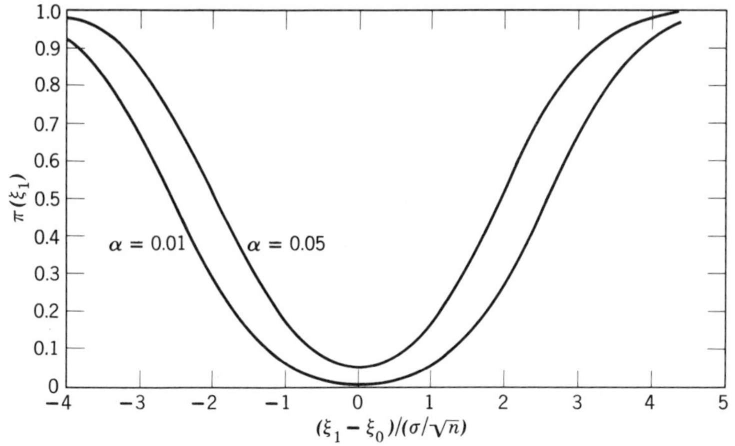

Figure 2.11

Table 2.3. Power of Two-Tailed Test at Level of Significance 0.05 of Mean of n Observations from a Normal Distribution

$\frac{\xi_1 - \xi_0}{\sigma/\sqrt{n}}$	−1.0	−0.5	0	0.5	1	1.5	2	2.5	3	3.5	4.0	4.5	5.0
$\pi(\xi_1)$	.170	.079	.05	.079	.170	.323	.516	.705	.851	.938	.979	.994	.999

When $\xi_1 = \xi_0$, the power coincides with the level of significance. The power curve for $\alpha = 0.01$ is also plotted in Figure 2.11. It is clear that we gain increased protection against the risk of committing an error of the first kind at the cost of decreased protection against the risk of committing an error of the second kind. For example, when $\delta = 3$, a test with $\alpha = 0.05$ has power 0.851, whereas a test with $\alpha = 0.01$ has power only 0.664.

Figure 2.12 shows graphically the basis of the power calculation for $\delta = 1$ with $\alpha = 0.05$. The mean of the alternative distribution ξ_1 is at a distance $1 \times \sigma/\sqrt{n}$ above the mean of the null distribution ξ_0. The probability density curves are represented in different parts of the figure to avoid confusing overlap. The critical region defined as $\alpha/2 = 0.05/2 = 0.025$ in the two tails of the null distribution $p\{\bar{x} : \xi_0, \sigma^2/n\}$ is marked in the upper curve

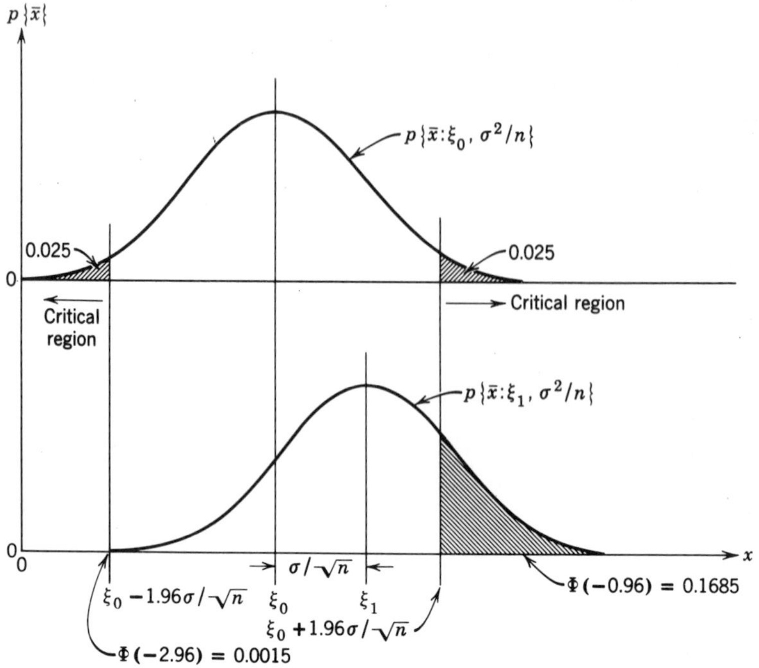

Figure 2.12

at $\pm 1.96\sigma/\sqrt{n}$ on either side of ξ_0. If $\bar{x}$ actually has the alternative distribution $p\{\bar{x} : \xi_1, \sigma^2/n\}$, it will be distributed as in the lower part of the figure, and the probability that $\bar{x}$ will fall in the region of rejection is

$$\int_{-\infty}^{\xi_0 - 1.96\sigma/\sqrt{n}} p\left\{\bar{x} : \xi_1, \frac{\sigma^2}{n}\right\} d\bar{x} + \int_{\xi_0 + 1.96\sigma/\sqrt{n}}^{\infty} p\left\{\bar{x} : \xi_1, \frac{\sigma^2}{n}\right\} d\bar{x}$$

$$= \int_{-\infty}^{\xi_1 - 2.96\sigma/\sqrt{n}} p\left\{\bar{x} : \xi_1, \frac{\sigma^2}{n}\right\} d\bar{x} + \int_{\xi_1 + 0.96\sigma/\sqrt{n}}^{\infty} p\left\{\bar{x} : \xi_1, \frac{\sigma^2}{n}\right\} d\bar{x}$$

$$= \Phi(-2.96) + 1 - \Phi(0.96) = \Phi(-2.96) + \Phi(-0.96)$$

$$= 0.0015 + 0.1685 = 0.1700.$$

We can use (9.7) to calculate the number of observations necessary to give a specified power $(1 - \beta)$, assuming that σ is known. Equation (9.7) can only be solved exactly for n by troublesome iterations. However, we note that in a typical situation one term is very much larger than the other:

For example, with $\delta = 1$ and $\alpha = 0.05$, the term $\Phi(u_{\alpha/2} + \delta)$ at 0.1685 was more than 100 times as large as the other at 0.0015. Even at $\delta = 0.5$, this term is over 10 times the other. For any calculation involving δ greater then 0.5, therefore, we can neglect the other term in (9.7) and write

$$\pi(\xi_1) \simeq \Phi\left(u_{\alpha/2} + \frac{\xi_1 - \xi_0}{\sigma/\sqrt{n}}\right)$$

and, putting $\pi(\xi_1) = 1 - \beta$, we get

$$u_{\alpha/2} + \frac{\xi_1 - \xi_0}{\sigma/\sqrt{n}} \simeq u_{1-\beta}$$

whence

$$n \simeq \left(u_{1-\beta} + u_{1-\alpha/2}\right)^2 \left(\frac{\sigma}{\xi_1 - \xi_0}\right)^2. \tag{9.8}$$

For example, suppose $\sigma = 0.12$, and we wish to make a test at the level of significance $\alpha = 0.01$, so that $u_{1-\alpha/2} = u_{0.995} = 2.58$. Suppose that, if $\xi_1 - \xi_0 = 0.02$, i.e., one-sixth of the standard deviation, we wish to have a probability of 0.95 of rejecting the null hypothesis; so $u_{1-\beta} = u_{0.95} = 1.645$. These values give $n = 641$. It is clear that a power as high as 0.95 of detecting a difference as small as one-sixth of a standard deviation is not easy to achieve.

2.10. A Two-Sided Test of an Observation from a Normal Distribution with Unknown Variance

Let us now construct a test for the null hypothesis that the mean of a normal distribution is ξ_0 against the alternative $\xi_1 \neq \xi_0$, the variance σ^2 not being specified. The likelihood function (3.3) is

$$L = \left(\frac{1}{2\pi\sigma^2}\right)^{n/2} \exp\left[-\frac{1}{2\sigma^2}\sum_i^n (x_i - \xi)^2\right]. \tag{10.1}$$

For the null hypothesis, the parameter ξ is specified to take the value ξ_0, but σ^2 is allowed to vary. Inserting $\xi = \xi_0$ in (10.1) and taking logarithms and then differentiating $\log L$ with respect to σ^2 to obtain the maximum-likelihood estimator of σ^2 in ω, we get

$$\frac{d \log L}{d\sigma^2} = -\frac{n}{2}\frac{1}{\sigma^2} + \frac{1}{2(\sigma^2)^2}\sum_i^n (x_i - \xi_0)^2.$$

Equating to zero and solving for $\hat{\sigma}^2$ gives

$$\hat{\sigma}^2 = \sum_i^n \frac{(x_i - \xi_0)^2}{n}. \tag{10.2}$$

Inserting this in (10.1) along with $\xi = \xi_0$ gives

$$L(\omega) = \left(\frac{n}{2\pi \sum_i^n (x_i - \xi_0)^2} \right)^{n/2} e^{-n/2}. \tag{10.3}$$

For the entire parameter space Ω, with no restrictions on the parameters ξ and σ^2, we saw in (3.6) that $\xi = \sum_i^n \frac{x_i}{n}$ and in (3.9) that $\hat{\sigma}^2 = \sum_i^n \frac{(x_i - \bar{x})^2}{n}$. Inserting these maximum-likelihood estimators in (10.1), we get

$$L(\Omega) = \left(\frac{n}{2\pi \sum_i^n (x_i - \bar{x})^2} \right)^{n/2} e^{-n/2}. \tag{10.4}$$

Hence the likelihood ratio as defined in (8.3) is

$$\lambda = \left(\frac{\sum_i^n (x_i - \bar{x})^2}{\sum_i^n (x_i - \xi_0)^2} \right)^{n/2}.$$

Any monotone function of λ can be used instead of λ itself for defining the critical region: Hence we may use the nth root of λ^2,

$$\lambda^{2/n} = \frac{\sum_i^n (x_i - \bar{x})^2}{\sum_i^n (x_i - \xi_0)^2} = \frac{\sum_i^n (x_i - \bar{x})^2}{\sum_i^n (x_i - \bar{x})^2 + n(\bar{x} - \xi_0)^2} = \frac{1}{1 + \dfrac{n(\bar{x} - \xi_0)^2}{\sum_i^n (x_i - \bar{x})^2}}$$

$$= \frac{1}{1 + \dfrac{1}{n-1} \dfrac{(\bar{x} - \xi_0)^2}{\dfrac{\sum_i^n (x_i - \bar{x})^2/(n-1)}{n}}} = \frac{1}{1 + \dfrac{t^2}{n-1}}, \tag{10.5}$$

if we define t as

$$t = \frac{\bar{x} - \xi_0}{\sqrt{\left[\sum_i^n (x_i - \bar{x})^2/(n-1) \right] / \sqrt{n}}} = \frac{\bar{x} - \xi_0}{s/\sqrt{n}} \tag{10.6}$$

with s defined as in (3.15). We recall that we reject the null hypothesis for small values of λ, which is equivalent from (10.5) to large values of $|t|$.

Thus t as defined by (10.6) can be used as a test statistic for the null hypothesis $\xi = \xi_0$ against the alternative $\xi \neq \xi_0$, σ^2 being unknown. We will obtain this same result later, in Section 9.5, by a different route.

2.11. The Comparison of Two Means

Suppose that we have random samples, with means $\bar{x}_1$ and $\bar{x}_2$, and sample sizes n_1 and n_2, drawn from two normal distributions $p\{x: \xi_1, \sigma_1^2\}$, $p\{x: \xi_2, \sigma_2^2\}$, and that the variances σ_1^2, σ_2^2 are known. Define $d = \bar{x}_1 - \bar{x}_2$. Then, by (1.22.4), $E[d] = \delta = E[\bar{x}_1 - \bar{x}_2] = \xi_1 - \xi_2$. The means $\bar{x}_1$ and $\bar{x}_2$ will have variances σ_1^2/n_1 and σ_2^2/n_2, and zero covariance; so, by (1.22.5) the variance of d, $V[d] = (\sigma_1^2/n_1) + \sigma_2^2/n_2)$. Also, by Section 1.23, d is normally distributed; so

$$\frac{d - E[d]}{\sqrt{V[d]}} = \frac{d - \delta}{\sqrt{\sigma_1^2/n_1 + \sigma_2^2/n_2}} \tag{11.1}$$

is a standardized normal variable u. Just as in the two preceding sections we outlined tests for the null hypothesis that a sample mean $\bar{x}$ with variance σ^2/n came from a normal distribution with expectation ξ_0; so we can test the null hypothesis that d with variance $\{(\sigma_1^2/n_1) + (\sigma_2^2/n_2)\}$ comes from a normal distribution with expectation δ_0. For a one-sided test with $\delta = \delta_1 > \delta_0$, (7.6) gives the critical region as

$$d > \delta_0 + u_{1-\alpha}\sqrt{\frac{\sigma_1^2}{n_1} + \frac{\sigma_2^2}{n_2}} \tag{11.2}$$

and, for the two-sided test with $\delta = \delta_1 \neq \delta_0$, (9.4) gives the critical region as

$$d < \delta_0 + u_{\alpha/2}\sqrt{\frac{\sigma_1^2}{n_1} + \frac{\sigma_2^2}{n_2}} \quad \text{and} \quad d > \delta_0 + u_{1-\alpha/2}\sqrt{\frac{\sigma_1^2}{n_1} + \frac{\sigma_2^2}{n_2}}. \tag{11.3}$$

The null hypothesis in which we are most frequently interested is, of course, $\delta = 0$, since this corresponds to $\xi_1 = \xi_2$, the two populations having the same expectation.

2.12. The Concept of *P* Value

We have seen that for a one-tailed test against the alternative $\xi_1 > \xi_0$ on an observation x from a normal distribution the critical region was defined by (7.6) as

$$x > \xi_0 + u_{1-\alpha}\sigma \tag{12.1}$$

and for a two-tailed test, adapting (9.5) to the case of a single observation x with variance σ^2,

$$\left| \frac{x - \xi_0}{\sigma} \right| > u_{1-\alpha/2} \, . \tag{12.2}$$

The standard procedure is to observe x, and note whether it falls in the region of acceptance or rejection, and conclude accordingly. There are often advantages to an inverse procedure. Instead of working to a fixed level of significance α, and merely recording whether H_0 is to be accepted or rejected at this level, we may choose to insert the observed value of the test statistic x in (12.1) or (12.2), replace the inequality sign by an equality, and solve for α. The value of α so found is known as the P *value*. The P value is thus the value of α at which the decision regarding H_0 would just be changing from accept to reject.

For example, suppose we observe $x = 125$ from a normal population with variance known to be 100, and test the null hypothesis $\xi_0 = 100$ at the level of significance $\alpha = 0.05$ against two-sided alternatives. Then

$$\left| \frac{125 - 100}{\sqrt{100}} \right| = 2.5 > u_{0.975} = 1.96;$$

so we reject the null hypothesis at the level of significance 0.05. Alternatively we write

$$\left| \frac{125 - 100}{\sqrt{100}} \right| = 2.5 = u_{1-P/2}$$

whence $1 - P/2 = 0.99379$, and $P = 0.012$. It is often more satisfactory to know that the null hypothesis can be just rejected at an α as small as 0.012 rather than rejected at $\alpha = 0.05$.

2.13. Confidence Limits

As indicated in Section 2.2, obtaining a point estimate of a parameter is one thing, but we may also want to have some idea of how accurately we have determined it; i.e., in what interval we are fairly certain that it lies. For example, if we find 10 light bulbs defective in a sample of 100 from a large lot, the point estimate for the population fraction defective (see Section 2.3) is 10/100, but is this sample consistent with the population fraction defective being actually 0.07, or 0.15? The generally accepted method of handling this question is to construct what are known as confidence limits. We derive upper and lower $100(1 - \alpha)$ per cent limits such that, when we say that the true value of the parameter lies in that interval, $100(1-\alpha)$ per cent of all such statements will be correct and 100α per cent will be incorrect. Obviously we choose α small, for example, 0.05 or 0.01.

The general method of construction of confidence limits is as follows. We suppose that we have a family of populations each with a known density function $p\{x:\theta\}$, x being the random variable and θ the parameter in question. We suppose that we have an estimator T to estimate θ, that T is a function of the observed x, and that we can derive the density function of T, $p\{T:\theta\}$. For example, if $p\{x:\theta\}$ is $N(\xi, \sigma^2)$ with σ^2 known, we know from (3.6) that $\bar{x}$ is an appropriate estimator of ξ and that the density function of $\bar{x}$ is

$$p\left\{\bar{x}:\xi, \frac{\sigma^2}{n}\right\} = \frac{1}{\sqrt{2\pi}(\sigma/\sqrt{n})} \exp\left[-\frac{(\bar{x}-\xi)^2}{2\sigma^2/n}\right].$$

Reverting to the general argument, if we assume that θ equals some particular value, say θ', we can insert this value and get the density function $p\{T:\theta'\}$ of the distribution of T under this assumption.

Under the assumption $\theta = \theta'$, there will be a P_1 point for the distribution of T, say T_1, which will be determined by the equation

$$\Pr\{T \le T_1 : \theta = \theta'\} = \int_{-\infty}^{T_1} p\{T:\theta'\}\,dT = P_1 . \qquad (13.1)$$

Likewise, under the same assumption $\theta = \theta'$, there will be a P_2 point for the distribution of T, say T_2, determined by the equation

$$\Pr\{T \ge T_2 : \theta = \theta'\} = \int_{T_2}^{\infty} p\{T:\theta'\}\,dT = 1 - P_2 . \qquad (13.2)$$

These points are indicated in Figure 2.13. The area below T_2 is equal to P_2, and the area between T_1 and T_2 is equal to $(P_2 - P_1)$.

Now, in (13.1) and (13.2), if we change the value of θ' we change the corresponding values of T_1 and T_2. We can therefore regard T_1 and T_2 as functions of θ, say $T_1(\theta)$ and $T_2(\theta)$, respectively. In principle, we can plot these functions $T_1(\theta)$ and $T_2(\theta)$ against θ. In idealized form these are plotted in Figure 2.14.

Now assume that the true value of θ is actually θ_0. Then $T_1(\theta)$ and $T_2(\theta)$ take the values $T_1(\theta_0)$ and $T_2(\theta_0)$, respectively, and

$$\Pr\{T \le T_1(\theta_0)\} = P_1 ,$$

$$\Pr\{T \ge T_2(\theta_0)\} = 1 - P_2 ,$$

which imply

$$\Pr\{T_1(\theta_0) < T < T_2(\theta_0)\} = P_2 - P_1 . \qquad (13.3)$$

Now suppose that we have taken a sample observation and have computed the numerical value of the estimate, say T_0. We draw a horizontal line parallel to the θ axis through the point T_0 on the T axis. Let this line intercept the two curves $T_2(\theta)$ and $T_1(\theta)$ at points A and B. Drop the

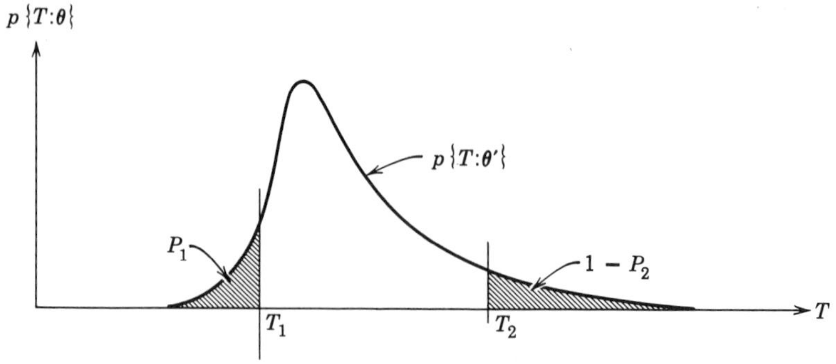

Figure 2.13

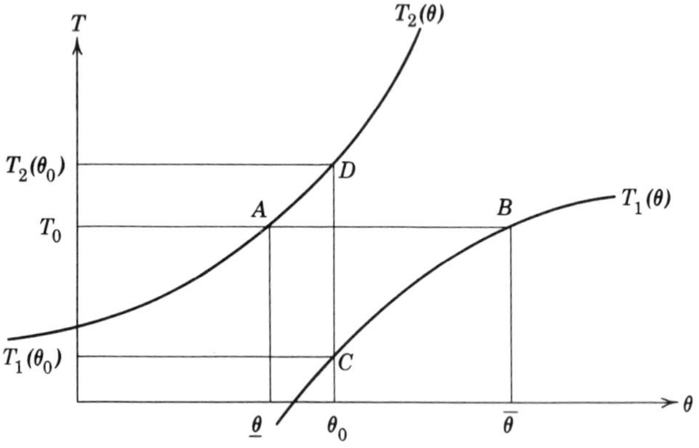

Figure 2.14

points A and B on to the θ axis to give $\underline{\theta}$ and $\bar{\theta}$. We assert that a $(P_2 - P_1)$ confidence interval for θ is $(\underline{\theta}, \bar{\theta})$, i.e.,

$$\Pr\{\underline{\theta} < \theta < \bar{\theta}\} = P_2 - P_1 . \tag{13.4}$$

The justification for this assertion is as follows. Enter the true value of θ_0 on the θ axis; erect the perpendicular at this point to cut the curves $T_1(\theta)$ at C and $T_2(\theta)$ at D. At both these points θ has the value θ_0; so, at C, $T = T_1(\theta_0)$, and, at D, $T = T_2(\theta_0)$. Now draw the horizontal lines through C and D: these will intersect the T axis at $T_1(\theta_0)$ and $T_2(\theta_0)$, respectively. Now examine Figure 2.14: θ_0 may be anywhere on the θ axis, but, if AB

intersects CD, then T_0 must lie in the interval $(T_1(\theta_0), T_2(\theta_0))$ and simultaneously the interval $(\underline{\theta}, \bar{\theta})$ must include θ_0. In other words, the two statements

(i) T_0 lies in the interval $(T_1(\theta_0), T_2(\theta_0))$,

and

(ii) The interval $(\underline{\theta}, \bar{\theta})$ includes θ_0,

are always true simultaneously or not true simultaneously. But by (13.3) the event (i) has probability $(P_2 - P_1)$; so the event (ii) must also have probability $(P_2 - P_1)$. Hence we can write

$$\Pr\{\underline{\theta} < \theta_0 < \bar{\theta}\} = P_2 - P_1, \tag{13.5}$$

and this completes the justification of (13.4).

At the point A, the function $T_2(\theta)$ has $\theta = \underline{\theta}$ and takes the value T_0, i.e.,

$$T_2(\underline{\theta}) = T_0. \tag{13.6}$$

Now $T_2(\theta)$ was defined as the solution of 13.2),

$$\int_{T_2}^{\infty} p\{T : \theta'\}\, dT = 1 - P_2;$$

so we can use this equation to find $\underline{\theta}$; $\underline{\theta}$ is obtained by solving

$$\int_{T_0}^{\infty} p\{T : \theta\}\, dT = 1 - P_2 = \Pr\{T \geq T_0 : \theta = \underline{\theta}\}. \tag{13.7}$$

Similarly, at the point B, the function $T_1(\theta)$ has $\theta = \bar{\theta}$ and takes the value T_0; so

$$T_1(\bar{\theta}) = T_0\,, \tag{13.8}$$

and $\bar{\theta}$ can be found as the solution of

$$\int_{-\infty}^{T_0} p\{T : \theta\}\, dT = P_1 = \Pr\{T \leq T_0 ; \theta = \bar{\theta}\}. \tag{13.9}$$

The idea of confidence intervals is due to Neyman [9].

We will now illustrate this procedure by an application to finding confidence limits for the mean ξ of a normal distribution from an observed mean $\bar{x}_0$. We assume that the variance of the distribution σ^2 is known. In (1.15.8) we saw that, for a normally distributed variable x,

$$\Pr\{x < x_a\} = \int_{-\infty}^{x_a} \frac{1}{\sqrt{2\pi}\,\sigma} \exp\left[-\frac{(x-\xi)^2}{2\sigma^2}\right] dx = \Phi\left(\frac{x_a - \xi}{\sigma}\right). \tag{13.10}$$

Similarly, since $\bar{x}$ has variance σ^2/n,

$$\Pr\{\bar{x} < x_a\} = \int_{-\infty}^{x_a} \frac{1}{\sqrt{2\pi}\,\sigma/\sqrt{n}} \exp\left[-\frac{(\bar{x}-\xi)^2}{2\sigma^2/n}\right] d\bar{x} = \Phi\left(\frac{x_a - \xi}{\sigma/\sqrt{n}}\right). \tag{13.11}$$

The estimator of ξ is $\bar{x}_0$. Thus (13.9) gives

$$\Pr\{\bar{x} < \bar{x}_0 : \xi = \bar{\xi}\} = \Phi\left(\frac{\bar{x}_0 - \bar{\xi}}{\sigma/\sqrt{n}}\right) = P_1;$$

so

$$\frac{\bar{x}_0 - \bar{\xi}}{\sigma/\sqrt{n}} = u_{P_1},$$

whence

$$\bar{\xi} = \bar{x}_0 - u_{P_1}\frac{\sigma}{\sqrt{n}}. \tag{13.12}$$

To obtain $\underline{\xi}$ from (13.7), we have

$$\Pr\{\bar{x} > \bar{x}_0 : \xi = \underline{\xi}\} = 1 - P_2;$$

so

$$\Pr\{\bar{x} < \bar{x}_0 : \xi = \underline{\xi}\} = P_2.$$

But

$$\Pr\{\bar{x} < \bar{x}_0 : \xi = \underline{\xi}\} = \Phi\left(\frac{\bar{x}_0 - \underline{\xi}}{\sigma/\sqrt{n}}\right);$$

so

$$\frac{\bar{x}_0 - \underline{\xi}}{\sigma/\sqrt{n}} = u_{P_2},$$

or

$$\underline{\xi} = \bar{x}_0 - u_{P_2}\frac{\sigma}{\sqrt{n}}. \tag{13.13}$$

So far we have left P_2 and P_1 unspecified, other than that $P_2 - P_1 = 1 - \alpha$. One rational basis for particularizing the choice would be to make the interval $(\underline{\theta}, \bar{\theta})$ as short as possible, in some sense. In practice, for symmetrical distributions it is standard practice to place equal probability in each tail, i.e., to put $P_1 = \alpha/2 = 1 - P_2$, so that $P_2 = 1 - \alpha/2$. For any common asymmetrical distribution, the possible gain in shortening the interval by adjusting the two tail areas is outweighed by the practical convenience of equal areas, and so here also equal probability is placed in each tail. Of course, if the consequences of being in error in one direction are more serious than the consequences of being in error in the other direction, then we may construct asymmetrical limits.

To revert to our example of the mean of a normal distribution, if we wanted 95 per cent confidence, so that $1 - \alpha = 0.95$, or $\alpha = 0.05$, then $u_{P_2} = u_{0.975} = +1.96$ and $u_{P_1} = u_{0.025} = -1.96$, and, substituting in (13.12) and (13.13), the 95 per cent confidence limits are

$$\underline{\xi} = \bar{x} - \frac{1.96\sigma}{\sqrt{n}}, \qquad \bar{\xi} = \bar{x} + \frac{1.96\sigma}{\sqrt{n}}. \tag{13.14}$$

A standard way of writing this is

$$\Pr\left\{\bar{x} - \frac{1.96\sigma}{\sqrt{n}} < \xi < \bar{x} + \frac{1.96\sigma}{\sqrt{n}}\right\} = 0.95. \tag{13.15}$$

The construction of confidence intervals has a close connection with the testing of hypotheses. Suppose that we have an observed value of an estimator T_0 and make a two-sided test at the level of significance α of the null hypothesis $\theta = \underline{\theta}$. The critical region is defined by $T < T_{\mathrm{CL}}$ and $T > T_{\mathrm{CU}}$, where T_{CL} and T_{CU} are determined by

$$\int_{-\infty}^{T_{\mathrm{CL}}} p\{T : \underline{\theta}\}\, dT = \frac{\alpha}{2}, \tag{13.16}$$

and

$$\int_{T_{\mathrm{CU}}}^{\infty} p\{T : \underline{\theta}\}\, dT = \frac{\alpha}{2}. \tag{13.17}$$

Now suppose that T_0 is on the lower edge of the upper part of the critical region, so that $T_0 = T_{\mathrm{CU}}$: then (13.17) becomes

$$\int_{T_0}^{\infty} p\{T : \underline{\theta}\}\, dT = \frac{\alpha}{2}. \tag{13.18}$$

This is exactly the same as (13.7), with $1 - P_2 = \alpha/2$. Thus $\underline{\theta}$ is the smallest value of θ which would be acceptable in a two-sided test at the level of significance α of the null hypothesis $\theta = \theta_0$.

In the same way the critical region for a two-sided test at the level of significance α of the null hypothesis $\theta = \bar{\theta}$ is $T < T'_{\mathrm{CL}}$ and $T < T'_{\mathrm{CU}}$, where T'_{CL} and T'_{CU} are determined by

$$\int_{-\infty}^{T'_{\mathrm{CL}}} p\{T : \bar{\theta}\}\, dT = \frac{\alpha}{2}, \tag{13.19}$$

and

$$\int_{T'_{\mathrm{CU}}}^{\infty} p\{T : \bar{\theta}\}\, dT = \frac{\alpha}{2}. \tag{13.20}$$

If T_0 is at the upper edge of the lower part of the critical region, then $T_0 = T'_{\mathrm{CL}}$, and (13.19) gives

$$\int_{-\infty}^{T_0} p\{T : \bar{\theta}\}\, dT = \frac{\alpha}{2}. \tag{13.21}$$

This is exactly the same as (13.9), with $P_1 = \alpha/2$. Thus θ is the largest value of θ_0 which would be acceptable in a two-sided test at the level of significance α of the null hypothesis $\theta = \theta_0$. Tests of all values of θ in the interval $(\underline{\theta}, \bar{\theta})$ would lead to acceptance of the null hypothesis, and tests of all values of θ outside the interval $(\underline{\theta}, \bar{\theta})$ would lead to rejection of the null hypothesis. The situation is represented graphically in Figure 2.15 for the case of the mean of a normal distribution.

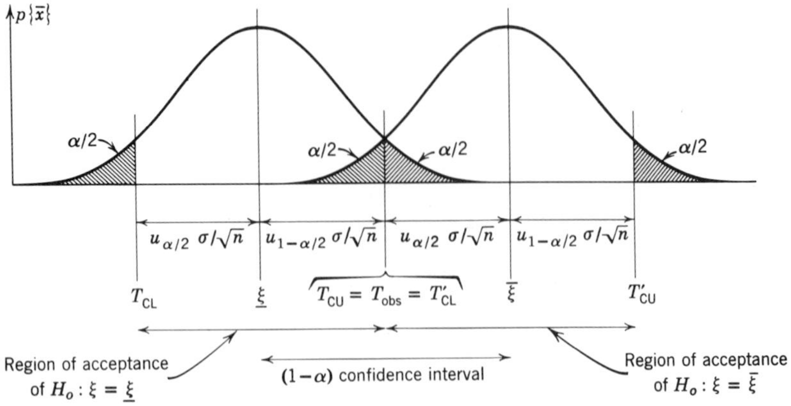

Figure 2.15

REFERENCES

1. Savage, L. J., "The theory of statistical decision," *Journal of the American Statistical Association*, 46(1951), 55–67.
2. Wald, A., *Statistical Decision Functions*. New York: John Wiley & Sons, 1950.
3. Chernoff, Herman, and Lincoln E. Moses, *Elementary Decision Theory*. New York: John Wiley & Sons, 1959.
4. Fisher, R. A., "The mathematical foundations of theoretical statistics," *Philosophical Transactions of the Royal Society*, A, 222(1922), 306–368.
5. Cramér, H., *Mathematical Methods of Statistics*. Princeton: University Press, 1951.
6. Neyman, J., and E. S. Pearson, "On the use and interpretation of certain test criteria for purposes of statistical inference," *Biometrika*, 20-A(1928), 175–240 and 263–294.
7. ——— and ——— "On the problem of the most efficient type of statistical hypotheses," *Philosophical Transactions of the Royal Society*, A, 231(1933), 289–337.
8. ——— and ——— "Contributions to the theory of testing statistical hypotheses," *Statistical Research Memoirs*, 1(1936), 1–37 and 2(1938), 25–57.
9. ——— "On the problem of confidence intervals," *Annals of Mathematical Statistics*, 6(1935), 111–116.

EXERCISES

2.1. A material is obtained in nominal pound packages from two suppliers *A* and *B*. From previous experience it is known that *A* and *B* have standard deviations 0.07 and 0.03 lb, respectively. A sample of 100 packages from *A* is found to have a mean weight of 0.99 lb, and a sample of 400 packages from *B* has a mean weight of 1.01 lb. Find the P value for the null hypothesis that A and B are supplying the same weight, the alternative hypothesis being that $A \neq B$. Give 95 per cent confidence limits for the difference $(B - A)$.

2.2. From long experience with a process for manufacturing an alcoholic beverage, it is known that the yield is normally distributed with a mean of 500 units and a standard deviation of 96 units. We receive a proposal for a modification which it is claimed will increase the yield (leaving the standard deviation unchanged). We propose to make a test of the null hypothesis that the yield remains unchanged at 500 units, using a level of significance 0.05. If the alternative hypothesis is $\xi > 500$,

(*a*) With 50 observations, what is the critical region?

(*b*) With 50 observations, if the yield actually is 535 units, what is the probability of rejecting the null hypothesis?

(*c*) How many observations should we take to make the probability of rejecting the null hypothesis equal to 0.9 when the yield is actually 535 units?

2.3. Same as Exercise 2.2, but the proposal is now for a modification which may change the yield, in one direction or the other. If the alternative hypothesis is now $\xi \neq 500$,

(*a*)
(*b*) As in Exercise 2.2.
(*c*)

2.4. Construct the best test at the level of significance $\alpha = 0.05$ for the null hypothesis that

$$p_0\{x\} = \begin{cases} 1/2, & -1 < x < 1, \\ 0, & \text{otherwise}, \end{cases}$$

against the alternative hypothesis that

$$p_1\{x\} = N(0, (1/2)^2).$$

Give the critical region, and compute the power of the test.

2.5. Same as Exercise 2.4, but interchange the null and the alternative hypotheses.

2.6. Samples of size n_i, $i = 1, \ldots, k$, are taken from a population with fraction defective θ, and the number of defectives in the ith sample is x_i. Form the minimum variance unbiased estimator of θ. What is its variance?

2.7. What is the best critical region for a test at the level of significance $\alpha = 0.05$ of the null hypothesis that an observation x comes from an exponential distribution $p\{x\} = \theta e^{-\theta x}$ where $\theta_0 = 1/2$, against the alternative hypothesis that $\theta_1 = 2$? What is the power of the test?

CHAPTER 3

Problems Involving the Use of the Binomial Distribution

3.1. Calculation of Individual Terms

If an event has a probability θ of occurring on each trial, then the probability that it will occur exactly x times in n independent trials, by (1.8.1), is

$$p_n\{x\} = \binom{n}{x}\theta^x(1-\theta)^{n-x}, \qquad x = 0, 1, \ldots, n. \tag{1.1}$$

The calculation of $p_n\{x\}$ when θ is a simple fraction and n and x are moderately small is comparatively easy. For example, for the probability of obtaining exactly 5 heads in 10 tosses of a fair coin we substitute $x = 5$, $n = 10$, and $\theta = 1/2$:

$$\begin{aligned} p_{10}\{5\} &= \binom{10}{5}\left(\frac{1}{2}\right)^5\left(1-\frac{1}{2}\right)^{10-5} = \frac{10!}{5!(10-5)!}\left(\frac{1}{2}\right)^5\left(\frac{1}{2}\right)^5 \\ &= \frac{10\times 9\times 8\times 7\times 6}{5\times 4\times 3\times 2\times 1}\frac{1}{2^{10}} = \frac{9\times 7\times 4}{1024} = 0.24609. \end{aligned}$$

For more awkward instances it may be easier to use logarithms:

$$\log_{10} p_n\{x\} = \log_{10}\binom{n}{x} + x\log_{10}\theta + (n-x)\log_{10}(1-\theta).$$

Table XIV of [1] gives $\log_{10}\binom{n}{x}$ for $n \leq 100$. Alternatively, we can use Table VII of the appendix which gives $\log_{10} n!$ to evaluate

$$\log_{10}\binom{n}{x} = \log_{10} n! - \log_{10} x! - \log_{10}(n-x)!\,.$$

If we need to evaluate many of these binomial probabilities, certain extensive tabulations [2], [3], or [4] may avoid these calculations. More frequently we are concerned with the sum of the terms in either the lower or upper tails, $\sum_{\nu=0}^{x} p_n\{\nu\}$ or $\sum_{\nu=x}^{n} p_n\{\nu\}$. The tables mentioned contain these cumulative sums for wide ranges of θ and n.

3.2. The Normal Approximation to the Binomial

In this section we shall sketch a proof that the binomial distribution can be approximated by a normal distribution with mean $n\theta$ and variance $n\theta(1-\theta)$. This was first demonstrated by Demoivre in 1733. We use Stirling's well-known approximation to $n!$,

$$n! \simeq n^{n+\frac{1}{2}}e^{-n}\sqrt{2\pi}, \tag{2.1}$$

for the factorials in $\binom{n}{x}$:

$$\begin{aligned}\binom{n}{x} &= \frac{n!}{x!(n-x)!}\\ &\simeq \frac{n^{n+\frac{1}{2}}e^{-n}\sqrt{2\pi}}{x^{x+\frac{1}{2}}e^{-x}\sqrt{2\pi}(n-x)^{n-x+\frac{1}{2}}e^{-(n-x)}\sqrt{2\pi}}\\ &\simeq \frac{1}{\sqrt{2\pi}}\,\frac{n^{n+\frac{1}{2}}}{x^{x+\frac{1}{2}}(n-x)^{n-x+\frac{1}{2}}}\,\frac{e^{-n}}{e^{-x-n+x}}.\end{aligned} \tag{2.2}$$

The exponential terms cancel each other. We now multiply the numerator and denominator by $n^{\frac{1}{2}}$: the numerator is then

$$n^{n+\frac{1}{2}}n^{\frac{1}{2}} = n^{x+\frac{1}{2}}n^{n-x+\frac{1}{2}}.$$

Thus (2.2) becomes

$$\binom{n}{x} \simeq \frac{1}{\sqrt{2\pi}\sqrt{n}}\left(\frac{n}{x}\right)^{x+\frac{1}{2}}\left(\frac{n}{n-x}\right)^{n-x+\frac{1}{2}} \tag{2.3}$$

We can also write

$$\theta^x(1-\theta)^{n-x} = \frac{\theta^{x+\frac{1}{2}}}{\sqrt{\theta}}\,\frac{(1-\theta)^{n-x+\frac{1}{2}}}{\sqrt{(1-\theta)}}. \tag{2.4}$$

Substituting (2.3) and (2.4) in (1.1), we get

$$\begin{aligned}p_n\{x\} &\simeq \frac{1}{\sqrt{2\pi}}\,\frac{1}{\sqrt{n\theta(1-\theta)}}\,\frac{\theta^{x+\frac{1}{2}}}{(x/n)^{x+\frac{1}{2}}}\,\frac{(1-\theta)^{n-x+\frac{1}{2}}}{[(n-x)/n]^{n-x+\frac{1}{2}}}\\ &\simeq \frac{1}{\sqrt{2\pi}}\,\frac{1}{\sqrt{n\theta(1-\theta)}}\,\frac{1}{\left(\dfrac{x}{n\theta}\right)^{x+\frac{1}{2}}}\,\frac{1}{\left[\dfrac{n-x}{n(1-\theta)}\right]^{n-x+\frac{1}{2}}}.\end{aligned} \tag{2.5}$$

Taking logarithms to base e:

$$\log_e p_n\{x\} \simeq -\log_e\sqrt{2\pi n\theta(1-\theta)} - \left(x+\frac{1}{2}\right)\log_e\left(\frac{x}{n\theta}\right) - \left(n-x+\tfrac{1}{2}\right)\log_e\left(\frac{n-x}{n(1-\theta)}\right). \tag{2.6}$$

Now define

$$z = \frac{x-n\theta}{\sqrt{n\theta(1-\theta)}}. \tag{2.7}$$

We will make the following substitutions in (2.6):

$$x = n\theta + z\sqrt{n\theta(1-\theta)}, \tag{2.8}$$

$$\frac{x}{n\theta} = 1 + z\sqrt{\frac{1-\theta}{n\theta}}, \tag{2.9}$$

$$n - x = n(1-\theta) - z\sqrt{n\theta(1-\theta)}, \tag{2.10}$$

$$\frac{n-x}{n(1-\theta)} = 1 - z\sqrt{\frac{\theta}{n(1-\theta)}}. \tag{2.11}$$

The logarithms of the expressions (2.9) and (2.11) appear in (2.6). For these we use the expansion

$$\log(1+y) = y - \frac{y^2}{2} + \frac{y^3}{3} - \cdots$$

which is convergent for $|y| < 1$ and for which the first terms are an approximation of increasing accuracy as $|y|$ tends to zero. Then

$$\log\left(\frac{x}{n\theta}\right) = \log\left(1 + z\sqrt{\frac{1-\theta}{n\theta}}\right) \simeq z\sqrt{\frac{1-\theta}{n\theta}} - z^2\frac{1-\theta}{2n\theta} + \cdots \tag{2.12}$$

and

$$\log\left[\frac{n-x}{n(1-\theta)}\right] = \log\left[1 - z\sqrt{\frac{\theta}{n(1-\theta)}}\right] \simeq -z\sqrt{\frac{\theta}{n(1-\theta)}} - z^2\frac{\theta}{2n(1-\theta)} - \cdots. \tag{2.13}$$

Making these substitutions in (2.6), we obtain

$$\begin{aligned}\log p_n\{x\} \simeq & -\log\sqrt{2\pi n\theta(1-\theta)} \\ & - \left[n\theta + z\sqrt{n\theta(1-\theta)} + \frac{1}{2}\right]\left[z\sqrt{\frac{1-\theta}{n\theta}} - z^2\frac{1-\theta}{2n\theta} + \cdots\right] \\ & - \left[n(1-\theta) - z\sqrt{n\theta(1-\theta)} + \frac{1}{2}\right] \\ & \left[-z\sqrt{\frac{\theta}{n(1-\theta)}} - z^2\frac{\theta}{2n(1-\theta)} - \cdots\right].\end{aligned}$$

Collecting terms in powers of z, the coefficient of z is zero except for $(1/2\sqrt{n})[\sqrt{\theta/(1-\theta)} - \sqrt{(1-\theta)/\theta}]$, which tends to zero as n tends to infinity. The coefficient of z^2 is $-1/2$ plus a component in $1/n$, which tends to zero as n tends to infinity. Higher terms in z also tend to zero; so

$$\log p_n\{x\} \simeq -\log\sqrt{2\pi n\theta(1-\theta)} - \frac{z^2}{2}.$$

Substituting (2.7) for z, we get

$$p_n\{x\} \simeq \frac{1}{\sqrt{2\pi}\sqrt{n\theta(1-\theta)}} \exp\left[-\frac{(x-n\theta)^2}{2n\theta(1-\theta)}\right] \tag{2.14}$$

which is the normal probability density function with the expectation $n\theta$ (1.13.6), and variance $n\theta(1-\theta)$ (1.14.7), of the binomial distribution. We have thus shown that the binomial distribution can be approximated by a normal distribution with the appropriate mean and variance.

Sometimes we may prefer to deal with the observed proportion $h = x/n$, for which

$$p\{h\} \simeq \frac{1}{\sqrt{2\pi}\sqrt{\theta(1-\theta)/n}} \exp\left[-\frac{(h-\theta)^2}{2\theta(1-\theta)/n}\right]. \tag{2.15}$$

The corresponding cumulative distribution functions are

$$\Phi\left(\frac{x-n\theta}{\sqrt{n\theta(1-\theta)}}\right) \quad \text{and} \quad \Phi\left(\frac{h-\theta}{\sqrt{\theta(1-\theta)/n}}\right). \tag{2.16}$$

However, we are approximating a discrete distribution by a continuous distribution. In the discrete distribution of x the probability is concentrated at the integers, and, when we approximate it by a continuous distribution, the corresponding probability is spread over a figure approximately a rectangle with base stretching from $-1/2$ to $+1/2$ on either side of the integer. In Figure 3.1 the integral $\int_{-\infty}^{x_1} p\{x\}\,dx$ will omit the shaded area from x_1 to $(x_1 + 1/2)$ which properly belongs to x_1. We therefore change the upper limit of integration to $(x_1 + 1/2)$:

$$\Pr\{x \le x_1\} \simeq \int_{-\infty}^{x_1+\frac{1}{2}} p\{x\}\,dx = \Phi\left(\frac{x_1 + 1/2 - n\theta}{\sqrt{n\theta(1-\theta)}}\right). \tag{2.17}$$

If on the other hand we wanted the probability that $x < x_1$, the integral $\int_{-\infty}^{x_1} p\{x\}\,dx$ would improperly include the area between $(x_1 - 1/2)$ and x_1: We therefore integrate to $(x_1 - 1/2)$:

$$\Pr\{x < x_1\} \simeq \int_{-\infty}^{x_1-\frac{1}{2}} p\{x\}\,dx = \Phi\left(\frac{x_1 - 1/2 - n\theta}{\sqrt{n\theta(1-\theta)}}\right). \tag{2.18}$$

This constant 1/2 that is added or subtracted to the limit of integration is known as the *correction for continuity*.

Formulas (2.17) and (2.18) can be combined to give

$$\Pr\{x = x_1\} = \Pr\{x \le x_1\} - \Pr\{x < x_1\}$$
$$\simeq \Phi\left(\frac{x_1 + 1/2 - n\theta}{\sqrt{n\theta(1-\theta)}}\right) - \Phi\left(\frac{x_1 - 1/2 - n\theta}{\sqrt{n\theta(1-\theta)}}\right). \quad (2.19)$$

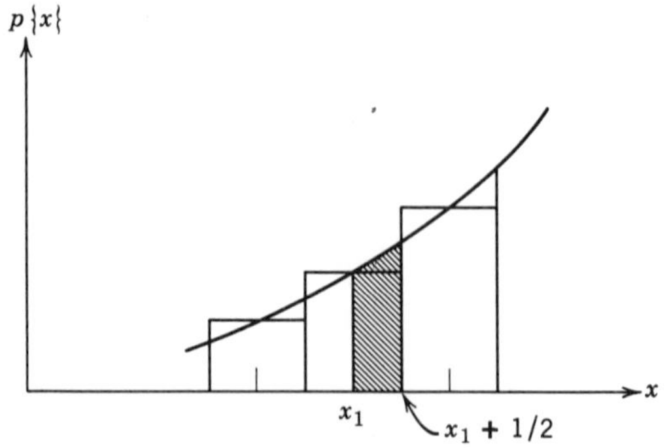

Figure 3.1

As an illustration, let $n = 100$, $\theta = 0.1$, $x_1 = 10$: Then

$$\Pr\{x = 10\} \simeq \Phi\left(\frac{10 + 1/2 - 100 \times 0.1}{\sqrt{100 \times 0.1 \times 0.9}}\right) - \Phi\left(\frac{10 - 1/2 - 100 \times 0.1}{\sqrt{100 \times 0.1 \times 0.9}}\right)$$
$$\simeq \Phi(0.1667) - \Phi(-0.1667) = 0.5662 - 0.4338 = 0.1324.$$

The exact answer, obtained from tables or from direct calculation as indicated in Section 3.1, is 0.1319.

The alternative forms of (2.17) and (2.18) referring to $h = x/n$, obtained by dividing the numerator and denominator of the argument of $\Phi(\ )$ by n, are

$$\Pr\{h \le h_1\} \simeq \Phi\left(\frac{h_1 + 1/2n - \theta}{\sqrt{\theta(1-\theta)/n}}\right), \quad (2.20)$$

$$\Pr\{h < h_1\} \simeq \Phi\left(\frac{h_1 - 1/2n - \theta}{\sqrt{\theta(1-\theta)/n}}\right). \quad (2.21)$$

For a rigorous proof of the results of this section, with a careful attention to remainder terms, etc., the reader is referred to Uspensky [5] or Feller [6].

3.3. Testing Hypotheses about the Binomial Distribution Using the Normal Approximation

Suppose we observe x defectives in a sample of size n from a binomial distribution, and wish to test the null hypothesis that the population fraction defective θ is some particular value θ_0.

First, suppose that the alternative hypothesis is one-sided, $\theta = \theta_1 > \theta_0$. The most reasonable critical region will be that part of the x axis corresponding to an area α in the upper tail of the distribution of x under the null hypothesis. Let x_c be the x at the lower end of the critical region. Then the region of acceptance will reach up to $(x_c - 1)$. We want the probability of falling in the region of acceptance under H_0: $\theta = \theta_0$ to be $1 - \alpha$; so, using (2.18), x_c is determined by the equation

$$\Pr\{x < x_c\} \simeq \Phi\left(\frac{x_c - 1/2 - n\theta_0}{\sqrt{n\theta_0(1 - \theta_0)}}\right) = 1 - \alpha, \tag{3.1}$$

or

$$\frac{x_c - 1/2 - n\theta_0}{\sqrt{n\theta_0(1 - \theta_0)}} = u_{1-\alpha} .$$

Solving for x_c, we get

$$x_c = n\theta_0 + \frac{1}{2} + u_{1-\alpha}\sqrt{n\theta_0(1 - \theta_0)}. \tag{3.2}$$

Accordingly, if $x < x_c$, we accept the null hypothesis, and, if $x \geq x_c$, we reject the null hypothesis. In general, (3.2) will give a value for x_c which is not an integer. If we use as the lower edge of our critical region x_c' the integer just less than x_c, then our critical region will have an α larger than the value we wanted for our level of significance. If we use as x_c' the integer just larger than x_c, then our critical region will be too small. The conservative procedure will be to use as our actual α the smaller of the possibilities. Its approximate numerical value can be obtained by inserting x_c' in (3.1) and solving for the corresponding value of α, say α'.

Second, if the alternative hypothesis is $\theta = \theta_1 < \theta_0$, we want the probability to be α, under H_0, that x will fall in the region $\leq x_c$. From (2.17),

$$\Pr\{x \leq x_c\} \simeq \Phi\left(\frac{x_c + 1/2 - n\theta_0}{\sqrt{n\theta_0(1 - \theta_0)}}\right) = \alpha,$$

whence

$$x_c \simeq n\theta_0 - \frac{1}{2} + u_\alpha\sqrt{n\theta_0(1 - \theta_0)}. \tag{3.3}$$

Accordingly, if $x > x_c$, we accept the null hypothesis, and, if $x \leq x_c$, we reject the null hypothesis.

Third, if the alternative hypothesis is two-sided, $\theta = \theta_1 \neq \theta_0$, the natural critical region, symmetric in probability, is

$$x \leq n\theta_0 - \frac{1}{2} + u_{\alpha/2}\sqrt{n\theta_0(1 - \theta_0)}$$

and

$$x \geq n\theta_0 + \frac{1}{2} + u_{1-\alpha/2}\sqrt{n\theta_0(1 - \theta_0)}. \tag{3.4}$$

The critical regions for $\boldsymbol{h}$ are given by dividing both sides of each equation (3.2), (3.3), and (3.4), by n.

Instead of a strict testing procedure at a fixed level of significance α, we may wish to calculate the P value. For a one-tailed test with alternative $\theta = \theta_1 > \theta_0$, if x_1 is the observed number of defectives, we want

$$\Pr\{x \geq x_1\} = 1 - \Pr\{x < x_1\} \simeq 1 - \Phi\left(\frac{x_1 - 1/2 - n\theta_0}{\sqrt{n\theta_0(1 - \theta_0)}}\right) \simeq P; \tag{3.5}$$

so

$$\Phi\left(\frac{x_1 - 1/2 - n\theta_0}{\sqrt{n\theta_0(1 - \theta_0)}}\right) \simeq 1 - P,$$

and

$$\frac{x_1 - 1/2 - n\theta_0}{\sqrt{n\theta_0(1 - \theta_0)}} \simeq u_{1-P}, \tag{3.6}$$

which can be solved for P. For example, if we observe 60 heads in 100 tosses of a coin, and are testing the null hypothesis that the coin is fair, i.e., $H_0 : \theta_0 = 1/2$, we refer

$$u_{1-P} \simeq \frac{60 - 1/2 - 100 \times 1/2}{\sqrt{100 \times 1/2(1 - 1/2)}} = 1.900$$

to Table I of the appendix, the cumulative normal distribution, obtaining $1 - P \simeq 0.9713$, whence $P \simeq 0.0287$. In the opposite tail, with the alternative hypothesis $\theta = \theta < \theta_0$, we want

$$\Pr\{x \leq x_1\} \simeq \Phi\left(\frac{x_1 + 1/2 - n\theta_0}{\sqrt{n\theta_0(1 - \theta_0)}}\right) \simeq P;$$

so

$$u_P \simeq \frac{x_1 + 1/2 - n\theta_0}{\sqrt{n\theta_0(1 - \theta_0)}}. \tag{3.7}$$

For example, if we observe 40 heads in 100 tosses of a coin, and are testing the null hypothesis that the coin is fair, we calculate

$$u_P = \frac{40 + 1/2 - 100 \times 1/2}{\sqrt{100 \times 1/2(1 - 1/2)}} = -1.900$$

whence $P = 0.0287$.

The calculation of P values for two-sided alternatives is most easily carried out by observing whether the observed number x falls in the upper or lower tail, and calculating the appropriate single-tail P value as above, and doubling it to get the two-tailed P value.

In computing the power of these tests, since h is approximately a normally distributed variable with mean θ and variance $\theta(1-\theta)/n$, we can use the methods of Section 2.7 for one-sided tests and those of Section 2.9 for two-sided tests. There is, however, a slight complication here in that the variance is not a constant but instead is a function of θ. The calculation of the power for a specified alternative $\theta = \theta_1$, $\theta_1 > \theta_0$, proceeds as follows: Using (2.18),

$$\Pr\{x \geq x_1\} = 1 - \Pr\{x < x_1\} \simeq 1 - \Phi\left(\frac{x_1 - 1/2 - n\theta}{\sqrt{n\theta(1-\theta)}}\right). \tag{3.8}$$

From (3.2), for a one-sided test at the level of significance α, the lower edge of the critical region is

$$x_c = n\theta_0 + \frac{1}{2} + u_{1-\alpha}\sqrt{n\theta_0(1-\theta_0)}. \tag{3.9}$$

Thus, using (3.8) to give us the probability that an observed number x will lie in the critical region $\geq x_c$ when θ is equal to the alternative θ_1, the power is

$$\begin{aligned}\pi(\theta_1) &= \Pr\{x \geq x_c | \theta = \theta_1\} \\ &\simeq 1 - \Phi\left(\frac{n\theta_0 + 1/2 + u_{1-\alpha}\sqrt{n\theta_0(1-\theta_0)} - 1/2 - n\theta_1}{\sqrt{n\theta_1(1-\theta_1)}}\right) \\ &\simeq 1 - \Phi\left(\frac{\sqrt{n}(\theta_0 - \theta_1)}{\sqrt{\theta_1(1-\theta_1)}} + u_{1-\alpha}\frac{\sqrt{\theta_0(1-\theta_0)}}{\sqrt{\theta_1(1-\theta_1)}}\right).\end{aligned} \tag{3.10}$$

If we define $\sigma_0 = \sqrt{\theta_0(1-\theta_0)/n}$, $\sigma_1 = \sqrt{\theta_1(1-\theta_1)/n}$, this can be written as

$$\begin{aligned}\pi(\theta_1) &\simeq 1 - \Phi\left[\frac{\theta_0 - \theta_1}{\sigma_1} + u_{1-\alpha}\left(\frac{\sigma_0}{\sigma_1}\right)\right] \simeq 1 - \Phi\left[\left(u_{1-\alpha} + \frac{\theta_0 - \theta_1}{\sigma_0}\right)\frac{\sigma_0}{\sigma_1}\right] \\ &\simeq \Phi\left[\left(u_\alpha + \frac{\theta_1 - \theta_0}{\sigma_0}\right)\frac{\sigma_0}{\sigma_1}\right].\end{aligned} \tag{3.11}$$

When the alternative hypothesis is $\theta_1 < \theta_0$, similar manipulations yield

$$\pi(\theta_1) = \Phi\left[\left(u_\alpha + \frac{\theta_0 - \theta_1}{\sigma_0}\right)\frac{\sigma_0}{\sigma_1}\right]. \tag{3.12}$$

For a two-sided test, the critical region is defined by (3.4). The power of the test is the probability that the observed number falls in the critical region when $\theta = \theta_1$:

$$\pi(\theta_1) = \Pr\{x \leq n\theta_0 - \frac{1}{2} + u_{\alpha/2}\sqrt{n\theta_0(1-\theta_0)}|\theta = \theta_1\}$$

$$+ \Pr\left\{x \geq n\theta_0 + \frac{1}{2} + u_{1-\alpha/2}\sqrt{n\theta_0(1-\theta_0)}|\theta = \theta_1\right\}$$

$$\simeq \Phi\left[\frac{n\theta_0 - 1/2 + u_{\alpha/2}\sqrt{n\theta_0(1-\theta_0)} + 1/2 - n\theta_1}{\sqrt{n\theta_1(1-\theta_1)}}\right]$$

$$+ 1 - \Phi\left[\frac{n\theta_0 + 1/2 + u_{1-\alpha/2}\sqrt{n\theta_0(1-\theta_0)} - 1/2 - n\theta_1}{\sqrt{n\theta_1(1-\theta_1)}}\right]$$

$$\simeq \Phi\left[\frac{u_{\alpha/2}\sqrt{n\theta_0(1-\theta_0)} + n(\theta_0 - \theta_1)}{\sqrt{n\theta_1(1-\theta_1)}}\right]$$

$$+ \Phi\left[\frac{u_{\alpha/2}\sqrt{n\theta_0(1-\theta_0)} - n(\theta_0 - \theta_1)}{\sqrt{n\theta_1(1-\theta_1)}}\right]$$

$$\simeq \Phi\left[u_{\alpha/2}\left(\frac{\sigma_0}{\sigma_1}\right) + \frac{\theta_0 - \theta_1}{\sigma_1}\right] + \Phi\left[u_{\alpha/2}\left(\frac{\sigma_0}{\sigma_1}\right) - \frac{\theta_0 - \theta_1}{\sigma_1}\right]$$

$$\simeq \Phi\left[\left(u_{\alpha/2} + \frac{\theta_0 - \theta_1}{\sigma_0}\right)\frac{\sigma_0}{\sigma_1}\right] + \Phi\left[\left(u_{\alpha/2} - \frac{\theta_0 - \theta_1}{\sigma_0}\right)\frac{\sigma_0}{\sigma_1}\right]. \tag{3.13}$$

These formulas can be used to give the sample size necessary for a power of $(1 - \beta)$ of rejecting the null hypothesis at a level of significance α when $(\theta_1 - \theta_0)$ has any specified value. For the one-sided alternative $\theta_1 > \theta_0$, putting (3.11) equal to $(1 - \beta)$, we get

$$\left(u_\alpha + \frac{\theta_1 - \theta_0}{\sigma_0}\right)\frac{\sigma_0}{\sigma_1} = u_{1-\beta},$$

and, substituting $\sqrt{\theta_0(1-\theta_0)/n}$ for σ_0 and likewise for σ_1, and solving for n, we get

$$n = \frac{1}{(\theta_1 - \theta_2)^2}\left(u_{1-\beta}\sqrt{\theta_1(1-\theta_1)} + u_{1-\alpha}\sqrt{\theta_0(1-\theta_0)}\right)^2. \tag{3.14}$$

For example, if we wish to have a power $(1 - \beta)$ of 0.95 of rejecting the null hypothesis $\theta_0 = 0.05$ at the one-sided level of significance $\alpha = 0.01$ when actually θ is $\theta_1 = 0.10$, then

$$n = \frac{1}{(0.10 - 0.05)^2}\left(u_{0.95}\sqrt{0.10(1-0.10)} + u_{0.99}\sqrt{0.05(1-0.05)}\right)^2 = 400.$$

3.4. The Angular Transformation and Other Variance-Stabilizing Transformations

It is convenient to assume that the variance of a random variable, say x, is a constant, say σ^2. However, situations do arise in which the variance is instead a function, say $g(\xi)$, of the expected value of x, ξ. For example, the variance of a binomial proportion h, by (1.14.8), is $\theta(1 - \theta)/n$ which is a function of θ. In such a situation, to permit the use of statistical techniques which assume a constant variance, we need to transform x into a function of x, say $\phi(x)$, where the function $\phi(\ )$ is chosen so that the random variable so defined has a constant variance. This we can do in the following manner.

Let $\phi(X)$ be a function of a real variable X. By a Taylor series, $\phi(X)$ can be approximated by a linear function near any point ξ:

$$\phi(X) \simeq \phi(\xi) + \phi'(\xi)(X - \xi).$$

Let x be a random variable with an expected value $E[x] = \xi$. Then $y = \phi(x)$ defines a new random variable y. If the variance of x is small, then x does not vary greatly about ξ, and so the Taylor series will be a close approximation:

$$y \simeq \phi(\xi) + \phi'(\xi)(x - \xi). \tag{4.1}$$

Taking expectations,

$$E[y] \simeq \phi(\xi); \tag{4.2}$$

so

$$y - E[y] \simeq \phi'(\xi)(x - \xi), \tag{4.3}$$

and $V[y] = E[(y - E[y])^2] \simeq \{\phi'(\xi)\}^2 E[(x - \xi)^2] \simeq \{\phi'(\xi)\}^2 V[x]$. (4.4)

In general, $V[x]$ will depend on various parameters. If, however, it can be written as a function of the expected value ξ, say $g(\xi)$, then

$$V[y] \simeq \{\phi'(\xi)\}^2 g(\xi).$$

If we choose $\phi'(\xi)$ so that

$$\phi'(\xi) = \frac{1}{\sqrt{g(\xi)}}, \tag{4.5}$$

then we will have made $V[y] \simeq 1$. Equation (4.5) is equivalent to

$$\phi(\xi) = \int \frac{d\xi}{\sqrt{g(\xi)}}. \tag{4.6}$$

For example, for a binomial proportion h with expectation θ, the variance $V[h] = \theta(1 - \theta)/n$. Inserting this for $g(\xi)$ in (4.6), we have

$$\phi(\theta) = \int \frac{d\theta}{\sqrt{\theta(1-\theta)/n}} = \sqrt{n} \int \frac{d\theta}{\sqrt{\theta(1-\theta)}}. \tag{4.7}$$

This integral can be evaluated by changing the variable to $t = \sqrt{\theta}$, so that $t^2 = \theta$, $2t\,dt = d\theta$, and

$$\int \frac{d\theta}{\sqrt{\theta(1-\theta)}} = \int \frac{2t\,dt}{\sqrt{t^2(1-t^2)}} = 2\int \frac{dt}{\sqrt{1-t^2}} = 2 \arcsin t = 2 \arcsin \sqrt{\theta}. \tag{4.8}$$

Thus, if we use the transformation $\phi(h) = 2\sqrt{n} \arcsin \sqrt{h}$, the variance of $\phi(h)$ will be 1. If we omit the factor $\sqrt{n}$ and instead use $\psi(h) = 2 \arcsin \sqrt{h}$, then the variance of this transformed variable will be $1/n$. Table V of the appendix gives this latter transformation directly from a proportion h to $\psi(h) = y$ in radians: For example, if one enters the table with $h = 0.500$ it gives directly $2 \arcsin \sqrt{h}$ as $y = 1.5708$.

We will note here several other transformations of frequent utility. First, if the variance is proportional to the expected value, so that $V[x] = k\xi$, then

$$\phi(\xi) = \int \frac{d\xi}{\sqrt{k\xi}} = \frac{2}{\sqrt{k}}\sqrt{\xi}. \tag{4.9}$$

Thus a square-root transformation will give a constant variance. In particular, if $k = 1$, as occurs with the Poisson distribution, to be discussed in Section 4.4, $2\sqrt{x}$ will have variance 1, and $\sqrt{x}$ will have variance 1/4.

Second, if the standard deviation is proportional to the expected value, so that $V[x] = k^2 \xi^2$,

$$\phi(\xi) = \int \frac{d\xi}{\sqrt{k^2\xi^2}} = \frac{1}{k} \log_e \xi, \tag{4.10}$$

so that $\log_e x$ will have a constant variance k^2, and $\log_{10} x$ a constant variance $0.189k^2$. We might note that, if, $\psi(\xi) = \log_e \xi$, then $\psi'(\xi) = 1/\xi$ and $\psi''(\xi) = -1/\xi^2$. Using the Taylor series up to the second-degree term,

$$y \simeq \psi(\xi) + \psi'(\xi)(x - \xi) + \psi''(\xi)\frac{(x-\xi)^2}{2};$$

so

$$E[y] \simeq \psi(\xi) + \frac{1}{2}\psi''(\xi)\,E[(x-\xi)^2] \simeq \log_e \xi - \frac{V[x]}{2\xi^2}. \tag{4.11}$$

This shows that when we include the second-degree term in the Taylor series the expected value of the transformed variable y differs from (4.2), the transformation of the expected value of the original variable x, by an amount in this case $-V[x]/(2(E[x])^2)$. We might also note that on substituting $1/\xi$ for $\psi'(\xi)$ in (4.4) we get

$$V[y] = \frac{V[x]}{(E[x])^2}. \tag{4.12}$$

Third, if the standard deviation is proportional to the square of the expected value, so that $V[x] = k^2\xi^4$, then

$$\phi(\xi) = \int \frac{d\xi}{\sqrt{k^2\xi^4}} = \int \frac{d\xi}{k\xi^2} = -\frac{1}{k\xi}, \tag{4.13}$$

so that the reciprocal $1/x$ will have constant variance k^2.

To summarize these three results, to obtain constance variance, if $V[x] \propto \xi$ we use $\sqrt{x}$, if $V[x] \propto \xi^2$ we use $\log x$, and if $V[x] \propto \xi^4$ we use $1/x$.

We have discussed transformations from the point of view of obtaining constant variance in the transformed variable. If the original variable is normally distributed, then the transformed variable cannot be. However, it is an empirical fact that the lack of constancy of variance is usually simultaneously associated with a nonnormality, and the transformation that gives a constant variance also simultaneously gives a distribution closer to normal. In short, this is one case where usually we can both have our cake and eat it.

3.5. Testing Hypotheses about the Binomial Distribution Using the Angular Transformation

If h is a binomial proportion with expectation θ based on a sample of n, then $y = 2 \arcsin \sqrt{h}$ in radians is approximately normally distributed with approximate expectation $\eta = 2 \arcsin \sqrt{\theta}$ and variance $1/n$, and

$$\Pr\{h \le h_1\} \simeq \int_{-\infty}^{2 \arcsin\sqrt{h_1 + 1/2n}} p\{y\}\, dy \simeq \Phi\left(\frac{2 \arcsin\sqrt{h_1 + 1/2n} - \eta}{1/\sqrt{n}}\right), \tag{5.1}$$

where the $1/2n$ is a correction for continuity analogous to that used with the normal approximation. For a one-sided test of the null hypothesis $\theta = \theta_0$ against the alternative $\theta = \theta_1 < \theta_0$, the critical region will be determined by putting (5.1) equal to α and writing h_c for h_1, $\eta_0 = 2 \arcsin \sqrt{\theta_0}$ for η; on rearrangement we get

$$2 \arcsin\sqrt{h_c + \frac{1}{2n}} = 2 \arcsin\sqrt{\theta_0} + \frac{u_\alpha}{\sqrt{n}} \tag{5.2}$$

which for specified θ_0, α, and n will determine h_c. If $h \leq h_c$, we reject the null hypothesis. The other one-sided test and the two-sided test can be constructed similarly. However, the angular transformation appears to give approximations no better than the normal approximation, and these tests are not customarily used.

However, since the variance of the angular transformation is a constant, the calculation of powers and necessary sample sizes can be made more expeditiously with it than with the normal approximation, in which the variance is a function of θ. Ignoring the correction for continuity, the formula (2.7.8) for the power of a one-sided test applies immediately: For the alternative $\eta_1 > \eta_0$,

$$\pi(\eta_1) = \Phi\left(u_\alpha + \frac{\eta_1 - \eta_0}{1/\sqrt{n}}\right). \tag{5.3}$$

The same formula, with η_1 and η_0 interchanged, applies for the alternative $\eta_1 < \eta_0$. For the two-sided test, the analog of (2.9.7) is

$$\pi(\eta_1) = \Phi\left(u_{\alpha/2} - \frac{\eta_1 - \eta_0}{1/\sqrt{n}}\right) + \Phi\left(u_{\alpha/2} + \frac{\eta_1 - \eta_0}{1/\sqrt{n}}\right). \tag{5.4}$$

For calculating necessary sample sizes, for the one-sided test the analog of (2.7.12) is

$$n = (u_{1-\beta} + u_{1-\alpha})^2\left(\frac{1}{\eta_1 - \eta_0}\right)^2, \tag{5.5}$$

and for the two-sided test the analog of (2.9.8) is

$$n = (u_{1-\beta} + u_{1-\alpha/2})^2\left(\frac{1}{\eta_1 - \eta_0}\right)^2. \tag{5.6}$$

For example, if we wish to have a power of $(1 - \beta)$ of 0.95 of rejecting the null hypothesis $\theta_0 = 0.05$ at the level of significance $\alpha = 0.01$, making a one-sided test, when actually θ is $\theta_1 = 0.10$, we use (5.5) with $u_{1-\beta} = u_{0.95} = 1.645$, $u_{1-\alpha} = u_{0.99} = 2.326$, $\eta_0 = 2 \arcsin \sqrt{0.05} = 0.4510$, $\eta_1 = 2 \arcsin \sqrt{0.10} = 0.6435$; then

$$n = \frac{(1.645 + 2.326)^2}{(0.6435 - 0.4510)^2} = 425$$

which can be compared with the result $n = 400$ obtained for the same problem with the normal approximation in Section 3.3. Both these are approximations; there is no obvious reason for preferring one to the other. An exact calculation would be difficult and not worth the trouble.

3.6. Exact Testing of Hypotheses about the Binomial Distribution

If x is the number of defectives in a sample of n taken from a population with parameter θ, it can be shown that

$$\Pr\{x \leq x_0\} = \sum_{\nu=0}^{x_0} \binom{n}{\nu} \theta^\nu (1-\theta)^{n-\nu} = 1 - \Pr\left\{F < \frac{n - x_0}{x_0 + 1} \frac{\theta}{1-\theta}\right\}, \tag{6.1}$$

where F is a random variable with the variance ratio distribution with degrees of freedom $f_1 = 2(x_0 + 1)$, $f_2 = 2(n - x_0)$. The variance ratio distribution will be discussed in Section 9.2, and for the present it will be sufficient to note that a number of upper percentage points, e.g., 0.90, 0.95, etc., are tabulated in Table IV of the appendix. In Section 9.2 we will see that we can obtain lower percentage points, e.g., 0.10, 0.05, etc., from the equation

$$F_\alpha(f_1, f_2) = \frac{1}{F_{1-\alpha}(f_2, f_1)}. \tag{6.2}$$

For example, the 0.05 point of F with degrees of freedom 80 and 100 is $F_{0.05}(80, 100) = 1/F_{0.95}(100, 80) = 1/1.43 = 0.699$.

Although equation (6.1) is exact, in practice it will usually not give us exact probabilities since F is only tabulated for a relatively few probability levels. As an example, consider the occurrence of 40 heads on 100 tosses of a coin. Under the null hypothesis that the coin is fair, so that $\theta_0 = 1/2$, the P value is

$$\begin{aligned} \Pr\{x \leq 40\} &= 1 - \Pr\left\{F < \frac{100-40}{40+1} \frac{0.5}{1-0.5}\right\}, \qquad & f_1 &= 2(40+1), \\ & & f_2 &= 2(100-40), \\ &= 1 - \Pr\{F < 1.464\}, & f_1 &= 82, \quad f_2 = 120. \end{aligned}$$

The degrees of freedom corresponding to our problem, 82 and 120, are not tabulated in the F table, but we might use $F_{0.95}(80, 125) = 1.39$ and $F_{0.975}(80, 125) = 1.48$. We see that our observed value of F lies between these two values; so

$$0.95 < \Pr\{F < 1.464\} < 0.975,$$

and

$$0.025 < \Pr\{x \leq 40\} < 0.05.$$

The observed value of F, 1.464, lies closer to the 0.975 point than to the 0.95 point; so we might guess that $\Pr\{x \leq 40\} \simeq 0.03$. A more precise answer would require careful interpolation in the F tables.

As another example, consider the occurrence of $x_0 = 60$ heads in 100 tosses of a coin. Under the null hypothesis that the coin is fair, so that $\theta_0 = 1/2$, the P value is

$$\begin{aligned}
\Pr\{x \geq x_0\} &= 1 - \Pr\{x \leq x_0 - 1\} \\
&= \Pr\left\{F < \frac{n - x_0 + 1}{x_0} \frac{\theta_0}{1 - \theta_0}\right\}, & f_1 = 2x_0, \quad f_2 = 2(n - x_0 + 1), \qquad (6.3) \\
&= \Pr\left\{F < \frac{100 - 60 + 1}{60} \frac{0.5}{1 - 0.5}\right\}, & f_1 = 2 \times 60, \quad f_2 = 2(100 - 60 + 1), \\
&= \Pr\{F < 0.683\}, & f_1 = 120, \quad f_2 = 82, \\
&= P, \quad \text{say.}
\end{aligned}$$

We note that our observed value of F lies in the lower, untabulated part of the distribution. A simple procedure is as follows. In general $\Pr\{F < F_P\} = P$; so $F_P(120, 82) = 0.683$. Using (6.2),

$$\frac{1}{F_P(120, 82)} = F_{1-P}(82, 120) = \frac{1}{0.683} = 1.46.$$

We have just seen that $F_{0.97}(82, 120) \simeq 1.46$; so $1 - P = 0.97$, and $P = 0.03$.

Two-tailed tests are made conventionally by doubling the P value given by a one-tailed test.

3.7. Confidence Limits for the Parameter of a Binomial Distribution

Suppose that in a sample of n light bulbs from a very large (infinite) lot we find x_0 defectives. The maximum-likelihood point estimate for θ is x_0/n. We wish to place confidence limits on θ. By equations (2.13.7) and (2.13.9) the confidence limits are defined by the equations

$$\Pr\{x \geq x_0 | \theta = \underline{\theta}\} = 1 - P_2, \tag{7.1}$$

$$\Pr\{x \leq x_0 | \theta = \overline{\theta}\} = P_1. \tag{7.2}$$

Equation (7.1) can be written

$$\Pr\{x < x_0 | \theta = \underline{\theta}\} = P_2. \tag{7.3}$$

We then have to solve for $\underline{\theta}$ and $\overline{\theta}$, the equations

$$P\{x_0 - 1\} = \sum_{x=0}^{x_0 - 1} \binom{n}{x} \underline{\theta}^x (1 - \underline{\theta})^{n-x} = P_2, \tag{7.4}$$

$$P\{x_0\} = \sum_{x=0}^{x_0} \binom{n}{x} \bar{\theta}^x (1 - \bar{\theta})^{n-x} = P_1. \tag{7.5}$$

We will first use the normal approximation. Using (2.17), we have for (7.4),

$$\Phi\left(\frac{x_0 - 1/2 - n\underline{\theta}}{\sqrt{n\underline{\theta}(1 - \underline{\theta})}}\right) = P_2 ,$$

whence

$$\frac{x_0 - 1/2 - n\underline{\theta}}{\sqrt{n\underline{\theta}(1 - \underline{\theta})}} = u_{P_2} . \tag{7.6}$$

This gives a quadratic equation in $\underline{\theta}$, to which the solution, obtained by simple but tedious algebra, is

$$\underline{\theta} = \frac{1}{n + u_{P_2}^2}\left[x_0 - \frac{1}{2} + \frac{u_{P_2}^2}{2} - u_{P_2}\sqrt{\frac{(x_0 - 1/2)(n - x_0 + 1/2)}{n} + \frac{u_{P_2}^2}{4}}\right]. \tag{7.7}$$

Using (2.17), we have for (7.5)

$$\Phi\left(\frac{x_0 + 1/2 - n\bar{\theta}}{\sqrt{n\bar{\theta}(1 - \bar{\theta})}}\right) = P_1 ,$$

which likewise leads to

$$\bar{\theta} = \frac{1}{n + u_{P_1}^2}\left[x_0 + \frac{1}{2} + \frac{u_{P_1}^2}{2} - u_{P_1}\sqrt{\frac{(x_0 + 1/2)(n - x_0 - 1/2)}{n} + \frac{u_{P_1}^2}{4}}\right]. \tag{7.8}$$

As an example, suppose an automobile dealer observes 8 automobiles characterized by inexcusably shoddy workmanship in a presumably random consignment of 30, then straightforward substitution and the use of $P_2 = 0.975$, $P_1 = 0.025$ gives 95 per cent confidence limits of 0.130 and 0.462. Exact confidence limits can be obtained using the formula for the cumulative sum of the binomial in terms of the F distribution (6.1). To deal with $\bar{\theta}$ first, we substitute (6.1) in (7.5):

$$\Pr\{x \le x_0 | \theta = \bar{\theta}\} = 1 - \Pr\left\{F(2(x_0 + 1), 2(n - x_0)) < \frac{n - x_0}{x_0 + 1}\frac{\bar{\theta}}{1 - \bar{\theta}}\right\} = P_1 .$$

Thus $\bar{\theta}$ is determined by the equation

$$\Pr\left\{F(2(x_0 + 1), 2(n - x_0)) < \frac{n - x_0}{x_0 + 1}\frac{\bar{\theta}}{1 - \bar{\theta}}\right\} = 1 - P_1 .$$

But the $(1 - P_1)$ point of F is F_{1-P_1}; so

$$\frac{n - x_0}{x_0 + 1}\frac{\bar{\theta}}{1 - \bar{\theta}} = F_{1-P_1}(2(x_0 + 1), 2(n - x_0)),$$

whence, solving for $\bar{\theta}$,

$$\bar{\theta} = \frac{(x_0 + 1)F_{1-P_1}}{n - x_0 + (x_0 + 1)F_{1-P_1}}, \tag{7.9}$$

where F has degrees of freedom $2(x_0 + 1)$, $2(n - x_0)$. For $\underline{\theta}$, substituting (6.1) in (7.3),

$$\Pr\{x < x_0 | \theta = \underline{\theta}\} = 1 - \Pr\left\{F(2x_0, 2(n - x_0 + 1)) < \frac{n - x_0 + 1}{x_0} \frac{\underline{\theta}}{1 - \underline{\theta}}\right\}$$
$$= P_2;$$

so $$\Pr\left\{F(2x_0, 2(n - x_0 + 1)) < \frac{n - x_0 + 1}{x_0} \frac{\underline{\theta}}{1 - \underline{\theta}}\right\} = 1 - P_2,$$

whence $$\frac{n - x_0 + 1}{x_0} \frac{\underline{\theta}}{1 - \underline{\theta}} = F_{1-P_2}(2x_0, 2(n - x_0 + 1)). \tag{7.10}$$

This is somewhat awkward for when P_2 is, for example, 0.975, the $(1 - P_2)$ point of F lies in the untabulated lower tail of the distribution. However, by (6.2),

$$F_{1-P_2}(2x_0, 2(n - x_0 + 1)) = \frac{1}{F_{P_2}(2(n - x_0 + 1), 2x_0)}.$$

Inserting this in (7.10) and solving for θ, we get

$$\underline{\theta} = \frac{x_0}{x_0 + (n - x_0 + 1)F_{P_2}} \tag{7.11}$$

where F has degrees of freedom $2(n - x_0 + 1)$, $2x_0$.

For 95 per cent confidence limits for the example of 8 poor automobiles in a consignment of 30, used to illustrate the normal approximation confidence limits, we substitute in (7.9)

$$F_{1-0.025}(2(8 + 1), 2(30 - 8)) = F_{0.975}(18, 44) = 2.07,$$

giving $$\bar{\theta} = \frac{(8 + 1) \times 2.07}{30 - 8 + (8 + 1) \times 2.07} = 0.459.$$

Use of (7.11) involves

$$F_{0.975}(2(30 - 8 + 1), 2 \times 8) = F_{0.975}(46, 16) = 2.49$$

and gives $\underline{\theta} = 0.123$. Comparison with the approximate limits 0.130 to 0.462 shows that the approximation is not too bad, but evidently a sample of 30 is somewhat on the small side for close agreement.

3.8. Comparison of Two Observed Frequencies with the Normal Approximation

Suppose we have two infinite populations with fractions defective θ_1 and θ_2, and from each population we draw samples sizes n_1 and n_2, and observe x_1 and x_2 defectives. We wish to test the null hypothesis that $\theta_1 = \theta_2$. Let $h_1 = x_1/n_1$, $h_2 = x_2/n_2$. Under the null hypothesis, $(h_1 - h_2)$ will be distributed about zero with variance

$$V[h_1 - h_2] = \frac{\theta(1-\theta)}{n_1} + \frac{\theta(1-\theta)}{n_2} = \theta(1-\theta)\left(\frac{1}{n_1} + \frac{1}{n_2}\right).$$

A natural estimate h of θ under the null hypothesis is to pool the total number of defectives and divide by the sum of the sample sizes, i.e., $h = (x_1 + x_2)/(n_1 + n_2)$. Then under H_0

$$\frac{h_1 - h_2}{\sqrt{h(1-h)(1/n_1 + 1/n_2)}}$$

will be approximately a standardized normal deviate. An improvement in the approximation can be obtained by introducing corrections for continuity into the h_1 and h_2, with such signs as will reduce the absolute value of the numerator. Thus, if $h_1 > h_2$, we use

$$\frac{(h_1 - 1/2n_1) - (h_2 + 1/2n_2)}{\sqrt{h(1-h)(1/n_1 + 1/n_2)}} \tag{8.1}$$

as an approximate standardized normal deviate. For a two-sided test, if the absolute value of (8.1) exceeds $u_{1-\alpha/2}$, we reject the null hypothesis at the level of significance α.

Table 3.1

Type of rubber	Number of cases With reactions	Without reactions	Totals
A	27	13	40
B	5	10	15
Totals	32	23	55

As an example, Table 3.1 shows the number of cases with reactions observed on using two types of rubber tubing for injection of a certain substance. If we assume that patients were allocated at random to the two "treatments," rubber A and rubber B, any difference between the groups will be attributable to a difference between the rubbers. (On the other hand, if random allocation is not used, it will probably be impossible to conclude anything useful from the data. If there is a significant difference, we will not know what it is due to.)

We shall see later (Section 5.3) that there is a simple rule which tells us whether it is safe to use the normal approximation (8.1). In the present instance the answer is yes; so we calculate $h = 32/55 = 0.5818$. We then compute, for a two-tailed test,

$$\frac{\left(\frac{27}{40} - \frac{1}{2 \times 40}\right) - \left(\frac{5}{15} + \frac{1}{2 \times 15}\right)}{\sqrt{0.5818(1 - 0.5818)(1/40 + 1/15)}} = 1.981 = u_{1-P/2}$$

whence $P = 0.0476$. We would thus conclude at the 5 per cent level of significance that the two groups differed in their percentage reactions, presumably on account of the different rubber tubing.

For calculating powers and necessary sample sizes, the angular transformation is convenient: $y_1 = 2 \arcsin \sqrt{h_1}$, $y_2 = 2 \arcsin \sqrt{h_2}$ have variances $1/n_1$, $1/n_2$; so $V[y_1 - y_2] = 1/n_1 + 1/n_2$. Let η_1, η_2 be equal to $2 \arcsin \sqrt{\theta_1}$, $2 \arcsin \sqrt{\theta_2}$, respectively. The power of a two-sided test is given by appropriate substitutions in (2.9.7):

$$\pi(\theta_1 - \theta_2) = \Phi\left(u_{\alpha/2} - \frac{\eta_1 - \eta_2}{\sqrt{1/n_1 + 1/n_2}}\right) + \Phi\left(u_{\alpha/2} + \frac{\eta_1 - \eta_2}{\sqrt{1/n_1 + 1/n_2}}\right), \tag{8.2}$$

and, for a one-sided test against the alternative $\theta_1 > \theta_2$, (2.7.8) gives

$$\pi(\theta_1 - \theta_2) = \Phi\left(u_\alpha + \frac{\eta_1 - \eta_2}{\sqrt{1/n_1 + 1/n_2}}\right). \tag{8.3}$$

For calculating necessary sample sizes we need to make some assumption about the relative magnitudes of n_1 and n_2. It is easy to show that $(n_1 + n_2)$ for specified power, etc., is a minimum when $n_1 = n_2 = m$, say, so that the standard deviation of $(y_1 - y_2)$ is $\sqrt{2/m}$. For the two-sided test, (2.9.8) gives

$$m = (u_{1-\beta} + u_{1-\alpha/2})^2 \frac{2}{(\eta_1 - \eta_2)^2}, \tag{8.4}$$

and, for the one-sided test, (2.7.12) gives

$$m = (u_{1-\beta} + u_{1-\alpha})^2 \frac{2}{(\eta_1 - \eta_2)^2}. \tag{8.5}$$

For example, if we wish to have a power $(1 - \beta)$ of 0.95 of rejecting the null hypothesis $\theta_1 = \theta_2$ at the level of significance $\alpha = 0.01$, making a one-sided test, when in fact $\theta_1 = 0.10$, $\theta_2 = 0.05$, then

$$m = \frac{2(1.645 + 2.326)^2}{(0.6435 - 0.4510)^2} = 850.$$

Note that $m = 850$ implies that $n_1 = n_2 = 850$; i.e., we need 850 observations on each population, making a total of 1700 observations.

3.9. The Fisher Exact Test for the Comparison of Two Binomial Proportions

Section 3.8 gave a solution, based upon the normal approximation to the binomial, to the problem of comparing two observed frequencies. The normal approximation is excessively crude when one or more of the expected numbers are small, in a way to be described in Section 5.3. In this section we will develop an exact test that is not subject to this limitation.

Consider all possible outcomes of two sets of independent trials, n_1 in number in one case and n_2 in the other, all with the same probability of success θ. Denote the numbers of successes by x_1, x_2. A particular pair

Table 3.2

	Number of successes	Number of failures	Number of trials
First set	ν_1	$n_1 - \nu_1$	n_1
Second set	ν_2	$n_2 - \nu_2$	n_2
Totals	$\nu_1 + \nu_2$	$n_1 + n_2 - \nu_1 - \nu_2$	$n_1 + n_2$

of outcomes are $x_1 = \nu_1$, $x_2 = \nu_2$ (see Table 3.2). The Fisher exact test computes the probability of obtaining these outcomes ν_1, ν_2, given the two sample sizes n_1 and n_2 and the observed total number of successes $(\nu_1 + \nu_2)$, under the assumption that the probability of a success is the same for each set.

We define E_1 as the event $(x_1 = \nu_1,\ x_2 = \nu_2)$ and E_2 as the event $(x_1 + x_2 = \nu_1 + \nu_2)$. We are going to compute

$$\Pr\{x_1 = \nu_1, x_2 = \nu_2 | x_1 + x_2 = \nu_1 + \nu_2\} = \Pr\{E_1 | E_2\} = \frac{\Pr\{E_1 E_2\}}{\Pr\{E_2\}}, \quad (9.1)$$

by (1.4.1). The event $(E_1 E_2)$ is the joint occurrence of both E_1 and E_2.

But, if E_1 occurs, i.e., if $x_1 = \nu_1$ and $x_2 = \nu_2$, then automatically E_2 occurs, for we cannot have $x_1 = \nu_1$ and $x_2 = \nu_2$ without simultaneously $(x_1 + x_2) = (\nu_1 + \nu_2)$. Hence the probability of the joint event (E_1E_2) is the same as the probability of the single event E_1, i.e.,

$$\Pr\{E_1E_2\} = \Pr\{E_1\}; \tag{9.2}$$

so, substituting this in (9.1),

$$\Pr\{x_1 = \nu_1, x_2 = \nu_2 | x_1 + x_2 = \nu_1 + \nu_2\} = \frac{\Pr\{E_1\}}{\Pr\{E_2\}}. \tag{9.3}$$

We now need to evaluate the numerator and denominator of (9.3). For the numerator, since the two sets of trials are assumed independent

$$\begin{aligned}\Pr\{E_1\} &= \Pr\{x_1 = \nu_1, x_2 = \nu_2\} = \Pr\{x_1 = \nu_1\}\Pr\{x_2 = \nu_2\} \\ &= p_{n_1}\{\nu_1\} \cdot p_{n_2}\{\nu_2\} = \binom{n_1}{\nu_1}\theta^{\nu_1}(1-\theta)^{n_1-\nu_1}\binom{n_2}{\nu_2}\theta^{\nu_2}(1-\theta)^{n_2-\nu_2} \\ &= \frac{\binom{n_1}{\nu_1}\binom{n_2}{\nu_2}}{\binom{n_1+n_2}{\nu_1+\nu_2}}\binom{n_1+n_2}{\nu_1+\nu_2}\theta^{\nu_1+\nu_2}(1-\theta)^{n_1+n_2-\nu_1-\nu_2}.\end{aligned} \tag{9.4}$$

For the denominator, we supposedly have a single sample of size $(n_1 + n_2)$ which gave rise to $(\nu_1 + \nu_2)$ successes; so

$$\begin{aligned}\Pr\{E_2\} &= \Pr\{x_1 + x_2 = \nu_1 + \nu_2\} = p_{(n_1+n_2)}(\nu_1 + \nu_2) \\ &= \binom{n_1+n_2}{\nu_1+\nu_2}\theta^{\nu_1+\nu_2}(1-\theta)^{n_1+n_2-\nu_1-\nu_2}.\end{aligned} \tag{9.5}$$

Substituting (9.4) and (9.5) in (9.3):

$$\begin{aligned}\Pr\{x_1 = \nu_1, x_2 = \nu_2 | x_1 + x_2 = \nu_1 + \nu_2\} &= \frac{\binom{n_1}{\nu_1}\binom{n_2}{\nu_2}}{\binom{n_1+n_2}{\nu_1+\nu_2}} \\ &= \frac{n_1!n_2!(\nu_1+\nu_2)!(n_1+n_2-\nu_1-\nu_2)!}{\nu_1!(n_1-\nu_1)!\nu_2!(n_2-\nu_2)!(n_1+n_2)!}.\end{aligned} \tag{9.6}$$

A somewhat more common notation for Table 3.2 is given in Table 3.3. Using the notation of Table 3.3, (9.6) becomes

$$\Pr\{a, c | a + c\} = \frac{(a+b)!(c+d)!(a+c)!(b+d)!}{a!b!c!d!(a+b+c+d)!}. \tag{9.7}$$

Table 3.3

	Number of successes	Number of failures	Number of trials
First set	a	b	$a + b$
Second set	c	d	$c + d$
Totals	$a + c$	$b + d$	$a + b + c + d$

This is the probability of getting precisely the observed table, given the observed margins, under the null hypothesis that we have independent samples from populations with the same θ. For a test of significance, we want not only this probability, but also the sum of the probabilities of the possible results more extreme in the same direction; i.e., we need to sum the tail of the distribution. This may be somewhat tedious, but

$$\frac{(a+b)!(c+d)!(a+c)!(b+d)!}{(a+b+c+d)!} = C, \quad \text{say}, \tag{9.8}$$

common to all terms in the series, can be evaluated with Table VII of logarithms of $n!$. Table 3.4 contains an analysis of the data of Table 3.1. The logarithm of the constant C is

$$\log \frac{40!15!32!23!}{55!}$$
$$= 47.911645 + 12.116500 + 35.420172 + 22.412494 - 73.103681$$
$$= 44.757130.$$

Table 3.4

Observed table	27	13	28	12	29	11	30	10	31	9	32	8
and more	5	10	4	11	3	12	2	13	1	14	0	15
extreme tables												

$\log a!$	28.036983	29.484141	30.946539	32.423660	33.915022	35.420172
$\log b!$	9.794280	8.680337	7.601156	6.559763	5.559763	4.605521
$\log c!$	2.079181	1.380211	0.778151	0.301030	0.000000	0.000000
$\log d!$	6.559763	7.601156	8.680337	9.794280	10.940408	12.116500
Sum	46.470207	47.145845	48.006183	49.078733	50.415193	52.142193
$\log C$ − sum	$\bar{2}.286923$	$\bar{3}.611285$	$\bar{4}.750957$	$\bar{5}.678397$	$\bar{6}.341937$	$\bar{8}.614937$
Probability	0.01936	0.00409	0.00056	0.00005	0.00000	0.00000

In constructing the upper part of Table 3.4, in this instance the observed proportion of reactions with rubber B, 5/15, is less than 27/40, and so we write down all possible tables in which this proportion is smaller than 5/15, always subject to the restriction that the marginal totals are unchanged. When the entry in this cell has gone from 5 to 0, it can go no further. This gives the 2×2 tables across the upper part of Table 3.4. The sum of the probabilities in the last row is 0.02406. This is the P value for this tail. For a two-sided test, the usual procedure is to double it, setting 0.04812. For these data the normal approximation gave 0.0476, and so it is apparent that the normal approximation is close enough for most practical purposes in cases like the present one.

Calculation of P values by the Fisher exact test may be somewhat tedious, but tables have been prepared by Mainland [7] giving the probabilities of all possible samples for $n_1 = n_2 \leq 20$ and the probabilities of samples in the region of probabilities 0.005 and 0.025 for $n_1 < n_2 \leq 20$. Another set of tables by Finney [8] deals with all samples, equal and unequal, up to $n_1 = n_2 = 15$, and these were extended by Latscha [9] up to $n_1 = n_2 = 20$.

3.10. The Correlated Two × Two Table

The standard way of presenting the results of two sets of independent trials is a 2×2 table such as Table 3.3, and the null hypothesis that the proportions of "successes" is the same in each population can be tested by the methods of Section 3.8 or Section 3.9. However, there are some experimental situations which give rise to data which may also be put in a 2×2 table which cannot correctly be analyzed in that way.

If we were given Table 3.5 (from Mosteller [10]) and asked to test the null hypothesis that the probability of nausea was the same with either drug, we might be tempted to proceed with the normal approximation for the comparison of two proportions (Section 3.8) without pausing to inquire how the data were obtained. A naïve interpretation of Table 3.5 would be that we took two samples each of 100 patients and gave one set of 100 drug A and the other set of 100 drug B. In actual fact, the data were obtained from just 100 patients, each of whom received both drugs, with results as sketched in Table 3.6, where N and $\bar{N}$ mean nausea and no nausea. There were 9 patients like patient number 1 who had nausea with both drugs; 9 patients like number 2 who had nausea with drug A but not with drug B; only 1 patient, number 3, who had nausea with drug B but not with A; and 81 patients like patient number 4 who had no nausea with either drug. The data of Table 3.6 should therefore be condensed as in Table 3.7.

As can be seen from the column totals, there were 18 cases of nausea and 82 without nausea with drug *A*, which is how the first row of Table 3.5 was formed. Likewise the row totals, 10 and 90, are the figures for drug *B* in Table 3.5. The essential features of the original data in Table 3.6 have been lost in the summarization of Table 3.5 but have been retained in Table 3.7. Table 3.5 can be constructed from Table 3.7, but the reverse is not true.

Table 3.5

	Nausea	No nausea	
Drug *A*	18	82	100
Drug *B*	10	90	100
	28	172	200

Table 3.6

Patient	Drug *A*	Drug *B*
1	N	N
2	N	$\bar{N}$
3	$\bar{N}$	N
4	$\bar{N}$	$\bar{N}$
5		
⋮		
100		

Table 3.7

		Drug *A*		
		N	$\bar{N}$	
Drug *B*	N	9	1	10
	$\bar{N}$	9	81	90
		18	82	100

In Table 3.7, the 9 patients who had nausea with both drugs, and the 81 who had nausea with neither, tell us nothing about the difference between the drugs. All the information on this question is contained in the other diagonal, presented in Table 3.8. If there was no difference between the drugs, we would expect these 10 patients to be split on the average 50:50

Table 3.8. Patients Who Responded Differently to the Two Drugs

Favorably to *A* and unfavorably to *B*	1
Unfavorably to *A* and favorably to *B*	9
Total	10

between the two categories in Table 3.8. The one-sided P value for the null hypothesis is thus given by the sum of the terms in the binomial tail:

$$\Pr\{x \leq x_0 | n, \theta\} = \sum_{x=0}^{x_0} \binom{n}{x} \theta^x (1-\theta)^{n-x}$$

with $\theta = 1/2$. Here $n = 10$, $x_0 = 1$, and we can use (2.17)

$$\Pr\{x \leq x_0\} = \Phi\left(\frac{x_0 + 1/2 - n\theta}{\sqrt{n\theta(1-\theta)}}\right) = \Phi(-2.214) = P,$$

whence $P = 0.0134$ (one-sided). Alternatively,

$$\Pr\left\{x \leq x_0 = 1 | 10, \frac{1}{2}\right\} = \sum_{x=0}^{x_0=1} \binom{10}{x} \left(\frac{1}{2}\right)^x \left(1 - \frac{1}{2}\right)^{10-x} = \frac{1}{2^{10}} \sum_{x=0}^{1} \binom{10}{x}$$

$$= \frac{1}{2^{10}} \left(\frac{10!}{0!10!} + \frac{10!}{1!9!}\right) = \frac{11}{1024} = 0.01074.$$

REFERENCES

1. Hald, A., *Statistical Tables and Formulas.* New York; John Wiley & Sons, 1952.
2. National Bureau of Standards, *Table of the Binomial Probability Distribution,* Applied Mathematics Series 6 (1950).
3. *Tables of the Cumulative Binomial Probabilities.* Ordnance Corps Pamphlet ORDP 20–1. Washington, D.C.: U.S. Government Printing Office, 1952.
4. Staff of the Computation Laboratory, *Tables of the Cumulative Binomial Probability Distribution.* Cambridge: Harvard University Press, 1955.

5. Upsensky, J. V., *Introduction to Mathematical Probability*. New York: McGraw-Hill Book Co., 1937.
6. Feller, William, *An Introduction to Probability Theory and Its Applications*. Vol. 1. New York: John Wiley & Sons, 1957.
7. Mainland, Donald, "Statistical methods in medical research: I: Qualitative statistics (enumeration data)," *Canadian Journal of Research*, E, 26(1948), 1–166.
8. Finney, D. J., "The Fisher-Yates test of significance in 2 × 2 contingency tables," *Biometrika*, 35(1948), 145–156.
9. Latscha, R., "Test of significance in a 2 × 2 contingency table: extension of Finney's table," *Biometrika*, 40(1953), 74–86.
10. Mosteller, Frederick, "Some statistical problems in measuring the subjective response to drugs," *Biometrics*, 8(1952), 220–226.

EXERCISES

3.1. The manager of a large automobile repair shop suspects that in six-cylinder engines the valves of the front cylinder are in worse condition than those of the other cylinders. After records have been kept on 115 such jobs, it is found that in 27 of them the front cylinder is in worse condition. Can the manager reject the null hypothesis that the front cylinder is no worse than the other cylinders, using a one-sided test?

3.2. The Chevalier de Méré thought that it paid to bet evens on

(i) Getting one or more sixes in 4 throws of a die; but not on

(ii) Getting one or more double sixes in 24 throws with a pair of dice.

In point of fact the true probabilities (assuming fair dice) for these events are 0.51775 and 0.49141, respectively.

Suppose that you are planning experiments to test empirically the null hypotheses

(*a*) That the probability of (i) is 0.5, against the alternative that it is 0.51775.

(*b*) That the probability of (i) is equal to the probability of (ii), against the alternative that they are 0.51775 and 0.49141, respectively.

Assuming one-sided tests of significance with $\alpha = 0.05$, in each case (*a*) and (*b*), how many observations should be taken to give probability 0.9 of rejecting the null hypothesis?

3.3. Fertilizer was stored in drums of two types. After a certain period it was observed that of 57 of the first type, 7 had split seams, and of 63 of the second type, 1 had split seams. Calculate the one-sided P value for the null hypothesis that the two types of drums do not differ in their liability to splitting (*a*) with the Fisher exact test, (*b*) with the normal approximation, (*c*) with the angular transformation.

3.4. An oil company drilled 15 holes and found 7 dry holes. In this region the industry average for the proportion of dry holes was 0.25. Test the significance of the null hypothesis that this company was merely unlucky by making use of the F distribution; i.e., find the value of the relevant statistic, and quote the relevant F values from the F table to give lower and upper bounds for the P value of the null hypothesis. Assume a one-sided test.

Also find the P value, using the normal approximation and the angular transformation.

3.5. In a study of the safety of polio vaccine 127 lots were tested by both a tissue culture test and a monkey test. Of these, 110 lots were negative by both tests, 2 were positive by both tests, 12 were positive by the tissue culture test and negative by the monkey test, and 3 were positive by the monkey test and negative by the tissue culture test. (*a*) Present this data in a tabular form. (*b*) On the basis of this data, can you state a preference for either test?

3.6. Fertilizer was stored in drums of a certain type. After a certain period, it was observed that in a sample of 63 drums 1 had split seams. Calculate 90 per cent confidence limits for the proportion of split drums in that population of drums (*a*) by a normal approximation, (*b*) exactly.

3.7. In an experiment to test whether seeding clouds of a certain type causes them to produce radar echoes corresponding to the occurrence of rain (R. R. Braham, L. J. Battan, and H. R. Byers, "Artificial nucleation of cumulus clouds," *University of Chicago Cloud Physics Project Report* 24), on each suitable day a plane flew through two clouds that met certain criteria, and one of the pair, chosen at random, was seeded and the other not. For 46 flights, echoes occurred in both clouds 5 times, in the unseeded cloud only 6 times, in the seeded cloud only 17 times, and in neither cloud 18 times. Find the one-sided P value for the null hypothesis that seeding is without effect.

3.8. Suppose that you are planning a clinical trial for a proposed vaccine against a disease which has a low and variable incidence from year to year. Therefore it is necessary to run a control group. Suppose that the average incidence for a season is 1 per 50,000. Suppose that you wish the trial to have a probability of 0.99 of rejecting the null hypothesis that the vaccine is without effect if in fact the vaccine reduces the incidence by one-half. Suppose that a level of significance 0.01 is to be used, and only a one-sided alternative is to be considered. Assuming that the two groups will be made the same size, what is the total number of subjects required?

(Note that, for very small values of x, $\sin x \simeq x$ and $\arcsin x \simeq x$.)

CHAPTER 4

The Hypergeometric and Poisson Distributions

4.1. The Hypergeometric Distribution

Suppose that, from a population of N elements, of which M are "defective," we draw without replacement a sample of size n. What is the probability that our sample contains exactly x defectives?

There are $\binom{N}{n}$ different ways, all assumed equally likely, of drawing a sample of size n from a population of N elements. We want the number of ways which give samples with x defective elements. The x defective elements must have been drawn from the M defectives, and the $(n - x)$ nondefective elements must have been drawn from the $(N - M)$ nondefectives. These two drawings can be made independently in $\binom{M}{x}$ and $\binom{N-M}{n-x}$ different ways, respectively. There are thus $\binom{M}{x}\binom{N-M}{n-x}$ ways of drawing a sample which will give us x defectives. We therefore can write

$$p\{x\} = \left(\frac{\text{number of ways of drawing a sample of size } n \text{ with exactly } x \text{ defectives}}{\text{total number of ways of drawing a sample of size } n}\right)$$

$$= \binom{M}{x}\binom{N-M}{n-x} \bigg/ \binom{N}{n}, \qquad (1.1)$$

where there are certain restrictions on the variable x, namely, $0 \le x \le n$, $0 \le x \le M$, $0 \le n - x \le N - M$. Distributions with this form of frequency function are known as hypergeometric distributions. They are awkward to work with, but fortunately they can be frequently well approximated by binomial distributions.

We can write (1.1) in the form

$$\begin{aligned}
p\{x\} &= \frac{M!}{x!(M-x)!}\,\frac{(N-M)!}{(n-x)!(N-M-n+x)!}\,\frac{n!(N-n)!}{N!} \\
&= \frac{M(M-1)\cdots(M-x+1)}{x!} \\
&\quad\times\frac{(N-M)(N-M-1)\cdots(N-M-n+x+1)}{(n-x)!} \\
&\quad\times\frac{n!}{N(N-1)\cdots(N-n+1)} \\
&= \frac{n!}{x!(n-x)!} \\
&\quad\times\frac{M(M-1)\cdots(M-x+1)(N-M)(N-M-1)\cdots(N-M-n+x+1)}{N(N-1)\cdots(N-n+1)}.
\end{aligned}\tag{1.2}$$

Ignoring the first part of (1.2), $n!/x!(n-x)!$, the numerator is made up of two sequences of terms, the first sequence, $M(M-1)\cdots$ being x in number, and the second sequence, $(N-M)(N-M-1)\cdots$ being $(n-x)$ in number; so the total number of these terms is $x+(n-x)=n$. In the denominator, the sequence $N(N-1)\cdots$ is made up of n terms. Dividing both numerator and denominator by N^n, there will be one N for every term in the numerator and denominator. Denoting the proportion of defectives in the population M/N as θ, we get

$$\begin{aligned}
p\{x\} &= \frac{n!}{x!(n-x)!} \\
&\times\frac{\theta\left(\theta-\frac{1}{N}\right)\cdots\left(\theta-\frac{x+1}{N}\right)(1-\theta)\left(1-\theta-\frac{1}{N}\right)\cdots\left(1-\theta-\frac{n-x-1}{N}\right)}{1\left(1-\frac{1}{N}\right)\cdots\left(1-\frac{n-1}{N}\right)}.
\end{aligned}$$

If now N tends to infinity with θ held constant, and n and x also fixed

$$p\{x\} \simeq \binom{n}{x}\theta^x(1-\theta)^{n-x}, \tag{1.3}$$

which is the usual frequency function for a binomial distribution. We would expect to obtain this result, for when the population size N gets infinitely large our successive drawings without replacement approach independence, since each withdrawal has a vanishingly small effect on the composition of the remaining population. The binomial distribution assumes, of course, that successive drawings are independent. In many real situations, the population is not infinite: In sampling a lot of light bulbs, the lot size is finite though usually very large. One can roughly say that the binomial distribution is a close enough approximation to the hypergeometric for most people's purposes when $n/N < 0.1$, i.e., when the sample size is less than 10 per cent of the population size.

4.2. Fisher's Exact Test as an Illustration of the Hypergeometric Distribution

Consider a 2×2 table with its usual notation (Table 4.1). In the first sample of size $(a + b)$ we found a defectives, and in the second sample of size $(c + d)$ we found c defectives. The Fisher exact test operates conditionally on the observed marginal totals, and so from this viewpoint we have a population of size $N = a + b + c + d$ containing $M = a + c$ defectives. We can regard the first sample as a sample of size $n = a + b$ from this population, and in this sample we observe $x = a$ defectives. Substitution in (1.1) gives

$$p\{x\} = \frac{\binom{a+c}{a}\binom{b+d}{b}}{\binom{a+b+c+d}{a+b}} = \frac{(a+b)!(c+d)!(a+c)!(b+d)!}{a!b!c!d!(a+b+c+d)!}, \qquad (2.1)$$

which is identical with (3.9.7) obtained by another approach.

Table 4.1

	Defective	Nondefective	Totals
First sample	a	b	$a + b$
Second sample	c	d	$c + d$
Totals	$a + c$	$b + d$	$a + b + c + d$

4.3. An Application of the Hypergeometric Distribution to Wild Life Population Estimation

Suppose that we have an enclosed lake containing N fish. We wish to estimate N. We take a sample of size M and mark the fish and return them to the lake. We now have a population of size N containing M marked elements.

Suppose that there exists a period sufficiently long to allow adequate mixing but not so long that births and deaths will have appreciable effects on N and M. After such a period we take a second sample of size n and find x marked fish. The frequency function of x is, by (1.1),

$$p\{x\} = \binom{M}{x}\binom{N-M}{n-x}\Big/\binom{N}{n}. \tag{3.1}$$

We know M, n, and x. We may estimate N by the method of maximum likelihood; i.e., we find that N which maximizes $L = p\{x\}$. We regard $p\{x\}$ as a function of N, say $p_N\{x\}$, and consider the ratio $p_N\{x\}/p_{N-1}\{x\}$. Increasing N from M, we find the largest value of N for which this ratio is greater than one. Since each successive $p_N\{x\}$ in this sequence is larger than its immediate predecessor, the last in the sequence must give the maximum value for $L = p_N\{x\}$. The ratio

$$\frac{p_N\{x\}}{p_{N-1}\{x\}} = \frac{\binom{M}{x}\binom{N-M}{n-x}}{\binom{N}{n}} \frac{\binom{N-1}{n}}{\binom{M}{x}\binom{N-1-M}{n-x}}$$

$$= \frac{N^2 - MN - nN + nM}{N^2 - MN - nN + Nx}, \tag{3.2}$$

is greater than one for $nM > Nx$; so the maximum-likelihood estimator $\hat{N}$ is the integer just less than nM/x.

If we take $\hat{N} = nM/x$, we might note that maximum-likelihood estimators sometimes have disconcerting properties. Thus

$$E[\hat{N}] = E\left[\frac{nM}{x}\right] = nM\,E\left[\frac{1}{x}\right] = nM \sum_{x=0}^{\min n,M} \frac{1}{x} \cdot \frac{\binom{M}{x}\binom{N-M}{n-x}}{\binom{N}{n}}. \tag{3.3}$$

Since the summation includes the term for $x = 0$, for which $1/x = \infty$, the expected value of $\hat{N}$ is ∞. However, the expected value of $1/\hat{N}$ is better behaved:

$$E\left[\frac{1}{\hat{N}}\right] = E\left[\frac{x}{nM}\right] = \frac{1}{nM} E[x] = \frac{1}{nM} \cdot \frac{nM}{N} = \frac{1}{N}, \tag{3.4}$$

using the result of Exercise 4.4.

For a detailed examination of these topics see Chapman [1].

4.4. The Poisson Distribution

One approach to the Poisson distribution is to consider a limiting case of the binomial distribution. For the binomial, $E[x] \equiv \xi = n\theta$; we suppose that n tends to infinity and θ tends to zero in such a way that $n\theta = \xi$ remains a nonzero, noninfinite quantity. Then

$$\begin{aligned} p\{x\} &= \binom{n}{x}\theta^x(1-\theta)^{n-x} = \frac{n!}{x!(n-x)!}\left(\frac{\xi}{n}\right)^x\left(1-\frac{\xi}{n}\right)^{n-x} \\ &= \frac{n(n-1)\cdots(n-x+1)}{n^x}\frac{\xi^x}{x!}\left(1-\frac{\xi}{n}\right)^{n-x} \\ &= \left[1\left(1-\frac{1}{n}\right)\cdots\left(1-\frac{x-1}{n}\right)\right]\left(1-\frac{\xi}{n}\right)^{-x}\frac{\xi^x}{x!}\left(1-\frac{\xi}{n}\right)^n. \end{aligned}$$

As n tends to infinity, all the terms in [ ] tend to one, and $(1-\xi/n)^{-x}$ likewise: also the limit of $(1-\xi/n)^n$ is known to be $e^{-\xi}$; so

$$p\{x\} \to \frac{\xi^x}{x!}e^{-\xi}, \qquad x = 0, 1, \ldots \tag{4.1}$$

and this is the frequency function of the Poisson distribution.

The expectation is easily found:

$$\begin{aligned} E[x] &= \sum_{x=0}^{\infty} x\, p\{x\} = \sum_{x=0}^{\infty} x \cdot e^{-\xi} \cdot \frac{\xi^x}{x!} \\ &= e^{-\xi}\left[0 \cdot \frac{\xi^0}{0!} + 1 \cdot \frac{\xi^1}{1!} + 2 \cdot \frac{\xi^2}{2!} + \cdots\right] \\ &= e^{-\xi}\left[0 + \xi\left(1 + \frac{\xi^1}{1!} + \frac{\xi^2}{2!} + \cdots\right)\right] = e^{-\xi} \cdot \xi \cdot e^{\xi} = \xi. \end{aligned} \tag{4.2}$$

since
$$e^{\xi} = 1 + \frac{\xi^1}{1!} + \frac{\xi^2}{2!} + \cdots.$$

To find the variance we first need $E[x^2]$:

$$\begin{aligned} E[x^2] &= \sum_{x=0}^{\infty} x^2\, e^{-\xi}\frac{\xi^x}{x!} = e^{-\xi}\xi\sum_{x=1}^{\infty} x\frac{\xi^{x-1}}{(x-1)!} \\ &= e^{-\xi}\xi\sum_{x=1}^{\infty}[(x-1)+1]\frac{\xi^{x-1}}{(x-1)!} \\ &= e^{-\xi}\xi\left[\sum_{x=1}^{\infty}(x-1)\frac{\xi^{x-1}}{(x-1)!} + \sum_{x=1}^{\infty}\frac{\xi^{x-1}}{(x-1)!}\right] \\ &= e^{-\xi}\xi\left[\xi\sum_{x=2}^{\infty}\frac{\xi^{x-2}}{(x-2)!} + e^{\xi}\right] = e^{-\xi}\xi[\xi\, e^{\xi} + e^{\xi}] = \xi^2 + \xi; \end{aligned}$$

so $$V[x] = E[x^2] - (E[x])^2 = \xi^2 + \xi - (\xi)^2 = \xi. \tag{4.3}$$

For a random sample of observations from a Poisson distribution $x_1, \ldots, x_n$, the maximum-likelihood estimator is found by maximizing the likelihood

$$L = p\{x_1 : \xi\} \cdots p\{x_n : \xi\}$$

$$= e^{-\xi} \cdot \frac{\xi^{x_1}}{x_1!} \cdots e^{-\xi} \cdot \frac{\xi^{x_n}}{x_n!} = e^{-n\xi} \frac{\xi^{\sum_i^n x_i}}{\prod_i^n x_i!}$$

or, equivalently, maximizing the logarithm of the likelihood,

$$\log L = -n\xi + (\sum_i^n x_i) \log \xi - \log (\prod_i^n x_i!).$$

To maximize, we differentiate with respect to ξ and equate to zero.

$$\frac{d \log L}{d\xi} = -n + (\sum_i^n x_i) \cdot \frac{1}{\xi} = 0$$

whence $$\hat{\xi} = \sum_{i=1}^n x_i/n = \bar{x}. \tag{4.4}$$

As an example of data with a distribution closely represented by the Poisson frequency function, R. D. Clarke [2] gave the numbers of flying bombs falling into areas of 0.25 sq km in London over a certain period. There were 576 such areas, 229 of which received zero bombs, 211 which received one bomb, etc. (Table 4.2); i.e., $x = 0$ on 229 occasions, $x = 1$ on 211 occasions, etc. There were no areas which received more than seven bombs. Let n_x be the number of areas which received x bombs: $\sum_{x=0}^{\infty} n_x = n$. From (4.4) the maximum-likelihood estimator of ξ is

$$\hat{\xi} = \sum_{i=1}^n \frac{x_i}{n} = \frac{\sum_{x=0}^{\infty} n_x x}{\sum_{x=0}^{\infty} n_x}$$

$$= \frac{229 \times 0 + 211 \times 1 + 93 \times 2 + 35 \times 3 + 7 \times 4 + 0 \times 5 + 0 \times 6 + 1 \times 7}{576}$$

$$= \frac{537}{576} = 0.932292.$$

Inserting $\hat{\xi}$ in place of ξ in (4.1) we get the estimated probability that a random area will have a particular value of x. Multiplying $p\{x\}$ by n

gives the expected numbers of areas with particular values of x. For example,

$$p\{0\} = \frac{(0.932292)^0}{0!} e^{-0.932292} = 0.393650,$$

and $n\,p\{0\} = 226.742$. The agreement of n_x with $n\,p\{x\}$ seems satisfactory. The last two columns of Table 4.2 are required for a method of testing that the n_x are consistent with the hypothesis that their expected values are the values $n\,p\{x\}$ derived under the assumption that x is Poisson-distributed, to be discussed in Section 5.2.

Table 4.2

x	n_x	$p\{x\}$	$n\,p\{x\}$	d_i	d_i^2/e_i
0	229	0.393650	226.742	2.258	0.0225
1	211	0.366997	211.390	−0.390	0.0007
2	93	0.171074	98.539	−5.539	0.3114
3	35	0.053164	30.622	4.378	0.6259
4	7	0.012391	7.137	−0.706	0.0698
5	0	0.002310	1.331		
6	0	0.000359	0.207		
7	1	0.000048	0.028		
8	0	0.000000	0.003		
Totals	576	1.000001	575.999	0.001	1.0303

4.5. An Alternative Derivation of the Poisson Distribution

While the derivation of the density function of the Poisson distribution (4.1) as a limiting case of the binomial is simple, we may get more insight into its meaning and range of applicability from an alternative approach.

Let the probability of an event occurring in a time interval $(t, t + dt)$ be $\xi\,dt$, where ξ is a constant, and where the length of the time interval dt is so small that the probability of the event occurring more than once in this time interval is of a higher order of smallness than dt and may be neglected.

Let the probability that the event will occur x times in the interval $(0, t)$ be $P_x(t)$. With this notation $P_0(t + dt)$ is the probability that zero events will occur in the interval $(0, t + dt)$. To get zero events in this interval means that we must have zero events both in the interval $(0, t)$

and in the interval $(t, t + dt)$. The probability of the former is $P_0(t)$. The probability of the latter is $(1 - \xi\, dt)$. We assume that these probabilities are independent; so

$$P_0(t + dt) = P_0(t)(1 - \xi\, dt) = P_0(t) - \xi\, P_0(t)dt,$$

whence

$$\frac{P_0(t + dt) - P_0(t)}{dt} = -\xi\, P_0(t). \tag{5.1}$$

The left-hand side is just the derivative of $P_0(t)$ with respect to t, namely, $d\, P_0(t)/dt$. We thus have a differential equation

$$\frac{d\, P_0(t)}{dt} = -\xi\, P_0(t), \tag{5.2}$$

whose solution is

$$P_0(t) = e^{-\xi t}, \tag{5.3}$$

since, as we can readily check,

$$\frac{dP_0(t)}{dt} = \frac{d}{dt}(e^{-\xi t}) = -\xi e^{-\xi t} = -\xi\, P_0(t).$$

In (5.3), we see that the constant of integration is 0, since we must have $P_0(0) = 1$, and $e^{\xi \cdot 0} = 1$.

Now consider $P_x(t + dt)$ when $x > 0$:

$$\begin{aligned} P_x(t + dt) &= \Pr\{x \text{ events in interval } (0, t + dt)\} \\ &= \Pr\{x \text{ in interval } (0, t)\} \Pr\{0 \text{ in interval } (t, t + dt)\} \\ &+ \Pr\{(x - 1) \text{ in interval } (0, t)\} \Pr\{1 \text{ in interval } (t, t + dt)\} \\ &= P_x(t) \cdot (1 - \xi\, dt) + P_{x-1}(t) \cdot \xi\, dt. \end{aligned} \tag{5.4}$$

Rearranging gives

$$\frac{P_x(t + dt) - P_x(t)}{dt} = -\xi\, P_x(t) + \xi\, P_{x-1}(t).$$

The left-hand side is the derivative of $P_x(t)$ with respect to t; so we have the differential equation

$$\frac{d\, P_x(t)}{dt} = -\xi\, P_x(t) + \xi\, P_{x-1}(t). \tag{5.5}$$

A solution is

$$P_x(t) = \frac{(\xi t)^x}{x!} e^{-\xi t}, \tag{5.6}$$

as is easily checked, since

$$\begin{aligned}\frac{d\,P_x(t)}{dt} &= \frac{\xi^x x t^{x-1}}{x!}\,e^{-\xi t} + \frac{(\xi t)^x}{x!}\,(-\xi)\,e^{-\xi t}\\ &= \xi\,\frac{(\xi t)^{x-1}}{(x-1)!}\,e^{-\xi t} - \xi\,\frac{(\xi t)^x}{x!}\,e^{-\xi t}\\ &= \xi\,P_{x-1}(t) - \xi\,P_x(t).\end{aligned}$$

Thus (5.6) does satisfy (5.5). Therefore the distribution of the number of events in the time interval $(0, t)$ is given by (5.6), which is a Poisson distribution with parameter ξt. There is nothing special about the origin in the interval $(0, t)$; so (5.6) applies to any interval of length t.

From the present approach we see that, if the probability of each radioactive atom in a mass disintegrating is a constant, then the number of atoms disintegrating in a time period t has the distribution (5.6). Similarly, if over a given part of the day the probability of a telephone call being received by a switchboard is constant, then the distribution of the number of calls per time interval is given by (5.6). The same would apply to the number of flaws per yard of insulated wire, the number of misprints per page, the number of blood cells on individual squares on a hemocytometer, etc.

4.6. Tests of Hypotheses about the Poisson Distribution

It was stated in (3.6.1) that the cumulative sum of the terms of the binomial distribution is given exactly by

$$\Pr\{x \le x_0\} = P\{x_0\} = 1 - \Pr\left\{F < \frac{n - x_0}{x_0 + 1}\,\frac{\theta}{1 - \theta}\right\}$$

where the variance ratio F has degrees of freedom $2(x_0 + 1)$ and $2(n - x_0)$. We have derived the Poisson distribution as the limiting case of the binomial with $\theta = \xi/n$ and $n \to \infty$. Taking these limits, for a Poisson variable,

$$P\{x_0\} = 1 - \Pr\left\{F < \frac{n - x_0}{n - \xi}\,\frac{\xi}{x_0 + 1}\right\} = 1 - \Pr\left\{F < \frac{\xi}{x_0 + 1}\right\},$$

where the degrees of freedom are $f_1 = 2(x_0 + 1)$, $f_2 = \infty$. We will see in Section 9.3 that F with degrees of freedom f and ∞ is distributed as another quantity, χ^2 with f degrees of freedom, divided by f, i.e., $F(f, \infty) = \chi^2(f)/f$. Thus

$$P\{x_0\} = 1 - \Pr\left\{\frac{\chi^2}{2(x_0 + 1)} < \frac{\xi}{x_0 + 1}\right\} = 1 - \Pr\{\chi^2 < 2\xi\}, \qquad (6.1)$$

where χ^2 has $2(x_0 + 1)$ degrees of freedom. The χ^2 distribution is tabulated in Table III of the appendix. For example, in the case of

$\xi = 0.932292$, we have calculated the individual terms in Table 4.2; so we find by summation $\Pr\{x \le 3\} = 0.9849$. Using (6.1),

$$\Pr\{x \le 3\} = 1 - \Pr\{\chi^2(8) < 2 \times 0.9323\}.$$

For 8 degrees of freedom, the 0.01 and 0.025 points of the χ^2 distribution are 1.65 and 2.18; so 1.86 must correspond to about the 0.015 point. Hence $\Pr\{x \le 3\} \simeq 1 - 0.015 = 0.985$.

With such a simple formula as (6.1) for the cumulative Poisson distribution, there seems small practical need for approximations. However, substituting ξ for the expectation $n\theta$ and ξ for the variance $n\theta(1 - \theta)$ in (3.2.17) which is a good approximation to the cumulative binomial when $n\theta(1 - \theta)$ is greater than 9, which corresponds in the Poisson case to $\xi > 9$, gives

$$P\{x\} \simeq \Phi\left(\frac{x + 1/2 - \xi}{\sqrt{\xi}}\right). \tag{6.2}$$

Another approximation is easily obtained. In (3.4.9) and following we saw that if the variance of a random variable was equal to the expected value, then the square root of the variable had a variance 1/4. Hence

$$P\{x\} \simeq \Phi\left(\frac{\sqrt{x + 1/2} - \sqrt{\xi}}{\sqrt{1/4}}\right) = \Phi\left[2\left(\sqrt{x + \frac{1}{2}} - \sqrt{\xi}\right)\right]. \tag{6.3}$$

To illustrate these formulas, suppose that we observe 4 telephone calls in an hour when we have the null hypothesis that the mean hourly rate is 8. Formulas (6.1), (6.2), and (6.3) give

$$\Pr\{x \le 4\} = 1 - \Pr\{\chi^2(10) < 16\} = 1 - 0.90 = 0.10,$$

$$\Pr\{x \le 4\} \simeq \Phi\left(\frac{4 + 1/2 - 8}{\sqrt{8}}\right) = \Phi(-1.238) = 0.109,$$

$$\Pr\{x \le 4\} \simeq \Phi\left[2\left(\sqrt{4 + \frac{1}{2}} - \sqrt{8}\right)\right] = \Phi(-1.414) = 0.079.$$

It is clear that $\xi = 8$ is still somewhat on the small side for the approximations to be accurate.

4.7. Confidence Limits for a Poisson Parameter

Equations (2.13.7) and (2.13.9) will give confidence limits for the population parameter for a Poisson distribution from an observation. Using (6.1), the upper confidence limit $\bar{\xi}$ is defined by the equation

$$\Pr\{x \le x_0 | \xi = \bar{\xi}\} = P_1 = 1 - \Pr\{\chi^2(2(x_0 + 1)) < 2\bar{\xi}\};$$

so $$\Pr\{\chi^2(2(x_0+1)) < 2\bar{\xi}\} = 1 - P_1 ,$$

but in general

$$\Pr\{\chi^2(2(x_0+1)) < \chi^2_{1-P_1}(2(x_0+1))\} = 1 - P_1 ;$$

so $$\bar{\xi} = \tfrac{1}{2}\,\chi^2_{1-P_1}(2(x_0+1)). \tag{7.1}$$

Likewise the lower confidence limit is defined by

$$\Pr\{x \le x_0 - 1 | \xi = \underline{\xi}\} = P_2 = 1 - \Pr\{\chi^2(2x_0) < 2\underline{\xi}\};$$

so $$\Pr\{\chi^2(2x_0) < 2\underline{\xi}\} = 1 - P_2 ,$$

so $$\underline{\xi} = \tfrac{1}{2}\,\chi^2_{1-P_2}(2x_0). \tag{7.2}$$

For example, if on an airplane coming off an assembly line we find one missing rivet, and if we can assume that the distribution of the number of missing rivets is Poisson, i.e., with constant probability and independent, then 99 per cent confidence limits for the average number of missing rivets per plane in the population of planes are

$$\bar{\xi} = \tfrac{1}{2}\,\chi^2_{0.995}(2(1+1)) = \frac{14.9}{2} = 7.45,$$

$$\underline{\xi} = \tfrac{1}{2}\,\chi^2_{0.005}(2 \times 1) = \frac{0.010}{2} = 0.005.$$

4.8. The Addition Theorem for the Poisson Distribution

Suppose that $x_1, \ldots, x_k$ are independently distributed according to the Poisson frequency function with parameters $\xi_1, \ldots, \xi_k$. Then $x = \sum_{i=1}^{k} x_i$ has the Poisson distribution with parameter $\sum_{i=1}^{k} \xi_i$. To prove this it will be sufficient to consider the case of $k = 2$.

The variables x_1, x_2 take the values $0, 1, 2, \ldots$. We want the probability that their sum $(x_1 + x_2)$ is equal to r. The probability that x_1 has the value s and x_2 the value $(r - s)$, is, since x_1, x_2 are independent,

$$\Pr\{x_1 = s\}\Pr\{x_2 = r - s\} = e^{-\xi_1}\frac{\xi_1^s}{s!}\,e^{-\xi_2}\frac{\xi_2^{r-s}}{(r-s)!}. \tag{8.1}$$

All values of s from 0 to r will give $x = x_1 + x_2 = r$; so the probability that $x = r$ is given by summing (8.1) over all permitted values of s, namely, 0 to r:

$$\sum_{s=0}^{r} e^{-\xi_1} e^{-\xi_2}\frac{\xi_1^s \xi_2^{r-s}}{s!(r-s)!} = e^{-(\xi_1+\xi_2)}\sum_{s=0}^{r}\frac{\xi_1^s \xi_2^{r-s}}{s!(r-s)!}. \tag{8.2}$$

To evaluate the summation in (8.2), consider the expansion of $(\xi_1 + \xi_2)^r$ by the binomial theorem:

$$(\xi_1 + \xi_2)^r = \sum_{s=0}^{r} \binom{r}{s} \xi_1^s \xi_2^{r-s} = r! \sum_{s=0}^{r} \frac{\xi_1^s \xi_2^{r-s}}{s!(r-s)!}.$$

Hence the summation in (8.2) is $(\xi_1 + \xi_2)^r/r!$, and

$$\Pr\{x = r\} = e^{-(\xi_1+\xi_2)} \frac{(\xi_1 + \xi_2)^r}{r!}, \tag{8.3}$$

which is a Poisson frequency function with parameter $(\xi_1 + \xi_2)$. Thus the theorem is proved for the case of $k = 2$, and so it is obviously true for any k.

4.9. The Comparison of Two Poisson-Distributed Observations

Suppose that we observe in a certain yardage carpeting A has x_1 flaws and carpeting B has x_2 flaws. We wish to test the null hypothesis that the mean number of flaws per yard in the two populations of carpeting is the same, i.e., H_0: $\xi_1 = \xi_2 = \xi$, say. Under the null hypothesis, x_1 and x_2 will both be approximately normally distributed independently with expectation ξ and variance ξ; so $(x_1 - x_2)$ will be approximately normally distributed with expectation zero and variance 2ξ. We can estimate 2ξ as $(x_1 + x_2)$. Thus, under the null hypothesis, $(x_1 - x_2)/\sqrt{x_1 + x_2}$ will be approximately a unit normal deviate. The approximation will be improved by introducing corrections for continuity analogous to those used in the two-sample binomial problem (Section 3.8). For a test against the alternative hypothesis $\xi_1 > \xi_2$, the null hypothesis is rejected if

$$\frac{(x_1 - 1/2) - (x_2 + 1/2)}{\sqrt{x_1 + x_2}} > u_{1-\alpha}. \tag{9.1}$$

An exact test can be constructed along lines similar to Fisher's exact test for the comparison of two binomials (Section 3.9). We identify E_1 with getting x_1 equal to ν_1 and x_2 equal to ν_2, and E_2 with getting $(x_1 + x_2)$ equal to $(\nu_1 + \nu_2)$. Then

$$\begin{aligned}\Pr\{E_1E_2\} &= \Pr\{x_1 = \nu_1, \quad x_2 = \nu_2 \quad \text{and} \quad x_1 + x_2 = \nu_1 + \nu_2\} \\ &= \Pr\{x_1 = \nu_1, \quad x_2 = \nu_2\} = \Pr\{x_1 = \nu_1\} \cdot \Pr\{x_2 = \nu_2\} \\ &= e^{-\xi} \cdot \frac{\xi^{\nu_1}}{\nu_1!} \cdot e^{-\xi} \frac{\xi^{\nu_2}}{\nu_2!} = e^{-2\xi} \cdot \frac{\xi^{\nu_1+\nu_2}}{\nu_1!\nu_2!}\end{aligned}$$

under the null hypothesis. Also

$$\Pr\{E_2\} = \Pr\{x_1 + x_2 = \nu_1 + \nu_2\} = e^{-2\xi}\frac{(2\xi)^{\nu_1+\nu_2}}{(\nu_1 + \nu_2)!}$$

using (8.3). Then

$$\Pr\{x_1' = \nu_1, x_2 = \nu_2 | x_1 + x_2 = \nu_1 + \nu_2\} = \Pr\{E_1 | E_2\} = \frac{\Pr\{E_1 E_2\}}{\Pr\{E_2\}}$$

$$= \frac{\xi^{\nu_1+\nu_2}}{(2\xi)^{\nu_1+\nu_2}} \cdot \frac{(\nu_1 + \nu_2)!}{\nu_1!\nu_2!} = \binom{\nu_1 + \nu_2}{\nu_1}\left(\frac{1}{2}\right)^{\nu_1+\nu_2}$$

$$= \binom{\nu_1 + \nu_2}{\nu_1}\left(\frac{1}{2}\right)^{\nu_1}\left(1 - \frac{1}{2}\right)^{(\nu_1+\nu_2)-\nu_1} \tag{9.2}$$

which is the $(\nu_1 + 1)$th term in the binomial expansion for $n = \nu_1 + \nu_2$, $\theta = 1/2$. Equation (9.2) gives the probability that $x_1 = \nu_1$, given the sum $x_1 + x_2$, and as in the Fisher exact test we also want the probabilities of all values of x_1 more extreme than the observed one ν_1. Thus, if $\nu_1 > \nu_2$, we also want the probabilities given by (9.2) for $x_1 = \nu_1 + 1, \nu_1 + 2, \ldots, \nu_1 + \nu_2$, the last being the maximum possible value for x_1 since it corresponds with $x_2 = 0$. The probability we want, the sum of the tail probabilities, is then

$$\Pr\{x_1 \geq \nu_1 | \nu_1 + \nu_2\} = \sum_{x_1=\nu_1}^{\nu_1+\nu_2}\binom{\nu_1 + \nu_2}{x_1}\left(\frac{1}{2}\right)^{x_1}\left(1 - \frac{1}{2}\right)^{(\nu_1+\nu_2)-x_1}$$

$$= 1 - \sum_{x_1=0}^{\nu_1-1}\binom{\nu_1 + \nu_2}{x_1}\left(\frac{1}{2}\right)^{x_1}\left(1 - \frac{1}{2}\right)^{\nu_1+\nu_2-x_1}.$$

Using (3.6.1) for the sum of the lower terms of a binomial, here $\theta = 1/2$; so $\theta/(1 - \theta) = 1$, and we get

$$\Pr\{x_1 \geq \nu_1 | \nu_1 + \nu_2\} = \Pr\left\{F < \frac{\nu_2 + 1}{\nu_1}\right\} \tag{9.3}$$

where $f_1 = 2\nu_1$, $f_2 = 2(\nu_2 + 1)$. Our P value, for a one-sided test with alternative $\xi_1 > \xi_2$, is thus defined by

$$\Pr\left\{F(2\nu_1, 2(\nu_2 + 1)) < \frac{\nu_2 + 1}{\nu_1}\right\} = P$$

but, since $\Pr\{F < F_P\} = P$, P is determined by

$$F_P(2\nu_1, 2(\nu_2 + 1)) = \frac{\nu_2 + 1}{\nu_1} \tag{9.4}$$

or

$$F_{1-P}(2(\nu_2 + 1), 2\nu_1) = \frac{\nu_1}{\nu_2 + 1}. \qquad (9.5)$$

To revert to our initial example, suppose that the number of flaws in carpeting A is $\nu_1 = 9$ and in carpeting B is $\nu_2 = 2$. Then

$$F_{1-P}(2(2 + 1), 2 \times 9) = \frac{9}{2 + 1}$$

or $F_{1-P}(6, 18) = 3$. From Table IV of the appendix $F_{0.95}(6, 18) = 2.66$ and $F_{0.975}(6, 18) = 3.22$; so $1 - P \simeq 0.965$, and $P \simeq 0.035$. The normal approximation (9.1) gives

$$\Phi\left(\frac{(9 - 1/2) - (2 + 1/2)}{\sqrt{9 + 2}}\right) = \Phi(1.81) = \Phi(u_{1-P});$$

so $(1 - P) = 0.965$ and $P = 0.035$.

4.10. Comparison of Two Poisson-Distributed Observations with the Parameters in a Certain Hypothetical Ratio

Suppose that the number of breakdowns on machine 1 was x_1 in T_1 hours and the number of breakdowns on machine 2 was x_2 in T_2 hours. Then an interesting null hypothesis is that the probability of a breakdown per unit time interval is the same for the two machines. This is equivalent to the hypothesis that x_1 and x_2 are independent observations from two Poisson distributions whose parameters ξ_1 and ξ_2 are in the hypothetical ratio $\xi_1/\xi_2 = T_1/T_2$. The exact test of the previous section for the null hypothesis $\xi_1 = \xi_2$ can be extended to this new case.

If the null hypothesis is true, the probability of getting particular results ν_1 for x_1 and ν_2 for x_2 is

$$\Pr\{x_1 = \nu_1, x_2 = \nu_2\} = \Pr\{x_1 = \nu_1\} \Pr\{x_2 = \nu_2\}$$
$$= e^{-\xi_1} \frac{\xi_1^{\nu_1}}{\nu_1!} e^{-\xi_2} \frac{\xi_2^{\nu_2}}{\nu_2!} = e^{-(\xi_1+\xi_2)} \frac{\xi_1^{\nu_1}\xi_2^{\nu_2}}{\nu_1!\nu_2!}. \qquad (10.1)$$

The sum of observations from two Poisson distributions has a Poisson distribution with parameter equal to the sum of the parameters of the two distributions; so $(x_1 + x_2)$ has a Poisson distribution with parameter $(\xi_1 + \xi_2)$, and

$$\Pr\{x_1 + x_2 = \nu_1 + \nu_2\} = e^{-(\xi_1+\xi_2)} \frac{(\xi_1 + \xi_2)^{\nu_1+\nu_2}}{(\nu_1 + \nu_2)!}. \qquad (10.2)$$

hen $\Pr\{x_1 = \nu_1, x_2 = \nu_2 | x_1 + x_2 = \nu_1 + \nu_2\} = \dfrac{\Pr\{x_1 = \nu_1, x_2 = \nu_2\}}{\Pr\{x_1 + x_2 = \nu_1 + \nu_2\}}$

$$= \frac{e^{-(\xi_1+\xi_2)}(\xi_1^{\nu_1}\xi_2^{\nu_2}/\nu_1!\nu_2!)}{e^{-(\xi_1+\xi_2)}(\xi_1 + \xi_2)^{\nu_1+\nu_2}/(\nu_1 + \nu_2)!}$$

$$= \frac{(\nu_1 + \nu_2)!}{\nu_1!\nu_2!} \frac{\xi_1^{\nu_1}\xi_2^{\nu_2}}{(\xi_1 + \xi_2)^{\nu_1+\nu_2}}$$

$$= \binom{\nu_1 + \nu_2}{\nu_1} \left(\frac{\xi_1}{\xi_1 + \xi_2}\right)^{\nu_1} \left(1 - \frac{\xi_1}{\xi_1 + \xi_2}\right)^{(\nu_1+\nu_2)-\nu_1}, \tag{10.3}$$

which is equal to the probability of ν_1 successes in $(\nu_1 + \nu_2)$ binomial trials with $\theta = \xi_1/(\xi_1 + \xi_2)$.

We assume that we are in the case where the observed value of x_1 exceeds its expectation under the null hypothesis, (and conversely the observed value of x_2 is less than its expectation), i.e., where $x_1/T_1 > x_2/T_2$. We therefore need to sum our binomial series for $x_1 = \nu_1, \nu_1 + 1, \ldots, \nu_1 + \nu_2$:

$$\Pr\{x_1 \geq \nu_1 | \nu_1 + \nu_2\} = \sum_{x_1=\nu_1}^{\nu_1+\nu_2} \binom{\nu_1 + \nu_2}{x_1} \left(\frac{\xi_1}{\xi_1 + \xi_2}\right)^{x_1} \left(\frac{\xi_2}{\xi_1 + \xi_2}\right)^{(\nu_1+\nu_2)-x_1}. \tag{10.4}$$

From (3.6.3) the sum of the upper tail of a binomial distribution is given by

$$\Pr\{x \geq x_1\} = \Pr\left\{F < \frac{n - x_1 + 1}{x_1} \frac{\theta}{1 - \theta}\right\}, \quad \begin{aligned} f_1 &= 2x_1, \\ f_2 &= 2(n - x_1 + 1). \end{aligned} \tag{10.5}$$

In (10.4) the binomial parameter θ equals $\xi_1/(\xi_1 + \xi_2)$; so

$$\frac{\theta}{1 - \theta} = \frac{\xi_1/(\xi_1 + \xi_2)}{\xi_2/(\xi_1 + \xi_2)} = \frac{\xi_1}{\xi_2}.$$

Substituting in (10.5),

$$\Pr\{x_1 \geq \nu_1 | \nu_1 + \nu_2\} = \Pr\left\{F < \frac{\nu_1 + \nu_2 - \nu_1 + 1}{\nu_1} \frac{\xi_1}{\xi_2}\right\}, \quad \begin{aligned} f_1 &= 2\nu_1, \\ f_2 &= 2(\nu_2 + 1). \end{aligned}$$

Suppose that this probability is P_1. Then

$$\frac{\nu_2 + 1}{\nu_1} \frac{\xi_1}{\xi_2} = F_{P_1}(2\nu_1, 2(\nu_2 + 1)), \tag{10.6}$$

or

$$\frac{\nu_1}{\nu_2 + 1} \frac{\xi_2}{\xi_1} = F_{1-P_1}(2(\nu_2 + 1), 2\nu_1), \tag{10.7}$$

and P_1 is found from tables of the F distribution as the solution to this equation for the observed values of ν_1, ν_2 and the hypothetical value of ξ_1/ξ_2.

4.11. An Application of the Poisson Distribution to Vaccine Testing

Suppose that we are testing lots of vaccine containing γ live particles per liter and we test a sample of Ω mililiters (ml) drawn from the well-stirred lot. Then on the average the sample will contain $\gamma\Omega$ per 1000 live particles: Call this ξ. Suppose that the test of the sample will find a live particle if it is present, and that if one or more live particles are found then the lot is rejected. The probability of rejection will be

$$\Pr\{x > 0\} = 1 - \Pr\{x = 0\} = 1 - e^{-\xi} \frac{\xi^x}{x!}\bigg|_{x=0} = 1 - e^{-\xi}.$$

Suppose that $\gamma = 5$ particles per liter and $\Omega = 60$ ml; then $\xi = 0.3$, and the probability of rejection is $(1 - e^{-0.3}) = 0.259$. Thus 25.9 per cent of such lots will be rejected.

Suppose that we wish to determine the size of sample that will accept only a fraction β of lots containing 5 live particles per liter; i.e., we require $\Pr\{x = 0\} = \beta$. But $\Pr\{x = 0\} = e^{-\xi}$; so $\xi = -\log_e \beta$. Suppose that we require $\beta = 0.05$; then

$$\log_e \beta = \log_e 5 - \log_e 100 = 1.60944 - 4.60517 = -2.99563,$$

from a table of natural logarithms; so $\xi = 2.99563$. Then

$$\Omega = \xi/\gamma = 2.99563/5 = 0.599 \text{ liter} = 599 \text{ ml}.$$

REFERENCES

1. Chapman, Douglas G., "Some properties of the hypergeometric distribution with application to zoological sample censuses," *University of California Publications in Statistics*, 1(1951), 131–160.
2. Clarke, R. D., "An application of the Poisson distribution," *Journal of the Institute of Actuaries*, 72(1946), 481.

EXERCISES

4.1. A small car-hire company has two cars which it rents out by the day. Suppose that the number of demands for a car on each day is distributed as a Poisson distribution with mean 1.5. (*a*) On what proportion of days is neither car required? (*b*) On what proportion of days is the demand in excess of the company's capacity? (Note that $e^{-1.5} = 0.223$).

4.2. A company installed two compressors at the same time. These compressors are used continuously. By the end of a year one of them has had

13 breakdowns and the other 3. Can one say that the first compressor is significantly inferior to the second? Make both exact and approximate tests. Discuss the assumptions underlying your test.

4.3. Suppose that the company in Exercise 4.2 above is going to expand its plant and acquire more compressors of the second type. They would like to know within what limits the average number of breakdowns per compressor per year, will lie, with 95 per cent confidence. Find these limits.

4.4. Show that the expectation of the hypergeometric distribution (1.1) is nM/N and that the variance is

$$\frac{nM}{N}\left(1 - \frac{M}{N}\right)\left(1 - \frac{n-1}{N-1}\right).$$

4.5. You are dealt a hand of 13 cards from a well-shuffled bridge deck of 52 cards. What is the probability of receiving (*a*) exactly zero aces, (*b*) exactly two aces?

CHAPTER 5

The χ^2 Distribution, the Multinomial Distribution, and Contingency Tables

5.1. The χ^2 Distribution

Suppose that we have n independent observations $x_1, \ldots, x_n$ from a normal distribution $N(\xi, \sigma^2)$. The standardized variables $u_i = (x_i - \xi)/\sigma$ will also be independent, and the sum of their squares will have a distribution whose functional form can be determined: we define $\chi^2(n)$ as the sum of the squares of n independent unit normal variables,

$$\chi^2(n) = \sum_i^n u_i^2. \tag{1.1}$$

The distribution of $\chi^2(n)$ is different for each value of n, and the parameter n is known as the number of degrees of freedom. Percentage points of the cumulative distribution of χ^2 are given in Table III of the appendix. Figure 5.1 shows the density function of χ^2 for degrees of freedom $n = 1, 2, 4$, and 20. Since u_i^2 can never be negative, all the χ^2 distributions are confined to the positive half of the χ^2 axis.

To obtain the expectation of the χ^2 distribution we need $E[u_i^2]$. Since u_i is a unit normal deviate, it has zero expectation and unit variance, and so

$$E[u_i^2] = E[(u_i - E[u_i])^2] = V[u_i] = 1.$$

Then

$$E[\chi^2(n)] = E[\sum_i^n u_i^2] = \sum_i^n E[u_i^2] = (1) = n. \tag{1.2}$$

The variance of χ^2 is

$$V[\chi^2(n)] = V[\sum_i^n u_i^2] = \sum_i^n V[u_i^2] = n\, V[u_i^2]. \tag{1.3}$$

We therefore need

$$V[u_i^2] = E[(u_i^2)^2] - (E[u_i^2])^2.$$

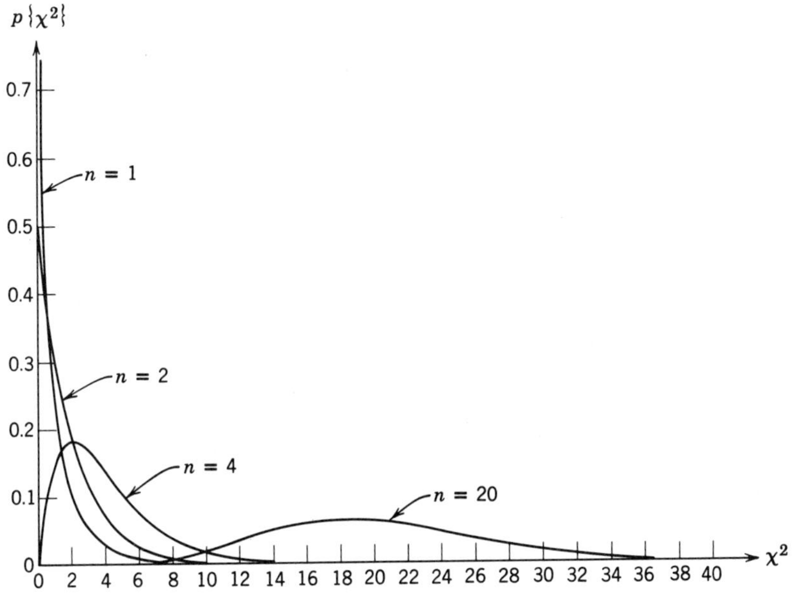

Figure 5.1

To obtain $E[u_i^4]$, we use the rule for integration by parts,

$$\int f(x)\, g'(x)\, dx = f(x)\, g(x) - \int g(x)\, f'(x)\, dx,$$

identifying $f(x)$ with u^3, so that $f'(x) = 3u^2$, and $g(x)$ with $-e^{-u^2/2}$, so that $g'(x) = u\, e^{-u^2/2}$. We now have

$$\begin{aligned}
E[u^4] &= \int_{-\infty}^{\infty} u^4\, p\{u\}\, du = \int_{-\infty}^{\infty} u^4 \cdot \frac{1}{\sqrt{2\pi}} e^{-u^2/2}\, du \\
&= \frac{1}{\sqrt{2\pi}} \int_{-\infty}^{\infty} u^3 \cdot u\, e^{-u^2/2}\, du \\
&= \frac{1}{\sqrt{2\pi}} u^3(-e^{-u^2/2}) \Big|_{-\infty}^{\infty} - \frac{1}{\sqrt{2\pi}} \int_{-\infty}^{\infty} (-e^{-u^2/2}) \cdot 3u^2\, du \\
&= 3 \cdot \frac{1}{\sqrt{2\pi}} \int_{-\infty}^{\infty} u^2\, e^{-u^2/2}\, du = 3\, E[u^2] = 3.
\end{aligned}$$

Hence

$$V[u_i^2] = 3 - (1)^2 = 2, \tag{1.4}$$

and, substituting this in (1.3),

$$V[\chi^2(n)] = 2n. \tag{1.5}$$

From the central-limit theorem, to be referred to in Section 7.1, $\chi^2(n)$ is asymptotically normal for large n. As can be seen from the distribution for $n = 20$ in Figure 5.1, the approach to normality is quite fast. We can thus obtain an approximation to the P point of the distribution from

$$\frac{\chi_P^2(n) - n}{\sqrt{2n}} \simeq u_P ,$$

whence

$$\chi_P^2(n) \simeq n + u_P\sqrt{2n}. \tag{1.6}$$

A better approximation is

$$\chi_P^2(n) \simeq n - \frac{1}{2} + u_P\sqrt{2n - 1} + \frac{u_P^2}{2} \simeq \frac{1}{2}(\sqrt{2n-1} + u_P)^2. \tag{1.7}$$

5.2. The Multinomial Distribution

The multinomial distribution can be regarded as a generalization of the binomial distribution. In the latter we suppose that the outcomes of a series of n independent trials are either A with probability θ or $\bar{A}$ with probability $(1 - \theta)$. In the multinomial distribution we have k, rather than 2 as in the binomial distribution, mutually exclusive and exhaustive outcomes $A_1, \ldots, A_k$ with probabilities $\theta_1, \ldots, \theta_k$, where $\sum_i^k \theta_i = 1$. We want the probability that, on n trials, A_1 occurs exactly x_1 times, $\ldots$, A_k occurs exactly x_k times, where $\sum_i^k x_i = n$. The probability of getting the specific sequence

$$\underbrace{A_1 \cdots A_1}_{x_1 \text{ times}} \cdots \underbrace{A_k \cdots A_k}_{x_k \text{ times}}$$

is, since successive trials are independent, $\theta^{x_1} \cdots \theta^{x_k}$. The ordering of the sequence is irrelevant to our purpose, as we are merely interested in the total number of times A_1 occurs, etc. All sequences with a specified set of x_i have the same probability. It remains to evaluate the number of sequences with a specified set of x_i. Equation (1.7.4) gave the number of arrangements of x_1 objects of type A_1, x_2 objects of type A_2, etc., as $n!/x_1!x_2! \cdots x_k!$; so

$$\Pr\{x_1, \ldots, x_k\} = \frac{n!}{x_1! \cdots x_k!} \theta_1^{x_1} \cdots \theta_k^{x_k} \tag{2.1}$$

is the frequency function of the multinomial distribution.

The multivariate distribution considered in Section 1.16 is an example of a multinomial distribution, with $\theta_U = 1/2$, $\theta_F = 1/3$, $\theta_G = 1/6$. In that section we calculated from first principles the entire distribution, giving the results in Table 1.13. Equation (2.1) will give the same results directly. For example,

$$\Pr\{2, 0, 1\} = \frac{3!}{2!\,0!\,1!}\left(\frac{1}{2}\right)^2\left(\frac{1}{3}\right)^0\left(\frac{1}{6}\right)^1 = \frac{1}{8} = \frac{27}{216}.$$

In the case of $k = 2$, the multinomial distribution reduces immediately to the binomial. In general, however, it is awkward to work with, and we will outline the development of an approximation to (2.1) which can then be used to obtain certain cumulative probabilities.

We use the symbol P^* for the probability defined in (2.1). As in the derivation of an approximation to the binomial distribution, so here we use Stirling's approximation,

$$n! \simeq \sqrt{2\pi}\, n^{n+\frac{1}{2}}e^{-n},$$

for the factorials in (2.1). Thus

$$P^* \simeq \frac{\sqrt{2\pi}\, n^{n+\frac{1}{2}}e^{-n}}{\prod_i^k \sqrt{2\pi}\, x_i^{x_i+\frac{1}{2}}e^{-x_i}} \prod_i^k \theta_i^{x_i}$$

$$\simeq (2\pi)^{-\frac{1}{2}(k-1)} n^{n+\frac{1}{2}} \prod_i^k x_i^{-(x_i+\frac{1}{2})} \prod_i^k \theta_i^{x_i}. \tag{2.2}$$

This involves n to the $(n + \frac{1}{2})$th power. We can write

$$n + \frac{1}{2} = -\frac{1}{2}(k-1) + \sum_i^k \left(x_i + \frac{1}{2}\right),$$

and also

$$\prod_i^k \theta_i^{x_i} = \prod_i^k \theta_i^{-\frac{1}{2}}\theta_i^{(x_i+\frac{1}{2})}.$$

Substituting in (2.2) gives

$$P^* \simeq (2\pi n)^{-\frac{1}{2}(k-1)}\left(\prod_i^k \theta_i\right)^{-\frac{1}{2}} \prod_i^k \left(\frac{n\theta_i}{x_i}\right)^{x_i+\frac{1}{2}}.$$

Taking logarithms,

$$\log P^* \simeq -\frac{1}{2}(k-1)\log(2\pi n) - \frac{1}{2}\sum_i^k \log\theta_i - \sum_i^k \left(x_i + \frac{1}{2}\right)\log\left(\frac{x_i}{n\theta_i}\right). \tag{2.3}$$

The expected value for the ith cell is $n\theta_i$: Use the symbol e_i for this, not to be confused, of course, with e, the base of natural logarithms. Define the deviation of the observed value in the ith cell from its expected value as $d_i = x_i - e_i$. Then

$$\frac{x_i}{n\theta_i} = \frac{d_i + e_i}{e_i} = 1 + \frac{d_i}{e_i},$$

and $(x_i + 1/2) = (e_i + d_i + 1/2)$. Substituting in (2.3),

$$\log P^* \simeq -\frac{1}{2}(k-1)\log(2\pi n) - \frac{1}{2}\sum_i^k \log\theta_i - \sum_i^k \left(e_i + d_i + \frac{1}{2}\right)\log\left(1 + \frac{d_i}{e_i}\right). \quad (2.4)$$

Again as in the binomial case we use the expansion

$$\log(1+y) = y - \frac{y^2}{2} + \frac{y^3}{3} - \cdots. \quad (2.5)$$

For the first terms of this series to give a good approximation we need $|y| \ll 1$. Here we are going to substitute $y = d_i/e_i$. We therefore need to check on the magnitude of $|d_i/e_i|$. From (1.15.12) we have, when x has the distribution $N(\xi, \sigma^2)$,

$$\Pr\{|x - \xi| > k\sigma\} = 2\Phi(-k). \quad (2.6)$$

We can regard x_i as a binomial variable which will be approximately normally distributed with expectation $n\theta_i = e_i$ and variance $n\theta_i(1 - \theta_i)$. Hence

$$\Pr\{|x_i - e_i| > k\sqrt{n\theta_i(1-\theta_i)}\} = 2\Phi(-k).$$

Choose for k the value $\sqrt{n\theta_i/(1-\theta_i)}$. Then we have

$$\Pr\left\{|d_i| > \sqrt{\frac{n\theta_i}{1-\theta_i}}\sqrt{n\theta_i(1-\theta_i)}\right\} = 2\Phi\left(-\sqrt{\frac{n\theta_i}{1-\theta_i}}\right),$$

or, since $\sqrt{n\theta_i/(1-\theta_i)}\sqrt{n\theta_i(1-\theta_i)} = n\theta_i = e_i$,

$$\Pr\{|d_i| > e_i\} = 2\Phi\left(-\sqrt{\frac{n\theta_i}{1-\theta_i}}\right). \quad (2.7)$$

For moderate values and beyond of $e_i = n\theta_i$, say 5 or greater, $\sqrt{n\theta_i/(1-\theta_i)}$ will be greater than $\sqrt{5}$, and hence $\Phi(-\sqrt{n\theta_i/(1-\theta_i)})$ will be very small. Hence $\Pr\{|d_i/e_i| > 1\}$ will be very small, and we will be justified in using the expansion (2.5). We note here that d_i will be of the order of its standard deviation $\sqrt{n\theta_i(1-\theta_i)}$, or approximately $\sqrt{e_i}$. We now examine the second summation term in (2.4), using (2.5) to expand $\log(1 + d_i/e_i)$:

$$\sum_i^k \left(e_i + d_i + \frac{1}{2}\right)\left[\frac{d_i}{e_i} - \frac{1}{2}\left(\frac{d_i}{e_i}\right)^2 + \frac{1}{3}\left(\frac{d_i}{e_i}\right)^3 - \frac{1}{4}\left(\frac{d_i}{e_i}\right)^4 + \cdots\right]$$
$$= \sum_i^k \left(d_i - \frac{1}{2}\frac{d_i^2}{e_i} + \frac{1}{3}\frac{d_i^3}{e_i^2} - \cdots + \frac{d_i^2}{e_i} - \frac{1}{2}\frac{d_i^3}{e_i^2} + \cdots + \frac{1}{2}\frac{d_i}{e_i} - \frac{1}{4}\frac{d_i^2}{e_i^2} + \cdots\right). \tag{2.8}$$

We note that $\sum_i^k d_i = \sum_i^k (x_i - e_i) = \sum_i^k x_i - \sum_i^k e_i = 0$. Examining the terms in powers of e_i, recalling that d_i is of order $\sqrt{e_i}$, the zero order terms are

$$\sum_i^k \left(-\frac{1}{2}\frac{d_i^2}{e_i} + \frac{d_i^2}{e_i}\right) = \frac{1}{2}\sum_i^k \frac{d_i^2}{e_i},$$

and the terms of order $1/\sqrt{e_i}$ are

$$\frac{1}{2}\sum_i^k \frac{d_i}{e_i} + \left(-\frac{1}{2} + \frac{1}{3}\right)\sum_i^k \frac{d_i^3}{e_i^2}.$$

For moderately large e_i, say greater than 5, all terms except those of zero order may be neglected. Hence, substituting back in (2.4) and taking antilogarithms, we get

$$P^* \simeq (2\pi n)^{-\frac{1}{2}(k-1)}\left(\prod_i^k \theta_i\right)^{-\frac{1}{2}}\exp\left[-\frac{1}{2}\sum_i^k \frac{d_i^2}{e_i}\right]. \tag{2.9}$$

Here all the terms preceding the exponential part, involving π, n, k, and the θ_i, are constant parameters. Thus P^* is, to this approximation, determined by $\sum_i^k \frac{d_i^2}{e_i}$ and historically the symbol χ^2 was given to this statistic:

$$\chi^2 = \sum_i^k \frac{d_i^2}{e_i}. \tag{2.10}$$

For a test of significance based on this statistic, we need to be able to calculate the probability of obtaining a value of the statistic as large as or larger than the observed value. We can write (2.10) in the form

$$\chi^2 = \sum_i^k \frac{d_i^2}{e_i} = \sum_i^k \frac{(x_i - e_i)^2}{n\theta_i} = \sum_i^k \frac{(x_i - e_i)^2}{n\theta_i(1-\theta_i)}(1-\theta_i)$$
$$= \sum_i^k \left(\frac{x_i - e_i}{\sqrt{n\theta_i(1-\theta_i)}}\right)^2 (1-\theta_i).$$

If we consider a particular cell, say the ith, and regard ourselves as in a binomial situation, then

$$\frac{x_i - e_i}{\sqrt{n\theta_i(1 - \theta_i)}} \sim N(0, 1).$$

Hence our "χ^2," as defined by (2.10), is a weighted sum, the weights being $(1 - \theta_i)$, of squares of approximate unit normal deviates. These approximate unit normal deviates are not quite independent, since $\sum_i^k (x_i - e_i) = 0$. Thus our "χ^2," because of this restriction, and on account of the weights, is not a true $\chi^2(k)$ as defined in (1.1). However, it may be shown that it is approximately a true $\chi^2(k - 1)$.

As an example, suppose that the lost-time accidents reported for a certain period for three shifts are 1, 7, and 7. We wish to test the null hypothesis that $\theta_1 = \theta_2 = \theta_3$, i.e., that $\theta_i = 1/3$. There are total of $n = 15$ accidents; so the expected number for each shift is $e_i = n\theta_i = 15 \times (1/3) = 5$, and the corresponding values of $d_i = x_i - e_i$ for the three shifts are $1 - 5 = -4$, $7 - 5 = 2$, and $7 - 5 = 2$. The test statistic, with degrees of freedom $k - 1 = 2$, is

$$\chi^2 = \sum_i^3 \frac{d_i^2}{e_i} = \frac{(-4)^2}{5} + \frac{2^2}{5} + \frac{2^2}{5} = 4.80.$$

The 0.90 and 0.95 points of χ^2 with 2 degrees of freedom are 4.61 and 5.99. The observed value of 4.80 being intermediate between these two points, our P value is approximately $1 - 0.91 = 0.09$.

As another example, consider the data of Table 4.2. Under the null hypothesis that the observations are Poisson-distributed, we have a sample of size 576 which should be multinomially distributed with θ_i, given by the column headed $p\{x\}$. The columns headed $n\,p\{x\}$ give the expected numbers e_i; the last two columns are $d_i = x_i - e_i$ and d_i^2/e_i. Since the χ^2 approximation for the multinomial distribution is not very satisfactory for $e_i < 5$, the cells for $x \geqq 4$ are combined into a single cell. Summing the entries in the last column gives $\chi^2 = 1.03$. As regards the degrees of freedom for this χ^2, here we have five classes; so $k = 5$, and we have constrained Σd_i to be zero, and we have also estimated the parameter ξ of the Poisson distribution which we fitted to the data. The degrees of freedom are therefore $5 - 1 - 1 = 3$. Table III of the appendix gives for three degrees of freedom the 0.10 and 0.25 points of the χ^2 distribution as 0.58 and 1.21; so $1 - P \simeq 0.20$ and $P \simeq 0.8$. The data of Table 4.2 are thus very well fitted by a Poisson distribution.

5.3. Contingency Tables

Suppose we have a random sample of n objects, cross-classified according to two attributes A_i, B_j. Let the probability of an object having the attributes A_i, B_j be θ_{ij}, and the number observed in the sample be n_{ij}: $\sum_i^k \sum_j^m n_{ij} = n$, $\sum_i^k \sum_j^m \theta_{ij} = 1$. Let the marginal row probabilities be $\theta_{i.}$ and the marginal row sums be $n_{i.}$ as in Tables 5.1 and 5.2. By (1.16.1) and (1.16.2),

$$\theta_{i\cdot} = \sum_j^m \theta_{ij}, \qquad \theta_{\cdot j} = \sum_i^k \theta_{ij}.$$

Table 5.1

	B_1	$\cdots B_j \cdots$	B_m	
A_1	θ_{11}	θ_{1j}	θ_{1m}	$\theta_{1\cdot}$
$\vdots$				
A_i	θ_{i1}	θ_{ij}	θ_{im}	$\theta_{i\cdot}$
$\vdots$				
A_k	θ_{k1}	θ_{kj}	θ_{km}	$\theta_{k\cdot}$
	$\theta_{\cdot 1}$	$\theta_{\cdot j}$	$\theta_{\cdot m}$	1

Table 5.2

	B_1	$\cdots B_j \cdots$	B_m	
A_1	n_{11}	n_{1j}	n_{1m}	$n_{1\cdot}$
$\vdots$				
A_i	n_{i1}	n_{ij}	n_{im}	$n_{i\cdot}$
$\vdots$				
A_k	n_{k1}	n_{kj}	n_{km}	$n_{k\cdot}$
	$n_{\cdot 1}$	$n_{\cdot j}$	$n_{\cdot m}$	$n_{\cdot\cdot}$

In Table 5.2, the sum of the row sums equals the sum of the column sums equals the grand sum:

$$\sum_i^k n_{i\cdot} = \sum_j^m n_{\cdot j} = n_{\cdot\cdot} = n.$$

If the true probabilities θ_{ij} are known, the agreement between the observed and hypothetical distribution can be tested by the statistic (2.10) developed in the previous section,

$$\chi^2 = \sum_i^k \sum_j^m \frac{(n_{ij} - n\theta_{ij})^2}{n\theta_{ij}}, \qquad f = km - 1. \tag{3.1}$$

However, usually in practice the θ_{ij} have to be estimated from the data. We are usually interested in testing the hypothesis that the row and column classifications are independent, i.e., that

$$\Pr\{A_i, B_j\} = \Pr\{A_i\} \Pr\{B_j\},$$

i.e.,

$$\theta_{ij} = \theta_{i\cdot} \theta_{\cdot j}. \tag{3.2}$$

Assuming that we have a multinomial distribution of the form (2.1), if we take a sample of size one, the frequency function can be written

$$\frac{n!}{x_{11}!\cdots x_{km}!}\theta_{11}^{x_{11}}\cdots\theta_{km}^{x_{km}}=\prod_{i=1}^{k}\prod_{j=1}^{m}\theta_{ij}^{x_{ij}}$$

where the x_{ij} are all zero except for one, which has the value 1; so $n! = 1$, $x_{ij}! = 0!$, or $1! = 1$. If we take a sequence of n samples, by (2.3.1) the likelihood function is

$$L=\prod^{n}\prod_{i}^{k}\prod_{j}^{m}\theta_{ij}^{x_{ij}}=\prod_{i}^{k}\prod_{j}^{m}\theta_{ij}^{n_{ij}} \tag{3.3}$$

where n_{ij} is the sum of the x_{ij} in the (i, j)th cell. Under the hypothesis of independence of the row and column classifications (3.2),

$$\begin{aligned}L&=\prod_{i}^{k}\prod_{j}^{m}\left(\theta_{i\cdot}\,\theta_{\cdot j}\right)^{n_{ij}}=\left(\prod_{i}^{k}\prod_{j}^{m}\theta_{i\cdot}^{n_{ij}}\right)\left(\prod_{j}^{m}\prod_{i}^{k}\theta_{\cdot j}^{n_{ij}}\right)\\&=\left\{\prod_{i}^{k}\left(\theta_{i\cdot}\right)^{\sum_{j}^{m}n_{ij}}\right\}\left\{\prod_{j}^{m}\left(\theta_{\cdot j}\right)^{\sum_{i}^{k}n_{ij}}\right\}=\prod_{i}^{k}\theta_{i\cdot}^{n_{i\cdot}}\prod_{j}^{m}\theta_{\cdot j}^{n_{\cdot j}}\,.\end{aligned} \tag{3.4}$$

But $\sum_{i=1}^{k}\theta_{i\cdot}=1$; so

$$\theta_{k\cdot}=1-\sum_{i=1}^{k-1}\theta_{i\cdot}\,. \tag{3.5}$$

Substituting in (3.4), we get

$$L=\left(1-\sum_{i=1}^{k-1}\theta_{i\cdot}\right)^{n_{k\cdot}}\prod_{i=1}^{k-1}\theta_{i\cdot}^{n_{i\cdot}}\prod_{j=1}^{m}\theta_{\cdot j}^{n_{\cdot j}}\,,$$

and, taking logarithms,

$$\log L=n_{k\cdot}\log\left(1-\sum_{i=1}^{k-1}\theta_{i\cdot}\right)+\sum_{i=1}^{k-1}n_{i\cdot}\log\theta_{i\cdot}+\sum_{j=1}^{m}n_{\cdot j}\log\theta_{\cdot j}\,.$$

To find the value of $\theta_{i\cdot}$ which maximizes this, we differentiate with respect to $\theta_{i\cdot}$ and equate to zero:

$$\frac{d\log L}{d\theta_{i\cdot}}=n_{k\cdot}(-1)\frac{1}{1-\sum_{i=1}^{k-1}\theta_{i\cdot}}+n_{i\cdot}\frac{1}{\theta_{i\cdot}}=0.$$

Using (3.5), this gives

$$\frac{n_{i\cdot}}{\hat{\theta}_{i\cdot}}=\frac{n_{k\cdot}}{\hat{\theta}_{k\cdot}}; \tag{3.6}$$

so

$$\sum_{i=1}^{k}\hat{\theta}_{i\cdot}=\frac{\hat{\theta}_{k\cdot}}{n_{k\cdot}}\sum_{i=1}^{k}n_{i\cdot}=\frac{n\hat{\theta}_{k\cdot}}{n_{k\cdot}}\,.$$

But
$$\sum_{i=1}^{k} \hat{\theta}_{i\cdot} = 1,$$

so $\hat{\theta}_{k\cdot}/n_{k\cdot} = 1/n$. Substituting in (3.6),

$$\hat{\theta}_{i\cdot} = n_{i\cdot}\left(\frac{\hat{\theta}_{k\cdot}}{n_{k\cdot}}\right) = \frac{n_{i\cdot}}{n}. \tag{3.7}$$

Similar arguments must apply to the estimation of $\theta_{\cdot j}$; so $\hat{\theta}_{\cdot j} = n_{\cdot j}/n$. The maximum-likelihood estimators of the θ_{ij} are thus

$$\hat{\theta}_{ij} = \frac{n_{i\cdot}}{n}\frac{n_{\cdot j}}{n}, \tag{3.8}$$

and these can be inserted in (3.1) to give

$$\chi^2 = \sum_{i}^{k}\sum_{j}^{m} \frac{(n_{ij} - n_{i\cdot}n_{\cdot j}/n)^2}{n_{i\cdot}n_{\cdot j}/n}. \tag{3.9}$$

However, this χ^2 does not have the degrees of freedom of the χ^2 in (3.1), namely $(km - 1)$, since we have estimated a number of parameters from the data. We have estimated k parameters $\theta_{i\cdot}$, but, in view of the restriction that $\sum_{i}^{k} \theta_{i\cdot} = 1$, only $(k - 1)$ of these are independent. Likewise $(m - 1)$ degrees of freedom are taken in estimation of the $\theta_{\cdot j}$. The degrees of freedom for the χ^2 in (3.10) are thus

$$(km - 1) - (k - 1) - (m - 1) = (k - 1)(m - 1). \tag{3.10}$$

The 2×2 table is a special case of a $k \times m$ contingency table. If rows correspond to two alternative treatments, and columns correspond to the numbers of successes and failures, we are back in the situation of comparing two binomial proportions as discussed in Section 3.8 where we developed the statistic (3.8.1), an approximate standardized normal deviate, for the test of the null hypothesis that the proportion of successes in the two populations was the same. In the present instance, if we regard the data as falling into a 2×2 contingency table, we will compute the statistic (3.10) as a χ^2 with one degree of freedom. It is easy to show that (3.10) is exactly the square of (3.8.1) if we omit the correction for continuity from the latter. Also, from the definition of χ^2 in (1.1) we see that χ^2 with one degree of freedom is the square of a single unit normal deviate. Thus the two approaches are fundamentally identical, and it makes no essential difference which we employ, except that the χ^2 approach automatically gives us a two-sided test whereas the other approach can be made one or two-sided. It is clear that, if we are going to use the statistic (3.9) in the 2×2 case, we will improve the approximation by introducing the correction for continuity. We bring each n_{ij} one-half unit closer to its expectation; i.e., instead of using $(n_{ij} - e_{ij})$, we use $\{|n_{ij} - e_{ij}| - 1/2\}$. In the general case of the $k \times m$ contingency table, there is no readily available method of making a correction for continuity.

Table 5.3

Type of pastry	Low	Medium	High	Totals
Éclairs	92	37	46	175
Napoleons	53	15	19	87
Coconut custard pies	75	19	12	106
Totals	220	71	77	368

Table 5.4

	Expectations e_{ij}	
104.620	33.764	36.617
52.001	16.785	18.204
63.370	20.451	22.179
	Observed minus expectation d_{ij}	
−12.620	3.236	9.383
0.989	−1.785	0.796
11.630	−1.451	−10.179
	d_{ij}^2/e_{ij}	
1.5223	0.3101	2.4044
0.0188	0.1898	0.0348
2.1344	0.1029	4.6716

We have remarked that the χ^2 approximation is regarded as a satisfactory approximation to the multinomial if all expectations e_i are greater than 5. This will also apply to the 2×2 table, whether we are computing (3.9) or (3.8.1). For Table 3.2, the smallest expectation is that, for no reaction with rubber B, $23 \times 15/55 = 6.273$. Since this is greater than 5, either of the statistics (3.9) or (3.8.1) will be an adequate approximation. In Section 3.9 we saw in fact that the P value obtained from the normal approximation for Table 3.2, 0.0476, was a close approximation to that given by the Fisher exact test, 0.0481. There is some reason to believe that the requirement that the minimum expectation should be greater than 5 is somewhat conservative and that we would not go far wrong with something like 3.5.

As an illustration of a contingency table, Abrahamson et al. [1] present data on the bacterial count of three types of pastry (Table 5.3). We ask whether the distribution of class of bacterial count varies according to type of pastry. We estimate the expected number for each cell as $n_{i\cdot}\, n_{\cdot j}/n$. For $i = 1, j = 1$, for example, this is $175 \times 220/368 = 104.620$. The calculations are given in detail in Table 5.4. Summing all the entries in the third part of this table, $\sum_i^k \sum_j^m d_{ij}^2 e_{ij} = 11.389$, and this will be distributed as χ^2 with degrees of freedom $(3-1)(3-1) = 4$ under the null hypothesis. The 0.975 point of $\chi^2(4)$ is 11.1; so $P < 0.025$, and therefore we reject the null hypothesis that the distribution of bacterial count is independent of the type of pastry. In other words, the pastries do differ in their distributions of bacterial counts.

For a general review of the χ^2 test see Cochran [2].

REFERENCES

1. Abrahamson, Abraham E., Rubin Field, Leon Buchbinder, and Anna V. Catilli, "A study of the control of sanitary quality of custard filled bakery products in a large city," *Food Research*, 17(1952), 268–277.
2. Cochran, William G., "The χ^2 test of goodness of fit," *Annals of Mathematical Statistics*, 23(1952), 315–345.

EXERCISES

5.1. A salesman made the following numbers of calls for a number of months. The table also gives the numbers of sales. Do you consider there is reason to believe that the efficiency of the salesman (or possibly the economic climate for his line of business) is varying?

Month	Calls	Sales
January	95	7
February	100	15
March	110	14
April	90	8
May	97	12
June	105	6
July	100	7
August	108	12
September	120	15
October	98	12
November	100	17
December	85	9

5.2. The number of window air conditioners in nine rows of row houses in an eastern city are as follows:

Row	1	2	3	4	5	6	7	8	9
Number of houses	23	43	43	41	41	42	42	39	36
Number of air conditioners	5	8	18	3	17	11	25	19	18

Test the null hypothesis that the probability that a house has an air conditioner is independent of which row it is in.

CHAPTER 6

Some Tests of the Hypothesis of Randomness: Control Charts

6.1. Introduction

Data are frequently obtained serially in time or space. For example, a series of determinations of the velocity of light may be spread over weeks or months. The quality of insulation of a long length of wire may be determined at a number of points along its length. In calculating the variance of the mean as σ^2/n, we are making the assumption that the observations are independent and are identically distributed. It is therefore desirable to have some method of checking on this assumption. In this chapter we will consider two such tests, the first appropriate for continuous observations with a normal distribution, and the second appropriate to a sequence of dissimilar elements of two types. This latter test is immediately adaptable to any continuous measurements by classifying them as above or below the median. The resulting test assumes continuity in the distribution but makes no assumptions about the form of the distribution, and is in fact an example of a nonparametric test, a class of tests to be discussed in Chapter 7.

6.2. The Mean-Square Successive Difference Test

The mean-square successive difference test is a test of the null hypothesis that we have a sequence of independent observations $x_1, \ldots, x_n$ from a population $N(\xi, \sigma^2)$. We compute estimates of σ^2 in two ways. The first is the unbiased estimator (2.3.15),

$$s^2 = \frac{1}{n-1} \sum_i^n (x_i - \bar{x})^2. \tag{2.1}$$

In computing this, it is usually convenient to use the identity

$$\begin{aligned}\sum_i^n (x_i - \bar{x})^2 &= \sum_i^n x_i^2 - 2\bar{x}\sum_i^n x_i + n\bar{x}^2 \\ &= \sum_i^n x_i^2 - 2\left(\sum_i^n \frac{x_i}{n}\right)\sum_i^n x_i + n\left(\sum_i^n \frac{x_i}{n}\right)^2 \\ &= \sum_i^n x_i^2 - \frac{1}{n}\left(\sum_i^n x_i\right)^2. \end{aligned} \tag{2.2}$$

The second estimator of σ^2 is $d^2/2$, where d^2 is defined as

$$d^2 = \frac{1}{n-1}\sum_{i=1}^{n-1}(x_{i+1} - x_i)^2. \tag{2.3}$$

It is easy to see that $E[d^2/2] = \sigma^2$, since

$$\begin{aligned} E[d^2] &= \frac{1}{n-1} E\left[\sum_{i=1}^{n-1} x_{i+1}^2 + \sum_{i=1}^{n-1} x_i^2 - 2\sum_{i=1}^{n-1} x_{i+1}x_i\right] \\ &= \frac{1}{n-1}\left\{\sum_{i=1}^{n-1} E[x_{i+1}^2] + \sum_{i=1}^{n-1} E[x_i^2] - 2\sum_{i=1}^{n-1} E[x_{i+1}]\, E[x_i]\right\} \\ &= 2\{E[x_i^2] - (E[x_i])^2\} = 2V[x] = 2\sigma^2. \end{aligned}$$

It was proved [1] that, under the null hypothesis,

$$E\left[\frac{d^2/2}{s^2}\right] = 1, \tag{2.4}$$

and

$$V\left[\frac{d^2/2}{s^2}\right] = \frac{n-2}{n^2-1}. \tag{2.5}$$

Thus the test statistic

$$\frac{(d^2/2)/s^2 - 1}{\sqrt{(n-2)/(n^2-1)}} \tag{2.6}$$

is approximately distributed as a unit normal deviate under the null hypothesis. The exact distribution under the null hypothesis has been tabulated for n over the range 4 to 60 (but note that in [2] the sample estimate s^2 was defined as in (2.3.9) with n in the denominator instead of $(n-1)$). This tabulation shows that even for n as small as 10 the normal approximation (2.6) is good.

The alternative to the null hypothesis is usually that consecutive observations tend to be correlated positively with their predecessors. The successive differences $(x_{i+1} - x_i)$ therefore tend to be smaller than they would be under complete randomness, and so the expected value of $d^2/2$

is less than σ^2. The numerator of (2.6) will tend to be negative, and the P value for the null hypothesis is obtained by putting (2.6) equal to u_P.

Table 6.1 gives the results of 23 determinations, ordered in time of, the gravitational constant G by Cavendish [3]. The right-hand column of the table is referred to in Section 6.4.

Table 6.1

x_i	d_i	
5.36		*B*
5.29	−0.07	*B*
5.58	+0.29	*A*
5.65	+0.07	*A*
5.57	−0.08	*A*
5.53	−0.04	*A*
5.62	+0.09	*A*
5.29	−0.33	*B*
5.44	+0.15	*B*
5.34	−0.10	*B*
5.79	+0.45	*A*
5.10	−0.69	*B*
5.27	+0.17	*B*
5.39	+0.12	*B*
5.42	+0.03	*B*
5.47	+0.05	*A*
5.63	+0.16	*A*
5.34	−0.29	*B*
5.46	+0.12	Median
5.30	−0.16	*B*
5.75	+0.45	*A*
5.68	−0.07	*A*
5.85	+0.17	*A*

Using (2.1) and (2.2), s^2 is computed as

$$s^2 = \left[(5.36^2 + \cdots + 5.85^2) - \frac{(5.36 + \cdots + 5.85)^2}{23}\right] \Big/ (23 - 1) = 0.036260.$$

We compute d^2 from (2.3):

$$d^2 = \left[\frac{(-0.07)^2 + \cdots + (0.17)^2}{22}\right] = 0.061941.$$

From (2.5) we get

$$V\left[\frac{(d^2/2)}{s^2}\right] = \frac{(23-2)}{(23^2-1)} = 0.03977.$$

Thus our test statistic is

$$u_P = \frac{(0.061941/2)/0.036260 - 1}{\sqrt{0.03977}} = \frac{-0.14588}{0.1944} = -0.732,$$

whence $P = 0.23$. This is substantially greater than 0.05; so we would not reject the null hypothesis of randomness at the 5 per cent level of significance.

6.3. Runs of Elements of Two Types

Suppose that we have m elements of type A and n of type B, and that these occur in a sequence, e.g.,

$$AABBABBBBAABAAAA:$$

Here $m = 9$, $n = 7$. Let $m + n = N$. We assume as a null hypothesis that every one of the possible permutations is equally likely. There are a number of characteristics of such a sequence which might be considered, for example, the length of the longest run of either type of element, a run being defined as an unbroken sequence of elements of the same type, i.e., a sequence of A's or a sequence of B's. We will consider the distribution of the number of runs, denoted by u. In the above example $u = 7$. The probability of each possible value of u, given m and n, can be evaluated by direct combinatorial methods. The resulting formulas are somewhat clumsy but have been tabulated in [4] for $m \leq n \leq 20$. Here we will develop a large sample approximation to the distribution of u under the null hypothesis based on the exact mean and variance.

It is convenient to consider the number of transitions t rather than the number of runs u: A transition is defined as the point where one run ends and another begins. The number of transitions must be one less than the number of runs, as the last run ends at the end of the sequence, and this point is not counted as a transition. Hence

$$t = u - 1. \tag{3.1}$$

We want to find $E[u] = E[t] + 1$ and $V[u] = V[t]$ under the null hypothesis.

Denote the total number of gaps between elements where transitions could occur as $N' = N - 1$. Define t_i as the number of transitions at the ith gap, i.e.,

$$t_i = \begin{cases} 0 & \text{if either } A, A \text{ or } B, B \text{ on the two sides of the gap,} \\ 1 & \text{if either } A, B \text{ or } B, A \text{ on the two sides of the gap.} \end{cases}$$

Then the total number of transitions $t = \sum_{i}^{N'} t_i$, and $E[t_i]$ is the probability that a pair of consecutive elements are dissimilar. We have

$$\Pr\{\text{first in a pair is an } A\} = \frac{m}{m+n},$$

$$\Pr\{\text{second in a pair is a } B \mid \text{first was an } A\} = \frac{n}{m+n-1};$$

so $$\Pr\{\text{a pair is an } AB\} = \frac{m}{m+n}\,\frac{n}{m+n-1}.$$

Also, $$\Pr\{\text{second in a pair is an } A \mid \text{first was an } A\} = \frac{m-1}{m+n-1};$$

so $$\Pr\{\text{a pair is an } AA\} = \frac{m}{m+n}\,\frac{m-1}{m+n-1}.$$

Using these and similar results we can tabulate the probabilities of all possible types of pairs (Table 6.2), along with the corresponding values of t_i and t_i^2.

Table 6.2

Type of pair	t_i	t_i^2	Probability
AA	0	0	$m(m-1)/(m+n)(m+n-1)$
AB	1	1	$mn/(m+n)(m+n-1)$
BA	1	1	$mn/(m+n)(m+n-1)$
BB	0	0	$n(n-1)/(m+n)(m+n-1)$

It follows that

$$E[t_i] = 1 \times \frac{mn}{(m+n)(m+n-1)} + 1 \times \frac{mn}{(m+n)(m+n-1)}$$

$$= \frac{2mn}{(m+n)(m+n-1)}, \tag{3.2}$$

$$E[t_i^2] = \frac{2mn}{(m+n)(m+n-1)}. \tag{3.3}$$

We thus obtain

$$E[t] = E[\sum_i^{N'} t_i] = \sum_i^{N'} E[t_i] = N' \frac{2mn}{(m+n)(m+n-1)} = \frac{2mn}{m+n},$$

since $N' = m + n - 1$, and the expected number of runs is

$$E[u] = 1 + \frac{2mn}{m+n}. \tag{3.4}$$

We now want the variance of u:

$$V[u] = V[t] = V[\sum_i^{N'} t_i]$$

$$= \sum_i^{N'} V[t_i] + 2 \sum_{i=1}^{N'-1} \sum_{j=i+1}^{N'} \text{Cov}[t_i, t_j]. \tag{3.5}$$

The first term is readily evaluated:

$$\sum_i^{N'} V[t_i] = N' \, V[t_i] = N'\{E[t_i^2] - (E[t_i])^2\}. \tag{3.6}$$

The second term in (3.5) involves the $\text{Cov}[t_i, t_j]$ which can be calculated as

$$\text{Cov}[t_i, t_j] = E[t_i t_j] - E[t_i]\, E[t_j] = E[t_i t_j] - (E[t_i])^2, \tag{3.7}$$

since $E[t_i] = E[t_j]$. The terms $t_i t_j$ are best considered in two groups:

1. The terms $t_i t_{i+1}$ which involve adjacent gaps, in which the pair of elements determining t_i has as its second element the first element of the second pair determining t_{i+1}.

2. The terms $t_i t_k$, where $k > i + 1$, for which the two pairs of elements do not have an element in common; i.e., the ith and kth gaps are separated by one or more other gaps.

We need the numbers of terms of these two types. The total number of pairs t_i, t_j, with $i < j$, is the number of combinations that can be formed from N' items taken two at a time, i.e.,

$$\binom{N'}{2} = \frac{N'!}{2!\,(N'-2)!} = \frac{N'(N'-1)}{2}.$$

The number of pairs of type 1 is $N - 2 = N' - 1$, since, if we consider a typical sequence of elements 1, 2, 3, 4, 5, then the only adjacent pairs of t's that can be formed are t_1, t_2 from elements 1, 2, 3; t_2, t_3 from elements 2, 3, 4; t_3, t_4 from elements 3, 4, 5. The number of pairs of type 2 can then be obtained as the total number of all pairs minus the number of pairs of type 1:

$$\frac{N'(N'-1)}{2} - (N'-1) = \frac{(N'-1)(N'-2)}{2}. \qquad (3.8)$$

To compute the Cov$[t_i, t_j]$ from (3.7) we need $E[t_i t_j]$ for the two types of pairs. For type 1, the pairs t_i, t_{i+1} are those pairs of transitions with one element in common. All possible examples are listed in Table 6.3.

Table 6.3

Sequences of elements	t_i	t_{i+1}	$t_i t_{i+1}$
AAA	0	0	0
AAB	0	1	0
ABA	1	1	1
ABB	1	0	0
BAA	1	0	0
BAB	1	1	1
BBA	0	1	0
BBB	0	0	0

The only sequences giving nonzero values for $t_i t_{i+1}$ are ABA and BAB. These have probabilities

$$\frac{m}{m+n} \cdot \frac{n}{m+n-1} \cdot \frac{m-1}{m+n-2} \quad \text{and} \quad \frac{n}{m+n} \cdot \frac{m}{m+n-1} \cdot \frac{n-1}{m+n-2}.$$

Thus

$$E[t_i t_{i+1}] = 1 \times \frac{mn(m-1)}{(m+n)(m+n-1)(m+n-2)} + 1 \times \frac{mn(n-1)}{(m+n)(m+n-1)(m+n-2)}$$
$$= \frac{mn}{(m+n)(m+n-1)}. \qquad (3.9)$$

Inserting this in (3.7) we get for the covariances of the pairs of the type t_i, t_{i+1}

$$\text{Cov}[t_i, t_{i+1}] = \frac{mn}{(m+n)(m+n-1)} - (E[t_i])^2. \qquad (3.10)$$

There are $N' - 1 = m + n - 2$ such terms.

To compute $\mathrm{Cov}[t_i, t_k]$, $k > i + 1$, we need $E[t_i t_k]$ for the pairs of t's formed by the types of pairs of elements listed in Table 6.4. The only types giving nonzero values for $t_i t_k$ are $AB \cdots AB$, $AB \cdots BA$, $BA \cdots AB$, and $BA \cdots BA$, all of which involve two A's and two B's: These types all have the same probability

$$\frac{m}{m+n} \cdot \frac{n}{m+n-1} \cdot \frac{m-1}{m+n-2} \cdot \frac{n-1}{m+n-3}.$$

Thus $$E[t_i t_k] = \frac{4mn(m-1)(n-1)}{(m+n)(m+n-1)(m+n-2)(m+n-3)}. \tag{3.11}$$

Table 6.4

Types of pairs	t_i	t_k	$t_i t_k$
$AA \cdots AA$	0	0	0
$AA \cdots AB$	0	1	0
$AA \cdots BA$	0	1	0
$AA \cdots BB$	0	0	0
$AB \cdots AA$	1	0	0
$AB \cdots AB$	1	1	1
$AB \cdots BA$	1	1	1
$AB \cdots BB$	1	0	0
$BA \cdots AA$	1	0	0
$BA \cdots AB$	1	1	1
$BA \cdots BA$	1	1	1
$BA \cdots BB$	1	0	0
$BB \cdots AA$	0	0	0
$BB \cdots AB$	0	1	0
$BB \cdots BA$	0	1	0
$BB \cdots BB$	0	0	0

Inserting this in (3.7), we get for the covariances of pairs of the type t_i, t_k, $k > i + 1$,

$$\mathrm{Cov}[t_i, t_k] = \frac{4mn(m-1)(n-1)}{(m+n)(m+n-1)(m+n-2)(m+n-3)} - (E[t_i])^2. \tag{3.12}$$

By (3.8), there are $(m + n - 2)(m + n - 3)/2$ such terms.

We now substitute in (3.5) the variance term (3.6) and the two covariance terms (3.10) and (3.12), the two latter with the appropriate coefficients, namely, the numbers of terms of the two types:

$$
\begin{aligned}
V[u] = {} & (m+n-1)\{E[t_i^2] - (E[t_i])^2\} \\
& + 2(m+n-2)\left\{\frac{mn}{(m+n)(m+n-1)} - (E[t_i])^2\right\} \\
& + 2 \times \frac{1}{2}(m+n-2)(m+n-3) \\
& \left\{\frac{4mn(m-1)(n-1)}{(m+n)(m+n-1)(m+n-2)(m+n-3)} - (E[t_i])^2\right\}.
\end{aligned}
\tag{3.13}
$$

The sum of the coefficients of $(E[t_i])^2$ is easily shown to be $-(m+n-1)^2$. Substituting for $E[t_i]$ from (3.2) and for $E[t_i^2]$ from (3.3), (3.13) reduces to

$$
V[u] = \frac{2mn(2mn-m-n)}{(m+n)^2(m+n-1)}. \tag{3.14}
$$

Thus, if u is an observed number of runs, the statistic

$$
\frac{u - \left(\dfrac{2mn}{m+n} + 1\right)}{\sqrt{2mn(2mn-m-n)/(m+n)^2(m+n-1)}} \tag{3.15}
$$

is under the null hypothesis a standardized variable which for large m and n is approximately normal.

The above statistic has been studied by Stevens [5] and Wald and Wolfowitz [6]. Wallis [7] suggested making a correction for continuity by bringing the observed u closer to its expectation by 1/2. For very small values of m and n the normal approximation will be unreliable, and the exact values of the distribution tabulated by Swed and Eisenhart [4] should be used.

Usually the alternative hypothesis envisaged is one-sided: Usually we anticipate the runs of like elements to be greater in length and hence fewer in number than under the hypothesis of randomness. For example, if a row of tomato plants contains diseased plants we might expect these to occur in groups. The usual critical region for the statistic (3.15) is therefore $< u_\alpha$.

As an example, in a street of row houses X represents the presence of an air conditioner and 0 the absence of an air conditioner:

00X0X000000000000XXXXXX000000000X000X00X00.

The number of runs $u = 13$: There are 31 0's and 11 X's; so

$$E[u] = \frac{2mn}{m+n} + 1 = \frac{2 \times 31 \times 11}{31 + 11} + 1 = 17.238,$$

$$V[u] = \frac{2mn(2mn - m - n)}{(m+n)^2(m+n-1)}$$

$$= \frac{2 \times 31 \times 11 \times (2 \times 31 \times 11 - 31 - 11)}{(31+11)^2(31+11-1)} = 6.0351,$$

and the approximate unit normal deviate is

$$\frac{u + 1/2 - E[u]}{\sqrt{V[u]}} = \frac{13 + 1/2 - 17.238}{\sqrt{6.0351}} = -1.522,$$

whence $P = 0.064$. The evidence in favor of nonrandomness using this test is thus not quite sufficient to allow the rejection of the null hypothesis at the 5 per cent level of significance, but certainly we would be encouraged to attempt to obtain more data.

The foregoing treatment of runs of two kinds of elements has been extended to the case of three kinds of elements: If the numbers of elements of the three types are a, b, and c,

$$E[u] = \frac{2(ab + ac + bc)}{a + b + c} + 1, \tag{3.16}$$

$$V[u] = \frac{[2(ab + ac + bc)]^2}{(a+b+c)^2(a+b+c-1)} - \frac{2(ab + ac + bc) + 6abc}{(a+b+c)(a+b+c-1)}. \tag{3.17}$$

6.4. Runs Above and Below the Median

The test of the previous section can readily be adapted to test the randomness of a sequence of continuous observations, $x_1, \ldots, x_N$. By classifying the observations as being above or below the sample median, each observation will be labeled either A or B. If the number of observations is odd, we ignore the observation which falls on the median. The number of observations above the median m equals the number of observations below the median n; so $m = n$. Equations (3.4) and (3.14) become

$$E[u] = 1 + m, \tag{4.1}$$

$$V[u] = \frac{m(m-1)}{2m-1}. \tag{4.2}$$

For the data of Table 6.1, the median is 5.46, and the observations are marked A or B accordingly in the last column. The number of runs $u = 8$, $m = n = 11$; $E[u] = 1 + 11 = 12$, and

$$V[u] = \frac{11 \times (11 - 1)}{2 \times 11 - 1} = 5.2381, \qquad u_P = \frac{8 + 1/2 - 12}{\sqrt{5.2381}} = -1.529,$$

whence $P = 0.063$.

This test is an example of a so-called nonparametric test, in that its only assumptions under the null hypothesis are that the observations are random and identically distributed from some continuous distribution whose form has not been specified. The mean-square successive difference test, in contrast, assumed normality. Usually, if such a stronger assumption is justified, then the test making use of such an assumption is more powerful against a particular alternative than an analogous test not making use of the assumption, assuming that both tests are oriented toward having power against this alternative. In the present instance, the assumption of normality appears reasonable, and, if the null hypothesis had been appreciably false, we might have anticipated a smaller P value with the mean-square successive difference test than the test for runs above and below the median. Actually the reverse occurred, though with both tests the null hypothesis was acceptable at the 5 per cent level of significance.

Other studies have been made of the distributions of runs of various types. The distributions of runs above and below the median of specified lengths, of runs up and down by number and by length, and so on, are available (see [8]—[11]).

6.5. Control Charts for the Mean and Range

The statistical control chart, due to Shewhart [12], [13], is a device for keeping a check on the stability of a repetitive process. For example, we may be filling cans with lubricating oil and wish to maintain the contents at a stable level. If x_i is the weight of the contents of the ith can, if the x_i are independent observations from a population normally distributed with known mean ξ and variance σ^2, then if we take samples of n cans the mean weights $\bar{x}$ will satisfy (1.15.12) with $\bar{x}$ written for x and $\sigma/\sqrt{n}$ written for σ:

$$\Pr\left\{\bar{x} < \xi - \frac{k\sigma}{\sqrt{n}}\right\} + \Pr\left\{\bar{x} > \xi + \frac{k\sigma}{\sqrt{n}}\right\} = 2[1 - \Phi(k)]. \qquad (5.1)$$

With $k = 3.09$, for example, 99.8 per cent of all sample means will lie in the interval $\xi \pm 3.09\sigma/n$. Should a sample mean lie outside this interval, since this will only happen twice in a thousand times under the stated assumptions, the natural conclusion is to suspect that the assumptions are incorrect in some respect. Usually the most likely way in which the system has deviated from the assumptions is for the mean to have shifted. So long as only the stated proportion of points lies outside the interval, the process is said to be in a *state of statistical control*, and, if more than that proportion of points is outside the interval, then the process is said to be *out of control*.

Usually the sample means are plotted on a chart serially as they are obtained, and lines, known as *control limits*, drawn in at $\xi \pm k\sigma/\sqrt{n}$. Usually ξ is estimated by the mean of the previous 30 or more sample means. The standard deviation σ can be estimated by (2.3.15), but almost invariably a quick but not fully efficient method is used, based on the *ranges*. The range w of a sample of n is defined as the difference between the largest and the smallest observations in the sample. For samples from a normal population $E[w] = d_n \sigma$, where d_n is a constant, tabulated in Table VI, dependent on n. The standard deviation is estimated by

$$\hat{\sigma} = \frac{\bar{w}}{d_n} \tag{5.2}$$

where $\bar{w}$ is the mean of 30 or more ranges. For example, if ξ is estimated as 100, and $\bar{w} = 10$ for a large number of samples of 5, then $\hat{\sigma} = 10/2.326$. For 99 per cent control limits, we have $2[1 - \Phi(k)] = 0.01$; so $\Phi(k) = 0.995$ and $k = 2.576$. The control limits are

$$100 \pm 2.576 \times \frac{10/2.326}{\sqrt{5}} = 100.00 \pm 4.62.$$

The object of this procedure is to enable the operator to distinguish between random variation and variation in excess of what would reasonably occur at random. The operator has to accept the variation represented by the fluctuation of the sample means as inevitable, given ξ and σ. However, the occurrence of an out-of-control point is a signal for him to suspect that something has changed, to find out what, and to restore the status quo.

It must be noted that, if σ increases, points on the mean chart can go out of control without any change in ξ. If the standard deviation increases by a factor of 4, and we are using 99 per cent control limits for the means, so that in (5.1) $k = 2.58$, the limits would now be effectively at $\pm 2.58(\sigma/4)/\sqrt{n} = \pm 0.645\ \sigma/\sqrt{n}$; so the probability of a point falling outside these limits is $2[1 - \Phi(0.645)] = 2(1 - 0.7405) = 0.519$, a drastic change from the supposed 0.01.

To guard against this ambiguity we can keep a control chart on the ranges. For samples of size n from a normal population with standard deviation σ, the sampling distribution of the range w is known,

$$\Pr\{w < \sigma W_P\} = P, \tag{5.3}$$

where W_P is tabulated in Table VI of the appendix. Thus $(P_2 - P_1)$ control limits for w are given by

$$\Pr\{\sigma W_{P_1} < w < \sigma W_{P_2}\} = P_2 - P_1\ . \tag{5.4}$$

For example, if $n = 10$, and we want 95 per cent control limits, then we need $P_2 = 0.975$, $P_1 = 0.025$. From Table VI for $n = 10$, $W_{0.975} = 4.79$, $W_{0.025} = 1.67$, and the limits are $(1.67\sigma, 4.79\sigma)$. If σ is estimated as $\bar{w}/d_n = \bar{w}/3.078$, then the lower control limit is $0.542\bar{w}$, and the upper control limit $1.556\bar{w}$. A control chart for ranges is kept in an analogous manner to that for means. The sample ranges are plotted from left to right as they occur in time, and the control lines drawn in. If a point lies outside a control limit, this is evidence that the standard deviation of the population has changed.

It will be noted that control limits are not the same as specification limits. If a process is in a state of statistical control, the sample averages with rare exceptions will be fluctuating inside the control limits $\xi \pm k\sigma/\sqrt{n}$ and the individual observations will be fluctuating with rare exceptions in the interval $\xi \pm k\sigma$: These limits, $+k\sigma$ and $-k\sigma$, will only coincide with the process specification limits, if it has any, by accident. It is important to note that the limits for the individual observations are wider than the control limits for the sample means by the factor $\sqrt{n}$.

To revert to our example of filling cans with lubricating oil, if ξ is equal to the claimed quantity, say ξ_0, then the individual observations x will be distributed around ξ_0 with standard deviation σ, and 50 per cent of all cans will have less than the claimed amount. If only 1 per cent of all cans are to have less than the claimed amount, we require that

$$\Pr\{x < \xi_0\} = 0.01 = \Phi\left[\frac{\xi_0 - \xi}{\sigma}\right]$$

by (1.15.8); so $(\xi_0 - \xi)/\sigma = u_{0.01} = -2.326$, and so the required overfill $\xi - \xi_0 = 2.326\sigma$. It may be economic to make quite an effort to reduce σ.

6.6. Control Charts for Poisson-Distributed Observations

Suppose that we wish to keep a control chart on the number x of defects in square-yard samples of carpeting. If the process is in control, then x

will be a Poisson-distributed variable with parameter ξ. We assume that ξ can be estimated accurately by (4.4.4) as $\bar{x} = \sum_i^n x_i/n$ where n is large.

The usual procedure is to use the normal approximation to the Poisson, (4.6.2). We assume that x is normally distributed with mean ξ and variance ξ, where ξ is estimated by $\bar{x}$, and the so-called three sigma limits are $\bar{x} \pm 3\sqrt{\bar{x}}$. Continuity corrections are usually omitted.

It may sometimes be justifiable to be more precise. Equating (4.6.1) with P gives

$$\Pr\{\chi^2 < 2\xi\} = 1 - P, \qquad f = 2(x_P + 1).$$

But, since $\Pr\{\chi^2 < \chi^2_{1-P}\} = 1 - P$,

$$2\xi = \chi^2_{1-P}, \qquad f = 2(x_P + 1). \tag{6.1}$$

This equation will determine x_P for a specified ξ and P: By changing x we change f and hence χ^2_{1-P} until it equals 2ξ. Since x has to change by integers, f will change by jumps of two units, and in general we will not be able to get an exact solution.

As an example, suppose that $\xi = 9$ (there is no reason, of course, why ξ should be an integer). If we want 95 per cent control limits, we will want P_1 to be as close as possible to 0.025 from the lower side. Substituting in (6.1), we want $2 \times 9 = \chi^2_{1-0.025}$. From the χ^2 table, $\chi^2_{0.975} = 17.5$, 19.0, and 20.5 for $f = 8$, 9, and 10, respectively. We cannot use an odd value of f, because that would make x fractional. We have to settle for $f = 8$, whence $x = 3$, and $\Pr\{x \le 3\} = 1 - \Pr\{\chi^2(8) < 18\} \simeq 1 - 0.976 = 0.024$, actually very close to the desired value of 0.025. If we used $f = 10$, to give $x = 4$, $\Pr\{x \le 4\} = 1 - \Pr\{\chi^2(10) < 18\} \simeq 1 - 0.94 = 0.06$, much larger than the desired figure. For the upper limit, we want

$$\Pr\{x \ge x_{P_2}\} = 1 - \Pr\{x \le x_{P_2} - 1\} = \Pr\{\chi^2(2x_{P_2}) < 2\xi\},$$

to be less than or equal to $1 - P_2 = 0.025$. We try $f = 30$, when $x = 15$, and

$$\Pr\{\chi^2(30) < 2 \times 9\} \simeq 0.035,$$

which is too large; so, trying $f = 32$, we have

$$\Pr\{\chi^2(32) < 2 \times 9\} \simeq 0.02,$$

and so we use our upper control limit, $x_{0.98} = 16$.

The crude limits $\bar{x} \pm 1.96\sqrt{\bar{x}}$ in this case, for $\bar{x} = 9$, are 3.12 and 14.88 which would be rounded outward to 3 and 15.

REFERENCES

1. von Neumann, J., R. H. Kent, H. R. Bellinson, and B. I. Hart, "The mean square successive differençe," *Annals of Mathematical Statistics*, 12(1941), 153–162.
2. Hart, B. I., "Significance levels for the ratio of the mean square successive difference to the variance," *Annals of Mathematical Statistics*, 13(1942), 445–447.
3. Cavendish, H., "Experiments to determine the density of the earth," *Philosophical Transactions of the Royal Society*, 88(1798), 469–526.
4. Swed, F. S., and C. Eisenhart, "Tables for testing randomness of grouping in a sequence of alternatives," *Annals of Mathematical Statistics*, 14(1943), 66–87.
5. Stevens, W. L., "Distribution of groups in a sequence of alternatives," *Annals of Eugenics*, 9(1939), 10–17.
6. Wald, A., and J. Wolfowitz, "On a test whether two samples are from the same population," *Annals of Mathematical Statistics*, 11(1940), 147–162.
7. Wallis, W. Allen, "Rough-and-ready statistical tests," *Industrial Quality Control*, 8(1952), 35–40.
8. Mosteller, Frederick, "Note on an application of runs to quality control charts," *Annals of Mathematical Statistics*, 12(1941), 228–232.
9. Olmstead, P. S., "Distribution of sample arrangements for runs up and down," *Annals of Mathematical Statistics*, 17(1946), 24–33.
10. Wolfowitz, J., "Asymptotic distribution of runs up and down," *Annals of Mathematical Statistics*, 15(1944), 163–172.
11. Moore, G. H., and W. Allen Wallis, "Time series significance tests based on signs of differences," *Journal of the American Statistical Association*, 38(1943), 153–164.
12. Shewhart, W. A., *Economic Control of Quality of Manufactured Product*. New York: D. Van Nostrand Co., 1931.
13. ——— *Statistical Method from the Viewpoint of Quality Control*. Washington, D.C.: Department of Agriculture, 1939.

EXERCISES

6.1. The number of hurricanes on the East Coast for the years 1930 through 1954 were reported as follows:

2,2,6,10,5,5,5,2,4,2,4,4,2,5,6,4,2,4,5,8,11,8,6,5,6.

Test the null hypothesis that this is a random sequence (*a*) with the mean-square successive difference test, assuming that the square root of the numbers observed is normally distributed (why?); (*b*) with the test for runs of two kinds of elements (Let years with 4 or fewer hurricanes be "good" and with 5 or more be "bad"); (*c*) with the test for runs of three kinds of elements (Let years with 4 or fewer hurricanes be "good", with 5 be "medium", and with 6 or more be "bad"). Report one-sided P values.

6.2. Construct a control chart for the data in the preceding example, using 99 per cent control limits.

6.3. We have a machine automatically filling tubes of toothpaste. We take a large number of samples of five tubes, find the weights of the individual tubes, and take the range of weights in each sample of 5. The mean weight is 16 grams, and the mean range is 0.7 gram.

(*a*) Suppose we want control limits that will contain 98 per cent of all sample means, on the average, when the system is under control. What should the control limits be? (*b*) What are the 98 per cent control limits for the ranges of the samples of five? (*c*) If the label claims that the tube contains 16 grams, what percentage of the customers are receiving less than they have a right to expect? (*d*) What percentage of the customers get less than 15.8 grams? (*e*) To give 99.9 per cent of the customers at least what the label claims, where should the process average be?

6.4. A mining company finds a body of ore, approximately rectangular. At equally spaced intervals along the length they bore through the body, and the cores are analyzed for a certain mineral. In this sample the minimum is 0.005, the median 0.05, and the maximum 1.32. It is apparent that this distribution is exceedingly skew, since the distance from the minimum to the median is 0.045 whereas the distance from the median to the maximum is 1.27. If we use logarithms, or more conveniently 100 times the (logarithms + 3), say x, the minimum, median, and maximum are 70, 170, and 312. It appears that the logarithm of the percentage is much more symmetrically distributed than the percentage itself.

Test the null hypothesis that this sequence of observations is a random sequence with

(*a*) The mean-square successive difference test.

(*b*) The test for number of runs above and below the median.

Bore	x	Bore	x	Bore	x
1	170	16	148	31	130
2	178	17	130	32	178
3	263	18	100	33	190
4	185	19	70	34	291
5	311	20	100	35	241
6	312	21	160	36	130
7	190	22	148	37	70
8	178	23	130	38	215
9	160	24	300	39	223
10	308	25	160	40	195
11	223	26	148	41	160
12	130	27	130	42	100
13	195	28	100	43	130
14	170	29	70	44	252
15	160	30	100	45	240
				46	274

What practical inferences might you draw if the hypothesis of randomness was

(*c*) Acceptable.

(*d*) Rejected at some reasonable significance level.

6.5. Construct a control chart for means and ranges for the data of the preceding exercise. Use samples of size 5 made up by grouping consecutive observations, and discard the 46th bore. Give 99 per cent control limits.

6.6. A process for purification of a fine chemical involved passing it in solution through a column containing a resin on which the chemical was adsorbed. A specified volume of solution constituted a batch, after which the flow was switched to another column. The figures in Table A give the concentration escaping from the outgoing end of the column at the conclusion of each batch operation.

(*a*) Construct a control chart for means and ranges of samples of 4 with 99 per cent control limits. Note that a chart of totals is equivalent for all practical purposes to a chart for means, with the obvious adjustment to the control limits, and saves some arithmetic. Comment on the charts.

(*b*) Comment on a graph of the ranges against the totals for each batch.

(*c*) Table B gives the logarithms of the data of Table A multiplied by a factor of 10. Construct charts as in (*a*) and comment.

Table A

Batches	1	5	9	13	17	21	25	29	33	37
	0.5	2.9	1.0	1.9	3.5	1.2	1.7	2.8	2.3	4.2
	3.0	3.0	2.5	4.6	0.7	2.0	2.2	2.9	1.7	3.0
	3.8	1.7	6.7	0.8	2.1	1.4	1.1	1.9	4.0	2.2
	1.1	3.1	1.9	3.7	3.0	1.6	2.7	3.2	0.8	2.1
Totals	8.4	10.7	12.1	11.0	9.3	6.2	7.7	10.8	8.8	11.5
Ranges	3.3	1.4	5.7	3.8	2.8	0.8	1.6	1.3	3.2	2.1

Batches	41	45	49	53	57	61	65	69	73	77
	2.3	1.8	1.3	4.2	0.5	0.8	1.2	2.3	1.2	0.7
	1.4	4.0	5.2	2.4	1.8	2.7	2.9	1.5	0.7	0.5
	2.2	2.6	0.9	1.0	0.6	0.9	1.0	0.3	3.4	1.3
	1.5	1.2	0.8	1.9	0.8	1.4	1.0	0.3	1.2	0.3
Totals	7.4	9.6	8.2	9.4	3.7	5.8	6.1	4.4	6.5	2.8
Ranges	0.9	2.8	4.4	3.2	1.3	1.9	1.9	2.0	2.7	1.0

Batches	81	85	89	93	97	101	105	109	113	117
	1.3	0.5	1.1	1.2	0.9	1.6	0.3	0.8	0.7	0.6
	0.1	0.9	0.5	1.2	1.3	0.6	0.7	0.4	0.8	1.4
	2.1	0.8	0.5	0.8	0.6	1.0	0.3	0.9	3.2	0.4
	2.0	0.4	0.7	0.6	1.1	0.9	0.8	1.3	0.5	1.1
Totals	5.5	2.6	2.8	3.8	3.9	4.1	2.1	3.4	5.2	3.5
Ranges	2.0	0.5	0.6	0.6	0.7	1.0	0.5	0.9	2.7	1.0

Table B

Batch	1	5	9	13	17	21	25	29	33	37
	0.70	1.46	1.00	1.28	1.54	1.08	1.23	1.45	1.36	1.62
	1.48	1.48	1.40	1.65	0.85	1.30	1.34	1.46	1.23	1.48
	1.58	1.23	1.83	0.90	1.32	1.15	1.04	1.28	1.60	1.34
	1.04	1.49	1.28	1.57	1.48	1.20	1.43	1.51	0.90	1.32
Totals	4.80	5.66	5.51	5.40	5.19	4.73	5.04	5.70	5.09	5.76
Ranges	0.99	0.26	0.83	0.75	0.69	0.22	0.39	0.39	0.23	0.70

Batch	41	45	49	53	57	61	65	69	73	77
	1.36	1.26	1.11	1.62	0.70	0.90	1.08	1.36	1.08	0.85
	1.15	1.60	1.72	1.38	1.25	1.43	1.46	1.18	0.85	0.70
	1.34	1.41	0.95	1.00	0.78	0.95	1.00	0.48	1.53	1.11
	1.18	1.08	0.90	1.26	0.90	1.15	1.00	0.48	1.08	0.48
Totals	5.03	5.35	4.68	5.26	3.63	4.43	4.54	3.50	4.54	3.14
Ranges	0.21	0.52	0.82	0.62	0.55	0.53	0.46	0.88	0.68	0.63

Batch	81	85	89	93	97	101	105	109	113	117
	1.11	0.70	1.04	1.08	0.95	1.20	0.48	0.09	0.85	0.78
	0.00	0.95	0.70	1.08	1.11	0.78	0.85	0.60	0.90	1.15
	1.32	0.90	0.70	0.90	0.78	1.00	0.48	0.95	1.51	0.60
	1.30	0.60	0.85	0.78	1.04	0.95	0.90	1.11	0.70	1.04
Totals	3.73	3.15	3.29	3.84	3.88	3.93	2.71	3.56	3.96	3.57
Ranges	1.32	0.35	0.34	0.30	0.33	0.42	0.42	0.51	0.81	0.55

CHAPTER 7

Some Nonparametric Tests

7.1. The Assumption of Normality

A large proportion of present-day statistical techniques for dealing with continuous variables relies on the assumption that the variable has an underlying normal distribution. This assumption is not so restrictive as it may seem at first sight, for, first, we can often transform a variable, if we know the general form of its distribution, into a variable which is approximately normally distributed. Second, we can often arrange to deal with means, and the central-limit theorem assures us, roughly, that if a population has a finite variance then the distribution of the sample mean approaches normality as n incresses. The central-limit theorem has a long history dating back to Demoivre, La Place, and Gauss; For a modern review see Cramer [1], sections 17.4 and 17.5. It is presumably on this foundation that applied statisticians have found empirically that usually there is no great need to fuss about the normality assumption. After a statistician has analyzed several quite widely differing transformations of a variable in a fair number of specific instances and found that the conclusions reached are substantially identical for all the transformations, then he ceases to worry unduly about the normality assumption in most situations.

This is a convenient place to interpolate a few more remarks about the importance of the assumption of normality. The importance of the assumption depends on

1. The nature of the departure from normality
2. The statistical technique being used
3. The ultimate purpose of the analysis

For example, marked skewness can badly upset the significance level of a one-sided test but have only a small effect on a two-sided test. Again deviation from normality in the extreme tails is rather unimportant in significance testing: To think that we are rejecting a null hypothesis at the level of significance 0.0001 when in fact the true level of significance is 0.001 is rarely going to tarnish our reputation, but to have 10 vacuum tubes failing per week in a system involving 10,000 when we have predicted only 1 could be embarrassing.

It is probable that deviations from normality cause fewer gross errors than two other departures from the usual assumptions:

1. Lack of constancy of variance
2. Lack of independence

Some of the effects of (1) are explored in Section 9.7 and of (2) in Section 10.5.

In recent years techniques have been developed which make no assumption about the form of the underlying distribution except that it be continuous. These methods are known as *nonparametric* or *distribution-free* methods, neither name being particularly satisfactory. The observations certainly do have a distribution, with parameters: What we are free of is assumptions about the form of that distribution.

7.2. The Sign Test

Let the yields of two varieties A, B of tomatoes grown at a number n of randomly selected locations be x_i, y_i. Then (x, y) will have a joint probability density $p\{x, y\}$. If the yields of the two varieties are identical in the sense that the two varieties are interchangeable, then $p\{a, b\} = p\{b, a\}$ for all a, b (see Figure 7.1). This implies that $p\{x, y\}$ is symmetrical about the line $y - x = 0$. Now define $z = y - x$. Then

$$\Pr\{y < x\} = \Pr\{y > x\} = \frac{1}{2};$$

so

$$\Pr\{y - x < 0\} = \Pr\{y - x > 0\} = \frac{1}{2},$$

and

$$\Pr\{z < 0\} = \Pr\{z > 0\} = \frac{1}{2}. \tag{2.1}$$

Thus z will have a zero median. Actually, the model we have supposed is somewhat stronger in that it implies not only a zero median for z but also a symmetrical distribution; for the sign test, however, all that is required is that the median be zero.

Now define a variable

$$Z_i = 1 \quad \text{if } z_i > 0,$$
$$= 0 \quad \text{if } z_i < 0.$$

We assume continuity in the original joint distribution $p\{x, y\}$ so that the distribution of z is also continuous, and "ties," in which $x_i = y_i$, so that $z_i = 0$, should occur with zero probability. The Z_i are independent; so we are in the binomial situation of making n independent trials, the probability of a success, the occurrence of $Z_i = 1$, being 1/2 on each trial. Thus $\sum_i^n Z_i$ has a binomial distribution with parameters n, $\theta = 1/2$.

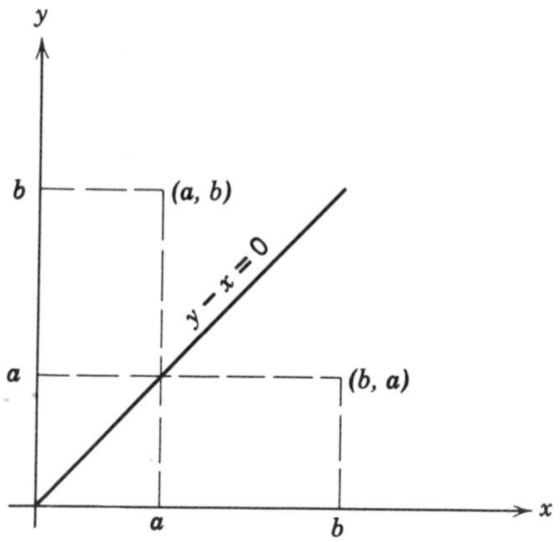

Figure 7.1

Actually, the joint distribution $p\{x, y\}$ can be different for each trial and we will still get $\Pr\{Z_i = 1\} = 1/2$, and so the distribution of $\sum_i^n Z_i$ will be unchanged.

The foregoing is under the null hypothesis. A reasonable alternative is that instead of x_i we have $x_i' = x_i - d_i$; i.e., each x_i is decreased by an amount d_i, $d_i > 0$. We then have the joint distribution $p\{x', y\}$ shifted leftward, and now

$$\Pr\{z_i > 0\} = \Pr\{y_i - x_i' > 0\} = \Pr\{y_i > x_i'\} > \frac{1}{2}.$$

Incidentally, in general $\Pr\{z_i > 0\}$, though greater than 1/2, is now not necessarily constant for different i, and so $\sum_i^n Z_i$ does not now necessarily have a binomial distribution. If under the alternative hypothesis $\sum_i^n Z_i$ will tend to have a value greater than the value expected under the null hypothesis, namely $n/2$, then an appropriate critical region will be the upper tail. Thus the sign test, when we have m positive differences in a sample of n, gives a P value of

$$\Pr\left\{\sum_i^n Z_i \geq m \middle| n, \theta = \frac{1}{2}\right\} = \sum_{x=m}^{n} \binom{n}{x} \left(\frac{1}{2}\right)^x \left(1 - \frac{1}{2}\right)^{n-x} = \frac{1}{2^n} \sum_{x=m}^{n} \binom{n}{x}$$

$$= \frac{1}{2^n} \sum_{x=0}^{n-m} \binom{n}{x}. \qquad (2.2)$$

In simple cases, for moderate n and m, this can be easily computed directly. For larger n and m we can use the normal approximation (3.3.5).

As an example of the use of the sign test, Table 7.1 gives the differences $(A - B)$ in potency of a series of lots of a pharmaceutical product as measured by two different methods A and B.

Table 7.1. Differences between Two Analytical Methods for 16 Lots

0.3,	6.3,	3.7,	2.8,	5.8,	−1.4,	1.7,	2.3,
−1.7,	1.6,	−1.8,	0.6,	4.5,	1.9,	2.4,	6.8.

The original observations were on each lot by each method: For the first lot the potencies were 89.7 and 89.4 by the methods A and B, but only the difference 0.3 is relevant. We have $Z_i = 1$ for 13 lots and 0 for 3 lots. Using (2.2),

$$\Pr\left\{\sum_i^n Z_i \geq 13 \middle| n = 16, \theta = \frac{1}{2}\right\} = \frac{1}{2^{16}} \sum_{x=0}^{16-13} \binom{16}{x}$$

$$= \frac{1}{65{,}536}\left[\frac{16!}{0!\,16!} + \frac{16!}{1!\,15!} + \frac{16!}{2!\,14!} + \frac{16!}{3!\,13!}\right] = 0.01064,$$

or, using (3.3.6),

$$u_{1-P} = \frac{13 - 1/2 - 16 \times 1/2}{\sqrt{16 \times (1/2)(1 - 1/2)}} = 2.25,$$

whence $1 - P = 0.9878$ and $P = 0.0122$.

The sign test assumes that the underlying distributions are continuous and hence the probability of a tie occurring, giving rise to a zero difference, is zero. However, in practice all continuous measurements are only recorded to a finite number of decimal places, and ties may occur. The best procedure when this happens is to delete the ties from all consideration. The tie is ignored in computing $\sum_{i}^{n} Z_i$, and the tie does not contribute to the sample size n either [2].

Our discussion so far has proceeded under the assumption that the null hypothesis was that the median of the differences $x_i - y_i = z_i$ was zero. If our null hypothesis is that the median of the z_i is ζ_0, then we can define a new variable $w_i = z_i - \zeta_0$ and make the foregoing sign test on the w_i.

This device immediately suggests a method of constructing $(1 - \alpha)$ confidence intervals for ζ. By trial and error we find that value for ζ, say $\underline{\zeta}$, which leads to rejection of the null hypothesis that $E[z] = \underline{\zeta}$ at the $\alpha/2$ level, and that value of ζ, say $\bar{\zeta}$, which leads to the rejection of the null hypothesis that $E[z] = \bar{\zeta}$ at the $\alpha/2$ level. We therefore put

$$\Pr\left\{\sum_{i}^{n} Z_i \geq r \middle| n, \theta = \frac{1}{2}\right\} = \frac{1}{2^n} \sum_{x=0}^{n-r} \binom{n}{x} \leq \frac{\alpha}{2},$$

and

$$\Pr\left\{\sum_{i}^{n} Z_i \leq s \middle| n, \theta = \frac{1}{2}\right\} = \frac{1}{2^n} \sum_{x=0}^{s} \binom{n}{x} \leq \frac{\alpha}{2},$$

and solve for r and s. Because of the discreteness of the binomial distribution we may not be able to approach very closely the desired value of $\alpha/2$. In the present example,

$$\Pr\left\{\sum_{i}^{n} Z_i \leq 4\right\} = 0.0384,$$

and

$$\Pr\left\{\sum_{i}^{n} Z_i \leq 3\right\} = 0.0106.$$

For 95 per cent confidence limits, we would want $\alpha/2 = 0.025$. To be conservative, we have to choose $s = 3$, which will give us $(1 - 2 \times 0.0106) \times 100 = 97.88$ per cent confidence. The choice of $s = 4$ would give us $(1 - 2 \times 0.0384) \times 100 = 92.32$ per cent confidence, which is far below our desired value of 95 per cent. From the symmetry of the binomial distribution with $\theta = 1/2$, $r = n - s = 16 - 3 = 13$. We now order the sample as in the first column of Table 7.2. We then select the minimum value of ζ, $\underline{\zeta}$, which gives $\sum Z_i = 13$, and the maximum value of ζ, $\bar{\zeta}$, which gives $\sum Z_i = 3$. Choosing $\underline{\zeta} = 0.2$, $\bar{\zeta} = 4.6$ gives the results in the second and third columns of Table 7.2. We could actually choose $\underline{\zeta}$ as large as 0.2999 and still have only three negative signs for $(z - \underline{\zeta})$, and $\bar{\zeta}$ as small as 4.50001 and still only have three positive signs for $(z - \bar{\zeta})$. Thus the

97.88 per cent confidence limits are roughly (0.29, 4.51), or more accurately just under 0.3 and just over 4.5. In practice, of course, we just order the sample and count in from the bottom end to the $(s + 1)$th observation and down from the top end likewise.

Table 7.2

z	$z - 0.2$	$z - 4.6$
−1.8	−2.0	−6.4
−1.7	−1.9	−6.3
−1.4	−1.6	−6.0
0.3	0.1	−4.3
0.6	0.4	−4.0
1.6	1.4	−3.0
1.7	1.5	−2.9
1.9	1.7	−2.7
2.3	2.1	−2.3
2.4	2.2	−2.2
2.8	2.6	−1.8
3.7	3.6	−0.9
4.5	4.3	−0.1
5.8	5.6	1.2
6.3	6.2	1.7
6.8	6.7	2.2

7.3. The Median Test

The sign test discussed in the previous section is appropriate when we have equal numbers of observations from the two distributions and natural pairing is present. In the median test we have samples of n_1 observations x_i from a distribution $p_1\{x\}$ and n_2 observations y_j from a distribution $p_2\{y\}$ and there is no natural pairing. We arrange the observations in a common sequence of increasing magnitude:

$$x_1, x_2, y_1, y_2, y_3, x_3, x_4, x_5, x_6, y_4, \ldots$$

Let the numbers of x's above and below the median of the common sequence be n_{1a} and n_{1b} and the numbers of y's above and below the same common sample median be n_{2a} and n_{2b}. Under the null hypothesis that the two samples come from identical distributions the proportion of each sample lying below any point should be the same.

We can compare the proportions below the joint sample median with Fisher's exact test. We have two samples of sizes n_1 and n_2 and a total of $(n_{1b} + n_{2b})$ observations classified as below the median (Table 7.3). The P value for the observed distribution can be calculated by the methods outlined in Section 3.9. For large samples we can use the normal approximation of Section 3.8.

Table 7.3

	Below median	Above median	Totals
Sample 1	n_{1b}	n_{1a}	n_1
Sample 2	n_{2b}	n_{2a}	n_2
Totals	$n_{1b} + n_{2b}$	$n_{1a} + n_{2a}$	$n_1 + n_2$

Table 7.4

A	32, 34, 35, 37, 42, 43, 47, 58, 59, 62, 69, 71, 78, 84	$n_1 = 14$
B	39, 48, 54, 65, 70, 76, 87, 90, 111, 118, 126, 127	$n_2 = 12$

Table 7.5

	Below median	Above median	Totals
Brand A	10	4	14
Brand B	3	9	12
Totals	13	13	26

If $(n_1 + n_2)$ is odd, then the median of the joint sample will be actually one of the observations: Suppose that it occurs in the first sample. This observation, since it lies on the joint sample median, contributes no information on the question of whether the distribution of the first sample has its median above or below the joint sample median. It appears reasonable, therefore, to delete this observation from all consideration, excluding it also from the sample total.

As an example of the application of the median test, Table 7.4 gives the lives in thousands of hours of samples of electron tubes of two brands A and B. Incidentally, survival time data are typically skewed with a long tail to the right, and usually quite appreciably nonnormal; so a test assuming normality would be inappropriate.

The median in Table 7.4 falls between 62 and 65, and so we have Table 7.5. By Fisher's exact test the two-tailed P value is 0.0472: The normal approximation, which we can consider reliable since the minimum expectation in any cell is 6, gives $P = 0.0449$.

7.4. The Mean and Variance of a Sample from a Finite Population

In the section to follow this, on the Wilcoxon two-sample rank test, and in Section 13.9 on the finite-population model in the analysis of variance, we need the mean and variance of a sample of size n from a finite population of N elements, the elements having attached to them numbers $x_1, x_2, \ldots, x_N$. We wish to express them in terms of the mean and variance of the population, which we define as

$$\xi = E[x] = \sum_i^N x_i p\{x_i\} = \frac{1}{N}\sum_i^N x_i\,, \tag{4.1}$$

since, for a finite population of size N, $p\{x_i\} = 1/N$, and

$$\begin{aligned}\sigma^2 = V[x] = E[x^2] - (E[x])^2 &= \sum_i^N x_i^2 p\{x_i\} - (E[x])^2 \\ = \frac{1}{N}(x_1^2 + \cdots + x_N^2) &- \left[\frac{1}{N}(x_1 + \cdots + x_N)\right]^2.\end{aligned} \tag{4.2}$$

This can be written in the form

$$\sigma^2 = (x_1^2 + \cdots + x_N^2)\left(\frac{1}{N} - \frac{1}{N^2}\right) - (x_1x_2 + x_1x_3 + \cdots + x_{N-1}x_N)\left(\frac{2}{N^2}\right). \tag{4.3}$$

The set of all possible samples of size n from the population will include

$$\begin{gathered}(x_1, x_2, \ldots, x_{n-1}, x_n) \\ (x_1, x_2, \ldots, x_{n-1}, x_{n+1}) \\ \vdots \\ (x_{N-n+1}, x_{N-n+2}, \ldots, x_N)\end{gathered} \tag{4.4}$$

These samples are formed by picking n elements at a time from N; by (1.7.6) there are $\binom{N}{n}$ ways of picking such a sample. It is axiomatic that every possible sample is equally likely, and so the probability of any particular sample being picked is $1/\binom{N}{n}$.

Suppose that the samples in (4.4) have means $\bar{x}_j$, $j = 1, 2, \ldots, \binom{N}{n}$. The expected value of $\bar{x}$ is

$$E[\bar{x}] = \sum_j^{\binom{N}{n}} \bar{x}_j p\{\bar{x}_j\} = \frac{1}{\binom{N}{n}} \sum_j^{\binom{N}{n}} \bar{x}_j$$

$$= \frac{1}{\binom{N}{n}} \left[\frac{1}{n}(x_1 + x_2 + \cdots + x_n) + \cdots + \frac{1}{n}(x_{N-n+1} + \cdots + x_N)\right]. \tag{4.5}$$

Now consider the number of times any particular x_i, say x_1, will occur in (4.5). The samples containing x_1 are made up by selecting $(n - 1)$ other elements from the available population of $(N - 1)$ elements, and this can be done in $\binom{N-1}{n-1}$ ways. There will therefore be $\binom{N-1}{n-1}$ samples containing x_1. In other words, x_1 occurs $\binom{N-1}{n-1}$ times in (4.5). The same will apply to every other x_i. Thus

$$E[\bar{x}] = \frac{1}{\binom{N}{n}} \left[\frac{1}{n}\binom{N-1}{n-1} \sum_i^N x_i\right] = \frac{1}{N} \sum_i^N x_i = \xi \tag{4.6}$$

by (4.1). The expected value of the sample mean is thus the population mean.

The variance of $\bar{x}$ is

$$V[\bar{x}] = E[\bar{x}^2] - (E[\bar{x}])^2. \tag{4.7}$$

We have already found $E[\bar{x}]$. Now consider $E[\bar{x}^2]$:

$$E[\bar{x}^2] = \sum_j^{\binom{N}{n}} \bar{x}_j^2 p\{\bar{x}_j\} = \frac{1}{\binom{N}{n}} \sum_j^{\binom{N}{n}} \bar{x}_j^2 . \tag{4.8}$$

But

$$\sum_j^{\binom{N}{n}} \bar{x}_j^2 = \left[\frac{1}{n}(x_1 + x_2 + \cdots + x_n)\right]^2 + \cdots + \left[\frac{1}{n}(x_{N-n+1} + \cdots + x_N)\right]^2. \tag{4.9}$$

When we square each term, each x_i will give rise to an x_i^2, and we have already seen that in the similar expression (4.5) each x_i occurs $\binom{N-1}{n-1}$ times; so the squared part of (4.9) is

$$\frac{1}{n^2}\binom{N-1}{n-1}\left(x_1^2 + \cdots + x_N^2\right).$$

The expression (4.9) will also give rise to product terms $x_i x_j$. Any particular x_i and x_j will occur together in a given sequence in $\binom{N-2}{n-2}$ of the samples; so the product part of (4.9) is

$$\frac{2}{n^2}\binom{N-2}{n-2}(x_1x_2 + x_1x_3 + \cdots + x_{N-1}x_N),$$

the factor 2 arising from the fact that $x_i x_j = x_j x_i$. Substituting these back into (4.8) gives

$$E[\bar{x}^2] = \frac{1}{\binom{N}{n}}\left[\frac{1}{n^2}\binom{N-1}{n-1}(x_1^2 + \cdots + x_N^2) + \frac{2}{n^2}\binom{N-2}{n-2}(x_1x_2 + \cdots + x_{N-1}x_N)\right]. \tag{4.10}$$

We thus have $E[\bar{x}^2]$ ready for substitution into (4.7) to give $V[\bar{x}]$. Equation (4.7) also requires $(E[\bar{x}])^2$. In (4.6) we found $E[\bar{x}]$) to be $\frac{1}{N}\sum_i^N x_i$; so

$$(E[\bar{x}])^2 = \frac{(x_1 + \cdots + x_N)^2}{N^2} = \frac{x_1^2 + \cdots + x_N^2}{N^2} + \frac{2(x_1x_2 + \cdots + x_{N-1}x_N)}{N^2}. \tag{4.11}$$

Substituting (4.10) and (4.11) in (4.7), we get

$$V[\bar{x}] = \left[\frac{1}{\binom{N}{n}}\frac{1}{n^2}\binom{N-1}{n-1} - \frac{1}{N^2}\right](x_1^2 + \cdots + x_N^2) + \left[\frac{1}{\binom{N}{n}}\frac{2}{n^2}\binom{N-2}{n-2} - \frac{2}{N^2}\right](x_1x_2 + \cdots + x_{N-1}x_N). \tag{4.12}$$

The coefficient of $(x_1^2 + \cdots + x_N^2)$ can be written as

$$\frac{\binom{N-1}{n-1}}{n^2\binom{N}{n}} - \frac{1}{N^2} = \frac{1}{n^2}\frac{(N-1)!}{(n-1)!(N-n)!}\frac{n!(N-n)!}{N!} - \frac{1}{N^2} = \frac{1}{nN} - \frac{1}{N^2}$$

$$= \frac{N-n}{N^2 n} = \frac{N-1}{N^2}\frac{N-n}{n(N-1)} = \left(\frac{1}{N} - \frac{1}{N^2}\right)\frac{N-n}{n(N-1)}, \tag{4.13}$$

and the coefficient of $(x_1 x_2 + \cdots + x_{N-1} x_N)^2$ is

$$\frac{2\binom{N-2}{n-2}}{n^2\binom{N}{n}} - \frac{2}{N^2} = \frac{2}{n^2}\frac{(N-2)!}{(n-2)!(N-n)!}\frac{n!(N-n)!}{N!} - \frac{2}{N^2}$$

$$= \frac{2(n-1)}{nN(N-1)} - \frac{2}{N^2} = -\frac{2\ (N-n)}{N^2 n(N-1)}. \tag{4.14}$$

Then, inserting these results in (4.12), we get

$$V[\bar{x}] = \frac{(N-n)}{n(N-1)}\left\{\left(\frac{1}{N} - \frac{1}{N^2}\right)(x_1^2 + \cdots + x_N^2) - \frac{2}{N^2}(x_1 x_2 + \cdots + x_{N-1}x_N)\right\}. \tag{4.15}$$

The part in { } is identical with the expression for σ^2, (4.3), so

$$V[\bar{x}] = \frac{\sigma^2}{n}\frac{N-n}{N-1} \tag{4.16}$$

$$= \frac{\sigma^2}{n}\left(1 - \frac{n-1}{N-1}\right). \tag{4.17}$$

Clearly, if N tends to infinity, then $V[\bar{x}]$ tends to σ^2/n, its customary form for an infinite population.

7.5. The Wilcoxon Two-Sample Rank Test

The Wilcoxon two-sample rank test [3] is a test of the null hypothesis that two populations are identical, against the alternative hypothesis that they differ by a linear translation. We substitute ranks for the actual observations. As an example, Table 7.6 lists five determinations of the atomic weight of carbon from one preparation and four determinations from another preparation [5]. Ranks are allocated to the observations in order of increasing magnitude without regard to the division into two samples.

Suppose that one sample is of size n and the other of size $(N - n)$. The test assumes that any combination of the ranks into these two groups is equally likely. The total number of ways of grouping the ranks, given N and n, is the number of ways of picking n elements out of N, $\binom{N}{n}$. The test then counts how many of the possible combinations give a rank sum as extreme as or more extreme than that observed.

Table 7.6

Preparation A		Preparation B	
Determination	Rank	Determination	Rank
12.0072	8	11.9853	1
12.0064	7	11.9949	2
12.0054	5	11.9985	3
12.0016	4	12.0061	6
12.0077	9		

In Table 7.6, regarding the observations from preparation B as the sample of size n, the rank sum is $1 + 2 + 3 + 6 = 12$. The only ways we could get a rank sum as small as or smaller than this, given $n = 4$, are

$$1 + 2 + 3 + 4 = 10, \quad 1 + 2 + 3 + 5 = 11,$$
$$1 + 2 + 3 + 6 = 12, \quad 1 + 2 + 4 + 5 = 12.$$

For example, $1 + 3 + 4 + 5 = 13$ is greater than our observed rank sum 12. The P value is equal to the ratio of the number of ways we can form a rank sum as extreme as or more extreme than that observed, namely, 4 ways, to the total possible number of ways of forming sums of $n = 4$ ranks, namely, $\binom{N}{n} = \binom{9}{4} = 126$ ways. Thus $P = 4/126 = 0.0317$ for a one-sided test. The rationale of this procedure is that, if one distribution is displaced relative to the other, the low ranks will tend to fall in one sample and the high ranks in the other sample, and so the rank sums will be relatively low or high.

In the case of small N and n, it is relatively easy to compute the P value directly as in the above example. For large samples, an approximate test is available based on the fact that the mean of the ranks of a sample is distributed around its expected value approximately normally with a variance to be calculated below.

Let R be the rank sum and $\bar{R}$ the mean of the ranks of the sample of size n. By (4.6), the expected value for $\bar{R}$ is $E[\bar{R}] = \frac{1}{N}\sum_i^N x_i$ where the x_i are the elements of the finite population, here the integers 1 to N. The sum of the first N integers is

$$1 + 2 + \cdots + N = \frac{N(N+1)}{2}, \tag{5.1}$$

and also the sum of their squares is

$$1^2 + 2^2 + \cdots + N^2 = \frac{N(N+1)(2N+1)}{6}. \tag{5.2}$$

Using (5.1),

$$E[\bar{R}] = \frac{N+1}{2}. \tag{5.3}$$

The variance of $\bar{R}$, $V[\bar{R}]$, will be given by (4.16) where σ^2 is given by substituting (5.1) and (5.2) in (4.2):

$$\sigma^2 = \frac{1}{N} \cdot \frac{N(N+1)(2N+1)}{6} - \left[\frac{1}{N} \cdot \frac{N(N+1)}{2}\right]^2 = \frac{N^2-1}{12}. \tag{5.4}$$

Thus, substituting this in (4.16),

$$V[\bar{R}] = \frac{(N^2-1)/12}{n} \frac{N-n}{N-1} = \frac{(N+1)(N-n)}{12n}. \tag{5.5}$$

We then have

$$\frac{\bar{R} - E[\bar{R}]}{\sqrt{V[\bar{R}]}} = \frac{\bar{R} - (N+1)/2}{\sqrt{(N+1)(N-n)/12n}} \tag{5.6}$$

$$= \frac{2R - n(N+1)}{\sqrt{n(N+1)(N-n)/3}} \tag{5.7}$$

asymptotically a unit normal deviate. Kruskal and Wallis [6] have observed that the approximation is improved when the one-sided P value is found to be greater than 0.02 by introducing a correction for continuity by bringing $\bar{R}$ closer to its expectation by $1/2n$, or $2R$ closer to its expectation by 1. If the one-sided P value is less than 0.02, this correction for continuity should be omitted.

In the example in Table 7.6, if we consider the results with preparation B as the sample of size n, then $n = 4$, $N = 9$, $R = 12$, $\bar{R} = 12/4 = 3$, and (5.6) is

$$u_P = \frac{3 - (9+1)/2}{\sqrt{(9+1)(9-4)/12 \times 4}} = -1.96;$$

so $P = 0.025$. This implies that we should use the continuity correction:

$$u_P = \frac{3 + (1/2 \times 4) - (9 + 1)/2}{\sqrt{(9 + 1)(9 - 4)/12 \times 4}} = -1.837;$$

so the one-sided $P = 0.033$. Even though N and n are small in this example, the normal approximation gives a P value close to the exact value, 0.0317, calculated earlier.

7.6. The Adjustment for Ties in the Wilcoxon Two-Sample Rank Test

If ties occur, so that two, or more, of the observations are identical, the best procedure is to allocate to these tied observations the mean of the ranks they would receive if they were not tied. Table 7.7 gives two series

Table 7.7

A		*B*	
Determination	Rank	Determination	Rank
95.6	$9\frac{1}{2}$	93.3	4
94.9	7	92.1	3
96.2	12	94.7	$5\frac{1}{2}$
95.1	8	90.1	2
95.8	11	95.6	$9\frac{1}{2}$
96.3	13	90.0	1
		94.7	$5\frac{1}{2}$

of determinations of the conversion efficiency of an ammonia oxidation plant for the production of nitric acid. If we allocate ranks to the observations in increasing order of magnitude, 90.0, 90.1, 92.1, and 93.3 receive ranks 1, 2, 3, and 4, respectively. We then encounter two observations at 94.7; these receive the ranks 5 and 6, so that the mean rank $5\frac{1}{2}$ is allocated to each of them. Later on, two observations at 95.6 both receive ranks $(9 + 10)/2 = 9\frac{1}{2}$. The effect of this procedure is to leave the sum of the ranks used unchanged, and so $E[\bar{R}]$ (5.3) is unchanged. The variance is somewhat affected, however.

The variance of the ranks, see (4.2), is formed from $E[x^2]$ and $(E[x])^2$. The latter involves the sum of the ranks, which is unchanged, and hence is unaltered. The former is the sum of the squares of the ranks, divided by N; this is affected by the substitution of mean ranks for individual ranks.

Consider one group of t ties. The integers $(x+1), (x+2), \ldots, (x+t)$ are replaced by their mean

$$\frac{(x+1)+(x+2)+\cdots+(x+t)}{t} = \frac{xt + t(t+1)/2}{t} = x + \frac{t+1}{2}.$$

The sum of squares $(x_1^2 + \cdots + x_N^2)$ in (4.2) is thus reduced by

$$(x+1)^2 + \cdots + (x+t)^2 - t\left(x + \frac{t+1}{2}\right)^2$$

which, after some simplification, can be written as

$$\frac{(t-1)\,t(t+1)}{12} = \frac{T}{12},$$

if we define $T = (t-1)\,t(t+1)$. The variance of the ranks is now no longer given by (5.4). Now the sum of squares of the ranks is

$$\frac{N(N+1)(2N+1)}{6} - \frac{T}{12}$$

and this is substituted for $(x_1^2 + \cdots + x_N^2)$ in the formula for σ^2 (4.2). The sum of the ranks is unchanged at $N(N+1)/2$, and this is substituted for $(x_1 + \cdots + x_N)$: Thus

$$\sigma^2 = \frac{1}{N}\left[\frac{N(N+1)(2N+1)}{6} - \frac{T}{12}\right] - \left[\frac{1}{N}\,\frac{N(N+1)}{2}\right]^2$$

$$= \frac{1}{12N}\left[N(N^2-1) - T\right]. \tag{6.1}$$

Using (4.16), the variance of $\bar{R}$ is

$$V[\bar{R}] = \frac{N(N^2-1) - T}{12Nn} \cdot \frac{N-n}{N-1}. \tag{6.2}$$

The term $T = (t-1)\,t(t+1)$ occurs for each group of ties, if there is more than one such group. In the example in Table 7.6, there are two groups of two ties; so the correction term $\sum_j T_j$ is

$$\sum_j T_j = (2-1)\cdot 2\cdot(2+1) + (2-1)\cdot 2\cdot(2+1) = 12.$$

Then $$V[\bar{R}] = \frac{13(13^2-1) - 12}{12 \times 13 \times 6} \cdot \frac{13-6}{13-1} = 1.3536,$$

and $$\bar{R} = \frac{9\tfrac{1}{2} + 7 + \cdots + 13}{6} = 10.083;$$

so we have an approximate unit normal deviate

$$u_{1-P} = \frac{10.083 - (13 + 1)/2}{\sqrt{1.3536}} = 2.650,$$

giving a one-sided P value of 0.0040. Since this is less than 0.02, we omit the correction for continuity.

We can find the level of significance by a direct enumeration as we did in the example without ties in Section 7.5. In Table 7.7 the rank sum for the smaller sample A is $60\frac{1}{2}$. The various ways in which a rank sum of $60\frac{1}{2}$ or greater can be formed from the ranks listed in Table 7.7 are given in Table 7.8, where tied ranks are distinguished from each other by the letters a and b.

Table 7.8. Ways in Which Six Ranks Can Be Selected from the Ranks of Table 7.7 Subject to Condition That Their Sum Is Greater than or Equal to $60\frac{1}{2}$

	13	13	13	13	13	13
	12	12	12	12	12	12
	11	11	11	11	11	11
	$9\frac{1}{2}a$	$9\frac{1}{2}a$	$9\frac{1}{2}a$	$9\frac{1}{2}a$	$9\frac{1}{2}a$	$9\frac{1}{2}b$
	$9\frac{1}{2}b$	$9\frac{1}{2}b$	$9\frac{1}{2}b$	$9\frac{1}{2}b$	8	8
	8	7	$5\frac{1}{2}a$	$5\frac{1}{2}b$	7	7
Rank sum	63	62	$60\frac{1}{2}$	$60\frac{1}{2}$	$60\frac{1}{2}$	$60\frac{1}{2}$

The total number of ways 6 ranks can be selected from 13 is $\binom{13}{6} = 1716$. The one-sided P value is thus $6/1716 = 0.00350$. The normal approximation, which gave $P = 0.0040$, is thus reasonably close in this instance.

7.7. The H Test

The H test, due to Kruskal and Wallis [6], is a generalization of the two-sample Wilcoxon test to the case of k samples, $k > 2$. As in the Wilcoxon test, the entire set of observations, here in k groups of size n_i rather than two groups as in the Wilcoxon test, are ranked, and mean ranks $\bar{R}_i$ are calculated for each group. $\bar{R}_i$ has an expectation $(N + 1)/2$ (5.3), and a variance $(N + 1)(N - n_i)/12n_i$ (5.5). The ratio $\{\bar{R}_i - E[\bar{R}_i]\}/\sqrt{V[\bar{R}_i]}$ will be a standardized variable approximately normal. Kruskal and Wallis showed that the sum of their squares, with a weighting factor $(1 - n_i/N)$, which they denoted by H, has approximately a $\chi^2(k-1)$ distribution; i.e.

$$H = \sum_i^k \frac{[\bar{R}_i - (N+1)/2]^2}{(N+1)(N-n_i)/12n_i} \cdot \left(1 - \frac{n_i}{N}\right) \underset{\text{approx}}{\sim} \chi^2(k-1).$$

Two identical forms for H, more convenient for calculation, are

$$H = \frac{N-1}{N} \sum_i^k \frac{[\bar{R}_i - (N+1)/2]^2}{(N^2-1)/12n_i} \tag{7.1}$$

$$= \frac{12}{N(N+1)} \sum_i^k \left(\frac{R_i^2}{n_i}\right) - 3(N+1). \tag{7.2}$$

If ties occur, H should be divided by the factor

$$1 - \frac{\sum T}{N^3 - N} \tag{7.3}$$

where $T = (t-1)\,t(t+1)$ is calculated and included in the sum for each group of ties. While H is distributed asymptotically as $\chi^2(k-1)$ for large k and n_i, in small samples the approximation is not very good, and Kruskal and Wallis [6] provided tables of the exact distribution for the case of $k = 3$, $n_i \leq 5$. For intermediate cases they proposed approximations based on the incomplete gamma and incomplete beta distributions, for details of which see their paper. Wallace [7] has discussed several approximations, and Box [8] suggested an approximation based on the F distribution.

As an example of the application of the H test, Table 7.9 gives the terminal digits of observations on six days on the mechanical equivalent of heat [9]. The first observation was 4.1849, but only the last two digits are given in Table 7.9. There are several groups of ties, the first being three observations at 27 which receive the mean rank $(4 + 5 + 6)/3 = 5$. Substituting in (7.2),

$$H = \frac{12}{23(23+1)}\left(\frac{(54\frac{1}{2})^2}{3} + \frac{(55)^2}{4} + \cdots\right) - 3 \times (23+1) = 8.753.$$

However, we need the correction for ties, there being two groups of three tied ranks and three groups of two tied ranks. For each of the triplets the correction $(t-1)t\,(t+1)$ is $(3-1)\cdot 3 \cdot (3+1) = 24$, and for each of the doublets the correction is $(2-1)\cdot 2 \cdot (2+1) = 6$. The correction factor (7.3) is

$$1 - \frac{24 \times 2 + 6 \times 3}{23^2 - 23} = 0.99457;$$

so the corrected H is $8.753/0.99457 = 8.801$ with $6 - 1 = 5$ degrees of freedom. The 0.90 point of $\chi^2(5)$ is 9.24, and so the null hypothesis is acceptable at the 0.10 level.

Table 7.9

	Day 1		Day 2		Day 3		Day 4		Day 5		Day 6	
	Obs.	Rank	Obs.	Rank	Obs.	Rank	Obs.	Rank	Obs.	Rank	Obs.	Rank
	49	18	42	12½	46	17	11	1	38	8	24	3
	52	21½	43	15	52	21½	27	5	50	19	40	9
	43	15	42	12½	27	5	71	23	41	10½	27	5
			43	15	51	20	23	2	41	10½	37	7
n_i	3		4		4		4		4		4	
R_i		54½		55		63½		31		48		24

We can apply the H test in the case where there are only two samples, so that $k = 2$. The H statistic (7.1) will then have approximately the χ^2 distribution with $2 - 1 = 1$ degree of freedom. In Section 5.1 we saw that $\chi^2(n)$ was defined as $\sum_i^n u_i^2$; so $\chi^2(1)$ is just the square of a single unit normal deviate. We shall see in Section 9.3 that specifically $\chi^2_{1-\alpha}(1) = u^2_{1-\alpha/2}$. It is easy to show that the H statistic in the case of $k = 2$ is identically equal to the square of the Wilcoxon statistic (5.7). In other words, the H test for the case of $k = 2$ is identical with the two-sample Wilcoxon test.

7.8. The Wilcoxon Paired-Sample Rank Test

Wilcoxon [3] proposed a test for paired observations in which we give ranks to the absolute magnitude of the differences and then give the ranks the signs of the corresponding differences. Our test statistic is the sum of the ranks of either sign. Essentially the test is of the null hypothesis that the distribution of the differences is symmetric about zero, so any rank is equally likely to be positive or negative.

Table 7.10 reproduces the data of Table 7.1 on the difference in potency for 16 lots of a pharmaceutical product reported by two methods of analysis, here with ranks attached to the absolute magnitude of the differences. Table 7.10 includes the complication of two differences 1.7 and -1.7

tieing in absolute magnitude. As in the unpaired Wilcoxon test, such ties receive the mean of the ranks necessary for the group of ties, here $\frac{1}{2}(5 + 6) = 5\frac{1}{2}$. The test statistic is the sum of the ranks of either sign, $15\frac{1}{2}$ for the negative ranks or $120\frac{1}{2}$ for the positive ranks, and the P value is the probability of getting a rank sum equal to or more extreme than the observed value.

Table 7.10

Difference	0.3	6.3	3.7	2.8	5.8	−1.4	1.7	2.3	−1.7	1.6	−1.8	0.6	4.5	1.9	2.4	6.8
Rank	1	15	12	11	14	−3	$5\frac{1}{2}$	9	$-5\frac{1}{2}$	4	−7	2	13	8	10	16

Under the null hypothesis any rank is equally likely to be positive or negative. The total number of ways rank sums can be produced is thus 2^N, 2^{16} in the case of Table 7.10. In moderate situations it is possible to enumerate all the rank sums less than or equal to the observed rank sum. Here the observed negative rank sum is $3 + 5\frac{1}{2} + 7 = 15\frac{1}{2}$. We proceed to write down all ways in which we can form rank sums less than or equal to $15\frac{1}{2}$. Starting with $0, 1, \ldots, 15$; continuing with $(1 + 2), \ldots, (1 + 14)$, $(2 + 3), \ldots, (2 + 13)$; continuing on up to $(7 + 8)$; then counting triplets such as $(1 + 2 + 3)$, quadruplets such as $(1 + 2 + 3 + 4)$, and the quintuplets $(1 + 2 + 3 + 4 + 5\frac{1}{2}a)$ and $(1 + 2 + 3 + 4 + 5\frac{1}{2}b)$; there are a total of 140 combinations of ranks with sums $\leq 15\frac{1}{2}$. The one-sided P value is thus $140/2^{16} = 0.00214$.

Obviously direct enumeration can be excessively slow and tedious, and a normal approximation is useful. Consider the ranks i, $i = 1, 2, \ldots, N$. Construct subsidiary variables $d_1, d_2, \ldots, d_N$, where d_i is attached to the ith rank. These variables d_i take the values 0 when a rank is negative and 1 when a rank is positive, under the null hypothesis each with probability 1/2. The sum of the positive ranks, say S, is $\sum_i^N d_i i$. Its expectation under the null hypothesis is

$$E[S] = E\left[\sum_i^N d_i i\right] = \sum_i^N i\, E[d_i].$$

Now, for each i, d takes the value 1 with probability 1/2 and the value 0 with probability 1/2; so

$$E[d_i] = 1 \times \left(\frac{1}{2}\right) + 0 \times \left(\frac{1}{2}\right) = \left(\frac{1}{2}\right),$$

and therefore

$$E[S] = \frac{1}{2}\sum_{i}^{N} i = \frac{1}{2}\cdot\frac{1}{2}N(N+1). \tag{8.1}$$

To obtain the variance of S we need

$$E[S^2] = E\left[\left(\sum_{i}^{N} d_i i\right)^2\right] = E\left[\sum_{i}^{N}\sum_{j}^{N} d_i i\, d_j j\right] = \sum_{i}^{N}\sum_{j}^{N} ij\, E[d_i d_j]. \tag{8.2}$$

This can be evaluated in two parts. The contribution to the sum when $i = j$ involves $E[d_i^2]$ which is

$$E[d_i^2] = 1^2 \times \frac{1}{2} + 0^2 \times \frac{1}{2} = \frac{1}{2};$$

so

$$\sum_{\substack{i \\ i=j}}^{N}\sum_{j}^{N} ij\, E[d_i\, d_j] = \sum_{i}^{N} i^2 \cdot \frac{1}{2} = \frac{1}{2}\sum_{i}^{N} i^2.$$

The contribution to the sum when $i \neq j$ involves $E[d_i d_j]$, $i \neq j$, which is

$$\underset{i\neq j}{E}[d_i d_j] = 0 \times 0 \times \frac{1}{4} + 0 \times 1 \times \frac{1}{4} + 1 \times 0 \times \frac{1}{4} + 1 \times 1 \times \frac{1}{4} = \frac{1}{4};$$

$$\sum_{\substack{i \\ i\neq j}}^{N}\sum_{j}^{N} ij\, E[d_i d_j] = \frac{1}{4}\sum_{\substack{i \\ i\neq j}}^{N}\sum_{j}^{N} ij.$$

Thus, substituting in (8.2),

$$E[S^2] = \frac{1}{2}\sum_{i}^{N} i^2 + \frac{1}{4}\sum_{\substack{i \\ i\neq j}}^{N}\sum_{j}^{N} ij = \frac{1}{2}\sum_{i}^{N} i^2 + \frac{1}{4}\left[\left(\sum_{i}^{N} i\right)^2 - \sum_{i}^{N}(i^2)\right]$$

$$= \frac{1}{4}\sum_{i}^{N} i^2 + \frac{1}{4}\left(\sum_{i}^{N} i\right)^2. \tag{8.3}$$

The variance of S is

$$V[S] = E[S^2] - (E[S])^2 = \frac{1}{4}\sum_{i}^{N} i^2 + \frac{1}{4}\left(\sum_{i}^{N} i\right)^2 - \left(\frac{1}{2}\sum_{i}^{N} i\right)^2 = \frac{1}{4}\sum_{i}^{N} i^2$$

$$= \frac{N(N+1)(2N+1)}{24}. \tag{8.4}$$

In the event that ties are present, $(t-1)\,t(t+1)/48$ must be subtracted from (8.4) for each group of ties.

For the data of Table 7.10, the sum of the positive ranks $S = 120\frac{1}{2}$, and there is one pair of ties; so

$$E[S] = \frac{N(N+1)}{4} = 16 \times \frac{16+1}{4} = 68,$$

$$\begin{aligned} V[S] &= \frac{N(N+1)(2N+1)}{24} - \frac{(t-1)\,t(t+1)}{48}, \\ &= \frac{16 \times (16+1)(2 \times 16+1)}{24} - \frac{(2-1) \times 2 \times (2+1)}{48} \\ &= 374 - 0.125 = 373.875, \end{aligned}$$

$$u_{1-P} = \frac{S - E[S]}{\sqrt{V[S]}} = \frac{120.5 - 68}{\sqrt{373.875}} = 2.715,$$

whence $P = 0.0033$, to be compared with the exact figure 0.0021 previously obtained. While nothing generally appears to be known about the use of a continuity correction with this approximation, its use does not seem to be indicated.

We have indicated how to handle ties in the absolute values of the ranks. However, if the observations are differences between paired samples, some samples may be tied in one or more pairs, giving rise to differences which are zero. It is not clear how these zeros should be handled. One procedure will be to ignore their existence completely, i.e., to delete them from the sample.

7.9. The Literature of Nonparametric Tests

The literature of nonparametric tests has grown very rapidly: A comprehensive survey up to 1953 by Richard Savage [10] contains 49 pages of references. The analog of the H test when there is cross classification and one observation per cell was developed by Friedman [11] and also by Kendall [12] under the designation the coefficient of concordance. A test for association in a two-dimensional graph was given by Olmstead and Tukey [13]. A careful development of the Wilcoxon unpaired two-sample test was given by Mann and Whitney [14]. Apart from that, the history of this test is a comedy of duplication: Kruskal [15] records at least four repetitious "discoveries" of it subsequent to Wilcoxon, and traces its first, though long neglected, appearance to a German psychometricist, Deuchler, in 1914.

A general textbook on ranking methods is by Kendall [12]. An advanced general textbook is by Fraser [16].

REFERENCES

1. Cramér, H., *Mathematical Methods of Statistics.* Princeton: University Press, 1951.
2. Putter, J., "The treatment of ties in some nonparametric tests," *Annals of Mathematical Statistics*, 26(1955), 368–386.
3. Wilcoxon, F., "Individual comparisons by ranking methods," *Biometrics Bulletin*, 1(1947), 80–83.
4. ——— "Probability tables for individual comparisons by ranking methods," *Biometrics*, 3(1947), 119–122.
5. Dean, G., "The atomic weight of carbon and silver," *Journal of the Chemical Society of London*, 125(1924), 2656–2672.
6. Kruskal, W. H., and W. Allen Wallis, "Use of ranks in one-criterion analysis of variance," *Journal of the American Statistical Association*, 47(1952), 583–621.
7. Wallace, D. L., "Simplified beta-approximations to the Kruskal–Wallis *H* test." *Journal of the American Statistical Association*, 54(1959), 225–230.
8. Box, G. E. P., and S. L. Andersen, "Permutation theory in the derivation of robust criteria and the study of departure from assumption," *Journal of the Royal Statistical Society*, B (methodological), 17(1955), 1–26.
9. Laby, T. H., and E. O. Hercus, "The mechanical equivalent of heat," *Philosophical Transactions of the Royal Society*, A, 227(1928), 63–91.
10. Savage, I. R., "Bibliography of nonparametric statistics and related topics," *Journal of the American Statistical Association*, 48(1953), 844–906.
11. Friedman, M., "The use of ranks to avoid the assumption of normality in the analysis of variance," *Journal of the American Statistical Association*, 32(1937), 675–701.
12. Kendall, M. G., *Rank Correlation Methods.* 2nd ed.; London: Griffin & Co., 1955.
13. Olmstead, P. S., and J. W. Tukey, "A corner test for association," *Annals of Mathematical Statistics*, 18(1939), 495–513.
14. Mann, H. B., and D. R. Whitney, "On a test of whether one of two random variables is stochastically larger than the other," *Annals of Mathematical Statistics*, 18(1947), 50–60.
15. Kruskal, W. H., "Historical notes on the Wilcoxon unpaired two-sample test," *Journal of the American Statistical Association*, 52(1957), 356–360.
16. Fraser, D. A. S., *Nonparametric Methods in Statistics.* New York: John Wiley & Sons, 1957.

EXERCISES

7.1. Apply the appropriate Wilcoxon rank test to the data of Table 7.4.

7.2. In a rain-making (?) experiment, rainfall measurements were made on 16 pairs of days. On one day in each pair the clouds were seeded and on the other day no seeding was done. The choice of which day in a pair to seed was made randomly. The total rainfall over the network of gages for the 16 pairs of days is below. Test the null hypothesis that seeding is without effect with

(*a*) The sign test.

(*b*) The appropriate Wilcoxon test.

Report one-sided *P* values.

Pair no.	S	NS
1	0	1.37
2	2.09	0
3	0.07	0
4	0.30	0.10
5	0	0.44
6	2.55	0
7	1.62	1.01
8	0	0.54
9	0	0
10	1.87	0.62
11	2.50	0
12	3.15	5.54
13	0.15	0.01
14	2.96	0
15	0	0
16	0	0.75

7.3. In a trial of two types of rain gage, 69 of type A and 12 of type B were distributed at random over a certain area. In a certain period 14 storms occurred, and the average amounts of rain found in the two types of gage were as shown in the accompanying table.

Storm	Type A	Type B
1	1.38	1.42
2	9.69	10.37
3	0.39	0.39
4	1.42	1.46
5	0.54	0.55
6	5.94	6.15
7	0.59	0.61
8	2.63	2.69
9	2.44	2.68
10	0.56	0.53
11	0.69	0.72
12	0.71	0.72
13	0.95	0.93
14	0.50	0.53

Data from E. L. Hamilton, "The problem of sampling rainfall in mountainous areas," pp. 469–475 of *Proceedings of the Berkeley Symposium on Mathematical Statistics and Probability*, J. Neyman (ed.), University of California Press, Berkeley and Los Angeles, 1949.

Obtain the one-sided P value for the hypothesis that the two types of gage are giving similar results, using

(*a*) The appropriate Wilcoxon test by exact enumeration.

(*b*) The appropriate Wilcoxon test using a normal approximation.

(*c*) The sign test.

7.4. A group of mice are allocated to individual cages randomly. The cages are allocated, in equal numbers, randomly, to two treatments, a control A and a certain drug B. All animals are infected, in a random sequence, with tuberculosis [Note: the experimenter usually wants to infect all the controls and then all the B group, but this is terrible]. The mice die on the following days following infection [one mouse got lost].

Control A:	5, 6, 7, 7, 8, 8, 8, 9, 12
Drug B:	7, 8, 8, 8, 9, 9, 12, 13, 14, 17.

A preliminary experiment having established that the drug is not toxic it can be assumed that the test group cannot be worse (die sooner) than the control group under any reasonable alternative hypothesis. Report the P value for the null hypothesis that the drug is without effect, using the appropriate Wilcoxon test.

7.5. Acid is concentrated continuously in a certain type of plant. Part of the plant corrodes and eventually fails. The throughput in hundreds of tons obtained between installation and failure is recorded. These parts were obtained from three separate foundries. Test the hypothesis that the median life is the same for the three foundries.

Foundry	Throughputs obtained
A	84, 60, 40, 47, 34, 46
B	67, 92, 95, 40, 98, 60, 59, 108, 86, 117
C	46, 93, 100, 92, 92

CHAPTER 8

The Partitioning of Sums of Squares

8.1. Introduction

Largely algebraic, the main part of this chapter is a demonstration of the relationship (4.19), which is the basis of the t test (Section 9.5), and of the theorem following (5.1), which is the basis of the analysis of variance (Chapter 10 and following). Some readers may prefer to omit this chapter temporarily and return later when the necessity of these results has made itself plain.

The account given here is based on an exposition by A. Hald [1].

8.2. The Distribution of Sample Estimates of Variance

In Section 5.1 the distribution of the sum of n independent unit normal deviates $\sum_i^n u_i^2$ was given the name the $\chi^2(n)$ distribution. Suppose that we have n independent observations $x_1, \ldots, x_n$ from a normal population of known mean ξ and unknown variance σ^2. To estimate σ^2 we can use the maximum-likelihood estimator (2.3.8),

$$\hat{\sigma}^2 = \frac{1}{n} \sum_i^n (x_i - \xi)^2. \tag{2.1}$$

This is unbiased, since its expected value is

$$E[\hat{\sigma}^2] = \frac{1}{n} \sum_i^n E[(x_i - E[x_i])^2] = \frac{1}{n} \cdot n\sigma^2 = \sigma^2.$$

We can write (2.1) in the form

$$\hat{\sigma}^2 = \frac{\sigma^2}{n} \sum_i^n \left(\frac{x_i - \xi}{\sigma}\right)^2, \tag{2.2}$$

in which $(x_i - \xi)/\sigma = u_i$ is a unit normal deviate. Since the x_i are supposed independent, so are the u_i, and

$$\hat{\sigma}^2 = \frac{\sigma^2}{n} \sum_i^n u_i^2 = \frac{\sigma^2 \chi^2(n)}{n}. \tag{2.3}$$

Thus the distribution of $\hat{\sigma}^2$ can be obtained from the χ^2 distribution.

When ξ is unknown, to estimate $\hat{\sigma}^2$ we use the unbiased estimator (2.3.15),

$$s^2 = \frac{1}{n-1} \sum_i^n (x_i - \bar{x})^2, \tag{2.4}$$

which can be written in the form

$$s^2 = \frac{\sigma^2}{n-1} \sum_i^n \left(\frac{x_i - \bar{x}}{\sigma}\right)^2, \tag{2.5}$$

which resembles (2.2) except for its use of $\bar{x}$ in place of ξ and $(n - 1)$ in place of n. We will prove in Section 8.4 that $\sum_i^n \left(\frac{x_i - \bar{x}}{\sigma}\right)^2$ has the χ^2 distribution with $(n - 1)$ degrees of freedom, so that

$$s^2 = \sigma^2 \frac{\chi^2(n-1)}{n-1}, \tag{2.6}$$

and hence we know the distribution of s^2.

8.3. The Additivity of χ^2's

If we have two independent χ^2-distributed random variables with degrees of freedom f_1 and f_2, then their sum has the χ^2 distribution with $(f_1 + f_2)$ degrees of freedom. For $\chi^2(f_1)$ can be written as the sums of squares of f_1 independent unit normal deviates

$$\chi^2(f_1) = u_1^2 + \cdots + u_{f_1}^2,$$

and $\chi^2(f_2)$ can be likewise written as

$$\chi^2(f_2) = u_{f_1+1}^2 + u_{f_1+2}^2 + \cdots + u_{f_1+f_2}^2;$$

so $$\chi^2(f_1) + \chi^2(f_2) = u_1^2 + \cdots + u_{f_1+f_2}^2 = \chi^2(f_1 + f_2). \tag{3.1}$$

This suggests a natural way of combining two independent estimates of a common variance. If we have two samples, one $x_{11}, x_{12}, \ldots, x_{1n_1}$ normally distributed with mean ξ_1 and variance σ^2, and the other $x_{21}, x_{22}, \ldots, x_{2n_2}$ normally distributed with mean ξ_2 and the same variance σ^2, then, from (2.6),

$$(n_1 - 1)s_1^2 = \sum_{\nu}^{n_1} (x_{1\nu} - \bar{x}_1)^2 \sim \sigma^2\chi^2(n_1 - 1)$$

$$(n_2 - 1)s_2^2 = \sum_{\nu}^{n_2} (x_{2\nu} - \bar{x}_2)^2 \sim \sigma^2\chi^2(n_2 - 1)$$

where $\sim$ is used to denote "is distributed as." Then, adding these together,

$$\sum_{\nu}^{n_1} (x_{1\nu} - \bar{x}_1)^2 + \sum_{\nu}^{n_2} (x_{2\nu} - \bar{x}_2)^2 \sim \sigma^2\chi^2(n_1 + n_2 - 2). \tag{3.2}$$

If we now define s^2 as

$$s^2 = \frac{\sum_{\nu}^{n_1} (x_{1\nu} - \bar{x}_1)^2 + \sum_{\nu}^{n_2} (x_{2\nu} - \bar{x}_2)^2}{n_1 + n_2 - 2} = \frac{\sum_{i}^{2}\sum_{\nu}^{n_i} (x_{i\nu} - \bar{x}_i)^2}{\sum_{i}^{2} (n_i - 1)}, \tag{3.3}$$

it is distributed as

$$\sigma^2 \frac{\chi^2(n_1 + n_2 - 2)}{n_1 + n_2 - 2}, \tag{3.4}$$

and it has an expected value σ^2. This generalizes to the case of k sample variances s_i^2 with f_i degrees of freedom:

$$s^2 = \frac{\sum_{i}^{k} f_i s_i^2}{\sum_{i}^{k} f_i} \sim \sigma^2 \frac{\chi^2\left(\sum_{i}^{k} f_i\right)}{\sum_{i}^{k} f_i}. \tag{3.5}$$

8.4. The Partitioning of Sums of Squares into Independent Components: I

We will now prove that s^2 as defined in (2.4) does have the distribution given by (2.6). We can write

$$\begin{aligned}\sum_{i}^{n} (x_i - \xi)^2 &= \sum_{i}^{n} [(x_i - \bar{x}) + (\bar{x} - \xi)]^2 \\ &= \sum_{i}^{n} (x_i - \bar{x})^2 + n(\bar{x} - \xi)^2.\end{aligned} \tag{4.1}$$

Dividing by σ^2,

$$\sum_i^n \left(\frac{x_i - \xi}{\sigma}\right)^2 = \sum_i^n \left(\frac{x_i - \bar{x}}{\sigma}\right)^2 + \left(\frac{\bar{x} - \xi}{\sigma/\sqrt{n}}\right)^2 . \tag{4.2}$$

Defining $u_i = (x_i - \xi)/\sigma$, the u_i are unit normal deviates, and their average is

$$\bar{u} = \frac{1}{n}\sum_i^n u_i = \frac{\bar{x} - \xi}{\sigma},$$

so (4.2) can be written as

$$\sum_i^n u_i^2 = \sum_i^n (u_i - \bar{u})^2 + (\sqrt{n}\bar{u})^2 \tag{4.3}$$

$$= Q_2 + Q_1, \qquad \text{say.} \tag{4.4}$$

The left-hand side $\sum_i^n u_i^2$ is distributed as $\chi^2(n)$. On the right-hand side, $\sqrt{n}\,\bar{u} = \bar{u}/(1/\sqrt{n})$ is a unit normal deviate, and hence its square Q_1 is distributed as $\chi^2(1)$. We shall now prove that Q_2 is distributed as $\chi^2(n - 1)$ and is independent of Q_1. This will establish that $\sum_i^n (x_i - \bar{x})^2$ is distributed as $\sigma^2\,\chi^2(n - 1)$ and is independent of $(\bar{x} - \xi)^2$.

Define $l_i = u_i - \bar{u}$, so that $Q_2 = \sum_i^n l_i^2$. Since

$$\bar{u} = \frac{u_1}{n} + \frac{u_2}{n} + \cdots + \frac{u_n}{n},$$

each l_i can be written in the form

$$l_i = -\frac{u_1}{n} - \frac{u_2}{n} - \cdots - \frac{u_{i-1}}{n} + u_i\left(1 - \frac{1}{n}\right) - \frac{u_{i+1}}{n} - \cdots - \frac{u_n}{n}. \tag{4.5}$$

The n variables l_i are subject to the restraint that $\sum_i^n l_i = 0$. The number of degrees of freedom for a set of variables is defined as the number of variables minus the number of independent linear relations or constraints between them. The number of degrees of freedom of the sum of squares of a set of variables is the same as the number of degrees of freedom of the variables themselves. In the present instance, $\sum_i^n u_i^2$ involves n variables u_i with no linear relationship between them, and so it has n degrees of freedom; but Q_2 involves n variables l_i with the restriction $\sum_i^n l_i = 0$, and so Q_2 has $(n - 1)$ degrees of freedom.

The l_i are linear functions of the normally distributed u_i, and hence are themselves normally distributed, with expected value

$$E[l_i] = E[u_i - \bar{u}] = E[u_i] - E[\bar{u}] = 0$$

and variance

$$\begin{aligned} V[l_i] &= \left(-\frac{1}{n}\right)^2 V[u_1] + \cdots + \left(1 - \frac{1}{n}\right)^2 V[u_i] + \cdots + \left(-\frac{1}{n}\right)^2 V[u_n] \\ &= (n-1)\left(\frac{1}{n}\right)^2 + \left(1 - \frac{1}{n}\right)^2 = \frac{n-1}{n}, \end{aligned}$$

since $V[u_i] = 1$. Their covariance is

$$\text{Cov}[l_i, l_j] = E[l_i l_j] - E[l_i]E[l_j] = E[l_i l_j]. \tag{4.6}$$

In evaluating $E[l_i l_j]$, $i \neq j$, multiplying l_i and l_j in the form (4.5) gives squared terms and cross-product terms. The squared terms are

$$\begin{aligned} \frac{u_1^2}{n^2} + \cdots + \frac{u_{i-1}^2}{n^2} - \frac{1}{n}\left(1 - \frac{1}{n}\right) u_i^2 + \frac{u_{i+1}^2}{n^2} + \cdots + \frac{u_{j-1}^2}{n^2} \\ - \frac{1}{n}\left(1 - \frac{1}{n}\right) u_j^2 + \frac{u_{j+1}^2}{n^2} + \cdots + \frac{u_n^2}{n^2}. \end{aligned}$$

Since $E[u_i^2] = 1$, and since there are $(n - 2)$ terms with coefficient $1/n^2$ and 2 terms with coefficient $(-1/n)(1 - 1/n)$, this (the squared part) has an expected value

$$(n-2) \cdot \frac{1}{n^2} - 2 \cdot \frac{1}{n}\left(1 - \frac{1}{n}\right) = -\frac{1}{n}.$$

The cross-product terms are of the form $k_{rs}u_r u_s$, where k_{rs} is some constant. Since the u_i are independent, $E[u_r u_s] = E[u_r]E[u_s] = 0$, and therefore the cross products contribute zero to the $E[l_i l_j)$. Thus

$$\text{Cov}[l_i, l_j] = -\frac{1}{n}, \tag{4.7}$$

and so the variables l_i, l_j must be statistically dependent, since, if they were independent, they would have zero covariance.

We will now prove that we can transform the n variables l_i into $(n - 1)$ variables v_i $(i = 2, 3, \ldots, n)$, where the v_i are unit normal deviates independent of each other and of v_1 defined as $\sqrt{n}\,\bar{u}$. This will imply that $Q_2 = \sum_{i=1}^{n} l_i^2 = \sum_{i=2}^{n} v_i^2$ is distributed as $\chi^2(n - 1)$ and is independent of $Q_1 = (\sqrt{n}\,\bar{u})^2 = v_1^2$.

We will look first at the simple special cases of $n = 2$ and 3. For $n = 2$,

$$Q_1 = v_1^2 = (\sqrt{n}\,\bar{u})^2 = \left(\sqrt{2}\,\frac{u_1 + u_2}{2}\right)^2 = \left(\frac{u_1 + u_2}{\sqrt{2}}\right)^2,$$

$$Q_2 = l_1^2 + l_2^2 = (u_1 - \bar{u})^2 + (u_2 - \bar{u})^2$$

$$= \left(\frac{2u_1 - u_1 - u_2}{2}\right)^2 + \left(\frac{2u_2 - u_1 - u_2}{2}\right)^2 = \left(\frac{u_1 - u_2}{\sqrt{2}}\right)^2.$$

Define $v_2 = (u_1 - u_2)/\sqrt{2}$. Then $E[v_2] = 0$, and

$$V[v_2] = \frac{1}{2}\{V[u_1] + V[u_2]\} = 1.$$

Also $$\text{Cov}[v_1, v_2] = E[v_1 v_2] - E[v_1]E[v_2]$$

$$= E\left[\frac{u_1 + u_2}{\sqrt{2}} \cdot \frac{u_1 - u_2}{\sqrt{2}}\right] = \frac{1}{2}\,E[u_1^2 - u_2^2] = 0.$$

It will be shown in Section 12.3 that, if v_1, v_2 are linear functions of normally distributed variables u_1, u_2, then v_1, v_2 are jointly distributed in the bivariate normal distribution, and that, if $\text{Cov}[v_1, v_2] = 0$, then v_1, v_2 are independent. We have thus transformed our l_i into a v_2, which is a unit normal deviate and is independent of v_1.

In the case of $n = 3$,

$$Q_1 = (\sqrt{n}\,\bar{u})^2 = \left(\frac{u_1 + u_2 + u_3}{\sqrt{3}}\right)^2 = v_1^2,$$

$$Q_2 = \sum_{i=1}^{n} l_i^2 = l_1^2 + l_2^2 + l_3^2 = 2(l_2^2 + l_2 l_3 + l_3^2),$$

substituting $l_1 = -(l_2 + l_3)$. We want to write Q_2 as a sum of squares of two terms, $Q_2 = v_2^2 + v_3^2$, where v_2 and v_3 are independent of each other and of v_1, and are unit normal deviates. This can be achieved by collecting all terms in l_2 and writing them as a square:

$$l_2^2 + l_2 l_3 = \left(l_2 + \frac{1}{2}\,l_3\right)^2 - \frac{1}{4}\,l_3^2.$$

Substituting this in Q_2,

$$Q_2 = 2\left(l_2 + \frac{1}{2}\,l_3\right)^2 - \frac{1}{2}\,l_3^2 + 2\,l_3^2 = 2\left(l_2 + \frac{1}{2}\,l_3\right)^2 + \left(\sqrt{\frac{3}{2}}\,l_3\right)^2.$$

Now define $v_2 = \sqrt{2}(l_2 + l_3/2)$ and $v_3 = \sqrt{3/2}\, l_3$, and express them in terms of the original observations u_i:

$$v_2 = \frac{1}{\sqrt{2}}(2l_2 + l_3) = \frac{1}{\sqrt{2}}\{2(u_2 - \bar{u}) + (u_3 - \bar{u})\} = -\frac{1}{\sqrt{2}}(u_1 - u_2),$$

$$v_3 = \frac{1}{\sqrt{6}} \cdot 3l_3 = \frac{1}{\sqrt{6}} \cdot 3(u_3 - \bar{u}) = -\frac{1}{\sqrt{6}}(u_1 + u_2 - 2u_3).$$

We see at once that $E[v_2] = 0 = E[v_3]$, and

$$V[v_2] = \left(-\frac{1}{\sqrt{2}}\right)^2 \{V[u_1] + V[u_2]\} = 1,$$

$$V[v_3] = \left(-\frac{1}{\sqrt{6}}\right)^2 \{V[u_1] + V[u_2] + (-2)^2 V[u_3]\} = 1,$$

$$\begin{aligned}\text{Cov}[v_2, v_3] &= E[v_2 v_3] - E[v_2]\, E[v_3] \\ &= E\left[\frac{(-1)}{\sqrt{2}}(u_1 - u_2) \cdot \frac{(-1)}{\sqrt{6}}(u_1 + u_2 - 2u_3)\right] \\ &= \frac{1}{\sqrt{12}} E[u_1^2 - u_1^2 - 2u_1u_3 + 2u_2u_3] = 0.\end{aligned}$$

Since v_2, v_3 are jointly normal and have zero covariance, they must be independent, by the theorem of Section 12.3, and hence $Q_2 = v_2^2 + v_3^2$ is distributed as $\chi^2(2)$. It is easy also to show that $\text{Cov}[v_1, v_2]$ and $\text{Cov}[v_1, v_3]$ are both zero, and hence Q_1 must be independent of Q_2.

Having proved that for the cases $n = 2$ and $n = 3$ we can transform the l_i into $(n - 1)$ independent v_i and that $Q_2 = \sum_{i=1}^{n} l_i^2 = \sum_{i=2}^{n} v_i^2$, we will now sketch the proof for any n. We have

$$Q_1 = (\sqrt{n}\,\bar{u})^2 = v_1^2, \tag{4.8}$$

$$Q_2 = \sum_{i=1}^{n} (u_i - \bar{u})^2 = \sum_{i=1}^{n} l_i^2. \tag{4.9}$$

Since $\sum_{i}^{n} l_i = 0$, $l_1 = -(l_2 + l_3 + \cdots + l_n)$, and its square is

$$\begin{aligned}l_1^2 = l_2^2 &+ 2(l_2l_3 + l_2l_4 + \cdots + l_2l_n) \\ &+ l_3^2 + 2(l_3l_4 + \cdots + l_3l_n) \\ &+ \cdots \qquad\qquad + \\ &\qquad\qquad \vdots \\ &\qquad\qquad + l_n^2.\end{aligned} \tag{4.10}$$

If we substitute this for l_1^2 in (4.9), we will eliminate l_1, and we will have Q_2 in the form of a function of the $(n-1)$ variables l_i, $i = 2, 3, \ldots, n$:

$$\begin{aligned} Q_2 = 2(l_2^2 &+ l_2 l_3 + l_2 l_4 + \cdots + l_2 l_n \\ &+ \quad l_3^2 + l_3 l_4 + \cdots + l_3 l_n \\ &+ \qquad \cdots + \\ &\qquad\qquad \vdots \\ &\qquad\qquad + \quad l_n^2). \end{aligned} \tag{4.11}$$

This can be expressed as the sum of $(n-1)$ squares, by first collecting all terms that involve l_2, the first row, and writing them as a perfect square plus whatever is left over:

$$\begin{aligned} 2(l_2^2 &+ l_2 l_3 + l_2 l_4 + \cdots + l_2 l_n) \\ &= \left\{\sqrt{2}\left[l_2 + \frac{1}{2}(l_3 + l_4 + \cdots + l_n)\right]\right\}^2 \\ &\quad -\frac{1}{2}l_3 - l_3 l_4 - \cdots - l_3 l_n \\ &\qquad -\frac{1}{2}l_4^2 - \cdots - l_4 l_n \\ &\qquad\qquad \vdots \\ &\qquad\qquad -\frac{1}{2}l_n^2 . \end{aligned} \tag{4.12}$$

Substituting this in (4.11),

$$\begin{aligned} Q_2 = &\left\{\sqrt{2}\left[l_2 + \frac{1}{2}(l_3 + l_4 + \cdots + l_n)\right]\right\}^2 \\ &+\frac{3}{2}l_3^2 + l_3 l_4 + \cdots + l_3 l_n \\ &\qquad \vdots \\ &\qquad + \frac{3}{2}l_n^2 . \end{aligned} \tag{4.13}$$

The next step is to collect all the terms in l_3 excluding those in the first row: They are set out in the second row of (4.13). We write them as a perfect square plus whatever is left over, just as we did for l_2. The square part is

$$\left\{\sqrt{\frac{3}{2}}\left[l_3 + \frac{1}{3}(l_4 + l_5 + \cdots + l_n)\right]\right\}^2 .$$

This procedure can be continued until we are finally left with only l_n^2. These squares can be denoted by v_i^2, $i = 2, \ldots, n$:

$$v_2 = \sqrt{2}\left[l_2 + \frac{1}{2}(l_3 + l_4 + \cdots + l_n)\right],$$

$$\begin{aligned} v_3 &= \sqrt{\frac{3}{2}}\left[l_3 + \frac{1}{3}(l_4 + l_5 + \cdots + l_n)\right], \\ &\vdots \\ v_i &= \sqrt{\frac{i}{i-1}}\left[l_i + \frac{1}{i}(l_{i+1} + l_{i+2} + \cdots + l_n)\right], \\ &\vdots \\ v_n &= \sqrt{\frac{n}{n-1}}\, l_n . \end{aligned} \tag{4.14}$$

We have thus expressed $Q_2 = \sum_{i=1}^{n} l_i^2$ as $\sum_{i=2}^{n} v_i^2$. It remains to show that these v_i are unit normal deviates and are independent of each other and of v_1. To do this we express the v_i, $i > 1$, in terms of the u_i by the substitution $l_i = u_i - \bar{u}$:

$$\begin{aligned} v_i &= \frac{1}{\sqrt{i(i-1)}}(il_i + l_{i+1} + \cdots + l_n) \\ &= \frac{1}{\sqrt{i(i-1)}}(iu_i - i\bar{u} + u_{i+1} - \bar{u} + \cdots + u_n - \bar{u}) \\ &= \frac{1}{\sqrt{i(i-1)}}(iu_i + u_{i+1} + \cdots + u_n - n\bar{u}) \\ &= \frac{1}{\sqrt{i(i-1)}}(iu_i + u_{i+1} + \cdots + u_n - u_1 - u_2 - \cdots - u_{i-1} \\ &\qquad\qquad - u_i - u_{i+1} - \cdots - u_n) \\ &= -\frac{1}{\sqrt{i(i-1)}}(u_1 + u_2 + \cdots + u_{i-1} - (i-1)u_i). \end{aligned} \tag{4.15}$$

The v_i will be normally distributed since they are linear functions of the u_i which are normally distributed, and

$$E[v_i] = -\frac{1}{\sqrt{i(i-1)}}\{E[u_1] + \cdots + E[u_{i-1}] - (i-1)\,E[u_i]\} = 0, \tag{4.16}$$

$$V[v_i] = \frac{1}{i(i-1)}\{V[u_1] + \cdots + V[u_{i-1}] + (i-1)^2\,V[u_i]\} = 1, \tag{4.17}$$

$$\begin{aligned} \text{Cov}[v_i, v_j] &= E[v_i v_j] - E[v_i]\,E[v_j] \\ &= \frac{1}{\sqrt{i(i-1)\,j(j-1)}}\,E[(u_1 + \cdots + u_{i-1} \\ &\qquad - (i-1)u_i)(u_i + \cdots + u_{j-1} - (j-1)u_j)]. \end{aligned}$$

For $i < j$, the expectation $E[\quad]$ will include the squared terms u_i^2 for $i < j$, and their expectation is

$$E[u_1^2 + \cdots + u_{i-1}^2 - (i-1)u_i^2] = 0.$$

The expectation $E[\quad]$ will also include cross products of the form $k_{rs}u_r u_s$, $r \neq s$, where k_{rs} is some constant. Their expectation is

$$E[k_{rs}u_r u_s] = k_{rs}E[u_r]\,E[u_s] = 0.$$

Thus $\text{Cov}[v_i, v_j] = 0$, and as v_i, v_j are jointly normal this implies that they are independent by the theorem of Section 12.3. Since the v_i have zero means and unit variances,

$$Q_2 = \sum_{i=2}^{n} v_i^2 \sim \chi^2(n-1), \tag{4.18}$$

where as before the symbol $\sim$ is used to denote "is distributed as." It is easy to show that v_1, v_i, $i = 2, \ldots, n$, are independent, and hence Q_1 is independent of Q_2.

To recapitulate, if we write

$$\sum_{i=1}^{n} u_i^2 = (\sqrt{n}\,\bar{u})^2 + \sum_{i=1}^{n} (u_i - \bar{u})^2 = Q_1 + Q_2,$$

then Q_1 and Q_2 have independent χ^2 distributions with degrees of freedom 1 and $(n-1)$. Substituting $u_i = (x_i - \xi)/\sigma$ and multiplying both sides by σ^2 gives

$$\sum_{i}^{n} (x_i - \xi)^2 = n(\bar{x} - \xi)^2 + \sum_{i}^{n} (x_i - \bar{x})^2, \tag{4.19}$$

for which the left-hand side is distributed as $\sigma^2\,\chi^2$ with n degrees of freedom and the two terms on the right-hand side are distributed as $\sigma^2\,\chi^2$ with degrees of freedom 1 and $(n-1)$, and are independent. This independence implies that $\bar{x}$ is independent of $\sum_{i}^{n} (x_i - \bar{x})^2$, and so that $\bar{x}$ is independent of $\sum_{i}^{n} (x_i - \bar{x})^2/(n-1) = s^2$. In other words, for normally distributed random variables the sample mean is independent of the usual sample estimate of the variance.

8.5. The Partitioning of Sums of Squares into Independent Components: II

The result of the preceding section will be used for the Student t test in Chapter 9. For the comparison of k means, in Chapter 10 and following, we need a stronger result, Cochran's theorem [2]. A restricted form of this theorem is as follows.

We have n unit normally distributed and independent random variables u_i, $i = 1, \ldots, n$. The sum of their squares is distributed as $\chi^2(n)$. Suppose that $Q_j, j = 1, \ldots, k$, are sums of squares with f_j degrees of freedom. Then, if

$$\sum_j^k Q_j = Q_1 + \cdots + Q_k = \sum_i^n u_i^2 \tag{5.1}$$

and

$$\sum_j^k f_j = f_1 + \cdots + f_k = n, \tag{5.2}$$

then the theorem states that the Q_j are independently distributed as $\chi^2(f_j)$. Actually the theorem is somewhat stronger in that the Q_j can be quadratic forms,

$$\sum_i \sum_j a_{ij} x_i x_j = a_{11}x_1^2 + a_{12}x_1x_2 + \cdots + a_{1n}x_1x_n$$
$$+ a_{21}x_1x_2 + a_{22}x_2^2 + a_{23}x_2x_3 + \cdots$$

where $a_{ij} = a_{ji}$. We will encounter expressions of this type in the consideration of multiple regression in Chapter 17, but even there we can get by without considering this more general form.

We assume that each Q_j is the sum of the squares of m_j variables l_{ij}, $i = 1, \ldots, m_j$; i.e.,

$$Q_j = l_{1j}^2 + l_{2j}^2 + \cdots + l_{m_jj}^2 = \sum_i^{m_j} l_{ij}^2 . \tag{5.3}$$

We assume that, among the m_j variables l_{ij}, there are r_j linear relations, so that the number of degrees of freedom for Q_j is $f_j = m_j - r_j$. We are going to show that each $Q_j = \sum_i^{m_j} l_{ij}^2$ can be written in the form $Q_j = \sum_i^{f_j} v_{ij}^2$, in which the v_{ij} are independent unit normal deviates. This will show that the Q_j have $\chi^2(f_j)$ distributions and are independent.

If there are r_j linear relations among the m_j variables l_{ij}, then we can use these relations to eliminate r_j of the l_{ij} and convert Q_j into a quadratic form in only $m_j - r_j = f_j$ variables l_{ij}. Thus it is possible to obtain

$$Q_j = \sum_i^{f_j} \sum_{i'}^{f_j} a_{ii'} \, l_{ij} \, l_{i'j} . \tag{5.4}$$

Further, this quadratic form can be linearly transformed into another quadratic form in f_j variables $v_{1j}, \ldots, v_{f_jj}$ involving only squares

$$Q_j = \sum_i^{f_j} b_{ij} \, v_{ij}^2 , \tag{5.5}$$

in which the $b_{ij} = \pm 1$ (see, for example, Section 51 of [3]). Combining (5.5) and (5.1), we have

$$\sum_i^n u_i^2 = \sum_j^k Q_j = \sum_j^k \sum_i^{f_j} b_{ij} v_{ij}^2 . \qquad (5.6)$$

Now, if the condition (5.2) for Cochran's theorem is satisfied, $\sum_j^k f_j = n$, so that the number of terms on the left-hand side of (5.6) equals the number of terms on the right-hand side. The theory of quadratic forms contains the result (see, for example, Section 50 of [3]) that, if a real quadratic form of rank r is reduced by two nonsingular transformations to the forms

$$(c_1 x_1'^2 + \cdots + c_r x_r'^2) \qquad \text{and} \qquad (k_1 x_1''^2 + \cdots + k_r x_r''^2),$$

then the number of positive c's equals the number of positive k's. In (5.6) all the coefficients of the u_i^2 are positive, in fact being all $+1$, and hence all the coefficients of the v_{ij}^2 must also be positive. They were already known to be ± 1; so it follows that they are all $+1$, and (5.5) becomes

$$Q_j = \sum_j^{f_j} v_{ij}^2 . \qquad (5.7)$$

We now have two sets of transformations of the quadratic form (5.4), one leading to $\sum_i^n u_i^2$ and the other to $\sum_j^k \sum_i^{f_j} v_{ij}^2$. In other words, $\sum_i^n u_i^2$ can be linearly transformed to $\sum_j^k \sum_i^{f_j} v_{ij}^2$, where $\sum_j^k f_j = n$; i.e., the n v_{ij}'s are linear functions of the n u_i's. It will be convenient at this point to change the index on v from $ij, i = 1, \ldots, k, j = 1, \ldots, f_j$, to $g = 1, \ldots, n$. If the transformation is

$$v_g = c_{g1} u_1 + c_{g2} u_2 + \cdots + c_{gn} u_n = \sum_j^n c_{gj} u_j, \qquad g = 1, \ldots, n, \qquad (5.8)$$

then
$$\begin{aligned}
\sum_g^n v_g^2 &= (c_{11} u_1 + c_{12} u_2 + \cdots + c_{1n} u_n)^2 + \cdots \\
&\qquad + (c_{n1} u_1 + c_{n2} u_2 + \cdots + c_{nn} u_n)^2 \\
&= u_1^2 (c_{11}^2 + \cdots + c_{n1}^2) + \cdots + u_n^2 (c_{1n}^2 + \cdots + c_{nn}^2) \\
&\qquad + 2u_1 u_2 (c_{11} c_{12} + \cdots + c_{n1} c_{n2}) \\
&\qquad + 2u_1 u_3 (c_{11} c_{13} + \cdots + c_{n1} c_{n3}) + \cdots \\
&= \sum_g^n \Big(\sum_j^n c_{gj} u_j\Big)^2 = \sum_g^n \sum_j^n \sum_{j'}^n c_{gj} c_{gj'} u_j u_{j'} \\
&= \sum_j^n \sum_{j'}^n \Big(\sum_g^n c_{gj} c_{gj'}\Big) u_j u_{j'} . \qquad (5.9
\end{aligned}$$

We know that $\sum_g^n v_g^2 = \sum_i^n u_i^2$; so

$$\sum_i^n u_i^2 = \sum_j^n \sum_{j'}^n (\sum_g^n c_{gj}c_{gj'})\, u_j u_{j'} \,, \tag{5.10}$$

and the coefficients of the u's on the two sides of this equation must be equal for each $i = j$. For example, for $i = j = j' = 1$, the coefficient of u_1^2 on the left-hand side is 1; so

$$\sum_g^n c_{g1}c_{g1} = \sum_g^n c_{g1}^2 = c_{11}^2 + c_{21}^2 + \cdots + c_{n1}^2 = 1,$$

and, for any $i = j = j'$,

$$\sum_g^n c_{gi}^2 = c_{1i}^2 + c_{2i}^2 + \cdots + c_{ni}^2 = 1. \tag{5.11}$$

There are no cross products $u_j u_{j'}, j \neq j'$, in the left-hand side of (5.10); so on the right-hand side the coefficient of $u_j u_{j'}, j \neq j'$, must be zero. For example, for $j = 1, j' = 2$, the coefficient of $u_1 u_2$ must be zero,

$$c_{11}c_{12} + c_{21}c_{22} + \cdots + c_{n1}c_{n2} = \sum_g^n c_{g1}c_{g2} = 0,$$

and, in general,

$$c_{1j}c_{1j'} + c_{2j}c_{2j'} + \cdots + c_{nj}c_{nj'} = \sum_g^n c_{gj}c_{gj'} = 0. \tag{5.12}$$

The relations (5.11) and (5.12) are unfortunately not in the form that we need, and we must prove the following relations:

$$\sum_j^n c_{gj}^2 = c_{g1}^2 + c_{g2}^2 + \cdots + c_{gn}^2 = 1\,, \tag{5.13}$$

$$\sum_j^n c_{gj}c_{g'j} = c_{g1}c_{g'1} + c_{g2}c_{g'2} + \cdots + c_{gn}c_{g'n} = 0. \tag{5.14}$$

If we multiply the first of the n equations (5.8) by c_{11}, the second by c_{21}, etc., we get

$$\begin{aligned} c_{11}v_1 &= c_{11}^2 u_1 + c_{11}c_{12}u_2 + \cdots + c_{11}c_{1n}u_n \\ c_{21}v_2 &= c_{21}^2 u_1 + c_{21}c_{22}u_2 + \cdots + c_{21}c_{2n}u_n \\ &\vdots \end{aligned}$$

Adding these n equations gives

$$\begin{aligned} c_{11}v_1 + c_{21}v_2 + \cdots + c_{n1}v_n \\ = u_1(c_{11}^2 + c_{21}^2 + \cdots + c_{n1}^2) + u_2(c_{11}c_{12} + c_{21}c_{22} + \cdots + c_{n1}c_{n2}) + \cdots \\ + u_n(c_{11}c_{1n} + c_{21}c_{2n} + \cdots + c_{n1}c_{nn}) \\ = u_1 \,, \end{aligned} \tag{5.15}$$

since by (5.11) the coefficient of u_1 equals 1 and by (5.12) the coefficients of $u_2, \ldots, u_n$ are all zero. Proceeding in this manner, we multiply the n equations (5.8) by c_{12}, c_{22}, etc., to get

$$c_{12}v_1 + c_{22}v_2 + \cdots + c_{n2}v_n = u_2, \tag{5.16}$$

and so on. We can thus assemble the set of equations

$$\begin{aligned} u_1 &= c_{11}v_1 + c_{21}v_2 + \cdots + c_{n1}v_n \\ u_2 &= c_{12}v_1 + c_{22}v_2 + \cdots + c_{n2}v_n \\ &\vdots \\ u_n &= c_{1n}v_1 + c_{2n}v_n + \cdots + c_{nn}v_n \, ; \end{aligned} \tag{5.17}$$

i.e., in general,

$$u_j = c_{1j}v_1 + c_{2j}v_2 + \cdots + c_{nj}v_n = \sum_g^n c_{gj}v_g \, . \tag{5.18}$$

Analogous to the derivation of (5.11) and (5.12) from (5.8), we have

$$\begin{aligned} \sum_j^n u_j^2 &= \sum_j^n \Big(\sum_g^n c_{gj}v_g\Big)^2 = \sum_j^n \sum_g^n \sum_{g'}^n c_{gj}c_{g'j}v_gv_{g'} \\ &= \sum_g^n \sum_{g'}^n \Big(\sum_j^n c_{gj}c_{g'j}\Big) v_gv_{g'} \, . \end{aligned} \tag{5.19}$$

But $\sum_j^n u_j^2 = \sum_g^n v_g^2$; so the coefficients of the v_g's on the two sides of the equation

$$\sum_g^n v_g^2 = \sum_g^n \sum_{g'}^n \Big(\sum_j^n c_{gj}c_{g'j}\Big) v_gv_{g'} \tag{5.20}$$

are equal. Thus, for $g = g'$,

$$\sum_j^n c_{gj}c_{g'j} = \sum_j^n c_{gj}^2 = c_{g1}^2 + c_{g2}^2 + \cdots + c_{gn}^2 = 1. \tag{5.21}$$

and, for $g \neq g'$,

$$\sum_j^n c_{gj}c_{g'j} = c_{g1}c_{g'1} + c_{g2}c_{g'2} + \cdots + c_{gn}c_{g'n} = 0. \tag{5.22}$$

Equations (5.21) and (5.22) correspond to (5.13) and (5.14) which we set out to prove. We will now use these relations to show that the v_g are independent unit normal deviates.

From the definition of v_g in (5.8), it follows that

$$E[v_g] = E[c_{g1}u_1 + \cdots + c_{gn}u_n] = 0, \tag{5.23}$$

$$\begin{aligned} V[v_g] &= c_{g1}^2\, V[u_1] + \cdots + c_{gn}^2\, V[u_n] \\ &= c_{g1}^2 + \cdots + c_{gn}^2 = 1, \end{aligned} \tag{5.24}$$

using (5.21). The v_g are thus unit normal deviates, and it remains to show that they are independent. This we do by showing that they have zero covariance, this implying independence by the theorem of Section 12.3. The covariance is

$$\begin{aligned}\text{Cov}[v_g, v_{g'}] &= E[v_g v_{g'}] - E[v_g]\,E[v_{g'}]\\ &= E[(c_{g1}u_1 + \cdots + c_{gn}u_n)(c_{g'1}u_1 + \cdots + c_{g'n}u_n)]\\ &= E[c_{g1}c_{g'1}u_1^2 + \cdots + c_{gn}c_{g'n}u_n^2] + E[\text{cross products in } u_g, u_{g'}].\end{aligned}$$

But $E[u_g u_{g'}] = E[u_g]\,E[u_{g'}] = 0$, since u_g, $u_{g'}$ are independent and have zero expectation. Hence

$$\begin{aligned}\text{Cov}[v_g, v_{g'}] &= c_{g1}c_{g'1}\,E[u_1^2] + \cdots + c_{gn}c_{g'n}\,E[u_n^2]\\ &= c_{g1}c_{g'1} + \cdots + c_{gn}c_{g'n} = 0,\end{aligned} \tag{5.25}$$

by (5.22). As stated earlier, this zero covariance implies independence. Since the v_g are independent unit normal deviates, each $Q_j = \sum_i^{f_j} v_{ij}^2$, changing the index on v back to ij from g, has the $\chi^2(f_j)$ distribution and is independent of the other Q_j. This completes the proof of the slightly restricted form of Cochran's theorem which we stated in (5.1) and (5.2).

The independence of the sample mean and variance, established at the end of Section 8.4, was required for Student's original exposition of the t test in 1908 [4]. A formal proof was given by Fisher in 1925 [5], an earlier proof by Helmert in 1876 being overlooked. Cochran's theorem was implicit in Fisher's early use of the analysis of variance [6], [7], but apparently did not receive a formal statement until 1934 [2]. Two papers by Irwin [8] and [9], reviewed the mathematical basis of the analysis of variance. For a modern proof see Section 11.11 of Cramér [10].

REFERENCES

1. Hald, A., *Statistical Theory with Engineering Applications.* New York; John Wiley & Sons, 1952.
2. Cochran, William G., "The distribution of quadratic forms in a normal system," *Proceedings of the Cambridge Philosophical Society*, 30(1934), 178–191.
3. Bocher, Maxime, *Introduction to Higher Algebra.* New York: Macmillan Co., 1907.
4. "Student," "The probable error of a mean," *Biometrika*, 6(1908), 1–25.
5. Fisher, R. A., "Applications of Student's distribution," *Metron*, 5(1925), 90–104.
6. ——— "The goodness of fit and regression formulae, and the distribution of regression coefficients", *Journal of the Royal Statistical Society*, 85(1922), 597–612.
7. ——— *Statistical Methods for Research Workers.* 1st ed.; Edinburgh: Oliver & Boyd, 1925.
8. Irwin, J. O., "Mathematical theorems involved in the analysis of variance," *Journal of the Royal Statistical Society*, 94(1931), 284–300.
9. ——— "On the independence of the constituent items in the analysis of variance," *Supplement to the Journal of the Royal Statistical Society*, 1(1934), 236–252.
10. Cramér, H., *Mathematical Methods of Statistics.* Princeton: University Press, 1951.

CHAPTER 9

Tests for Equality of Variances and Means

9.1. Uses of the Sample Estimate of Variance

We have seen in the previous chapter that $s^2 = \sum_i^n (x_i - \bar{x})^2 / (n - 1)$ is distributed as $\sigma^2\chi^2(n - 1)/(n - 1)$. If we use f for the number of degrees of freedom, the P point of the distribution of s^2 is $\sigma^2\chi_P^2(f)/f$, and $(P_2 - P_1)$ control limits for s^2 are determined by

$$\Pr\left\{\frac{\sigma^2\chi_{P_1}^2(f)}{f} < s^2 < \frac{\sigma^2\chi_{P_2}^2(f)}{f}\right\} = P_2 - P_1 . \tag{1.1}$$

For example, if we know σ^2 and want 95 per cent control limits, and we have samples of 5, so that $f = 4$, we substitute $\chi_{0.975}^2(4) = 11.1$ and $\chi_{0.025}^2(4) = 0.484$, and the control limits are

$$\Pr\{0.121\sigma^2 < s^2 < 2.775\sigma^2\} = 0.975 - 0.025 = 0.95.$$

To construct confidence limits for σ^2 from an observed estimate s^2, we can write

$$\Pr\{\chi_{P_1}^2(f) < \chi^2(f) < \chi_{P_2}^2(f)\} = P_2 - P_1 . \tag{1.2}$$

Since s^2 is distributed as $\sigma^2\chi^2(f)/f$, fs^2/σ^2 has the $\chi^2(f)$ distribution and can be substituted in (1.2):

$$\Pr\left\{\chi_{P_1}^2(f) < \frac{fs^2}{\sigma^2} < \chi_{P_2}^2(f)\right\} = P_2 - P_1 ,$$

which on rearranging becomes

$$\Pr\left\{\frac{s^2 f}{\chi^2_{P_2}} < \sigma^2 < \frac{s^2 f}{\chi^2_{P_1}}\right\} = P_2 - P_1 . \tag{1.3}$$

For example, if we observe $s^2 = 23.394$ with degrees of freedom $f = 66$, and want 90 per cent confidence limits, we need $\chi^2_{0.95}(66) = 86.0$ and $\chi^2_{0.05}(66) = 48.3$, whence the limits are

$$\left(23.394 \times \frac{66}{86.0}, 23.394 \times \frac{66}{48.3}\right) = (17.95, 31.97).$$

To make a test of significance of the null hypothesis that $E[s^2] = \sigma_0^2$ against the alternative that $E[s^2] = \sigma_1^2 > \sigma_0^2$, we observe that, since fs^2/σ_0^2 is distributed under the null hypothesis as $\chi^2(f)$,

$$\Pr\left\{\frac{fs^2}{\sigma_0^2} > \chi^2_{1-\alpha}(f) \middle| E[s^2] = \sigma_0^2\right\} = \Pr\{\chi^2(f) > \chi^2_{1-\alpha}(f)\} = 1 - (1 - \alpha) = \alpha;$$

so we reject the null hypothesis if $s^2/\sigma_0^2 > \chi^2_{1-\alpha}(f)/f$. The critical region is thus $s^2 > \sigma_0^2\chi^2_{1-\alpha}(f)/f$. The power of this test with respect to the alternative hypothesis is

$$\begin{aligned}\pi(\sigma_1^2) &= \Pr\left\{s^2 > \frac{\sigma_0^2\chi^2_{1-\alpha}(f)}{f} \mid E[s^2] = \sigma_1^2\right\} \\ &= \Pr\left\{\frac{fs^2}{\sigma_1^2} > \frac{\sigma_0^2}{\sigma_1^2}\chi^2_{1-\alpha}(f) \middle| E[s^2] = \sigma_1^2\right\} \\ &= \Pr\left\{\chi^2 > \frac{\sigma_0^2}{\sigma_1^2}\chi^2_{1-\alpha}(f)\right\}.\end{aligned} \tag{1.4}$$

For example, suppose that we are making a test with $\alpha = 0.05$, using $f = 19$. We want the probability of rejecting the null hypothesis if $\sigma_1^2/\sigma_0^2 = 3/2$. Substituting $\chi^2_{0.95}(19) = 30.1$,

$$\pi\left(\sigma_1^2 = \frac{3\sigma_0^2}{2}\right) = \Pr\left\{\chi^2(19) > \frac{2}{3} \times 30.1\right\} = \Pr\{\chi^2(19) > 20.0\} \simeq 0.39.$$

When the alternative hypothesis is $E[s^2] = \sigma_1^2 < \sigma_0^2$, the critical region for the test is $s^2 < \sigma_0^2\chi^2_\alpha(f)/f$, and the power is

$$\pi(\sigma_1^2) = \Pr\left\{\chi^2 < \frac{\sigma_0^2}{\sigma_1^2}\chi^2_\alpha\right\}. \tag{1.5}$$

When the alternative hypothesis is two-sided, $E[s^2] = \sigma_1^2 \neq \sigma_0^2$, the conventional procedure is to use critical regions for both upper and lower tails each at a level of significance $\alpha/2$.

Equations (1.4) and (1.5) can be used to calculate the number of degrees of freedom necessary to give specified power. When the alternative hypothesis is $E[s^2] = \sigma_1^2 > \sigma_0^2$, we put (1.4) equal to $(1 - \beta)$:

$$\pi(\sigma_1^2) = \Pr\left\{\chi^2 > \frac{\sigma_0^2}{\sigma_1^2}\chi_{1-\alpha}^2(f)\right\} = 1 - \beta.$$

But $\Pr\{\chi^2 > \chi_\beta^2\} = 1 - \beta$; so

$$\frac{\sigma_1^2}{\sigma_0^2} = \frac{\chi_{1-\alpha}^2(f)}{\chi_\beta^2(f)}. \tag{1.6}$$

For specified values of the ratio σ_1^2/σ_0^2, α, and β, this can be solved for f with the χ^2 table. For example, for $\sigma_1^2/\sigma_0^2 = 3/2$, $\alpha = 0.05$, $1 - \beta = 0.90$, we find that, for $f = 100$, $\chi_{0.95}^2(100) = 124.3$ and $\chi_{0.10}^2(100) = 82.4$; so $\chi_{0.95}^2(100)/\chi_{0.10}^2 = 124.3/82.4 = 1.508$, very close to the required value of 1.500. Thus the solution is f slightly greater than 100. An exact solution cannot be obtained since χ^2 is not tabulated beyond $f = 100$. For values of f beyond that, we can use the approximation (5.1.7),

$$\chi_P^2(f) \simeq \frac{1}{2}(\sqrt{2f-1} + u_P)^2. \tag{1.7}$$

Substitute this in (1.6),

$$\frac{\sigma_1^2}{\sigma_0^2} \simeq \frac{\frac{1}{2}(\sqrt{2f-1} + u_{1-\alpha})^2}{\frac{1}{2}(\sqrt{2f-1} + u_\beta)^2},$$

and solve for f:

$$f \simeq \frac{1}{2} + \frac{1}{2}\left(\frac{u_{1-\alpha} + u_{1-\beta}\sqrt{(\sigma_1^2/\sigma_0^2)}}{\sqrt{(\sigma_1^2/\sigma_0^2)} - 1}\right)^2. \tag{1.8}$$

For $\alpha = 0.05$, $u_{1-\alpha} = 1.645$, $1 - \beta = 0.90$, $u_{1-\beta} = 1.282$, and $\sigma_1^2/\sigma_0^2 = 3/2$, we obtain $f \simeq 102.9$.

9.2. The Variance Ratio

Let s_1^2, s_2^2 be independent sample estimates of σ^2 based on f_1, f_2 degrees of freedom. We have seen that s_i^2 is distributed as $\sigma^2\chi^2(f_i)/f_i$. Denote by F the ratio of two such independent mean squares which are estimates of the same σ^2:

$$F = \frac{s_1^2}{s_2^2}. \tag{2.1}$$

A variance ratio will have associated with it two numbers of degrees of freedom, one for the numerator sample variance and one for the denominator sample variance. We will, when necessary, attach these in parentheses following the F: for the F in (2.1), for example, we write $F(f_1, f_2)$. If we substitute $\sigma^2\chi^2(f_i)/f_i$ for s_i^2 in (2.1), we get

$$F = \frac{\sigma^2\chi^2(f_1)/f_1}{\sigma^2\chi^2(f_2)/f_2} = \frac{\chi^2(f_1)/f_1}{\chi^2(f_2)/f_2}. \tag{2.2}$$

The distribution of χ^2 is known, and the distribution of the ratio of two χ^2's, and hence of F, can be found. The cumulative form of F is tabulated in Table IV. Since χ^2 is never less than zero, F is distributed from 0 to ∞. It can be shown that $E[F] = f_2/(f_2 - 2)$, which tends to 1 as f_2 tends to ∞, and the mode is at $f_2(f_1 - 2)/f_1(f_2 + 2)$.

Table IV of the appendix gives only the upper tail of the F distribution. We obtain points in the lower tail as follows. Since

$$\Pr\left\{\frac{s_1^2}{s_2^2} < F_P(f_1, f_2)\right\} = P,$$

we have

$$\Pr\left\{\frac{s_1^2}{s_2^2} < F_{1-P}(f_1, f_2)\right\} = 1 - P.$$

Taking reciprocals of the inequality inside the braces { } will reverse the inequality sign:

$$\Pr\left\{\frac{s_2^2}{s_1^2} > \frac{1}{F_{1-P}(f_1, f_2)}\right\} = 1 - P;$$

so

$$\Pr\left\{\frac{s_2^2}{s_1^2} < \frac{1}{F_{1-P}(f_1, f_2)}\right\} = P.$$

But

$$\Pr\left\{\frac{s_2^2}{s_1^2} < F_P(f_2, f_1)\right\} = P;$$

so, comparing the last two expressions,

$$F_P(f_2, f_1) = \frac{1}{F_{1-P}(f_1, f_2)}. \tag{2.3}$$

For example, the 0.05 point of F for degrees of freedom 6 and 12 is found as $1/F_{0.95}(12, 6) = 1/4.00 = 0.250$.

If s_1^2, s_2^2 are sample estimates of σ_1^2, σ_2^2 based on f_1, f_2 degrees of freedom, their ratio will be distributed as

$$\frac{s_1^2}{s_2^2} \sim \frac{\sigma_1^2\chi^2(f_1)/f_1}{\sigma_2^2\chi^2(f_2)/f_2} = \left(\frac{\sigma_1^2}{\sigma_2^2}\right)F(f_1, f_2). \tag{2.4}$$

We can write

$$\Pr\left\{\left(\frac{\sigma_1^2}{\sigma_2^2}\right)F_{P_1}(f_1, f_2) < \frac{s_1^2}{s_2^2} < \left(\frac{\sigma_1^2}{\sigma_2^2}\right)F_{P_2}(f_1, f_2)\right\} = P_2 - P_1 \tag{2.5}$$

which for a known value of σ_1^2/σ_2^2 gives control limits for s_1^2/s_2^2. Taking reciprocals and multiplying by $(\sigma_1^2/\sigma_2^2)\,(s_1^2/s_2^2)$ gives

$$\Pr\left\{\left(\frac{s_1^2}{s_2^2}\right)\frac{1}{F_{P_2}(f_1,f_2)}<\frac{\sigma_1^2}{\sigma_2^2}<\left(\frac{s_1^2}{s_2^2}\right)\frac{1}{F_{P_1}(f_1,f_2)}\right\}$$
$$=\Pr\left\{\left(\frac{s_1^2}{s_2^2}\right)\frac{1}{F_{P_2}(f_1,f_2)}<\frac{\sigma_1^2}{\sigma_2^2}<\left(\frac{s_1^2}{s_2^2}\right)\cdot F_{1-P_1}(f_2,f_1)\right\}=P_2-P_1 \quad (2.6)$$

and hence $(P_2 - P_1)$ confidence limits for a variance ratio.

Suppose that we have a sample estimate s_1^2 of a variance σ_1^2 and similarly a sample estimate s_2^2 of a variance σ_2^2. To make a test of the null hypothesis $\sigma_1^2 = \sigma_2^2$, against the alternative $\sigma_1^2 > \sigma_2^2$, we note that, since s_1^2/s_2^2 is distributed under the null hypothesis as $F(f_1, f_2)$,

$$\Pr\left\{\frac{s_1^2}{s_2^2}>F_{1-\alpha}(f_1,f_2)\,\middle|\,E[s_1^2]=\sigma_1^2=\sigma_2^2=E[s_2^2]\right\}$$
$$=\Pr\{F(f_1,f_2)>F_{1-\alpha}(f_1,f_2)\}=1-(1-\alpha)=\alpha. \quad (2.7)$$

We therefore reject the null hypothesis at the level of significance α if

$$\frac{s_1^2}{s_2^2}>F_{1-\alpha}(f_1,f_2). \quad (2.8)$$

This inequality defines the critical region for the test. The power of the test for a specified value of the ratio $\sigma_1^2/\sigma_2^2 = \phi$ is

$$\pi(\phi)=\Pr\left\{\frac{s_1^2}{s_2^2}>F_{1-\alpha}(f_1,f_2)\,\middle|\,E[s_1^2]=\sigma_1^2=\phi\sigma_2^2=\phi\,E[s_2^2]\right\}$$
$$=\Pr\left\{\frac{s_1^2/\sigma_1^2}{s_2^2/\sigma_2^2}>\frac{1}{\phi}\,F_{1-\alpha}(f_1,f_2)\right\}. \quad (2.9)$$

But, by (2.4),

$$\frac{s_1^2/\sigma_1^2}{s_2^2/\sigma_2^2}\sim F(f_1,f_2). \quad (2.10)$$

Hence (2.9) is equivalent to

$$\pi(\phi)=\Pr\left\{F(f_1,f_2)>\frac{1}{\phi}\,F_{1-\alpha}(f_1,f_2)\right\}. \quad (2.11)$$

For example, if we are making a test of the null hypothesis $\sigma_1^2 = \sigma_2^2$ at the level of significance $\alpha = 0.05$, with $f_1 = 30$, $f_2 = 10$, then $F_{0.95}(30, 10) = 2.70$, and the power for $\phi = 2$ is

$$\pi(\phi=2)=\Pr\left\{F(30,10)>\frac{2.70}{2}\right\}\simeq 0.30.$$

To find the number of degrees of freedom necessary to achieve a specified power, we put (2.11) equal to $(1 - \beta)$. But also

$$\Pr\{F(f_1, f_2) > F_\beta(f_1, f_2)\} = 1 - \beta;$$

so

$$\phi = \frac{F_{1-\alpha}(f_1, f_2)}{F_\beta(f_1, f_2)} = F_{1-\alpha}(f_1, f_2)\, F_{1-\beta}(f_2, f_1), \tag{2.12}$$

which can be solved iteratively with the F tables. For example, with $\alpha = 0.05$, $1 - \beta = 0.90$, $F_{0.95}(80, 80) = 1.45$ and $F_{0.90}(80, 80) = 1.33$; so their product is 1.93. The solution for $\phi = 2$ will therefore require $f_1 = f_2$ slightly smaller than 80, about 75. For a given sum $(f_1 + f_2)$, it can be shown that an equal allocation of the total number of observations to the two samples so that $f_1 = f_2$ is not exactly optimum but so close that further consideration is unnecessary.

9.3. The Interrelations of Various Distributions

In (5.1.1), $\chi^2(n)$ was defined as $\sum_i^n u_i^2$, where the u_i were independent unit normal deviates. When $n = 1$, $\chi^2(1) = u^2$. To get corresponding probability levels for the two distributions u and χ^2, we proceed as follows. Consider small areas α in the lower and upper tails of the standardized normal distribution: These will be defined as $u < u_\alpha$ and $u > u_{1-\alpha}$. The sum of the areas in the two tails is 2α, and the area between u_α and $u_{1-\alpha}$ is $(1 - 2\alpha)$. Then

$$\Pr\{u_\alpha < u < u_{1-\alpha}\} = 1 - 2\alpha. \tag{3.1}$$

From the symmetry of the normal distribution, $u_\alpha = -u_{1-\alpha}$, and so (3.1) becomes

$$\Pr\{-u_{1-\alpha} < u < u_{1-\alpha}\} = 1 - 2\alpha.$$

This implies

$$\Pr\{u^2 < u_{1-\alpha}^2\} = 1 - 2\alpha. \tag{3.2}$$

Now put $1 - 2\alpha = P$, so that $1 - \alpha = (1 + P)/2$: Then (3.2) becomes

$$\Pr\{u^2 < u_{(1+P)/2}^2\} = P. \tag{3.3}$$

Also,

$$\Pr\{\chi^2(1) < \chi_P^2(1)\} = P. \tag{3.4}$$

Comparing (3.3) and (3.4), and, since $u^2 = \chi^2(1)$,

$$\chi_P^2(1) = u_{(1+P)/2}^2\,. \tag{3.5}$$

For example, if $P = 0.95$, $(1 + P)/2 = 0.975$, and

$$\chi^2_{0.95}(1) = 3.84 = (1.96)^2 = u^2_{0.975} \,.$$

Or, if $P = 0.10$, $(1 + P)/2 = 0.55$, and

$$\chi^2_{0.10}(1) = 0.0158 = (0.126)^2 = u^2_{0.55} \,.$$

In (5.1.2) we noted that $E[\chi^2(f)] = f$, and in (5.1.5) that $V[\chi^2(f)] = 2f$. It follows from the former that $E[\chi^2(f)/f] = f/f = 1$, and from the latter that $V[\chi^2(f)/f] = 2f/f^2 = 2/f$. Thus, as f tends to infinity, $\chi^2(f)/f$ becomes closer and closer to 1 with high probability. In (2.2) put $f_2 = \infty$: the denominator $\chi^2(f_2)/f_2$ becomes 1 and we get

$$F(f_1, \infty) = \frac{\chi^2(f_1)}{f_1}. \tag{3.6}$$

For example, the 0.99 point of χ^2 with 10 degrees of freedom is 23.2: the 0.99 point of F with degrees of freedom 10 and ∞ is 2.32, which equals 23.2/10.

An important distribution is the t distribution, defined as the ratio of a unit normal deviate to the square root of an independent χ^2 with f degrees of freedom, divided by f. The degrees of freedom of this χ^2 are also the degrees of freedom of the t:

$$t(f) = \frac{u}{\sqrt{\chi^2(f)/f}} \,. \tag{3.7}$$

As stated earlier, $\chi^2(f)/f$ tends to 1 as f tends to infinity. Thus the t distribution with infinite degrees of freedom is identical with the standardized normal distribution.

The t distribution is related to the F distribution, for, if we put $f_1 = 1$ in (2.2), the numerator becomes $\chi^2(1)/1$ which is just u^2. Hence

$$F(1, f_2) = \frac{u^2}{\chi^2(f_2)/f_2} \,. \tag{3.8}$$

Comparing (3.7) with (3.8), we see that $t^2 = F$. Corresponding probability levels of $t(f)$ and $F(1, f)$ are obtained in the same way that we found the relationship for u and $\chi^2(1)$. The t distribution is symmetric about zero; so, with $t(f)$ replacing u and $F(1, f)$ replacing $\chi^2(1)$, the argument proceeds exactly analogously to (3.1) through (3.5) and gives

$$F_P(1, f) = t^2_{(1+P)/2}(f). \tag{3.9}$$

For example, for $f = 12$ and $P = 0.95$,

$$F_{0.95}(1, 12) = 4.75 = (2.179)^2 = t^2_{0.975}(12).$$

9.4. Bartlett's Test for the Equality of Several Variances

We have seen that the null hypothesis that two sample variances are sample estimates of a common variance can be tested with the F test. Bartlett's test is the extension to the case of k variances $s_1^2, \ldots, s_k^2$ with degrees of freedom $f_1, \ldots, f_k$. The null hypothesis is

$$H_0: \sigma_1^2 = \sigma_2^2 = \cdots = \sigma_k^2 = \sigma^2.$$

As indicated in (8.3.5), if the null hypothesis is correct,

$$s^2 = \sum_i^k f_i s_i^2 \Big/ \sum_i^k f_i \tag{4.1}$$

will be a sample estimate of σ^2 with the distribution $\sigma^2\chi^2(f)/f$, where $f = \sum_i^k f_i$. Also each s_i^2 is distributed as $\sigma^2\chi^2(f_i)/f_i$. Thus the distribution of any function of $s_i^2/s^2, \ldots, s_k^2/s^2$ depends only on the parameters $f_1, \ldots, f_k$ and k. Bartlett [1] has shown that the ratio B/C, where

$$B = -\sum_i^k f_i \log_e\left(\frac{s_i^2}{s^2}\right), \tag{4.2}$$

$$C = 1 + \frac{1}{3(k-1)} \sum_i^k \left(\frac{1}{f_i} - \frac{1}{f}\right), \tag{4.3}$$

is distributed under the null hypothesis approximately as χ^2 with $(k-1)$ degrees of freedom. Alternative forms of the test statistic are

$$\frac{1}{C}\left(f \log_e s^2 - \sum_i^k f_i \log_e s_i^2\right), \tag{4.4}$$

and

$$\frac{2.3026}{C}\left(f \log_{10} s^2 - \sum_i^k f_i \log_{10} s_i^2\right). \tag{4.5}$$

As an example, the data of Table 9.1 are the final digits of determinations of the velocity of light by Michelson [2] made with six different rotating mirrors. The lower part of the table details the calculation of the s_i^2. Table 9.2 continues the calculation of B and C. s^2 is obtained from Table 9.2 as the sum of the sums of squares divided by the sum of the degrees of freedom, 22,191.317/83 = 267.365, and from a table of natural logarithms $\log_e s^2 = 5.58860$. Thus

$$B = 83 \times 5.58860 - (11 \times 5.54953 + \cdots + 15 \times 4.75214) = 9.95023,$$

$$C = 1 + \frac{1}{3(6-1)}\left(0.4532 - \frac{1}{83}\right) = 1.0294,$$

and under the null hypothesis $B/C = 9.95023/1.0294 = 9.666$ is distributed as $\chi^2(5)$. For 5 degrees of freedom, the 0.90 and 0.95 points of χ^2 are 9.236 and 11.070; hence $P \simeq 0.08$, and we cannot reject the null hypothesis at the 0.05 level of significance.

Table 9.1. Determinations of the Velocity of Light with Different Rotating Mirrors*

Table number	II		III		IV		V		VI		VII	
Material	Glass		Glass		Glass		Glass		Steel		Steel	
Number of sides	8		12		16		16		12		8	
	47	47	42	18	3	39	66	21	18	9	30	21
	38	62	36	45	27	66	27	33	12	30	33	18
	29	59	33	30	48	15	9	24	30	27	12	33
	92	44	0	27	3	7	6	39	30	39	24	23
	41	47	18	27	27	27	42	18	18	27	57	39
	44	41	57	66	42	37	12	63	48	24	44	33
			48	24	69	24			18		30	24
			15		63	15					24	30
					30	27						
					42	42						
					60							
n_i	12		15		21		12		13		16	
$\sum_{\nu}^{n_i} x_{i\nu}$	591		486		713		360		330		475	
$\sum_{\nu}^{n_i} x_{i\nu}^2$	31,935		19,890		32,081		15,030		9756		15,839	
$\left(\sum_{\nu}^{n_i} x_{i\nu}\right)^2 / n_i$	29,106.750		15,746.400		24,208.048		10,800.000		8376.923		14,101.562	
$\sum_{\nu}^{n_i} (x_{i\nu} - \bar{x}_i)^2$	2,828.250		4,143.600		7,872.952		4,230.000		1379.077		1,737.438	
s_i^2	257.114		295.971		393.648		384.545		114.923		115.829	

* Data from [2].

It is suggestive that four of the six mirrors were made of glass and the remaining two of steel, and that there is not much variation in the s_i^2 within each group. Forming pooled sample variances with (4.1), we get estimates of 340.621 with 56 degrees of freedom for the glass mirrors and 115.426 with 27 degrees of freedom for the steel mirrors. The variance ratio 2.951 is at about the 0.9975 point of the F distribution. A two-sided test is called for, since there is no a priori reason to expect either variance to be less than the other; so the P value is about 0.005. However, since we are testing a null hypothesis to some extent suggested by the data, this P value is not

Table 9.2

Table number	Sums of squares	Degrees of freedom (f_i)	Mean squares (s_i^2)	$\log_e s_i^2$	$1/f_i$
II	2,828.250	11	257.114	5.54953	0.0909
III	4,143.600	14	295.971	5.69026	0.0714
IV	7,872.952	20	393.648	5.97545	0.0500
V	4,230.000	11	384.545	5.95208	0.0909
VI	1,379.077	12	114.923	4.74426	0.0833
VII	1,737.438	15	115.829	4.75214	0.0667
Totals	22,191.317	83			0.4532

legitimate, but, if we knew how to allow for this fact, probably the result would still be significant.

Hartley [3] has shown that the approximation involved in Bartlett's test is poor for small f_i (i.e., 2 or 3 or thereabouts) and has given a modification with the necessary tables.

Hartley [4] has also proposed an alternative for the case where the f_i are all equal. A tabulation by H. A. David of the 0.95 and 0.99 points of the largest variance ratio in a group of k, $k \leq 12$, for an adequately representative set of f_i, is reproduced in the *Biometrika Tables* [5].

9.5. The One-Sample t Test

Suppose that we have a sample of n independent observations $x_1, \ldots, x_n$ from a normal population with mean ξ and variance σ^2. We wish to test the null hypothesis that $\xi = \xi_0$: We not do assume knowledge of σ^2.

In Section 8.4 we developed most of what we need. In (8.4.19),

$$\sum_i^n (x_i - \xi)^2 = n(\bar{x} - \xi)^2 + \sum_i^n (x_i - \bar{x})^2,$$

the two terms were independently distributed as $\sigma^2\chi^2$ with degrees of freedom 1 and $(n - 1)$. Hence

$$E[n(\bar{x} - \xi)^2] = E[\sigma^2\chi^2(1)] = \sigma^2, \tag{5.1}$$

and

$$E[\sum_i^n (x_i - \bar{x})^2] = E[\sigma^2\chi^2(n - 1)] = (n - 1)\sigma^2. \tag{5.2}$$

Define

$$s^2 = \frac{1}{(n - 1)} \sum_i^n (x_i - \bar{x})^2 \tag{5.3}$$

and

$$s_2'^2 = n(\bar{x} - \xi)^2. \tag{5.4}$$

Then $s^2, s_2'^2$ are distributed as $\sigma^2\chi^2(n - 1)/(n - 1)$ and $\sigma^2\chi^2(1)/1$, respectively, and by (2.2) their ratio $s_2'^2/s^2$ is distributed as F with degrees of freedom 1 and $(n - 1)$. However, since we do not know ξ, we cannot compute $s_2'^2$. Define

$$s_2^2 = n(\bar{x} - \xi_0)^2 \tag{5.5}$$

where ξ_0 is the value of ξ to be tested under the null hypothesis. We find the expected value of s_2^2 as follows. We can write

$$s_2^2 = n[(\bar{x} - \xi) + (\xi - \xi_0)]^2 = n(\bar{x} - \xi)^2 + n(\xi - \xi_0)^2 + 2n(\xi - \xi_0)(\bar{x} - \xi).$$

Since

$$E[2n(\xi - \xi_0)(\bar{x} - \xi)] = 2n(\xi - \xi_0)\, E[\bar{x} - \xi] = 0,$$

we have, using (5.1),

$$E[s_2^2] = E[n(\bar{x} - \xi)^2] + n(\xi - \xi_0)^2 = \sigma^2 + n(\xi - \xi_0)^2. \tag{5.6}$$

Under the null hypothesis, when $\xi = \xi_0$, $s_2^2 = s_2'^2$ and so is distributed as $\sigma^2\chi^2(1)/1$ and has expected value σ^2, and therefore

$$\frac{s_2^2}{s^2} \sim F(1, n - 1). \tag{5.7}$$

If the null hypothesis is false, the numerator in this ratio will have an expected value greater than σ^2, and so the $(1 - \alpha)$ point of the F distribution will be reached more frequently than α of the time. The test will therefore have power against the alternative $\xi \neq \xi_0$.

An alternative approach is as follows. We saw at the end of Section 8.4 that the sample mean $\bar{x}$ was independent of the sample estimate of the variance, $s^2 = \frac{1}{n - 1} \sum_i^n (x_i - \bar{x})^2$. Now under the null hypothesis that

$E[x] = \xi_0$, $(\bar{x} - \xi_0)/(\sigma/\sqrt{n})$ is distributed as a unit normal deviate u. Also, since $\sum_i^n (x_i - \bar{x})^2$ is distributed as $\sigma^2\chi^2(n-1)$, s^2 is distributed as $\sigma^2\chi^2(n-1)/(n-1)$, and s^2/σ^2 is distributed as $\chi^2(n-1)/(n-1)$. We can now substitute $(\bar{x} - \xi_0)/(\sigma/\sqrt{n})$ for the numerator in (3.7) and $\sqrt{s^2/\sigma^2}$ for the denominator, having established their independence above: Then

$$\frac{(\bar{x} - \xi_0)/(\sigma/\sqrt{n})}{s/\sigma} = \frac{\bar{x} - \xi_0}{s/\sqrt{n}} \sim t(n-1). \tag{5.8}$$

Essentially this procedure is the same as the test based on s_2^2/s^2 in (5.7), for the square of (5.8) is $n(\bar{x} - \xi_0)^2/s^2 = s_2^2/s^2$, and we saw in Section 9.3 that $t^2(n-1) = F(1, n-1)$. The statistic (5.8) was derived earlier from a likelihood ratio viewpoint in (2.10.6). For a one-sided test against the alternative $\xi > \xi_0$ the critical region cf (2.7.6) is

$$\bar{x} > \xi_0 + t_{1-\alpha}\frac{s}{\sqrt{n}}, \tag{5.9}$$

and, against the alternative $\xi < \xi_0$,

$$\bar{x} < \xi_0 + t_\alpha \frac{s}{\sqrt{n}}, \tag{5.10}$$

and, for a two-sided test cf (2.9.5),

$$\left| \frac{\bar{x} - \xi_0}{s/\sqrt{n}} \right| > t_{1-\alpha/2}. \tag{5.11}$$

These critical regions are the analogs of those obtained when σ was assumed known: The only difference is that the use of s in place of σ implies that we use the t distribution instead of the normal distribution. Similar to (2.13.14), we can write confidence limits for ξ as

$$\underline{\xi} = \bar{x} - t_{P_2}\frac{s}{\sqrt{n}}, \qquad \bar{\xi} = \bar{x} - t_{P_1}\frac{s}{\sqrt{n}}. \tag{5.12}$$

As an example, we will consider the data of Table 7.1 on the difference in potency of a series of lots of a pharmaceutical analyzed by two methods A and B. These data were used in Section 7.2 to illustrate the sign test and in Section 7.8 to illustrate the Wilcoxon one-sample test, the one-sided P values for the null hypothesis that the median was zero being 0.0106 and 0.00214 by exact calculation and 0.0122 and 0.0033 by normal approximations to the exact nonparametric probabilities. To apply the t test, we need $\bar{x} = 2.2375$ and

$$s^2 = \frac{\sum_i^n (x_i - \bar{x})^2}{n-1} = \frac{\sum_i^n x_i^2 - (\sum_i^n x_i)^2/n}{n-1} \tag{5.13}$$

$$= \frac{(0.3)^2 + \cdots + (6.8)^2 - (0.3 + \cdots + 6.8)^2/16}{16-1}$$

$$= 7.3265.$$

We could compute $s_2^2 = n(\bar{x} - \xi_0)^2 = 16 \times (2.2375 - 0)^2 = 80.1025$ when the null hypothesis is that $\xi_0 = 0$, and refer the ratio $s_2^2/s^2 = 80.1025/7.3265 = 10.933$ to the F table with degrees of freedom 1 and 15. The 0.995 point of F with these degrees of freedom is 10.8; so the two-sided P value is just less than 0.005.

It is, however, customary, though really the same thing, to use (5.8),

$$\frac{\bar{x} - \xi_0}{s/\sqrt{n}} = \frac{2.2375 - 0}{\sqrt{7.3265}/\sqrt{16}} = \frac{2.2375}{0.67669} = 3.3065,$$

and refer this value to the t table with 15 degrees of freedom. The 0.995 and 0.999 levels of t with these degrees of freedom are 2.947 and 3.733. The one-sided P value is between 0.005 and 0.001. We can construct 95 per cent confidence limits for ξ with (5.12): $t_{0.975}(15) = 2.131$, $t_{0.025}(15) = -2.131$, $s/\sqrt{n} = 0.67669$, and $\bar{x} = 2.2375$; so the confidence limits are $2.2375 \pm 2.131 \times 0.67669 = (0.796, 3.679)$.

9.6. The Two-Sample t Test

Suppose that we have two samples, $x_{11}, \ldots, x_{1n_1}$ and $x_{21}, \ldots, x_{2n_2}$, from normal populations with means ξ_1 and ξ_2 and both with the same variance σ^2. We wish to test the null hypothesis that $\xi_1 = \xi_2$: We do not assume knowledge of σ^2.

For each sample, $i = 1, 2$, we can write (8.4.19)

$$\sum_\nu^{n_i} (x_{i\nu} - \xi_i)^2 = n_i(\bar{x}_i - \xi_i)^2 + \sum_\nu^{n_i} (x_{i\nu} - \bar{x}_i)^2. \tag{6.1}$$

As in (5.1) and (5.2),

$$E[n_i(\bar{x}_i - \xi_i)^2] = \sigma^2, \tag{6.2}$$

$$E[\sum_\nu^{n_i} (x_{i\nu} - \bar{x}_i)^2] = (n_i - 1)\sigma^2. \tag{6.3}$$

As in (8.3.3), if we sum the sums of squares and the degrees of freedom, we will get a pooled estimate of σ^2 defined as

$$s^2 = \frac{\sum_{\nu}^{n_1} (x_{1\nu} - \bar{x}_1)^2 + \sum_{\nu}^{n_2} (x_{2\nu} - \bar{x}_2)^2}{n_1 - 1 + n_2 - 1} \tag{6.4}$$

distributed as $\sigma^2\chi^2(n_1 - 1 + n_2 - 1)/(n_1 - 1 + n_2 - 1)$ and with the expected value σ^2. Since $n_i(\bar{x}_i - \xi_i)^2$ is distributed as $\sigma^2\chi^2$ with 1 degree of freedom, if we sum these two items for $i = 1, 2$, we have

$$n_1(\bar{x}_1 - \xi_1)^2 + n_2(\bar{x}_2 - \xi_2)^2 \sim \sigma^2\chi^2(2). \tag{6.5}$$

This sum of squares, with 2 degrees of freedom, is distributed independently of s^2.

Define $\bar{x}$ as the mean of the separate sample means weighted by the sample sizes:

$$\bar{x} = \frac{n_1\bar{x}_1 + n_2\bar{x}_2}{n_1 + n_2}. \tag{6.6}$$

Define ξ similarly in terms of the population parameters:

$$\xi = \frac{n_1\xi_1 + n_2\xi_2}{n_1 + n_2}. \tag{6.7}$$

Let η_i be the deviation of the ith population mean from the over-all average ξ:

$$\eta_i = \xi_i - \xi. \tag{6.8}$$

We can write the deviation of the ith sample mean from the corresponding population mean in the following form:

$$\bar{x}_i - \xi_i = (\bar{x}_i - \bar{x}) - (\xi_i - \xi) + (\bar{x} - \xi) = [(\bar{x}_i - \bar{x}) - \eta_i] + (\bar{x} - \xi).$$

Squaring and summing over i and ν (here summing over ν is equivalent to multiplying by n_i) gives

$$\sum_i^2 n_i(\bar{x}_i - \xi_i)^2 = \sum_i^2 n_i[(\bar{x}_i - \bar{x}) - \eta_i]^2 + (\bar{x} - \xi)^2 \sum_i^2 n_i + \sum_i^2 2n_i(\bar{x}_i - \bar{x} - \eta_i)(\bar{x} - \xi).$$

The last term here is

$$\sum_i^2 2n_i(\bar{x}_i - \bar{x} - \eta_i)(\bar{x} - \xi) = 2(\bar{x} - \xi) \sum_i^2 n_i(\bar{x}_i - \bar{x} - \eta_i)$$
$$= 2(\bar{x} - \xi)[n_1\bar{x}_1 + n_2\bar{x}_2 - (n_1 + n_2)\bar{x} - (n_1\eta_1 + n_2\eta_2)] = 0,$$

using the definitions (6.6), (6.7), and (6.8). The left-hand side of (6.5) can therefore be written as

$$\sum_i^2 n_i(\bar{x}_i - \xi_i)^2 = \sum_i^2 n_i[(\bar{x}_i - \bar{x}) - \eta_i]^2 + (n_1 + n_2)(\bar{x} - \xi)^2. \quad (6.9)$$

From (6.5) the left-hand side is distributed as $\sigma^2\chi^2(2)$. On the right-hand side we have two sums of squares, the first involving two variables $\bar{x}_i$ subject to the one restriction (6.6) and hence with $2 - 1 = 1$ degree of freedom, and the second sum of squares, actually just a single square, involving merely one variable $\bar{x}$ and hence with 1 degree of freedom. We are in a situation similar to that of (8.4.19), and we can infer that the two sums of squares on the right-hand side of (6.9) are independently distributed each as $\sigma^2\chi^2(1)$.

Define $s_2'^2$ as

$$s_2'^2 = \sum_i^2 n_i[(\bar{x}_i - \bar{x}) - \eta_i]^2. \quad (6.10)$$

Then $E[s_2'^2] = E[\sigma^2\chi^2(1)] = \sigma^2$, so $s_2'^2$ and s^2 are independent estimates of σ^2, and their ratio will be distributed as $F(1, n_1 + n_2 - 2)$. We cannot calculate $s_2'^2$ as it involves the η_i which are unknown. We can, however, calculate s_2^2 defined as

$$s_2^2 = \sum_i^2 n_i(\bar{x}_i - \bar{x})^2. \quad (6.11)$$

To find the expected value of s_2^2, we note that

$$E[s_2'^2] = \sigma^2 = E[n_1(\bar{x}_1 - \bar{x})^2 + n_2(\bar{x}_2 - \bar{x})^2 + n_1\eta_1^2 + n_2\eta_2^2 - 2n_1\eta_1(\bar{x}_1 - \bar{x}) - 2n_2\eta_2(\bar{x}_2 - \bar{x})];$$

$$\text{so } \sigma^2 = E\left[\sum_i^2 n_i(\bar{x}_i - \bar{x})^2\right] + n_1\eta_1^2 + n_2\eta_2^2 - 2n_1\eta_1\, E[\bar{x}_1 - \bar{x}] - 2n_2\eta_2\, E[\bar{x}_2 - \bar{x}],$$

whence after some manipulation we obtain

$$E\left[\sum_i^2 n_i(\bar{x}_i - \bar{x})^2\right] = E[s_2^2] = \sigma^2 + n_1\eta_1^2 + n_2\eta_2^2 \quad (6.12)$$

$$= \sigma^2 + \frac{n_1 n_2}{n_1 + n_2}(\xi_1 - \xi_2)^2; \quad (6.13)$$

(6.13) resulting from simple manipulation following inserting of $(\xi_i - \xi)$ for η_i in (6.12). Therefore, if the null hypothesis $\xi_1 = \xi_2$ is true, then $s_2^2 = s_2'^2$ and so is distributed as $\sigma^2\chi^2(1)$, and

$$\frac{s_2^2}{s^2} \sim F(1, n_1 + n_2 - 2). \quad (6.14)$$

If $\xi_1 \neq \xi_2$, then s_2^2 will have an expected value greater than σ^2, and the ratio s_2^2/s^2 will reach the $(1 - \alpha)$ point of the F distribution more than α of the time. The test will thus have appreciable power against the alternative $\xi_1 \neq \xi_2$.

An alternative approach is as follows. The sample means $\bar{x}_1$ and $\bar{x}_2$ are independent of $\sum_{\nu}^{n_1} (x_{1\nu} - \bar{x}_1)^2$ and $\sum_{\nu}^{n_2} (x_{2\nu} - \bar{x}_2)^2$; so they are independent of s^2 as defined in (6.4). s^2 is distributed as $\sigma^2\chi^2(n_1 + n_2 - 2)/(n_1 + n_2 - 2)$; so s^2/σ^2 is distributed as $\chi^2(n_1 + n_1 - 2)/(n_1 + n_2 - 2)$. Under the null hypothesis $\xi_1 = \xi_2$, $(\bar{x}_1 - \bar{x}_2)$ will be distributed about zero with variance $(\sigma^2/n_1 + \sigma^2/n_2) = \sigma^2(1/n_1 + 1/n_2)$; so

$$\frac{\bar{x}_1 - \bar{x}_2}{\sigma\sqrt{1/n_1 + 1/n_2}} \sim u.$$

Substituting this for the numerator and $\sqrt{s^2/\sigma^2}$ for the denominator in (3.7), we get

$$\frac{\bar{x}_1 - \bar{x}_2}{\sigma\sqrt{1/n_1 + 1/n_2}} \cdot \frac{1}{s/\sigma} = \frac{\bar{x}_1 - \bar{x}_2}{s\sqrt{1/n_1 + 1/n_2}} \sim t(n_1 + n_2 - 2). \qquad (6.15)$$

The test of the null hypothesis $\xi_1 = \xi_2$ is usually made in this form. Essentially the test of (6.14) is identical, however, for we can write

$$\begin{aligned} s_2^2 &= n_1(\bar{x}_1 - \bar{x})^2 + n_2(\bar{x}_2 - \bar{x})^2 \\ &= n_1\left(\bar{x}_1 - \frac{n_1\bar{x}_1 + n_2\bar{x}_2}{n_1 + n_2}\right)^2 + n_2\left(\bar{x}_2 - \frac{n_1\bar{x}_1 + n_2\bar{x}_2}{n_1 + n_2}\right)^2 \\ &= \frac{(\bar{x}_1 - \bar{x}_2)^2}{(n_1 + n_2)^2}(n_1n_2^2 + n_1^2n_2) = \frac{(\bar{x}_1 - \bar{x}_2)^2}{1/n_1 + 1/n_2}; \end{aligned} \qquad (6.16)$$

so

$$\frac{s_2^2}{s^2} = \frac{(\bar{x}_1 - \bar{x}_2)^2}{s^2(1/n_1 + 1/n_2)},$$

which is the square of (6.15). Since $t^2(n_1 + n_2 - 2) = F(1, n_1 + n_2 - 2)$, the two tests are identical. Confidence limits for $(\xi_1 - \xi_2)$ are obtained from (6.15) as

$$\Pr\left\{(\bar{x}_1 - \bar{x}_2) - t_{P_2}s\sqrt{\frac{1}{n_1} + \frac{1}{n_2}} < \xi_1 - \xi_2 < (\bar{x}_1 - \bar{x}_2) - t_{P_1}s\sqrt{\frac{1}{n_1} + \frac{1}{n_2}}\right\} = P_2 - P_1. \qquad (6.17)$$

As an illustration of the two-sample t test, we will use two series of determinations of the atomic weight of scandium by Honigschmid [6] (Table 9.3.) The figures are given in units in the third decimal place; so 79 corresponds to 45.079. Certain calculations are given in Table 9.4. From (6.4),

$$s^2 = \frac{1937.50 + 2546.50}{8 - 1 + 10 - 1} = 280.25.$$

Table 9.3

Series *A*	79, 84, 108, 114, 120, 103, 122, 120,
Series *B*	91, 103, 90, 113, 108, 87, 100, 80, 99, 54.

Table 9.4

	n_i	$\sum_{\nu}^{n_i} x_{i\nu}$	$\bar{x}_i$	$\sum_{\nu}^{n_i} x_{i\nu}^2$	$\frac{\left(\sum_{\nu}^{n_i} x_{i\nu}\right)^2}{n_i}$	$\sum_{\nu}^{n_i} (x_{i\nu} - \bar{x}_i)^2$
Series *A*	8	850	106.25	92,250	90,312.50	1,937.50
Series *B*	10	925	92.50	88,109	85,562.50	2,546.50

To perform the test of (6.14) we could compute s_2^2 as defined in (6.11), but the identity (6.16) is more convenient:

$$s_2^2 = \frac{(106.25 - 92.50)^2}{1/8 + 1/10} = 840.278.$$

Under the null hypothesis $\xi_1 = \xi_2$, the ratio (6.14), $s_2^2/s^2 = 840.278/280.25 = 2.998$, has the F distribution with degrees of freedom 1 and 16. The 0.90 point of F with these degrees of freedom is 3.05, and so we could not reject the null hypothesis at the 0.10 level of significance.

It would be more customary to use (6.15);

$$\frac{106.25 - 92.50}{\sqrt{280.25}\sqrt{1/8 + 1/10}} = \frac{13.75}{7.9408} = 1.732$$

is referred to the t table with 16 degrees of freedom. The 0.90 and 0.95 points of $t(16)$ are 1.337 and 1.746, and so the two-sided P value is just greater than 0.10. It will be noted that the square of our t $(1.732)^2 = 3.00$, equals the F previously found, within rounding errors.

For 95 per cent confidence limits we need $t_{0.975}(16) = 2.120$, $t_{0.025}(16) = -2.120$, $\bar{x}_1 - \bar{x}_2 = 13.75$, and $s\sqrt{1/n_1 + 1/n_2} = 7.9408$, to get $13.75 \pm 2.120 \times 7.9408 = (-3.08, 30.58)$.

9.7. The Two-Sample Test with Unequal Variances

Suppose that we have two independent samples $x_{11}, \ldots, x_{1n_1}$ and $x_{21}, \ldots, x_{2n_2}$ from normal distributions with means ξ_1 and ξ_2 and variances σ_1^2 and σ_2^2. We wish to test the null hypothesis that $\xi_1 = \xi_2$: We do not assume knowledge of σ_1^2 or σ_2^2, and in distinction to the previous section we do not assume that $\sigma_1^2 = \sigma_2^2$. This problem has proved difficult, and all the proposed solutions have been criticized. The problem is frequently referred to as the Behrens–Fisher problem on account of Fisher's advocacy of a solution proposed by Behrens. An alternative approach, due to Welch [7], [8], admittedly an approximation, is somewhat easier to follow and is also useful in other contexts.

We saw in Section 2.9 that the means $\bar{x}_1$, $\bar{x}_2$ are normally distributed with variances σ_1^2/n_1, σ_2^2/n_2, and

$$\frac{(\bar{x}_1 - \bar{x}_2) - (\xi_1 - \xi_2)}{\sqrt{\sigma_1^2/n_1 + \sigma_2^2/n_2}} \tag{7.1}$$

is a unit normal deviate. However, we do not know the σ_i^2, and the problem is to determine the distribution of (7.1) when we insert sample estimates s_i^2 based on degrees of freedom f_i. Here the s_1^2 and s_2^2 correspond to the s^2 in (5.3) calculated separately for each sample. We want the distribution of

$$\frac{(\bar{x}_1 - \bar{x}_2) - (\xi_1 - \xi_2)}{\sqrt{s_1^2/n_1 + s_2^2/n_2}}. \tag{7.2}$$

We will first discuss a more general question. Suppose that S_i are independent sums of squares with f_i degrees of freedom such that the mean squares $s_i^2 = S_i^2/f_i$ have expected values σ_i^2, $i = 1, \ldots, k$. Suppose that we are concerned with a linear combination of the mean squares,

$$S^2 = a_1 s_1^2 + \cdots + a_k s_k^2 = \sum_i^k a_i s_i^2, \tag{7.3}$$

where the a_i are known constants.

We shall need $V[s_i^2]$. From (8.2.6), s_i^2 is distributed as $\sigma_i^2\, \chi^2(f_i)/f_i$, and, from Section 9.3 $V[\chi^2(f_i)/f_i] = 2/f_i$;

$$V[s_i^2] = V\left[\frac{\sigma_i^2 \chi^2(f_i)}{f_i}\right] = (\sigma_i^2)^2\, V\left[\frac{\chi^2(f_i)}{f_i}\right] = \frac{2(\sigma_i^2)^2}{f_i}. \tag{7.4}$$

We propose to approximate the distribution of S^2, defined in (7.3) as a linear combination of the s_i^2, by the distribution of a mean square with some number, say f', of degrees of freedom. The approach is to make the expectation and variance of the approximating distribution the same as the expectation and variance of the actual distribution. The variance of S^2 is

$$V[S^2] = V[\sum_i^k a_i s_i^2] = \sum_i^k a_i^2 V[s_i^2] = \sum_i^k a_i^2 \frac{2(\sigma_i^2)^2}{f_i}. \tag{7.5}$$

On the other hand, the variance of a genuine mean square with the same expectation as S^2, namely $\sum_i^k a_i\sigma_i^2$, and degrees of freedom f', is, from (7.4)

$$\frac{2(\sum_i^k a_i\sigma_i^2)^2}{f'}. \tag{7.6}$$

We now equate the variances (7.5) and (7.6) and solve for f':

$$f' = \frac{(\sum_i^k a_i\sigma_i^2)^2}{\sum_i^k a_i^2 \frac{(\sigma_i^2)^2}{f_i}}. \tag{7.7}$$

In practice, we do not know the values of the σ_i^2, and so we have to substitute the sample estimates s_i^2; so f' is estimated as

$$f' \simeq \frac{(\sum_i^k a_i s_i^2)^2}{\sum_i^k a_i^2 \frac{(s_i^2)^2}{f_i}}. \tag{7.8}$$

To revert to our particular problem, we are concerned with the linear combination of two variances s_1^2 and s_2^2, namely, $(s_1^2/n_1) + (s_2^2/n_2)$, and so our coefficients are $a_1 = 1/n_1$, $a_2 = 1/n_2$. Substituting these values of the coefficients in (7.8), we get

$$\begin{aligned} f' &\simeq \frac{[(s_1^2/n_1) + (s_2^2/n_2)]^2}{(1/n_1)^2(s_1^2)^2/(n_1 - 1) + (1/n_2)^2(s_2^2)^2/(n_2 - 1)} \\ &\simeq \frac{[(s_1^2/n_1) + (s_2^2/n_2)]^2}{(s_1^2/n_1)^2/(n_1 - 1) + (s_2^2/n_2)^2/(n_2 - 1)}. \end{aligned} \tag{7.9}$$

If we define

$$c = \frac{s_1^2/n_1}{s_1^2/n_1 + s_2^2/n_2}, \tag{7.10}$$

we can derive

$$\frac{1}{f'} = \frac{c^2}{f_1} + \frac{(1-c)^2}{f_2}. \tag{7.11}$$

It is then easy to show, by differentiating $1/f'$ with respect to c and then equating to zero, that the maximum value that f' can take is $(f_1 + f_2)$: This occurs when

$$\frac{s_1^2}{n_1(n_1 - 1)} = \frac{s_2^2}{n_2(n_2 - 1)} . \tag{7.12}$$

The smallest value that f' can approach is the minimum of f_1 and f_2: This occurs when either $(1 - c)$ or c approaches zero, i.e., when $(s_2^2/n_2)/(s_1^2/n_1)$ or $(s_1^2/n_1)/(s_2^2/n_2)$ approaches zero.

As an example of this procedure we will use the data of Dean on the atomic weight of carbon quoted in Table 7.6 for an illustration of the Wilcoxon two-sample test which gave an exact one-sided P value of 0.0317 and a normal approximation of 0.033. Here we need to compute the separate s_i^2. Using (5.13), for the first sample A, we can subtract a constant, 12.0000, from all observations:

$$s_1^2 = \frac{(0.0072)^2 + \cdots + (0.0077)^2 - (0.0072 + \cdots + 0.0077)^2/5}{5 - 1}$$

$$= \frac{(18{,}381 - 16{,}017.80) \times 10^{-8}}{4} = 590.80 \times 10^{-8}.$$

Similarly $s_2^2 = 7460.00 \times 10^{-8}$. Also $\bar{x}_1 = 12.00566$ and $\bar{x}_2 = 11.99620$. For the null hypothesis $\xi_1 = \xi_2$, the test statistic (7.2) is

$$\frac{(12.00566 - 11.99620) - 0}{\sqrt{590.80 \times 10^{-8}/5 + 7460.00 \times 10^{-8}/4}} = 2.124.$$

The approximate number of degrees of freedom of this t-like statistic is given by (7.9): First calculating

$$\frac{s_1^2}{n_1} = \frac{590.80 \times 10^{-8}}{5} = 118.16 \times 10^{-8},$$

$$\frac{s_2^2}{n_2} = \frac{7460.00 \times 10^{-8}}{4} = 1865.00 \times 10^{-8},$$

we get

$$f' \simeq \frac{(118.16 + 1865.00)^2}{(118.16)^2/(5 - 1) + (1865.00)^2/(4 - 1)} = 3.38.$$

The t table (Table II of the appendix) shows that for degrees of freedom 3 and 4 the 0.95 point is 2.353 and 2.132. For 3.38 degrees of freedom the 0.95 point will be approximately 2.27. The one-sided P value for the observed value of the statistic, 2.124, is thus greater than 0.05.

If we had treated this problem as an ordinary two-sample t test we would have obtained $t = 2.372$ with 7 degrees of freedom corresponding to a one-sided P value of just less than 0.025, so making the assumption that the variances are from the same population makes a substantial difference in the conclusions reached. The two-sample Wilcoxon test agrees closely with the two-sample t test, but it too makes the assumption that the variances of the two populations are the same.

It is interesting to note the results of falsely assuming that the two sample variances are samples of a common variance and using (6.15) instead of (7.2). The numerators of these two statistics are identical and they differ only in their denominators. If $f_i = n_i - 1$, and if $s_1^2/s_2^2 = F$, so that $s_1^2 = Fs_2^2$, the square of the denominator of (6.16) is

$$\frac{f_1 s_1^2 + f_2 s_2^2}{f_1 + f_2}\left(\frac{1}{f_1 + 1} + \frac{1}{f_2 + 1}\right), \tag{7.13}$$

and the square of the denominator of (7.2) is

$$\frac{s_1^2}{f_1 + 1} + \frac{s_2^2}{f_2 + 1}. \tag{7.14}$$

The ratio of (7.14) to (7.13) is reducible to

$$\frac{(Ff_1 + f_2)(f_1 + f_2 + 2)}{(f_1 + f_2)(f_1 + Ff_2 + F + 1)}. \tag{7.15}$$

If we are using equal sample sizes, so that $f_1 = f_2 = f$, say, then the ratio (7.15) equals

$$\frac{(Ff + f)(2f + 2)}{2f(Ff + F + f + 1)} = 1$$

no matter what the value of F. Thus, for equal sample sizes, the test statistic has the same numerical value, and the only difference would be that we would refer (6.16) to the t table with $2f$ degrees of freedom whereas we would refer (7.2) to the t table with degrees of freedom given by (7.9), which in the case of $f_1 = f_2 = f$ becomes

$$f' = f\frac{(F + 1)^2}{F^2 + 1}, \tag{7.16}$$

which will always be less than $2f$ except when $F = 1$. But, for $0.5 < F < 2$, the reduction in the number of degrees of freedom does not exceed 10 per cent; for $0.333 < F < 3$, not 20 per cent; so that, when the sample sizes are equal and sample variances nearly equal, there is little difference between the procedures.

However, when the sample sizes are unequal, for example, when $f_1 \gg f_2$, (7.15) tends to F; i.e., the test statistic will be in error by a ratio approaching $\sqrt{F}$. Since there are no theoretical bounds on F, the test statistic could be in error by any amount.

We conclude, therefore, that the two-sample t test is rather sensitive to the assumption that the sample variances come from a common population, unless the sample sizes are close to equality. For markedly unequal sample sizes, and when the assumption that the sample variances are from a common population cannot be justified, a preferable procedure would be to use the methods of this section. A further conclusion is that the sample sizes should be made equal if possible.

The treatment of the two-sample test with unequal variances is subject to disagreements which are still unresolved; see Fisher [10]. However important the controversy from the point of view of statistical theory, it seems that the Welch procedure described here is close enough to the truth to be used in practice without qualms. The k-sample form appears to have been first published by Satterthwaite [11].

9.8. A Comparison of Simple Tests for Means and Medians

We have now discussed seven tests, listed in Table 9.5, for means or medians, and the question arises: Which is appropriate in any particular situation? The four tests listed under the heading "Unpaired" are for the case of two sets of independent observations $x_{11}, x_{12}, \ldots, x_{1n_1}$ and $x_{21}, x_{22}, \ldots, x_{2n_2}$. At the head of the table, we require normality and equality of variances. At the next stage, on the one hand the Welch modification of the t test dispenses with the requirement of equality of variance but continues to require normality, and on the other hand the two-sample Wilcoxon test requires equality of variances but dispenses with the requirement of normality. The t test and its modification, of course, are tests for the mean, but, since they assume normality, and since the normal distribution is symmetric, and hence has its median coinciding with its mean, they can also be regarded as tests for the median. The Wilcoxon and median tests are tests for the median and will only be tests for the mean if the distributions happen to have their means and medians coinciding, as will be the case, for example, if the distributions are symmetric. The median test, requiring only independence, continuity, and identity, is probably affected only slightly by moderate departures from the assumption of identity.

The three tests under the heading "one sample or paired" in Table 9.5 are strictly for a single set of independent observations $d_1, d_2, \ldots, d_n$. In practice, these observations very often arise as the differences between pairs of observations, and hence Table 9.4 gives the implications that follow from assumptions about the d_i when the d_i are so formed. It is interesting to note that, whereas the unpaired two-sample t test requires equality of variances, this assumption is not necessary for the paired test. In going from the one-sample t test to the one-sample Wilcoxon test, the assumption of normality is replaced by the weaker assumption of symmetry

Table 9.5. Assumptions Involved in Various Tests
All tests assume that the observations are independent.

Test	Two sample or unpaired	One sample or paired
t test	Normality and equality of variances (Welch's modification is an approximate treatment of the case of unequal variances)	Normality. If the observations are formed as paired differences, the parent populations must be normal but may have different variances
Wilcoxon	Identity of distributions for the two samples. This implies equality of variances. Continuity is also assumed	Symmetry of the distribution of the observations about zero and continuity. If the observations are formed as paired differences, this requires either (1) that the two distributions be identical, or (2) if the distributions be not identical, then that they both be symmetrical.
Sign and median	Median test assumes identity and continuity	Sign test assumes that the observations have median zero, and are continuous

about zero. For the case of paired differences, this condition can be satisfied in either of the two ways listed in the table. The sign test makes even weaker demands, the symmetry about zero required by the corresponding Wilcoxon test being relaxed to merely that the observations have median zero.

Obviously, the price involved in the use of the tests with the stronger assumptions is not wasted: We get in return greater power if in fact the stronger assumptions are satisfied. Conversely, the tests employing weaker assumptions have lower power. Yet it is rash to use the more powerful tests unless their assumptions are satisfied: It is pointless to obtain a greater nominal power if in fact the test is giving seriously incorrect probabilities of error of the first kind.

Technical definitions and discussions of the power of these tests are beyond the scope of this textbook. Even though we do not attempt these definitions, the reader will not be led astray if we say that the power of the Wilcoxon tests is of the order of 90 per cent of the corresponding t tests, and the power of the median and sign tests is of the order of 67 per cent.

An important, but rather elusive, topic of applied statistics is the question of the *robustness* of the procedures. A *robust* procedure is one which is relatively insensitive to departures from its assumptions. For example, a numerical comparison of the two-sample t test with the Wilcoxon two-sample test for distributions with known nonnormality shows that the t test is robust with respect to mild departures from normality. Using (7.15) and (7.16), we saw that the two-sample t test could be made very insensitive to departures from the assumption of equality of variances by using equal sample sizes. Box and Andersen [9] have concluded, on the other hand, that Bartlett's test for equality of variances is excessively sensitive to departures from the assumption of normality, but the analysis of variance, to be discussed in Chapter 10, is remarkably insensitive to what they call "general nonnormality," i.e., the case where the observations all have the same nonnormal distribution with possibly different means.

REFERENCES

1. Bartlett, M. S., "Properties of sufficiency and statistical tests," *Proceedings of the Royal Society of London*, A, 160(1937), 268–282.
2. Michelson, A. A., "Measurement of the velocity of light between Mount Wilson and Mount San Antonio," *Astrophysical Journal*, LXV(1927), 1–14.
3. Hartley, H. O., "Testing the homogeneity of a set of variances," *Biometrika*, 31(1940), 249–255.
4. ——— "The maximum F ratio as a short-cut test for heterogeneity of variance," *Biometrika*, 37(1950), 308–312.
5. Pearson, E. S., and H. O. Hartley (eds.), *Biometrika Tables for Statisticians*, vol.I. Cambridge, England: University Press, 1954.
6. Honigschmid, O., "Neure Atomgewichtsbestimmungen," *Zeitschrift fur Electrochemie*, 25(1919), 91–96.
7. Welch, B. L., "The significance of the difference between two means when the population variances are unequal," *Biometrika*, 29(1937), 350–362.
8. ——— "The generalization of 'Student's' problem when several different population variances are involved," *Biometrika*, 34(1947), 28–35.
9. Box, G. E. P., and S. L. Andersen, "Permutation theory in the derivation of robust criteria and the study of the departures from assumption," *Journal of the Royal Statistical Society*, B (Methodological), 17(1955), 1–26.
10. Fisher, R. A., "Comment on the notes by Neyman, Bartlett, and Welch in this journal," *Journal of the Royal Statistical Society*, B, 19(1957), 179.
11. Satterthwaite, F. E., "An approximate distribution of estimates of variance components," *Biometrics Bulletin*, 2(1946), 110–114.

EXERCISES

9.1. A laboratory handles large numbers of microbiological assays each day. To check on the variance of the assay, six samples of the identical material are distributed at random throughout the day's samples, every day. The sample estimate of the variance is calculated each day from the results of these six samples. Over a long period it has been found that the average variance is 10 (units)^2. Construct 90 per cent control limits for these sample variances.

9.2. A new analytical procedure for the determination of titanium was developed. To show its reproducibility the author presented the following six presumably independent determinations on the same sample:

0.0087, 0.0091, 0.0094, 0.0096, 0.0098, 0.0098.

(*a*) Give 95 per cent confidence limits for the variance.

(*b*) Supposing that another analytical method has a variance estimated with 10 degrees of freedom as 94.0×10^{-8}, test the null hypothesis that the two population variances are equal.

(*c*) Construct 95 per cent confidence limits for the ratio of these two variances.

9.3. A new analytical procedure is proposed as a replacement for the procedure currently in use. The variance of the latter is known. We wish to test at the 0.01 level of significance the null hypothesis that the variance of the new procedure is equal to the variance of the old against the alternative hypothesis that it is greater. If it is greater in the ratio 5/3, we want to have a 0.95 probability of rejecting the null hypothesis. How many degrees of freedom do we need for our estimate of the variance of the new procedure? Suppose that the alternative hypothesis is that the variance of the new procedure is less than that of the old, and that, if it is smaller in the ratio 3/5, we want to have a 0.95 probability of rejecting the null hypothesis. How many degrees of freedom do we need for our estimate of the variance of the new procedure?

9.4. Two new analytical procedures A and B are developed. A is somewhat more difficult than B. We wish to test at the 0.01 level of significance the null hypothesis that the variances are equal against the alternative that the variance of B is greater than the variance of A. If it is greater by the ratio 3/1, we want to have a 0.95 probability of rejecting the null hypothesis. Assuming that we run equal numbers of replicates with the two procedures, how many degrees of freedom do we need in each sample?

9.5. Samples of very pure iron prepared by two different methods had the following melting points:

A:	1493, 1519, 1518, 1512, 1512, 1514, 1489, 1508, 1508, 1494.
B:	1509, 1494, 1512, 1483, 1507, 1491.

(*a*) Test the null hypothesis that the two methods give iron with the same melting point. (*b*) Construct 95 per cent confidence limits for the difference $(A - B)$.

Assume normality, and (i) assume the variances are the same, and (ii) do not assume that the variances are the same.

9.6. For the data of Exercise 7.3, obtain the one-sided P value for the null hypothesis that the difference between the two types of gages is zero, using (*a*) the data as it stands, (*b*) the logarithms of the data. Give an explanation for the difference between the results, and indicate which you would prefer.

9.7. For the data of Exercise 7.4, test the null hypothesis that the variances of the two samples could come from populations with the same variance. Is a one-sided or a two-sided test appropriate here?

9.8. For the data of Exercise 7.4, obtain the one-sided P value for the null hypothesis that the means are the same, (*a*) assuming normality and equality of variances, (*b*) assuming normality but making no assumption about equality of variances.

9.9. The table below gives the reciprocals of the data of Exercise 7.4. Perform the same tests on these data as were required in Exercises 7.4, 9.7, and 9.8.

Control *A*:	0.200, 0.167, 0.143, 0.143, 0.125, 0.125, 0.125, 0.111, 0.083.
Drug *B*:	0.143, 0.125, 0.125, 0.125, 0.111, 0.111, 0.083, 0.077, 0.071, 0.059.

Discuss possible reasons for differences between the various results.

9.10. The data below are the results of octane determinations on samples of gasoline obtained in four regions of the northeastern United States in the summer of 1953.

Region *A*	Region *B*	Region *C*	Region *D*
84.0	82.4	83.2	80.2
83.5	82.4	82.8	82.9
84.0	83.4	83.4	84.6
85.0	83.3	80.2	84.2
83.1	83.1	82.7	82.8
83.5	83.3	83.0	83.0
81.7	82.4	85.0	82.9
85.4	83.3	83.0	83.4
84.1	82.6	85.0	83.1
83.0	82.0	83.7	83.5
85.8	83.2	83.6	83.6
84.0	83.1	83.3	86.7
84.2	82.5	83.8	82.6
82.2		85.1	82.4
83.6		83.1	83.4
84.9		84.2	82.7
		80.6	82.9
		82.3	83.7
			81.5
			81.9
			81.7
			82.5

Data from O. C. Blade, "National motor-gasoline survey," *Bureau of Mines Report of Investigation* 5041.

Test the null hypothesis that the variability in octane number is the same for all four regions.

Some calculations which may be useful are summarized below.

Region	*A*	*B*	*C*	*D*
n_i	16	13	18	22
$\sum_{\nu}^{n_i} x_{i\nu}$	62.0	37.0	58.0	66.2
$\sum_{\nu}^{n_i} x_{i\nu}^2$	258.06	107.98	215.86	232.24

A constant 80 has been subtracted from all observations before making these calculations.

9.11. Rosa and Dorsey (see Exercise 10.2) measured the ratio of the electromagnetic to the electrostatic unit of electricity with great precision. In a long series of observations they on occasion disassembled their apparatus, cleaned it, and reassembled it. The variances of the groups of observations, multiplied by 10^8, and numbers of observations in each group, were as follows.

Group	Number of observations	Variance
1	11	1.5636
2	8	1.1250
3	6	3.7666
4	24	4.1721
5	15	4.2666

Test the null hypothesis that these sample variances could come from a common population.

CHAPTER 10

One-Way Analysis of Variance

10.1. Introduction: Models I and II

We have seen in Section 9.6 that two sample means can be compared with the two-sample t test. The generalization of this problem to k groups, $k > 2$, brings us to the body of techniques known as the analysis of variance. In this chapter we shall be concerned with the case in which the data are subject to only one dimension of classification. There are two somewhat different situations. In the first, known as model I, the groups in the sample represent the particular groups in which we are interested. In the second, known as model II, we have no particular interest in the particular groups that happen to be in the sample, our concern being to estimate the variance of the infinite population of group means from which our sample has been randomly selected.

As an illustration of the difference between models I and II, consider a machine tool manufacturer producing a standard model in quantity, who is interested in some variable associated with the quality of the items produced by the tool. A customer may purchase k tools, and the manufacturer may supply him with a sample taken at random from his current production. The measurements are made on a sample of the items produced by these k tools, and the data analyzed by both the customer and the manufacturer. From the point of view of the customer, he is concerned solely with these k tools sitting on his floor, and he uses a model I approach. From the point of view of the manufacturer, these k tools are merely a random sample, and he is only concerned with using these measurements to estimate the variance of the population of tools; therefore he uses a model II approach.

The problem of whether any particular situation is model I or model II is often clarified by asking the question, "If we were to repeat the experiment, would we have the same groups or not?" Clearly in the model I case we would; in the model II case, the probability of getting the identical sample, or even any single group, a second time is zero.

Model I can be regarded as the case where the sample consists of all groups in the population, and model II as the case where the interest is in the infinite population from which the sample came. In Sections 13.9 and 13.10 we shall consider the intermediate case in which the population is finite; there, by letting the population size decrease to the sample size or increase to infinity, we will get models I and II as special cases.

10.2. One-way Analysis of Variance: Model I

Suppose that we have k groups of independent observations $x_{11}, \ldots, x_{1n_1}, x_{21}, \ldots, x_{2n_2}, \ldots, x_{k1}, \ldots, x_{kn_k}$ from normally distributed populations with means $\xi_1, \ldots, \xi_k$, all with the same variance σ^2. Thus the model is

$$x_{i\nu} = \xi_i + z_{i\nu}; \qquad i = 1, \ldots, k, \quad \nu = 1, \ldots, n_i \tag{2.1}$$

where the ξ_i are fixed constants and the $z_{i\nu}$ are independent random normal deviates with zero mean and variance σ^2.

It is often helpful, but not always essential, when averaging over a suffix to replace that suffix with a dot. Thus $\bar{x}_{i\cdot} = \sum_{\nu}^{n_i} \frac{x_{i\nu}}{n_i}$. We also define $\bar{x}_{\cdot\cdot}$ as the weighted average of the $\bar{x}_{i\cdot}$, or what comes to the same thing, as the grand average of all the $x_{i\nu}$, since $n_i\bar{x}_{i\cdot} = \sum_{\nu}^{n_i} x_{i\nu}$:

$$\bar{x}_{\cdot\cdot} = \frac{\sum_i^k n_i\bar{x}_{i\cdot}}{\sum_i^k n_i} = \frac{\sum_i^k \sum_\nu^{n_i} x_{i\nu}}{\sum_i^k n_i}. \tag{2.2}$$

In consequence of these definitions,

$$\sum_i^k n_i(\bar{x}_{i\cdot} - \bar{x}_{\cdot\cdot}) = \sum_i^k n_i\bar{x}_{i\cdot} - \bar{x}_{\cdot\cdot} \sum_i^k n_i = 0. \tag{2.3}$$

From (8.4.19), for each group we can write

$$\sum_\nu^{n_i} (x_{i\nu} - \xi_i)^2 = n_i(\bar{x}_{i\cdot} - \xi_i)^2 + \sum_\nu^{n_i} (x_{i\nu} - \bar{x}_{i\cdot})^2, \tag{2.4}$$

where the sums of squares are distributed as $\sigma^2\chi^2$ with degrees of freedom n_i, 1, and $(n_i - 1)$, respectively, and the two terms on the right-hand side are independent. Now sum (2.4) over all k groups:

$$\sum_i^k \sum_\nu^{n_i} (x_{i\nu} - \xi_i)^2 = \sum_i^k n_i(\bar{x}_{i.} - \xi_i)^2 + \sum_i^k \sum_\nu^{n_i} (x_{i\nu} - \bar{x}_{i.})^2. \qquad (2.5)$$

We saw in (8.3.1) that the sum of a number of $\chi^2(f_i)$ is itself distributed as $\chi^2 (\sum_i^k f_i)$; so the sums of squares in (2.5) are distributed as $\sigma^2\chi^2$ with degrees of freedom $\sum_i^k n_i$, k, $\sum_i^k (n_i - 1) = (\sum_i^k n_i) - k$, respectively. If we define

$$s_1^2 = \frac{\sum_i^k \sum_\nu^{n_i} (x_{i\nu} - \bar{x}_{i.})^2}{(\sum_i^k n_i) - k}, \qquad (2.6)$$

it has expected value

$$E[s_1^2] = \frac{E[\sigma^2\chi^2(\sum_i^k n_i - k)]}{\sum_i^k n_i - k} = \sigma^2 ; \qquad (2.7)$$

so s_1^2 is an estimate of σ^2 with $(\sum_i^k n_i - k)$ degrees of freedom.

Now define

$$\xi = \frac{\sum_i^k n_i \xi_i}{\sum_i^k n_i}, \qquad (2.8)$$

and

$$\eta_i = \xi_i - \xi. \qquad (2.9)$$

Then

$$\sum_i^k n_i \eta_i = \sum_i^k n_i(\xi_i - \xi) = \sum_i^k n_i \xi_i - \xi \sum_i^k n_i = 0. \qquad (2.10)$$

The first term on the right-hand side of (2.5) involves $(\bar{x}_{i.} - \xi_i)$, which we can write in the form

$$\bar{x}_{i.} - \xi_i = (\bar{x}_{i.} - \bar{x}_{..}) - (\xi_i - \xi) + (\bar{x}_{..} - \xi) = (\bar{x}_{i.} - \bar{x}_{..} - \eta_i) + (\bar{x}_{..} - \xi).$$

Squaring and summing over i and ν gives

$$\sum_i^k n_i(\bar{x}_{i.} - \xi_i)^2 = \sum_i^k n_i(\bar{x}_{i.} - \bar{x}_{..} - \eta_i)^2 + (\bar{x}_{..} - \xi)^2 \sum_i^k n_i, \qquad (2.11)$$

since the cross product

$$2(\bar{x}_{..} - \xi)\sum_i^k n_i(\bar{x}_{i.} - \bar{x}_{..} - \eta_i) = 2(\bar{x}_{..} - \xi)[\sum_i^k n_i(\bar{x}_{i.} - \bar{x}_{..}) - \sum_i^k n_i\eta_i] = 0,$$

by (2.3) and (2.10). In (2.11) the left-hand side is distributed as $\sigma^2\chi^2(k)$. We have partitioned this sum of squares into two sums of squares. The first of these components involves k variables $(\bar{x}_{i.} - \bar{x}_{..})$, on which there is the one restriction (2.3); so it will have $(k - 1)$ degrees of freedom. The second involves the single variable $\bar{x}_{..}$, on which there is no restriction; so it will have one degree of freedom. The situation is thus analogous to (8.4.19), and the two sums of squares will be distributed as $\sigma^2\chi^2$ and will be independent. If we define

$$s_2'^2 = \frac{\sum_i^k n_i(\bar{x}_{i.} - \bar{x}_{..} - \eta_i)^2}{k - 1}, \tag{2.12}$$

it will have expected value

$$E[s_2'^2] = \frac{E[\sigma^2\chi^2(k - 1)]}{k - 1} = \sigma^2, \tag{2.13}$$

with $(k - 1)$ degrees of freedom, and be independent of s_1^2. Hence $s_2'^2$, s_1^2 are independent estimates of σ^2, and their ratio has the F distribution with degrees of freedom $k - 1, \sum_i^k n_i - k$.

Define

$$s_2^2 = \frac{\sum_i^k n_i(\bar{x}_{i.} - \bar{x}_{..})^2}{k - 1}. \tag{2.14}$$

To find the expected value of s_2^2, we note that, using (2.12) and (2.13),

$$E[s_2'^2] = \sigma^2 = E\left[\frac{\sum_i^k n_i(\bar{x}_{i.} - \bar{x}_{..} - \eta_i)^2}{k - 1}\right];$$

so, multiplying out the square and multiplying by $(k - 1)$ throughout,

$$\begin{aligned}(k - 1)\sigma^2 &= E[\sum_i^k n_i(\bar{x}_{i.} - \bar{x}_{..})^2] + \sum_i^k n_i\eta_i^2 - 2\sum_i^k n_i\eta_i\, E[\bar{x}_{i.} - \bar{x}_{..}] \\ &= (k - 1)\, E[s_2^2] - \sum_i^k n_i\eta_i^2.\end{aligned}$$

Thus

$$E[s_2^2] = \sigma^2 + \frac{\sum_i^k n_i(\xi_i - \xi)^2}{k - 1}. \tag{2.15}$$

If the null hypothesis that $\xi_i = \xi_k$ for all i is true, $\xi_i - \xi = 0$, $s_2^2 = s_2'^2$, and so s_2^2 will have the distribution $\sigma^2\chi^2(k-1)/(k-1)$. Therefore

$$\frac{s_2^2}{s_1^2} \sim F\left(k-1, \sum_i^k n_i - k\right) \tag{2.16}$$

under the null hypothesis.

These results are conventionally and conveniently summarized in an analysis-of-variance table (Table 10.1).

Table 10.1

Source of variance	Sums of squares	Degrees of freedom	Mean squares	E[M.S.]
Between groups	$\sum_i^k(\bar{x}_{i\cdot} - \bar{x}_{\cdot\cdot})^2$	$k-1$	s_2^2	$\sigma^2 + \frac{1}{k-1}\sum_i^k n_i(\xi_i - \xi)^2$
Within groups	$\sum_i^k\sum_\nu^{n_i}(x_{i\nu} - \bar{x}_{i\cdot})^2$	$(\sum_i^k n_i) - k$	s_1^2	σ^2
Total	$\sum_i^k\sum_\nu^{n_i}(x_{i\nu} - \bar{x}_{\cdot\cdot})^2$	$(\sum_i^k n_i) - 1$		

While s_1^2 and s_2^2 can be calculated from (2.6) and (2.14), it is usually easier to use identities that involve working with totals rather than means: Thus the between-group sum of squares is

$$\begin{aligned}
\sum_i^k n_i(\bar{x}_{i\cdot} - \bar{x}_{\cdot\cdot})^2 &= \sum_i^k n_i\bar{x}_{i\cdot}^2 + \sum_i^k n_i\bar{x}_{\cdot\cdot}^2 - 2\bar{x}_{\cdot\cdot}\sum_i^k n_i\bar{x}_{i\cdot} \\
&= \sum_i^k n_i\left(\frac{\sum_\nu^{n_i} x_{i\nu}}{n_i}\right)^2 + \sum_i^k n_i\left(\frac{\sum_i^k\sum_\nu^{n_i} x_{i\nu}}{\sum_i^k n_i}\right)^2 - 2\left(\frac{\sum_i^k\sum_\nu^{n_i} x_{i\nu}}{\sum_i^k n_i}\right)\sum_i^k n_i\left(\frac{\sum_\nu^{n_i} x_{i\nu}}{n_i}\right) \\
&= \sum_i^k\frac{\left(\sum_\nu^{n_i} x_{i\nu}\right)^2}{n_i} - \frac{\left(\sum_i^k\sum_\nu^{n_i} x_{i\nu}\right)^2}{\sum_i^k n_i}.
\end{aligned} \tag{2.17}$$

The within-group sum of squares is

$$\sum_i^k \sum_\nu^{n_i} (x_{i\nu} - \bar{x}_{i.})^2 = \sum_i^k \sum_\nu^{n_i} x_{i\nu}^2 + \sum_i^k n_i \left(\frac{\sum_\nu^{n_i} x_{i\nu}}{n_i} \right)^2 - 2 \sum_i^k \left(\frac{\sum_\nu^{n_i} x_{i\nu}}{n_i} \right) \sum_\nu^{n_i} x_{i\nu}$$

$$= \sum_i^k \sum_\nu^{n_i} x_{i\nu}^2 - \sum_i^k \frac{\left(\sum_\nu^{n_i} x_{i\nu} \right)^2}{n_i} . \tag{2.18}$$

The total sum of squares is

$$\sum_i^k \sum_\nu^{n_i} (x_{i\nu} - \bar{x}_{..})^2 = \sum_i^k \sum_\nu^{n_i} x_{i\nu}^2 - \frac{\left(\sum_i^k \sum_\nu^{n_i} x_{i\nu} \right)^2}{\sum_i^k n_i} . \tag{2.19}$$

Thus for arithmetical computation we need only three items:

A: $\sum_i^k \sum_\nu^{n_i} x_{i\nu}^2$ = sum of squares of all observations x_i (2.20)

B: $\sum_i^k \frac{\left(\sum_\nu^{n_i} x_{i\nu} \right)^2}{n_i}$ = sum of (squares of group totals, each squared group total being divided by the number in that group) (2.21)

C: $\frac{\left(\sum_i^k \sum_\nu^{n_i} x_{i\nu} \right)^2}{\sum_i^k n_i}$ = (square of sum of all observations) divided by total number of observations (2.22)

The three sums of squares in Table 10.1 are then found as $B - C$, $A - B$, and $A - C$, respectively.

As an example of one-way model I analysis of variance, Table 10.2 gives the units in the third decimal place for determinations by Heyl [1] of the gravitational constant G; e.g., 83 corresponds to an observation of 6.683. Balls of three different materials were used. The lower part of the table contains the calculation of items A and B defined by (2.20) and (2.21). We further need C, defined in (2.22), as $(1159)^2/16 = 83{,}955.062$.

Table 10.2

	Gold	Platinum	Glass	Sums
	83	61	78	
	81	61	71	
	76	67	75	
	78	67	72	
	79	64	74	
	72			
n_i	6	5	5	16
$\sum_{\nu}^{n_i} x_{i\nu}$	469	320	370	1,159
$\sum_{\nu}^{n_i} x_{i\nu}^2$	36,735	20,516	27,410	84,661 $= A$
$\dfrac{(\sum_{\nu}^{n_i} x_{i\nu})^2}{n_i}$	36,660.167	20,480.000	27,380.000	84,520.167 $= B$

Then

$$\sum_{i}^{k} n_i(\bar{x}_{i\cdot} - \bar{x}_{\cdot\cdot})^2 = B - C = 84{,}520.167 - 83{,}955.062 = 565.105,$$

$$\sum_{i}^{k} \sum_{\nu}^{n_i} (x_{i\nu} - \bar{x}_{i\cdot})^2 = A - B = 84{,}661 - 84{,}520.167 = 140.833,$$

$$\sum_{i}^{k} \sum_{\nu}^{n_i} (x_{i\nu} - \bar{x}_{\cdot\cdot})^2 = A - C = 84{,}661 - 83{,}955.062 = 705.938.$$

We assemble these results in Table 10.3.

Table 10.3

Source of variance	Sums of squares	Degrees of freedom	Mean squares
Materials	565.105	2	282.553
Within materials	140.833	13	10.833
Total	705.938	15	

The test of the null hypothesis that the ξ_i are all equal is given by the variance ratio 282.553/10.833 = 26.08 with degrees of freedom 2 and 13; this is overwhelmingly significant as the 0.9995 point for these degrees of freedom is 14.4.

10.3. The Problem of Multiple Comparisons

An F test as performed in the previous section may reject the null hypothesis that the ξ_i are all equal, but it does not tell us which ξ_i are significantly different from which. A single prechosen pair may be compared by an ordinary two-sample t test, either using a within-group mean square calculated only from the two groups in question, or using the within-group mean square from all the groups, and confidence limits for the difference constructed in the usual way. This is valid only for one prechosen comparison; if we start making comparisons suggested by the data, and several of them, the significance level becomes hopelessly incorrect. Several systems of procedure have been proposed for this problem. We will discuss those offered by Scheffé [2] and Tukey [3].

Scheffé's system is more general than simple comparison between pairs of means. Suppose that we have estimates $\bar{x}_i$ of true means ξ_i, with variances σ^2/n_i estimated as s^2/n_i, s^2 being estimated with f degrees of freedom. We are interested in *contrasts*, defined as

$$\theta = \sum_i^k c_i\xi_i, \tag{3.1}$$

where $\sum_i^k c_i = 0$. The contrast θ is estimated as

$$H = \sum_i^k c_i\bar{x}_i \tag{3.2}$$

with variance $$V[H] = \sum_i^k c_i^2 \cdot \frac{\sigma^2}{n_i}.$$

The estimated variance of H is

$$\hat{V}[H] = \sum_i^k c_i^2 \cdot \frac{s^2}{n_i} = s^2 \sum_i^k \frac{c_i^2}{n_i}. \tag{3.3}$$

Scheffé's result is that we can construct $(1 - \alpha)$ confidence limits for all imaginable contrasts θ,

$$\Pr\{H - S\sqrt{\hat{V}[H]} < \theta < H + S\sqrt{\hat{V}[H]}\} = 1 - \alpha, \tag{3.4}$$

where $$S^2 = (k-1)F_{1-\alpha}(k-1, f). \tag{3.5}$$

If, for each experiment we perform, we construct confidence limits according to (3.4), then, in a fraction $(1 - \alpha)$ of these experiments, all the confidence statements will be correct: in a fraction α, one or more of the statements will be incorrect.

Tukey's procedure is somewhat similar but requires that the $\bar{x}_i$ have equal variances. We construct confidence limits for each contrast as

$$\Pr\{H - Ts < \theta < H + Ts\} = 1 - \alpha, \tag{3.6}$$

where s^2 is the estimated variance of individual observations, as before, and T is defined as

$$T = \frac{1}{2}\sum_i^k |c_i| \cdot q \cdot \frac{1}{\sqrt{n}}, \tag{3.7}$$

where q is the $(1 - \alpha)$ point of the studentized range for a sample of k and f degrees of freedom (Table VIII of the appendix). The function q is the distribution of $(x_{\max} - x_{\min})/s$, where s is estimated with f degrees of freedom.

These two procedures have somewhat different properties. In the first place, Scheffé's can be used when the n_i are different; Tukey's requires that the n_i be all equal to n. Second, Tukey's gives somewhat shorter confidence intervals for simple differences, e.g., a contrast formed by coefficient $c_i = -1, 1, 0, \ldots, 0$, whereas Scheffé's gives shorter confidence intervals for more complex contrasts, e.g., the difference between the sum of the first three means minus three times the mean of the fourth, which would be given by coefficients $c_i = 1, 1, 1, -3, 0, \ldots, 0$.

To illustrate the use of these methods we will use the data of Table 10.2. So that the results of the different methods will be comparable, and since Tukey's method requires equal n_i, we will omit the last observation from the gold balls, so that the three means will be 79.4, 64.0, and 74.00, respectively, but we will use the estimate of variance of a single observation unchanged at 10.833 with 13 degrees of freedom.

Suppose that we wish to construct confidence limits for the differences between the metal balls and the glass ball, i.e., the contrast

$$\theta = \xi_1 + \xi_2 - 2\xi_3,$$

which will be defined by the coefficients c_i taking the values $c_1 = 1$, $c_2 = 1$, $c_3 = -2$. Then

$$H = 1 \times 79.4 + 1 \times 64.0 - 2 \times 74.0 = -4.6,$$

$$\hat{V}[H] = \frac{10.833}{5}[(1)^2 + (1)^2 + (-2)^2] = 13.00,$$

$$S^2 = (3 - 1)F_{0.95}(2, 13) = 2 \times 3.81 = 7.62,$$

$$S\sqrt{\hat{V}[H]} = \sqrt{7.62}\sqrt{13.00} = 9.951;$$

so the Scheffé limits are -4.6 ± 9.95. If this were the only contrast for which we wanted confidence limits, and the choice had been made before we saw the data, it would be legitimate to use $t_{0.975}(13) = 2.160$ in place of S, which would give limits -4.6 ± 7.8. The Tukey limits involve q for three means and a variance estimated on 13 degrees of freedom. From Table VIII, $q = 3.73$ for these values of the parameters. We need

$$T = \frac{1}{2}\sum_i^k |c_i| \cdot q \cdot \frac{1}{\sqrt{n}} = \frac{1}{2}(|1| + |1| + |-2|) \times 3.73 \times \frac{1}{\sqrt{5}} = 3.336;$$

so $Ts = 3.336 \times \sqrt{10.833} = 10.98$, and the confidence limits are 4.6 ± 11.0.

A third type of multiple confidence intervals was developed by Dunnett [5] for the special but important case where we have tested $(1 + k)$ treatments, of which one is a control and we wish to compare the other k with the control. These limits are easy to construct, being $\pm\, ds\sqrt{1/n_0 + 1/n_i}$ where n_0 is the number of observations on the control, n_i on the treatments, and d is a parameter analogous to t tabulated in his paper.

10.4. One-Way Analysis of Variance: Model II

In model I analysis of variance we defined the model in (2.1) as $x_{i\nu} = \xi_i + z_{i\nu}$, and in (2.9) we defined $\eta_i = \xi_i - \xi$; so the model was

$$x_{i\nu} = \xi + \eta_i + z_{i\nu} \tag{4.1}$$

where $\sum_i^k \eta_i = 0$ and $z_{i\nu} \sim N(0, \sigma^2)$. The η_i were fixed constants. A model II analysis is based on the model

$$x_{i\nu} = \xi + y_i + z_{i\nu} \tag{4.2}$$

where the $y_i \sim N(0, \omega^2)$ and the $z_{i\nu} \sim N(0, \sigma^2)$. Regarding the relevant populations as infinite, such a model could correspond to the situation where we take a number of sacks of wool from a large consignment and the sack means are distributed about a mean ξ with variance ω^2: We then take a sample from the sack which is distributed about the sack mean with variance σ^2. Both y_i and $z_{i\nu}$ are random samples from infinite populations, and our only interest in the particular y_i and $z_{i\nu}$ we happen to get in the sample is insofar as they enable us to estimate ξ, ω^2, and σ^2. The parameters ω^2 and σ^2 are known as *components of variance*.

Since the model is so similar to model I, much of the analysis proceeds along similar lines. The total sum of squares about the grand mean is split up as before into two components:

$$\sum_i^k \sum_v^{n_i} (x_{iv} - \bar{x}_{..})^2 = \sum_i^k n_i(\bar{x}_{i} - \bar{x}_{..})^2 + \sum_i^k \sum_v^{n_i} (x_{iv} - \bar{x}_{i.})^2, \tag{4.3}$$

where the two terms on the right-hand side are the numerators of s_2^2 (2.14) and s_1^2 (2.6), with degrees of freedom $(k-1)$ and $(\sum_i^k n_i - k)$. The mean square s_1^2 as before has expected value σ^2, but the change in the model affects the expected value and the distribution of s_2^2. To find this we proceed as follows:

$$\begin{aligned} E\,[\sum_i^k n_i(\bar{x}_{i\cdot} - \bar{x}_{..})^2] &= E\,[\sum_i^k n_i\bar{x}_{i\cdot}^2] + E\,[\bar{x}_{..}^2 \sum_i^k n_i] - 2E\,[\bar{x}_{..} \sum_i^k n_i\bar{x}_{i\cdot}] \\ &= \sum_i^k n_i\, E[\bar{x}_{i\cdot}^2] - (\sum_i^k n_i)E[\bar{x}_{..}^2]. \end{aligned} \tag{4.4}$$

To evaluate this we need $E[\bar{x}_{i\cdot}^2]$ and $E[\bar{x}_{..}^2]$. The averages $\bar{x}_{i\cdot}$ and $\bar{x}_{..}$ are formed by averaging the model (4.2) first over v to give $\bar{x}_{i\cdot}$; we then average $\bar{x}_{i\cdot}$ over i to get $\bar{x}_{..}$:

$$\bar{x}_{i\cdot} = \xi + y_i + \frac{1}{n_i}\sum_v^{n_i} z_{iv}\,, \tag{4.5}$$

$$\bar{x}_{..} = \frac{\sum_i^k n_i\bar{x}_{i\cdot}}{\sum_i^k n_i} = \xi + \frac{\sum_i^k n_i y_i}{\sum_i^k n_i} + \frac{\sum_i^k \sum_v^{n_i} z_{iv}}{\sum_i^k n_i}. \tag{4.6}$$

We see that $E[\bar{x}_{i\cdot}] = \xi$ and likewise $E[\bar{x}_{..}] = \xi$. From the definition of variance, $V[\bar{x}_{i\cdot}] = E[\bar{x}_{i\cdot}^2] - (E[\bar{x}_{i\cdot}])^2$, we have

$$E[\bar{x}_{i\cdot}^2] = V[\bar{x}_{i\cdot}] + (E[\bar{x}_{i\cdot}])^2 = V[y_i] + \frac{1}{n_i^2}\,V[\sum_v^{n_i} z_{iv}] + \xi^2 = \omega^2 + \frac{\sigma^2}{n_i} + \xi^2. \tag{4.7}$$

Similarly,

$$\begin{aligned} E[\bar{x}_{..}^2] = V[\bar{x}_{..}] + (E[\bar{x}_{..}])^2 &= \frac{1}{(\sum_i^k n_i)^2}\{V[\sum_i^k n_i y_i] + V[\sum_i^k \sum_v^{n_i} z_{iv}]\} + \xi^2 \\ &= \frac{1}{\left(\sum_i^k n_i\right)^2}\left(\omega^2 \sum_i^k n_i^2 + \sigma^2 \sum_i^k n_i\right) + \xi^2. \end{aligned} \tag{4.8}$$

We now substitute (4.7) and (4.8) in (4.4):

$$E\Big[\sum_i^k n_i(\bar{x}_{i\cdot} - \bar{x}_{\cdot\cdot})^2\Big]$$
$$= \sum_i^k n_i\Big(\omega^2 + \frac{\sigma^2}{n_i} + \xi^2\Big) - \Big(\sum_i^k n_i\Big)\left[\frac{1}{\left(\sum_i^k n_i\right)^2}\Big(\omega^2 \sum_i^k n_i^2 + \sigma^2 \sum_i^k n_i\Big) + \xi^2\right]$$
$$= (k-1)\sigma^2 + \left(\sum_i^k n_i - \frac{\sum_i^k n_i^2}{\sum_i^k n_i}\right)\omega^2;$$

so the expected value of s_2^2 is

$$E[s_2^2] = E\left[\frac{\sum_i^k n_i(\bar{x}_{i\cdot} - \bar{x}_{\cdot\cdot})^2}{k-1}\right] = \sigma^2 + \frac{1}{k-1}\left(\sum_i^k n_i - \frac{\sum_i^k n_i^2}{\sum_i^k n_i}\right)\omega^2. \quad (4.9)$$

In the case when the n_i are all equal, say to n, then (4.9) becomes

$$E[s_2^2] = \sigma^2 + n\omega^2. \quad (4.10)$$

It is apparent that model I and II one-way analyses of variance are very similar. The partitioning of the total sum of squares and the arithmetic are identical, and the only difference that emerges is the change in the expectation and distribution of s_2^2. In the case of equal n_i, the change in the expectation of s_2^2 is the substitution of ω^2 for $\sum_i^k (\xi_i - \xi)^2/(k-1)$. For equal $n_i = n$, (4.5) is

$$\bar{x}_{i\cdot} = \xi + y_i + \bar{z}_{i\cdot},$$

and so $\bar{x}_{i\cdot}$ has expectation $E[\bar{x}_{i\cdot}] = \xi$ and variance

$$V[\bar{x}_{i\cdot}] = V[y_i] + V[\bar{z}_{i\cdot}] = \omega^2 + \frac{\sigma^2}{n}.$$

Also, since y_i and z_i are normally distributed, $\bar{x}_{i\cdot}$ is normally distributed. Therefore $s_2^2 = \sum_i^k (\bar{x}_{i\cdot} - \bar{x}_{\cdot\cdot})^2/(k-1)$ is an ordinary sample estimate of variance, where the variance is $(\omega^2 + \sigma^2/n)$, and will have the distribution $(\omega^2 + \sigma^2/n)\,\chi^2(k-1)/(k-1)$.

10.5. Interpretation of a Model II One-Way Analysis of Variance

Under the null hypothesis that $\omega^2 = 0$, s_2^2/s_1^2 will be distributed as F with degrees of freedom $(k-1)$ and $(\sum_i^k n_i - k)$; so this is the test for this null hypothesis.

We have seen that $E[\bar{x}..] = \xi$; so $\bar{x}..$ is an obvious estimator of ξ. The expectation of $\bar{x}^2_{..}$ (4.8), in the case $n_i = n$, reduces to

$$\frac{n\omega^2 + \sigma^2}{kn} + \xi^2,$$

and so the variance of $\bar{x}..$ in the case of equal n_i is

$$V[\bar{x}..] = \frac{\sigma^2 + n\omega^2}{kn}. \tag{5.1}$$

Hence
$$\frac{\bar{x}.. - E[\bar{x}..]}{\sqrt{V[\bar{x}..]}} = \frac{\bar{x}.. - \xi}{\sqrt{(\sigma^2 + n\omega^2)/kn}} \sim N(0, 1). \tag{5.2}$$

Substituting the sample estimate of $(\sigma^2 + n\omega^2)$, namely, s_2^2, based on $(k-1)$ degrees of freedom, gives

$$\frac{\bar{x}.. - \xi}{\sqrt{s_2^2/kn}} \sim t(k-1), \tag{5.3}$$

which will give confidence limits for ξ as in (9.5.12).

The variance of the $z_{i\nu}$, σ^2, is estimated by s_1^2 and ω^2 is estimated as

$$\hat{\omega}^2 = \frac{s_2^2 - s_1^2}{n}. \tag{5.4}$$

Confidence limits for σ^2 can be obtained as in (9.1.3). Confidence limits for ω^2 are considerably more troublesome. We can use either a large sample approximation or a somewhat more exact approximation. The large sample treatment applies (9.7.4), $V[s^2] = 2(\sigma^2)^2/f$, to s_2^2 and s_1^2:

$$V[s_2^2] = \frac{2(n\omega^2 + \sigma^2)^2}{k-1}, \qquad V[s_1^2] = \frac{2(\sigma^2)^2}{k(n-1)},$$

and so
$$V[\hat{\omega}^2] = V\left[\frac{1}{n}(s_2^2 - s_1^2)\right] = \frac{2(n\omega^2 + \sigma^2)^2}{n^2(k-1)} + \frac{2(\sigma^2)^2}{n^2k(n-1)}.$$

Substituting the sample estimates s_2^2 and s_1^2 for $(n\omega^2 + \sigma^2)$ and σ^2, we get

$$\hat{V}[\hat{\omega}^2] = \frac{2}{n^2}\left[\frac{(s_2^2)^2}{k-1} + \frac{(s_1^2)^2}{k(n-1)}\right]. \tag{5.5}$$

We then assume $\hat{\omega}^2$ to be normally distributed with this variance, and obtain confidence limits in the usual way. This approximation is poor except for large k. Probably k should be greater than 50 before the approximation ceases to be crude.

The better approximation is due to Bross [6], and the reader is referred to his article for the derivation of what strictly are known as fiducial limits. At the present level of sophistication we will regard these limits as effectively the same as confidence limits. Bross's results are that $(1-\alpha)$ approximate confidence limits for $\hat{\omega}^2$ are $\underline{L}\hat{\omega}^2$, $\overline{L}\hat{\omega}^2$, where

$$\underline{L} = \frac{(F/F_{1-\alpha/2})-1}{(F'_{1-\alpha/2}F/F_{1-\alpha/2})-1}, \qquad \overline{L} = \frac{(F/F_{\alpha/2})-1}{(F'_{\alpha/2}F/F_{\alpha/2})-1}, \tag{5.6}$$

where F is the observed variance ratio s_2^2/s_1^2; $F_{1-\alpha/2}$ and $F_{\alpha/2}$ have degrees of freedom the same as F, namely $(k-1)$ and $k(n-1)$; and $F'_{1-\alpha/2}$ and $F'_{\alpha/2}$ have degrees of freedom $(k-1)$ and ∞.

Although we have only approximations for confidence limits for ω^2, we are able to obtain exact confidence limits for the ratio ω^2/σ^2. In the derivation of (9.2.6), s_1^2 and s_2^2 were sample estimates of σ_1^2 and σ_2^2 with f_1 and f_2 degrees of freedom. Here s_1^2 is an estimate of σ^2 with the distribution $\sigma^2\chi^2(k(n-1))/k(n-1)$ and s_2^2 is an estimate of $(\sigma^2+n\omega^2)$ with the distribution $(\sigma^2+n\omega^2)\chi^2(k-1)/(k-1)$. The arguments of (9.2.4) to (9.2.6) are valid here; so, substituting s_2^2 here for the s_1^2 in (9.2.6) and vice versa, we have

$$\Pr\left\{\left(\frac{s_2^2}{s_1^2}\right)\frac{1}{F_{P_2}(k-1,k(n-1))} < \frac{\sigma^2+n\omega^2}{\sigma^2} < \left(\frac{s_2^2}{s_1^2}\right)F_{1-P_1}(k(n-1),k-1)\right\} = P_2 - P_1,$$

which rearranges to

$$\Pr\left\{\frac{1}{n}\left(\frac{s_2^2}{s_1^2}\frac{1}{F_{P_2}(k-1,k(n-1))}-1\right) < \frac{\omega^2}{\sigma^2} < \frac{1}{n}\left(\frac{s_2^2}{s_1^2}F_{1-P_1}(k(n-1),k-1)-1\right)\right\} = P_2 - P_1. \tag{5.7}$$

It is interesting to note what can happen if we are presented with kn observations, without being informed that they are really k groups of n observations, and asked to calculate confidence limits for the mean. We would start by computing as s^2,

$$s^2 = \sum_{i,\nu}^{k,n}(x_{i\nu}-\bar{x}_{..})^2/(kn-1).$$

But

$$E\left[\sum_{i\nu}^{k,n}(x_{i\nu}-\bar{x}_{..})^2\right] = E\left[n\sum_{i}^{k}(\bar{x}_{i.}-\bar{x}_{..})^2\right] + E\left[\sum_{i}^{k}\sum_{\nu}^{n}(x_{i\nu}-\bar{x}_{i.})^2\right]$$
$$= (k-1)(\sigma^2+n\omega^2) + k(n-1)\sigma^2;$$

so $$E[s^2] = \frac{(k-1)(\sigma^2 + n\omega^2) + k(n-1)\sigma^2}{kn-1} = \frac{n(k-1)}{kn-1}\omega^2 + \sigma^2,$$

and the incorrectly estimated variance of $\bar{x}..$ would have expected value

$$V_{\text{inc}}[\bar{x}..] = \frac{[n(k-1)/(kn-1)]\omega^2 + \sigma^2}{kn}. \tag{5.8}$$

But we saw in (5.1) that the correct variance of $\bar{x}..$, say $V_{\text{cor}}[\bar{x}..]$, equals

$$V_{\text{cor}}[\bar{x}..] = \frac{\sigma^2 + n\omega^2}{kn}. \tag{5.9}$$

The ratio of incorrect to correct variances is the ratio of (5.8) to (5.9), which can be written in the form

$$\frac{V_{\text{inc}}[\bar{x}..]}{V_{\text{cor}}[\bar{x}..]} = 1 - \left(\frac{1-1/n}{1-1/nk}\right)\frac{1}{1+(1/n)(\sigma^2/\omega^2)}. \tag{5.10}$$

The magnitude of the error is going to depend on the values of the various parameters and particularly on σ^2/ω^2. If $\sigma^2/\omega^2 \to \infty$, then the ratio (5.10) tends to 1, but, if $\sigma^2/\omega^2 \to 0$ and n is large, then the ratio tends to $(k-1)/(nk-1)$, which for large k will tend to $1/n$. Thus a very serious error may be made by assuming that we have *kn independent* observations when in point of fact we do not.

In this section we have so far made the simplification that the n_i were all equal to n. As an illustration of the difficulties that arise when this is not the case we will compute $V[\bar{x}..]$. In (2.2) $\bar{x}..$ was defined as

$$\bar{x}.. = \frac{\sum_i^k \sum_\nu^{n_i} x_{i\nu}}{\sum_i^k n_i},$$

and so $$V[\bar{x}..] = \frac{1}{(\sum_i^k n_i)^2} \sum_i^k V\left[\sum_\nu^{n_i} x_{i\nu}\right]. \tag{5.11}$$

Summing the model (4.2) over ν gives

$$\sum_\nu^{n_i} x_{i\nu} = n_i\xi_i + n_i y_i + \sum_\nu^{n_i} z_{i\nu},$$

and the variance of this is

$$V[\sum_\nu^{n_i} x_{i\nu}] = n_i^2\, V[y_i] + \sum_\nu^{n_i} V[z_{i\nu}] = n_i^2\omega^2 + n_i\sigma^2.$$

Substituting this in (5.11) gives

$$V[\bar{x}_{..}] = \frac{\sum_i^k n_i^2}{(\sum_i^k n_i)^2}\omega^2 + \frac{1}{\sum_i^k n_i}\sigma^2. \tag{5.12}$$

Whereas, in the case of equal n_i, $V[\bar{x}_{..}]$ was found in (5.1) to be $(\sigma^2 + n\omega^2)/kn$, where we had a mean square, s_2^2, for estimating $(\sigma^2 + n\omega^2)$, here we do not have a mean square to estimate (5.12). An approximate procedure would be to insert the appropriate estimators of ω^2 and σ^2, involving s_2^2 and s_1^2, and reduce the resulting expression to a linear combination of these two mean squares, and then estimate the approximate degrees of freedom of this linear combination by (9.7.8). This is clearly an awkward business of unknown accuracy. All this trouble can be avoided by the use of equal n_i.

An alternative approach to the estimation of ξ is to use the results of Section 2.4 on the formation of weighted means of minimum variance. There we saw that $\bar{x}$ defined as $\sum w_i x_i / \sum w_i$ had minimum variance, actually $1/\sum w_i$, if the weights w_i were chosen as $1/\sigma_i^2$. Here, from (4.5),

$$\bar{x}_{i\cdot} = \xi + y_i + \sum_\nu^{n_i} \frac{z_{i\nu}}{n_i},$$

and so

$$V[\bar{x}_{i\cdot}] = V[y_i] + \sum_\nu^{n_i} \frac{V[z_{i\nu}]}{n_i^2} = \omega^2 + \frac{\sigma^2}{n_i}; \tag{5.13}$$

so we might use weights based on the estimates of ω^2 and σ^2:

$$\hat{w}_i = \left(\hat{\omega}^2 + \frac{\hat{\sigma}^2}{n_i}\right)^{-1}. \tag{5.14}$$

For the construction of approximate confidence limits for ξ, Cochran [7] suggests using $\bar{x} \pm t\sqrt{\hat{V}[\bar{x}]}$ where t is given $(k - 1)$ degrees of freedom.

Cochran, in the same paper [7], also discusses how to handle the still more awkward situation where in the model

$$x_i = \xi + y_i + z_i$$

the z_i are distributed normally with mean zero and variances σ_1^2, i.e., where the within-group component of variance varies from group to group. This situation can arise, for example, when different laboratories determine some quantity. There is no a priori reason why the variance of the measurements within a laboratory should be the same from laboratory to laboratory. The reader is referred to Cochran's paper for details.

Table 10.4

Batch	1	2	3	4	5	6	7	8	9	10	11	12	13	14	15	16	17	18	19	20	21	22	Totals
	58	49	45	28	54	47	45	49	43	37	48	45	55	42	45	41	43	53	41	43	34	50	995
	48	41	44	55	49	45	54	47	48	43	52	43	42	41	43	46	42	44	43	45	34	48	997
	47	46	44	50	53	47	50	46	49	47	57	44	47	46	48	41	38	49	41	44	40	48	1022
	65	46	44	41	52	47	57	50	47	27	51	44	52	50	45	30	35	52	35	46	40	48	1004
Totals	218	182	177	174	208	186	206	192	187	154	208	176	196	179	181	158	158	198	160	178	148	194	4018

10.6. An Example of a Model II One-Way Analysis of Variance with Equal Group Sizes

Table 10.4 gives the measurements of a certain physical property on 88 successive subbatches of a plasticlike material. The raw material goes through a number of stages of processing in batches, which then are split into four subbatches, which go through several more stages of processing. In Table 10.4 each column gives the measurements on the four subbatches from one batch. A glance at the results shows that there is considerable variation, which was in excess of that which could be tolerated. If we suppose that the individual observations $x_{i\nu}$ are represented by the model $x_{i\nu} = \xi + y_i + z_{i\nu}$, then the variance of the y_i, ω^2 will represent the variation due to the earlier stages and the variance of the $z_{i\nu}$, σ^2 the variation due to the later stages.

The analysis of variance follows the same lines as in the model I example discussed in Section 10.2, except that the n_i being all equal to n makes the calculation slightly simpler. We need

$$A = \sum_i^k \sum_\nu^n x_{i\nu}^2 = 58^2 + 48^2 + \cdots + 48^2 = 186{,}922,$$

$$B = \frac{1}{n} \sum_i^k \left(\sum_\nu^n x_{i\nu} \right)^2 = \frac{1}{4}(218^2 + 182^2 + \cdots 194^2) = 185{,}378,$$

$$C = \frac{1}{kn} \left(\sum_i^k \sum_\nu^n x_{i\nu} \right)^2 = \frac{(4018)^2}{22 \times 4} = 183{,}458.227.$$

With these figures we construct Table 10.5.

Table 10.5

Source of variance	Sums of squares	Degrees of freedom	Mean squares	E[M.S.]
Between batches	$B - C =$ 1919.773	21	91.418	$\sigma^2 + 4\omega^2$
Between sub-batches	$A - B =$ 1544.000	66	23.394	σ^2
Total	$A - C =$ 3463.733	87		

The succeeding analysis runs as follows. Under the null hypothesis that $\omega^2 = 0$, $s_2^2/s_1^2 = 91.418/23.394 = 3.91 \sim F(21, 66)$. The 0.9995 point of F with these degrees of freedom is 2.94, and so we reject the null hypothesis at the level of significance $\alpha = 0.0005$. The mean square $s_1^2 = 23.394$ is an estimate of σ^2, and

$$\hat{\omega}^2 = \frac{91.418 - 23.394}{4} = 17.006.$$

It appears, therefore, that the variability is arising in roughly equal amounts from the two parts of the process. Application of (9.1.3) gives (17.95, 31.97) as 90 per cent confidence limits for σ^2, as were calculated immediately following that equation. The large sample approach to confidence limits for ω^2 uses (5.5):

$$\hat{V}[\hat{\omega}^2] = \frac{2}{4^2}\left[\frac{(91.418)^2}{22-1} + \frac{(23.296)^2}{22(4-1)}\right] = 50.78;$$

so 90 per cent confidence limits for ω^2 are $17.006 \pm 1.65 \times 7.126 = (5.29, 28.7)$.

Alternatively, and better, Bross's formulas (5.6) involve $F = 91.418/23.394 = 3.908$, $F_{0.95}(21, 66) = 1.72$, $F'_{0.95}(21, \infty) = 1.56$, $F_{0.05}(21, 66) = 1/F_{0.95}(66, 21) = 1/1.91 = 0.5236$, $F'_{0.05}(21, \infty) = 1/F_{0.95}(\infty, 21) = 1/1.81 = 0.5525$:

$$\underline{L} = \frac{3.908/1.72 - 1}{(1.56 \times 3.908)/1.72 - 1} = 0.500,$$

$$\bar{L} = \frac{3.908/0.5236 - 1}{(0.5525 \times 3.908)/0.5236 - 1} = 2.069.$$

Since $\hat{\omega}^2 = 17.006$, the limits are $\underline{L}\hat{\omega}^2 = 0.500 \times 17.006 = 8.503$ and $\bar{L}\hat{\omega}^2 = 2.069 \times 17.006 = 35.185$. Comparing these with the cruder approximate limits, we see that the crude limits fall down particularly in being, from their very method of construction, symmetric about the point estimate $\hat{\omega}^2$.

Confidence limits for the ratio ω^2/σ^2 are obtained with (5.7). Inserting $s_2^2/s_1^2 = 91.418/23.394 = 3.91$, $k(n-1) = 22(4-1) = 66$, $k - 1 = 22 - 1 = 21$, $F_{0.95}(21, 66) = 1.72$, $F_{0.95}(66, 21) = 1.91$, we get

$$\left(\frac{1}{4}(3.91 \times \frac{1}{1.72} - 1) < \frac{\omega^2}{\sigma^2} < \frac{1}{4}(3.91 \times 1.91 - 1)\right) = (0.32, 1.62).$$

This has the somewhat disagreeable implication that, though the point estimate of ω^2/σ^2 is $17.006/23.394 = 0.727$, we have determined this ratio with rather poor precision, even in spite of having quite a lot of data, since the 90 per cent confidence limits range from less than half to more than twice the point estimate.

Finally, if we wanted 90 per cent confidence limits for the grand mean, we would use (5.3), inserting $\bar{x}_{..} = 4018/88 = 45.659$, $s_2^2 = 91.418$, $kn = 88$, and using $t_{0.05}(21) = -1.721 = -t_{0.95}(21)$: $\pm t\sqrt{s_2^2/kn} = \pm 1.721\sqrt{91.418/88} = \pm 1.754$, whence the 90 per cent confidence limits for ξ are (43.9, 47.4).

10.7. An Example of Model II One-Way Analysis of Variance with Unequal Group Sizes

To illustrate a model II one-way analysis of variance with unequal group sizes we will use the data of Table 9.1, assuming that the different groups correspond to random replications. This may not actually be the case, as the groups have mirrors with identifiably different properties. For the purpose of illustrating the arithmetical procedures, however, we will assume that the mirrors were drawn at random from a large population of mirrors. A straightforward analysis of variance proceeds by obtaining

$$\sum_i^k \sum_\nu^{n_i} x_{i\nu}^2 = 124{,}531, \qquad \sum_i^k \frac{\left(\sum_\nu^{n_i} x_{i\nu}\right)^2}{n_i} = 102{,}339.683,$$

$$\frac{\left(\sum_i^k \sum_\nu^{n_i} x_{i\nu}\right)^2}{\sum_i^k n_i} = 98{,}112.640,$$

leading to Table 10.6.

Table 10.6

Source of variance	Sum of squares	Degrees of freedom	Mean squares	E[M.S.]
Between groups	4,227.043	5	845.409	$\sigma^2 + 14.701\omega^2$
Within groups	22,191.317	83	267.365	σ^2
Total	26,418.360	88		

The coefficient of ω^2 in the expected mean square for between groups is, by (4.9),

$$\frac{1}{k-1}\left(\sum_i^k n_i - \frac{\sum_i^k n_i^2}{\sum_i^k n_i}\right) = \frac{1}{6-1}\left(89 - \frac{1379}{89}\right) = 14.701.$$

The null hypothesis that $\omega^2 = 0$ is tested by the variance ratio $845.409/267.365 = 3.16$. Since $F_{0.975}(5, 83) = 2.72$, we reject the null hypothesis and estimate ω^2 as $(845.409 - 267.365)/14.701 = 39.320$.

To form a weighted mean with approximately minimum variance, we compute the weights $\hat{w}_i$ from (5.14). For $i = 1$ for example,

$$\hat{w}_1 = \frac{1}{39.320 + 267.365/12} = \frac{1}{61.60} = 0.016234.$$

We then form

$$\bar{x} = \frac{\sum_i^k \hat{w}_i \bar{x}_{i\cdot}}{\sum_i^k \hat{w}_i} = \frac{3.459562}{0.103726} = 33.353.$$

This will have a variance estimated as

$$\hat{V}[\bar{x}] = \frac{1}{\sum_i^k \hat{w}_i} = \frac{1}{0.103726} = 9.6408.$$

Making the conservative assumption that this has the usual distribution with $(k - 1) = 5$ degrees of freedom, confidence limits for ξ are $33.353 \pm 2.571\sqrt{9.6408} = 33.35 \pm 7.98$. If we made the incorrect assumption that we had 89 independent observations we would have calculated $\bar{x}_{\cdot\cdot} = 2{,}955/89 = 33.202$ and $s^2 = 26{,}418.360/88 = 300.209$, whence $\hat{V}[\bar{x}_{\cdot\cdot}] = 300.209/89 = 3.373$ and the confidence limits for ξ would be $33.202 \pm 1.987\sqrt{3.373} = 33.20 \pm 3.65$. The length of this (incorrect) confidence interval would thus be a serious underestimate of the better estimate, being too short by a factor of more than 2.

10.8. One-Way Analysis of Variance with Unequal Variances

In Section 10.1 we saw that one-way analysis of variance could be regarded as the generalization of the two-sample Student t test of Section 9.6 to k samples. In Section 9.7 we saw that differing variances in the two samples posed awkward problems that could be handled with an approximation due to Welch. Welch has extended this approach to the k-sample case [8].

For a model I case we have the model

$$x_{i\nu} = \xi_i + z_{i\nu}; \qquad i = 1, \ldots, k, \quad \nu = 1, \ldots, n_i \tag{8.1}$$

where the $z_{i\nu}$ are independent normal deviates with zero mean and variance σ_i^2 [in (2.1) the $z_{i\nu}$ were $N(0, \sigma^2)$]. Welch proposes the use of the statistic

$$F = \frac{\left[\sum_i^k w_i(\bar{x}_{i\cdot} - \bar{x}_{\cdot\cdot})^2\right]/(k-1)}{\left[1 + \frac{2(k-2)}{k^2-1} \sum_i^k \frac{1}{f_i}\left(1 - \frac{w_i}{\sum w_i}\right)^2\right]}, \tag{8.2}$$

where the weights w_i are defined by

$$w_i = \frac{n_i}{s_i^2}, \tag{8.3}$$

and the weighted average $\bar{x}$ is

$$\bar{x}_{\cdot\cdot} = \sum_i^k w_i \bar{x}_{i\cdot} \Big/ \sum_i^k w_i \,. \tag{8.4}$$

This statistic, under the null hypothesis that $\xi_i = \xi$ for all i, has approximately the F distribution with degrees of freedom

$$f_1 = k - 1, \tag{8.5}$$

$$f_2 = \left[\frac{3}{k^2-1} \sum_i^k \frac{1}{f_i}\left(1 - \frac{w_i}{\sum w_i}\right)^2\right]^{-1}. \tag{8.6}$$

In the case of $k = 2$, this procedure reduces to that of Section 9.7: Specifically, (8.2), an F-like statistic, becomes the square of (9.7.2) with $\xi_1 = \xi_2$, a t-like statistic, and (8.6) becomes equal to (9.7.9).

We will illustrate this procedure on the data of Table 9.1. For those data Bartlett's test gave a P value of about 0.08. The null hypothesis of equal variances in the groups, while strictly acceptable at the 0.05 level of significance, looks somewhat dubious. However, a straightforward analysis of variance gives Table 10.7, for which $F(5, 83) = 3.16$, which exceeds the 0.975 point, 2.72, and is quite close to the 0.99 point, 3.25.

The calculation of the numerator of (8.2) proceeds as in Table 10.8. Having w_i and $\bar{x}_{i\cdot}$, we then calculate $\sum w_i \bar{x}_{i\cdot} = 13.660$ and $\sum w_i = 0.433159$, whence by (8.4) $\bar{x}_{\cdot\cdot} = 31.536$. After the next two columns we can cumulate on the calculating machine $\sum w_i(\bar{x}_{i\cdot} - \bar{x}_{\cdot\cdot})^2 = 19.820$.

Table 10.7

Source of variance	Sums of squares	Degrees of freedom	Mean squares
Between groups	4,227.043	5	845.409
Within groups	22,191.317	83	267.365
Total	26,418.360	88	

Table 10.8

n_i	$\sum x_{i\nu}$	$\bar{x}_{i\cdot}$	s_i^2	$w_i = n_i/s_i^2$	$\bar{x}_{i\cdot} - \bar{x}_{\cdot\cdot}$	$(\bar{x}_{i\cdot} - \bar{x}_{\cdot\cdot})^2$
12	591	49.250	257.114	0.046671	17.713	313.759
15	486	32.400	295.971	0.050680	0.863	0.745
21	713	33.952	393.648	0.053347	2.415	5.835
12	360	30.000	384.545	0.031205	−1.536	2.361
13	330	25.384	114.923	0.113119	−6.152	37.848
16	475	29.687	115.829	0.138136	−1.849	3.419
				$0.433159 = \sum w_i$		

Table 10.9

$\dfrac{w_i}{\sum w_i}$	$1 - \dfrac{w_i}{\sum w_i}$	f_i	$\dfrac{1}{f_i}\left(1 - \dfrac{w_i}{\sum w_i}\right)^2$
0.107747	0.892252	11	0.072374
0.117002	0.882997	14	0.055691
0.123158	0.876841	20	0.038442
0.072042	0.927957	11	0.078282
0.261149	0.738850	12	0.045491
0.318900	0.681099	15	0.030926
1.000000	5.000000		0.321208 $= \sum \dfrac{1}{f_i}\left(1 - \dfrac{w_i}{\sum w_i}\right)^2$

Table 10.9 sets out the calculation of $\sum (1/f_i)(1 - w_i/\sum w_i)^2$. Since $k = 6$, substituting in (8.2), we get

$$F = \frac{19.820/(6-1)}{1 + 2(6-2)/(6^2-1) \times 0.321208} = \frac{3.964061}{1.073419} = 3.693.$$

This will have degrees of freedom approximately $f_1 = k - 1 = 5$ and f_2, by (8.6),

$$f_2 = \left(\frac{3}{6^2-1} \times 0.321208\right)^{-1} = 36.32.$$

Comparing this with the simple analysis of Table 10.7, we see that the degrees of freedom for the denominator have decreased from 83 to 36. This changes the 0.99 point of F with 5 degrees of freedom in the numerator from 3.25 to 3.56. However, the variance ratio happens to change from 3.16 for the simple analysis to 3.69 for the present analysis.

It has been shown by several writers (see Box [9] for references) that, just as the two-sample t test becomes very insensitive to departures from the assumption of equality of variances in the two samples when the sample sizes approach equality, so does the analysis of variance become insensitive to departures from equality of variance when the several sample sizes approach equality. This suggests that it becomes particularly important to use the technique of the present section only when the sample sizes are markedly unequal.

10.9. The Power Function of Model II One-Way Analysis of Variance

In (9.2.11) we found that the power function $\pi(\phi)$ for a ratio of variances $\sigma_1^2/\sigma_2^2 = \phi$, when the null hypothesis was $\sigma_1^2 = \sigma_2^2$,

$$\pi(\phi) = \Pr\left\{F(f_1, f_2) > \frac{1}{\phi} F_{1-\alpha}(f_1, f_2)\right\}. \tag{9.1}$$

Here we are dealing with mean squares s_2^2 and s_1^2 with expected values $(\sigma^2 + n\omega^2)$ and σ^2: We put ϕ equal to the ratio of the expected values as before:

$$\phi = \frac{\sigma^2 + n\omega^2}{\sigma^2} = 1 + n\frac{\omega^2}{\sigma^2}. \tag{9.2}$$

The procedure is best illustrated by an example. Suppose we are using $k = 22$ groups of $n = 4$ observations, with a level of significance, $\alpha = 0.05$. Then $f_1 = 21, f_2 = 66$. We ask what is the probability of rejecting the null hypothesis when in fact $\omega^2/\sigma^2 = 3/4$. Then $\phi = 1 + 4 \times (3/4) = 4$, and $F_{0.95}(21, 66) = 1.72$, and

$$\pi\left(\frac{\omega^2}{\sigma^2} = \frac{3}{4}\right) = \Pr\{F(21, 66) > \frac{1}{4} \times 1.72\} = \Pr\{F(21, 66) > 0.43\}$$
$$= \Pr\{F(66, 21) < 2.326\},$$

taking reciprocals and reversing the sign of the inequality. Since $\Pr\{F(66, 21) < 2.173\} = 0.975$, the power is somewhat greater than 0.975.

REFERENCES

1. Heyl, Paul R., "A redetermination of the constant of gravitation," *Journal of Research of the Bureau of Standards*, 5(1930), 1243–1250.
2. Scheffé, H., "A method for judging all contrasts in the analysis of variance," *Biometrika*, 40(1933), 87–104.
3. Tukey, John W., "The problem of multiple comparisons." Unpublished dittoed manuscript.
4. Pearson, E. S., and H. O. Hartley (eds.), *Biometrika Tables for Statisticians*, vol. I. Cambridge, England: University Press, 1954.
5. Dunnett, Charles W., "A multiple comparison procedure for comparing several treatments with a control," *Journal of the American Statistical Association*, 50(1955), 1096–1121.
6. Bross, Irwin, "Fiducial intervals for variance components," *Biometrics*, 6(1950), 136–144.
7. Cochran, William G., "The combination of estimates from different experiments," *Biometrics*, 10(1954), 101–129.
8. Welch, B. L., "On the comparison of several mean values—an alternative approach," *Biometrika*, 38(1951), 330–336.
9. Box, G. E. P., and S. L. Anderson, "Permutation theory in the derivation of robust criteria and the study of departures from assumption," *Journal of the Royal Statistical Society*, B (Methodological), 17(1955), 1–26.

EXERCISES

10.1. For the data of Exercise 9.10, irrespective of the outcome of that exercise:

(*a*) Test the null hypothesis that the mean octane number is the same in the four regions.

(*b*) Construct 95 per cent confidence limits for the difference in means of regions A and B (i) assuming that it had been your original intention so to do, (ii) assuming that the idea occurred to you after looking at the data.

(*c*) Construct 95 per cent confidence limits for the contrast defined by the difference between region A and the mean of the other three regions. Assume that this contrast was suggested by the data.

10.2. The data below give some of the results of Rosa and Dorsey ["A new determination of the ratio of the electromagnetic to the electrostatic unit of electricity," *Bulletin of the National Bureau of Standards*, 3(1907), 433–604] on the ratio of electromagnetic to the electrostatic units of electricity, a constant which is equal to the velocity of light. The figures below have had 2.99 subtracted from them and have been multiplied by 10,000 to give numbers simple to work with. The groups correspond to successive dismantling and reassembly of the apparatus. Certain sums which may be useful are given in the lower part of the table.

(*a*) Make a conventional analysis of variance of these data, giving the expectations of the mean squares.

(*b*) Obtain estimates of the components of variance for within groups and between groups. Test the null hypothesis that the latter is zero.

(*c*) Form the weighted mean which has minimum variance.

(*d*) What is the estimated variance of this mean?

(*e*) Supposing that all 64 observations were regarded as 64 independent observations, what would the variance of the simple mean be?

Group	1	2	3	4		5		$\sum_i^k$
	62	65	65	62	65	66	64	
	64	64	64	66	63	65	65	
	62	63	67	64	63	65	64	
	62	62	62	64	63	66		
	65	65	65	63	61	67		
	64	63	62	62	56	66		
	65	64		64	64	69		
	62	63		64	64	70		
	62			66	65	68		
	63			64	64	69		
	64			66	64	63		
				63	65	65		
n_i	11	8	6	24		15		64
$\sum_{\nu}^{n_i} x_{i\nu}$	695	509	385	1,525		992		4,106
$\sum_{\nu}^{n_i} x_{i\nu}^2$	43,927	32,393	24,723	96,997		65,664		26,3704

10.3. A manufacturer has been making all his product from a single large uniform batch of raw material and has achieved a reputation for uniformity of product. This reputation has brought him more business, and he now needs to consider a much larger output. The raw material is no longer obtainable in very large batches, and he must now use relatively large numbers of small batches.

He considers that he will lose his reputation for uniformity if the standard deviation of his new output exceeds by 20 per cent the standard deviation of the old. In other words, if the new standard deviation is $\sigma_{T'}$ and the old σ_T, then $\sigma_{T'}$ must not exceed $1.2\sigma_T$.

He decides to run a trial on a random sample of five batches of raw material. He is going to make a number, say n, of parts from each batch and test for batch differences with a one-way analysis of variance using α as his level of significance.

(*a*) Suppose he chooses $n = 9$, $\alpha = 0.01$, what is the probability of his detecting a deterioration, i.e., an increase in total standard deviation of the magnitude specified above?

(*b*) Suppose he uses $\alpha = 0.1$, what then?

(*c*) Suppose he requires $\alpha = 0.01$ and a probability of detecting the specified deterioration in uniformity of 0.99, what should n be?

CHAPTER 11

Simple Linear Regression

11.1. Introduction

When an investigator observes simultaneously two variables x and y, usually with good reason he plots the observations on a graph. If there is any sign of an association, he is usually seized with the impulse to fit a line, usually a straight line or rather infrequently a parabola or cubic. The purpose of this arithmetic penance of curve fitting is often not very clearly defined; one purpose, however, might be to predict x from a new observed y or vice versa. Another purpose is to use the route of testing the significance of the parameters of the line as a means of testing for association between x and y. The standard technique for fitting a line is known as "least squares," and the line so fitted is known as a regression line for curious historical reasons (see, e.g., [1]).

In this chapter we shall consider the case in which a series of values of x have been selected by the experimenter and he observes y at those values of x. The so-called independent variable x is assumed to be measured without appreciable error. The situation in which the variables x and y vary at random outside the control of the experimenter and are only observed will be discussed in the next chapter.

The present chapter is of unusual length, and some guidance to the reader is called for. Sections 11.2 and 11.3 give the usual fitting of a straight line to data by the method of least squares, and Section 11.4 is a numerical example. This is as much as is found in some elementary textbooks. Section 11.5 deals with finding confidence limits for x from an observed y. In Section 11.6 the problem of comparing two regression lines is covered.

An important application of this statistical technique is to parallel-line biological assay (Section 11.7), a numerical example following in Section 11.8. The line discussed thus far is the two-parameter line $Y = a + b(x - \bar{x})$. In Section 11.9 the one-parameter line through the origin $Y = bx$ is described, with its use in reverse in Section 11.10. The construction of joint confidence regions for (α, β) is considered in Section 11.11. In Sections 11.12 to 11.15 the techniques for two- and one-parameter lines are extended to the case where the variance of y at a fixed x is not a constant but instead a known function of x. Section 11.16 deals with confidence limits when weighted regression lines are used to predict x, given an observed y. Sections 11.17 and 11.18 discuss the case where we have several observations on y at some of the x's and it becomes possible to check the line for goodness of fit. Section 11.19 extends the methods of Section 11.6, for comparing two regression lines, to the case of more than two lines: This technique is also known as the analysis of covariance as it amounts to making an analysis of variance of y adjusted for concommitant variation in x.

On a first reading, the reader might consider only Sections 11.2 through 11.4. For further study Sections 11.5 through 11.8 might be added, followed by Section 11.19. The omitted material (Sections 11.9 through 11.18) could be covered at a later time, though some statisticians would consider that Sections 11.17 and 11.18 should follow Section 11.4.

For a thorough review of linear regression see Acton [2].

In general we assume that we have observations $y_{i\nu}$ as follows:

$$\begin{array}{ll} y_{11}, \ldots, y_{1n_1} & \text{at } x_1, \\ \vdots & \\ y_{i1}, \ldots, y_{in_i} & \text{at } x_i, \end{array}$$

where $i = 1, \ldots, k$. If all the $n_i = 1$, so that there is only one observation on y at each x, we have a special, and important case, for which the analysis, both theoretical and arithmetical, is simpler. We will therefore deal with this case first. The general case, where all the n_i are not equal to 1, can always be treated as the special case by merely ignoring the fact that some of the x_i happen to be identical. For example, if $n_1 = 2$, $n_2 = 3$, and $n_3 = 1$, we can regard the observations

$$(y_{11}, x_1), (y_{12}, x_1), (y_{21}, x_2), (y_{22}, x_2), (y_{23}, x_2), (y_{31}, x_3)$$

as

$$(y_1, x_1), (y_2, x_2), (y_3, x_3), (y_4, x_4), (y_5, x_5), (y_6, x_6).$$

The fact that in this second set of observations $x_1 = x_2$, etc., can in general be disregarded. The only case in which it would matter is where all the x's are identical; then it is obviously meaningless to attempt to fit a line. The case where some of the n_i are greater than 1 permits a more detailed analysis in that a check on the goodness of fit of the function selected can be made (Section 11.17). For the present, however, we will deal with the simpler situation and suppose that we have observations (x_i, y_i), $i = 1, \ldots, k$. Except where otherwise obvious or explicitly stated, all summation operations, $\sum_i^k$, will be over $i = 1, \ldots, k$, and so we will omit the index of the summation and write merely $\sum$.

11.2. The Model

We assume that y is distributed normally about an expected value η with variance σ^2, and that all observations are independent. We further assume that η is a simple linear function of x:

$$\eta = \alpha + \beta(x - \bar{x}). \tag{2.1}$$

The problem is to obtain, from the data, sample estimates a, b, and s^2 of α, β, and σ^2 and to determine the distribution of these estimates. The estimated regression equation is

$$Y = a + b(x - \bar{x}). \tag{2.2}$$

where $\bar{x} = \sum x_i/k$. The standard method of estimation in regression is the *method of least squares*; this is to use those values of a, b which will minimize the sum of squares of deviations, say R, between the observed values y_i and the predictions Y_i given by inserting the values of x_i in the estimated equation (2.2). Thus we minimize

$$R = \sum(y_i - Y_i)^2 = \sum[y_i - a - b(x_i - \bar{x})]^2. \tag{2.3}$$

The method of least squares appears to be largely due to Gauss. As far as estimation of the parameters is concerned, it does not require the assumption of normality, but this assumption is necessary for construction of confidence intervals for or tests of hypotheses about the parameters. With the assumption of normality, the method of maximum likelihood gives results identical with those of the method of least squares. The method of least squares has the desirable properties that the estimators it gives are unbiased and, among all unbiased linear estimators, have minimum variance. Detailed discussions have been given by David and Neyman [3] and Plackett [4].

To find the values of a and b which minimize R we differentiate (2.3) with respect to a and b and equate to zero:

$$\frac{\partial R}{\partial a} = -2\sum[y_i - a - b(x_i - \bar{x})] = 0, \tag{2.4}$$

$$\frac{\partial R}{\partial b} = -2\sum[y_i - a - b(x_i - \bar{x})](x_i - \bar{x}) = 0. \tag{2.5}$$

Rearranging, we have

$$ka + b\sum(x_i - \bar{x}) = \sum y_i, \tag{2.6}$$

$$a\sum(x_i - \bar{x}) + b\sum(x_i - \bar{x})^2 = \sum(x_i - \bar{x})y_i. \tag{2.7}$$

Since $\sum(x_i - \bar{x}) = 0$, we have as estimators for α and β:

$$a = \frac{\sum y_i}{k} = \bar{y}, \tag{2.8}$$

$$b = \frac{\sum(x_i - \bar{x})y_i}{\sum(x_i - \bar{x})^2}. \tag{2.9}$$

The numerator of this expression for b can be written slightly differently: Since $\sum(x_i - \bar{x}) = 0$, then $\bar{y}\sum(x_i - \bar{x}) = 0$, and

$$\sum(x_i - \bar{x})y_i = \sum(x_i - \bar{x})y_i - \bar{y}\sum(x_i - \bar{x}) = \sum(x_i - \bar{x})(y_i - \bar{y}). \tag{2.10}$$

Thus an alternative form for b is

$$b = \frac{\sum(x_i - \bar{x})(y_i - \bar{y})}{\sum(x_i - \bar{x})^2}. \tag{2.11}$$

We can readily check that b is an unbiased estimator of β. We assumed that the expected value of y_i was η_i, given by (2.1) with $x = x_i$. Then

$$\begin{aligned} E[b] &= \frac{\sum(x_i - \bar{x})\, E[y_i]}{\sum(x_i - \bar{x})^2} = \frac{\sum(x_i - \bar{x})[\alpha + \beta(x_i - \bar{x})]}{\sum(x_i - \bar{x})^2} \\ &= \alpha\frac{\sum(x_i - \bar{x})}{\sum(x_i - \bar{x})^2} + \beta\frac{\sum(x_i - \bar{x})^2}{\sum(x_i - \bar{x})^2} = \beta. \end{aligned} \tag{2.12}$$

The variances of a and b can be obtained directly, for inspection of (2.8) and (2.9) shows that they are linear functions of the y_i, which are assumed to be independent and have a normal distribution with variance σ^2:

$$V[a] = V\left[\frac{\sum y_i}{k}\right] = \frac{1}{k^2}\sum V[y_i] = \frac{\sigma^2}{k}, \tag{2.13}$$

$$V[b] = V\left[\frac{\sum(x_i - \bar{x})y_i}{\sum(x_i - \bar{x})^2}\right] = \frac{\sum(x_i - \bar{x})^2\, V[y_i]}{[\sum(x_i - \bar{x})^2]^2} = \frac{\sigma^2}{\sum(x_i - \bar{x})^2}. \tag{2.14}$$

We will defer the estimation of σ^2 to the next section.

A demonstration that in general the method of least squares produces estimators of smallest variance amongst all linear estimators is somewhat involved, [2], [3], but it is often quite easy to show that a least-squares estimator, when it has been obtained, is of minimum variance.

We shall show that the estimator b (2.9) has the smallest variance of all unbiased linear estimators. Suppose that there exists an alternative linear estimator b',

$$b' = \sum c_i y_i \,. \tag{2.15}$$

We have

$$E[b'] = \sum c_i\, E[y_i] = \sum c_i[\alpha + \beta(x_i - \bar{x})] = \alpha \sum c_i + \beta \sum (x_i - \bar{x})c_i \,. \tag{2.16}$$

For b' to be an unbiased estimator, so that $E[b'] = \beta$, we require

$$\sum c_i = 0, \tag{2.17}$$

$$\sum (x_i - \bar{x})c_i = 1. \tag{2.18}$$

The variance of this alternative estimator b' is

$$\begin{aligned} V[b'] &= \sum c_i^2\, V[y_i] = \sigma^2 \sum c_i^2 = \sigma^2 \sum \left[c_i - \frac{x_i - \bar{x}}{\sum (x_i - \bar{x})^2} + \frac{x_i - \bar{x}}{\sum (x_i - \bar{x})^2} \right]^2 \\ &= \sigma^2 \sum \left[c_i - \frac{x_i - \bar{x}}{\sum (x_i - \bar{x})^2} \right]^2 + \sigma^2 \cdot \frac{\sum (x_i - \bar{x})^2}{[\sum (x_i - \bar{x})^2]^2} \,, \end{aligned} \tag{2.19}$$

since the cross-product term is zero, for

$$\begin{aligned} 2\sigma^2 \sum \left[c_i - \frac{x_i - \bar{x}}{\sum (x_i - \bar{x})^2} \right] \frac{(x_i - \bar{x})}{\sum (x_i - \bar{x})^2} \\ = 2\sigma^2 \frac{\sum c_i (x_i - \bar{x})}{\sum (x_i - \bar{x})^2} - 2\sigma^2 \frac{\sum (x_i - \bar{x})^2}{[\sum (x_i - \bar{x})^2]^2} = 0, \end{aligned}$$

using (2.18). Thus

$$V[b'] = \sigma^2 \sum \left[c_i - \frac{x_i - \bar{x}}{\sum (x_i - \bar{x})^2} \right]^2 + \frac{\sigma^2}{\sum (x_i - \bar{x})^2}, \tag{2.20}$$

in which the last term is a constant. Hence to minimize $V[b']$ we can only make adjustments to the first term; by putting

$$c_i = \frac{x_i - \bar{x}}{\sum (x_i - \bar{x})^2} \tag{2.21}$$

we make the first term zero and hence make $V[b']$ a minimum. But, with this value of c_i, our alternative estimator (2.15) is

$$b' = \sum c_i y_i = \frac{\sum (x_i - \bar{x}) y_i}{\sum (x_i - \bar{x})^2}$$

which is our original least-squares estimator b (2.9). Therefore $b' = b$, and b is the minimum-variance unbiased linear estimator. Incidentally, from (2.20) we see that when c_i is given the value in (2.21) $V[b] = \sigma^2/\sum(x_i - \bar{x})^2$, as found earlier in (2.14).

11.3. An Analysis-of-Variance Representation

We will now consider regression analysis from the point of view of analysis of variance. From this approach we will obtain the variances of a and b (which we have already found directly), and in addition we will be

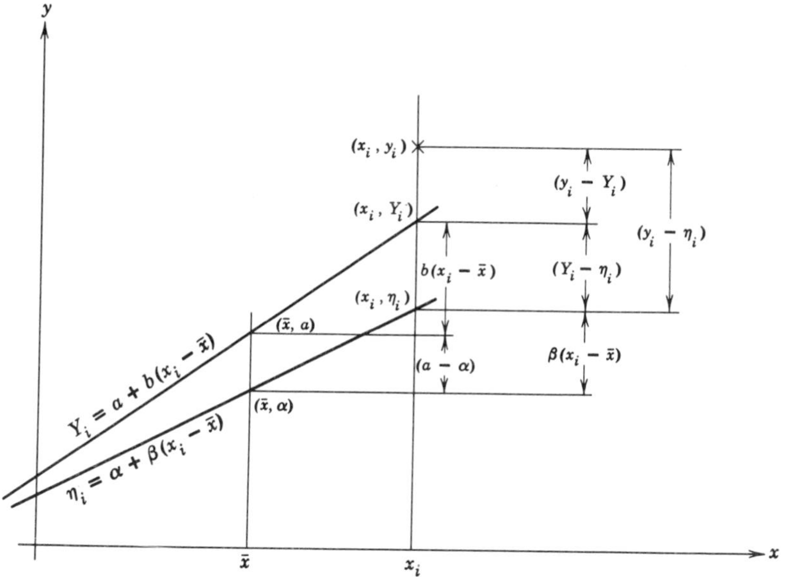

Figure 11.1

able to show that a and b are independent of each other and of s^2, our estimate of σ^2.

The deviation of an observation y_i from the value predicted by the true regression equation (2.1) can be written as

$$\begin{aligned} y_i - \eta_i &= (y_i - Y_i) + (Y_i - \eta_i) \\ &= (y_i - Y_i) + [a + b(x_i - \bar{x}) - \{\alpha + \beta(x_i - \bar{x})\}] \\ &= (y_i - Y_i) + (a - \alpha) + (b - \beta)(x_i - \bar{x}). \end{aligned} \tag{3.1}$$

This equation is represented graphically in Figure 11.1. Squaring and summing over i gives an equation which can be written in tabular form as the second column of Table 11.1; the various cross products are easily shown to be zero.

In Table 11.1, $\sum(y_i - \eta_i)^2$ is a sum of squares with k degrees of freedom and is distributed as $\sigma^2\chi^2(k)$. It is partitioned into three components. The first and second each involve only one variable, a and b, respectively, and these will each have one degree of freedom. The third component involves k variables $(y_i - Y_i)$, but in equating (2.4) and (2.5) to zero we imposed two restrictions and so the degrees of freedom for this component are $(k - 2)$. Thus the sum of the three sums of the squares in the upper part of the table equals the sum of squares in the bottom line, and the sum of the degrees of freedom likewise; so, by Cochran's theorem, the sums of

Table 11.1

Source of variation	Degrees of freedom	Sums of squares	Mean squares
Deviation of a from α	1	$k(a - \alpha)^2$	s_3^2
Deviation of b from β	1	$(b - \beta)^2 \sum(x_i - \bar{x})^2$	s_2^2
Deviation of observed values from estimated line	$k - 2$	$\sum(y_i - Y_i)^2$	s^2
Deviations of observed values from true line	k	$\sum(y_i - \eta_i)^2$	

squares in the upper part of the table are distributed as $\sigma^2\chi^2$ with the corresponding degrees of freedom and are independent. It follows that $\sum(y_i - Y_i)^2$ is distributed as $\sigma^2\chi^2(k - 2)$; so

$$E[s^2] = E\left[\frac{\sum(y_i - Y_i)^2}{k - 2}\right] = \frac{\sigma^2}{k - 2} E[\chi^2(k - 2)] = \sigma^2. \tag{3.2}$$

Thus s^2 is an estimator of σ^2, and is independent of a and b. It also follows that $k(a - \alpha)^2$ is distributed as $\sigma^2\chi^2(1)$; so

$$E[k(a - \alpha)^2] = E[\sigma^2\chi^2(1)] = \sigma^2,$$

and

$$V[a] = E[(a - \alpha)^2] = \sigma^2/k. \tag{3.3}$$

By a similar argument, $V[b] = \sigma^2/\sum(x_i - \bar{x})^2$. Since a and b are independent, their covariance is zero, and for any fixed x,

$$V[Y] = V[a + b(x - \bar{x})] = V[a] + (x - \bar{x})^2\, V[b] = \sigma^2\left[\frac{1}{k} + \frac{(x - \bar{x})^2}{\sum(x_i - \bar{x})^2}\right]. \tag{3.4}$$

The expected value of Y is $\alpha + \beta(x - \bar{x}) = \eta$. Y is a linear function of a and b, and a and b are linear functions of the y_i which are normally distributed. So Y is normally distributed; inserting s^2 for σ^2 in (3.4), we have

$$\frac{Y - \eta}{\sqrt{\hat{V}[Y]}} \sim t(k - 2). \tag{3.5}$$

This gives confidence limits for η, the true value at some specified x:

$$\Pr\{Y - t_{P_2}\sqrt{\hat{V}[Y]} < \eta < Y - t_{P_1}\sqrt{\hat{V}[Y]}\} = P_2 - P_1. \tag{3.6}$$

A new single observation at x will be distributed about η, with a variance σ^2, independently of Y, so

$$V[y - Y] = V[y] + V[Y] = \sigma^2\left[1 + \frac{1}{k} + \frac{(x - \bar{x})^2}{\sum(x_i - \bar{x})^2}\right]. \tag{3.7}$$

We now write the deviation of y_i from the over-all mean as

$$y_i - \bar{y} = (y_i - Y_i) + (Y_i - \bar{y}),$$

and square this expression and sum over i:

$$\sum(y_i - \bar{y})^2 = \sum(y_i - Y_i)^2 + \sum(Y_i - \bar{y})^2. \tag{3.8}$$

The sum of the cross products is zero by (2.5), since

$$\begin{aligned} 2\sum(y_i - Y_i)(Y_i - \bar{y}) &= 2\sum[y_i - a - b(x_i - \bar{x})][a + b(x_i - \bar{x}) - a] \\ &= 2b\sum[y_i - a - b(x_i - \bar{x})](x_i - \bar{x}) = 0. \end{aligned}$$

The left-hand side is the usual sum of squares of deviations of observations from the mean, with $(k - 1)$ degrees of freedom. On the right-hand side, $\sum(y_i - Y_i)^2$ is the sum of squares of deviations of the observed values from the estimated line. We have already seen that the expected value of the corresponding mean square $\sum(y_i - Y_i)^2/(k - 2)$ is σ^2. To find the expected value of the other term on the right-hand side of (3.8), $\sum(Y_i - \bar{y})^2$, we write

$$\sum(Y_i - \bar{y})^2 = \sum[a + b(x_i - \bar{x}) - a]^2 = b^2\sum(x_i - \bar{x})^2. \tag{3.9}$$

We have seen that $(b - \beta)^2\sum(x_i - \bar{x})^2$ is distributed as $\sigma^2\chi^2(1)$, and has expected value σ^2. But

$$(b - \beta)^2\sum(x_i - \bar{x})^2 = b^2\sum(x_i - \bar{x})^2 + \beta^2\sum(x_i - \bar{x})^2 - 2b\beta\sum(x_i - \bar{x})^2.$$

Taking expectations, and substituting for $b^2\sum(x_i - \bar{x})^2$ from (3.9),

$$\begin{aligned} \sigma^2 &= E[\sum(Y_i - \bar{y})^2] + \beta^2\sum(x_i - \bar{x})^2 - 2\beta\sum(x_i - \bar{x})^2\, E[b] \\ &= E[\sum(Y_i - \bar{y})^2] - \beta^2\sum(x_i - \bar{x})^2 \end{aligned}$$

since, from (2.12), $E[b] = \beta$. Rearranging gives

$$E[\sum(Y_i - \bar{y})^2] = \sigma^2 + \beta^2\sum(x_i - \bar{x})^2. \tag{3.10}$$

We can now put (3.8) in a tabular form (Table 11.2, p. 281) and enter the expectations of the mean squares we have just found.

11.4. An Example of Linear Regression

The data of Table 11.3 (personal communication from Dr. D. W. Cugel), plotted in Fig. 11.2, give the results of an experiment to determine the behavior of a method of measuring blood flow. The y_i are rates of flow

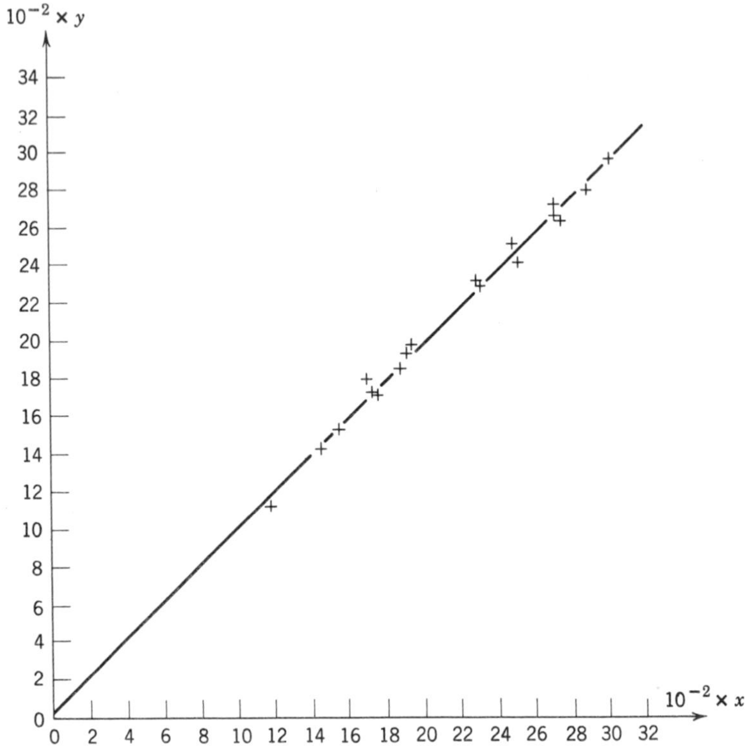

Figure 11.2

estimated by this method for a series of x_i: the x_i were accurately determined by a direct method. The columns headed Y_i and $(Y_i - y_i)$ will be referred to later.

Table 11.2

Source of variance	Degrees of freedom	Sums of squares	Mean squares	E[M.S.]
Slope of line	1	$\sum(Y_i - \bar{y})^2$	s_2^2	$\sigma^2 + \beta^2 \sum(x_i - \bar{x})^2$
Deviations of observed values about estimated line	$k - 2$	$\sum(y_i - Y_i)^2$	s^2	σ^2
Total	$k - 1$	$\sum(y_i - \bar{y})^2$		

Table 11.3

x_i	y_i	$Y_i = bx_i$	$Y_i - y_i$
1190	1115	1167.692	52.692
1455	1425	1427.725	2.725
1550	1515	1520.944	5.944
1730	1795	1697.569	−97.431
1745	1715	1712.288	−2.712
1770	1710	1736.820	26.820
1900	1830	1864.383	34.383
1920	1920	1884.008	−35.992
1960	1970	1923.258	−46.742
2295	2300	2251.978	−48.022
2335	2280	2291.228	11.228
2490	2520	2443.322	−76.678
2720	2630	2669.011	39.011
2710	2740	2659.198	−80.802
2530	2390	2482.573	92.573
2900	2800	2845.636	45.636
2760	2630	2708.261	78.261
3010	2970	2953.574	−16.426

To carry out the analysis of variance of Table 11.2 we need the following:

$$\sum x = 38{,}970, \qquad \sum y = 38{,}255, \qquad k = 18,$$
$$\sum x^2 = 89{,}394{,}900, \qquad \sum y^2 = 86{,}125{,}825, \qquad \sum xy = 87{,}719{,}100,$$

from which we derive

$$\sum(x_i - \bar{x})^2 = \sum x_i^2 - \frac{(\sum x_i)^2}{k} = 89{,}394{,}900 - \frac{(38{,}970)^2}{18} = 5{,}024{,}850,$$

$$\sum(y_i - \bar{y})^2 = \sum y_i^2 - \frac{(\sum y_i)^2}{k} = 86{,}125{,}825 - \frac{(38{,}255)^2}{18} = 4{,}823{,}323.6,$$

$$\sum(x_i - \bar{x})(y_i - \bar{y}) = \sum x_i y_i - \frac{\sum x_i \sum y_i}{k}$$
$$= 87{,}719{,}100 - \frac{38{,}970 \times 38{,}255}{18} = 4{,}897{,}025.0.$$

The sum of squares due to regression is, from (3.8),

$$\sum(Y_i - \bar{y})^2 = b^2 \sum(x_i - \bar{x})^2 = \frac{[\sum(x_i - \bar{x})(y_i - \bar{y})]^2}{\sum(x_i - \bar{x})^2} \tag{4.1}$$
$$= \frac{(4{,}897{,}025.0)^2}{5{,}024{,}850.0} = 4{,}772{,}451.7.$$

We can now assemble Table 11.4, finding the residual sum of squares by difference.

Table 11.4

Source of variance	Sums of squares	Degrees of freedom	Mean squares	E[M.S.]
Due to regression line	4,772,451.7	1	4,772,451.7	$\sigma^2 + \beta^2 \sum(x_i - \bar{x})^2$
Residual	50,871.9	16	3,179.49	σ^2
Total	4,823,323.6	17		

Under the null hypothesis $\beta = 0$ the variance ratio 4,772,451.7/3179.49 = 1501.0 is distributed as $F(1, 16)$. Here the result is obviously significant. An alternative test would be to use the fact that

$$\frac{b - \beta}{\sqrt{\hat{V}[b]}} \sim t(k - 2), \tag{4.2}$$

for which we need b, from (2.11),

$$b = \frac{\sum(x_i - \bar{x})(y_i - \bar{y})}{\sum(x_i - \bar{x})^2} = \frac{4,897,025.0}{5,024,850.0} = 0.974561,$$

and $\hat{V}[b]$, which we get by replacing σ^2 in (2.14) by s^2:

$$\hat{V}[b] = \frac{s^2}{\sum(x_i - \bar{x})^2} \tag{4.3}$$
$$= \frac{3179.49}{5,024,850.0} = 6.32753 \times 10^{-4}.$$

A test of the null hypothesis that $\beta = 0$ is given by

$$\frac{b - 0}{\sqrt{\hat{V}[b]}} = \frac{0.974561 - 0}{\sqrt{6.32753 \times 10^{-4}}} = 38.74,$$

which will be distributed as $t(16)$. The null hypothesis obviously has to be rejected. Of course, $t^2 = (38.74)^2 = 1501.0 = F$ of the previous test.

In this particular example there is no reason to doubt the significance of the regression. A more interesting null hypothesis is that $\beta = 1$; for this, (4.2) gives

$$\frac{0.974561 - 1}{\sqrt{6.32753 \times 10^{-4}}} = -1.012,$$

which is distributed as $t(16)$ under this null hypothesis. Clearly the null hypothesis that $\beta = 1$ can be accepted. We may wish to construct 95 per cent confidence limits for β; for these, $t_{0.975}(16) = 2.120$ and $\sqrt{\hat{V}[b]} = 0.02515$; so $t\sqrt{\hat{V}[b]} = 0.05333$, and the 95 per cent confidence limits are 0.97456 ± 0.05333 or $(0.9212, 1.028)$.

To construct the estimated regression line we need $\bar{y} = 38,255/18 = 2125.278$, $\bar{x} = 38,970/18 = 2,165.000$, and $b = 0.974561$, whence the estimated regression line is

$$Y = 2125.278 + 0.974561(x - 2165.000).$$

At $x = 0$, $(Y)_{x=0} = 15.352$. From (3.4),

$$\hat{V}[(Y)_{x=0}] = 3179.49\left[\frac{1}{18} + \frac{(0 - 2165.000)^2}{5,024,850.0}\right] = 3142.493.$$

Under the hypothesis that $(\eta)_{x=0} \doteq 0$, the ratio

$$\frac{15.352 - 0}{\sqrt{3142.493}} = 0.274$$

is distributed as $t(16)$: Clearly the null hypothesis of a zero intercept is acceptable. Confidence limits for the intercept are

$$15.352 \pm 2.120 \times \sqrt{3142.493} = (-103.5, 134.2).$$

Let us summarize what has been so far established:

(i) The estimated regression line of y on x is

$$Y = 2125.3 + 0.97456(x - 2165.0).$$

(ii) 95 per cent confidence limits for the regression coefficient β are (0.921, 1.028); so the null hypothesis $\beta = 1$ is acceptable.

(iii) The intercept on the y axis has 95 per cent confidence limits (−103, 134); so the null hypothesis that the intercept is zero is acceptable.

(iv) The estimated variance of an observation around its true value is 3179.49, corresponding to a standard deviation of 56.83.

We might ask, if we observe a new value of y, what is our estimate of x, and what are confidence limits on the true value of x corresponding to this observed y? This question is investigated in the following section.

A further question arising from items (ii) and (iii) above is the following: While the null hypothesis that $\beta = 1$, the intercept unspecified, is acceptable, and also the null hypothesis that the intercept is zero, β being unspecified, is acceptable, is the null hypothesis that $\beta = 1$ and the intercept is zero simultaneously acceptable? This question is discussed from the testing point of view in Section 11.9 and from the confidence region point of view in Section 11.11.

11.5. The Use of the Regression Line in Reverse

Suppose that we have a regression line $Y = a + b(x - \bar{x})$, based on k observations (x_i, y_i). Suppose that we now observe a new $\bar{y}'$, the mean of m new observations known to have arisen from the same x, and we wish to predict the x corresponding to this $\bar{y}'$, and to construct confidence limits for this prediction. Of course, m may equal 1, so that we just have a single observation y'. We can solve the estimated regression equation (2.2) for x, inserting $\bar{y}'$ for Y, where $\bar{y}'$ is the mean of the new set of observations on y, to get

$$\hat{x} = \bar{x} + \frac{\bar{y}' - a}{b}, \tag{5.1}$$

a point estimate of the value of x corresponding to the new observed value $\bar{y}'$. The expected value of the new $\bar{y}'$ is $E[\bar{y}] = \eta$. Corresponding to this value of η is a value of x given by solving the true regression equation (2.1) for x: Denote this value of x by ξ. Then

$$\xi = \bar{x} + \frac{\eta - \alpha}{\beta}$$

and

$$\eta - \alpha - \beta(\xi - \bar{x}) = 0. \tag{5.2}$$

We now define a new variable z as

$$z = \bar{y}' - a - b(\xi - \bar{x}). \tag{5.3}$$

This variable will have expected value

$$E[z] = E[\bar{y}'] - E[a] - (\xi - \bar{x})\, E[b] = \eta - \alpha - (\xi - \bar{x})\beta = 0$$

by (5.2). Its variance is

$$V[z] = V[\bar{y}'] + V[a] + (\xi - \bar{x})^2\, V[b] = \frac{\sigma^2}{m} + \frac{\sigma^2}{k} + (\xi - \bar{x})^2 \frac{\sigma^2}{\sum(x_i - \bar{x})^2}$$

$$= \sigma^2\left[\frac{1}{m} + \frac{1}{k} + \frac{(\xi - \bar{x})^2}{\sum(x_i - \bar{x})^2}\right]. \tag{5.4}$$

The random variable z is a linear function of three random normally distributed variables $\bar{y}'$, a, and b, and hence will itself be normally distributed. Thus $z/\sqrt{V[z]}$ is $N(0, 1)$, and, on replacing σ^2 in (5.4) by its estimate s^2 from Table 11.2, we have

$$\frac{\bar{y}' - a - b(\xi - \bar{x})}{s\sqrt{1/m + 1/k + (\xi - \bar{x})^2/\sum(x_i - \bar{x})^2}} \sim t(k - 2). \tag{5.5}$$

We can insert the above expression in place of t in the statement $\Pr\{t_1 < t < t_2\} = P_2 - P_1$, to get confidence limits for ξ. If ξ_2 is the lower confidence limit, it is given by the equation

$$\frac{\bar{y}' - a - b(\xi_2 - \bar{x})}{s\sqrt{1/m + 1/k + (\xi_2 - \bar{x})^2/\sum(x_i - \bar{x})^2}} = t_2, \tag{5.6}$$

where t_2 is the P_2 point of t with the degrees of freedom of s, namely $(k - 2)$. Squaring and expanding and collecting terms in ξ_2^2, ξ_2, we get a quadratic equation in ξ_2:

$$\xi_2^2\left[b^2 - \frac{t_2^2 s^2}{\sum(x_i - \bar{x})^2}\right] + 2\xi_2\left[\frac{t_2^2 s^2}{\sum(x_i - \bar{x})^2}\,\bar{x} - b^2\bar{x} - b(\bar{y}' - a)\right]$$
$$+ (\bar{y}' - a + b\bar{x})^2 - t_2^2 s^2\left[\frac{1}{m} + \frac{1}{k} + \frac{\bar{x}^2}{\sum(x_i - \bar{x})^2}\right] = 0. \tag{5.7}$$

For a quadratic equation of the conventional form $A\xi^2 + B\xi + C = 0$ the standard solutions are

$$\xi = -\frac{B}{2A} \pm \frac{\sqrt{B^2 - 4AC}}{2A} = -\frac{B}{2A} \pm \sqrt{\frac{(B/2)^2 - AC}{A^2}}. \tag{5.8}$$

The first term is

$$\begin{aligned} -\frac{B}{2A} &= \frac{-2\{[t_2^2s^2/\sum(x_i - \bar{x})^2]\bar{x} - b^2\bar{x} - b(\bar{y}' - a)\}}{2[b^2 - t_2^2s^2/\sum(x_i - \bar{x})^2]} \\ &= \bar{x} + \frac{b(\bar{y}' - a)}{b^2 - t_2^2s^2/\sum(x_i - \bar{x})^2}. \end{aligned} \tag{5.9}$$

The numerator of the square of the second term of (5.8) is

$$\begin{aligned} \left(\frac{B}{2}\right)^2 - AC &= \left[\frac{t_2^2s^2}{\sum(x_i - \bar{x})^2}\bar{x} - b^2\bar{x} - b(\bar{y}' - a)\right]^2 - \left[b^2 - \frac{t_2^2s^2}{\sum(x_i - \bar{x})^2}\right] \\ &\qquad \left\{(\bar{y}' - a + b\bar{x})^2 - t_2^2s^2\left[\frac{1}{m} + \frac{1}{k} + \frac{\bar{x}^2}{\sum(x_i - \bar{x})^2}\right]\right\} \\ &= \left[b^2 - \frac{t_2^2s^2}{\sum(x_i - \bar{x})^2}\right]\left(\frac{1}{m} + \frac{1}{k}\right)t_2^2s^2 + \frac{t_2^2s^2(\bar{y}' - a)^2}{\sum(x_i - \bar{x})^2}. \end{aligned} \tag{5.10}$$

Thus the second term of (5.8) is

$$\begin{aligned} &\sqrt{\frac{(B/2)^2 - AC}{A^2}} \\ &\quad = \frac{t_2 s}{b^2 - t_2^2s^2/\sum(x_i - \bar{x})^2}\sqrt{\left[b^2 - \frac{t_2^2s^2}{\sum(x_i - \bar{x})^2}\right]\left(\frac{1}{m} + \frac{1}{k}\right) + \frac{(\bar{y}' - a)^2}{\sum(x_i - \bar{x})^2}}. \end{aligned} \tag{5.11}$$

Substituting (5.9) and (5.11) in (5.8), using the negative sign for the square-root term, gives as the solution for the lower confidence limit,

$$\begin{aligned} \xi_2 &= \bar{x} + \frac{b(\bar{y}' - a)}{b^2 - t_2^2s^2/\sum(x_i - \bar{x})^2} \\ &\quad - \frac{t_2 s}{b^2 - t_2^2s^2/\sum(x_i - \bar{x})^2}\sqrt{\left[b^2 - \frac{t_2^2s^2}{\sum(x_i - \bar{x})^2}\right]\left(\frac{1}{m} + \frac{1}{k}\right) + \frac{(\bar{y}' - a)^2}{\sum(x_i - \bar{x})^2}}. \end{aligned} \tag{5.12}$$

The upper confidence limit ξ_1 is obtained in the identical manner, using t_1 in place of t_2, and the solution is the same as (5.12) with this change.

We now note an important property of the formula (5.12) for the lower confidence limit ξ_2. Consider the case where b is positive and a test of the null hypothesis $\beta = 0$ tends to the $(1 - P_2)$ level of significance, i.e.,

$$\frac{b - 0}{\sqrt{\hat{V}[b]}} \to t_{P_2}. \tag{5.13}$$

Substituting for $\hat{V}[b]$ from (4.3), squaring, and rearranging gives

$$b^2 - \frac{t_2^2 s^2}{\sum(x_i - \bar{x})^2} \to 0. \tag{5.14}$$

Inspecting the formulas for ξ_2 (5.12) and ξ_1 shows that in this case meaningful confidence limits do not exist.

Now consider the other case in which b is positive and highly significant at the $(1 - P_2)$ level of significance, so that $b/\sqrt{\hat{V}[b]} \gg t_2$, and

$$b^2 \gg \frac{t_2^2 s^2}{\sum(x_i - \bar{x})^2}. \tag{5.15}$$

Now define a quantity g as

$$g = \left(\frac{t_2\sqrt{\hat{V}[b]}}{b}\right)^2 = \frac{t_2^2 s^2}{b^2 \sum(x_i - \bar{x})^2}. \tag{5.16}$$

If (5.15) is satisfied, $0 < g \ll 1$, and replacing

$$b^2 - \frac{t_2^2 s^2}{\sum(x_i - \bar{x})^2} = b^2(1 - g)$$

by b^2 in (5.12) and its analog for ξ_1, we get

$$\begin{aligned} \xi_2 &\simeq \bar{x} + \frac{\bar{y}' - a}{b} - \frac{t_2 s}{|b|}\sqrt{\left(\frac{1}{m} + \frac{1}{k}\right) + \frac{(\bar{y}' - a)^2}{b^2 \sum(x_i - \bar{x})^2}} \\ \xi_1 &\simeq \bar{x} + \frac{\bar{y}' - a}{b} - \frac{t_1 s}{|b|}\sqrt{\left(\frac{1}{m} + \frac{1}{k}\right) + \frac{(\bar{y}' - a)^2}{b^2 \sum(x_i - \bar{x})^2}} \end{aligned} \tag{5.17}$$

as approximate confidence limits for ξ. These are usually considered valid for most purposes when $g < 0.1$.

To illustrate these results, suppose that in the example of Section 11.4 we observe a single new observation $y = 3000$. To construct 95 per cent confidence limits for ξ we need $t_{0.975} = -t_{0.025}$. For that example $s^2 = 3179.49$, $b = 0.974561$, $\sum(x_i - \bar{x})^2 = 5{,}024{,}850$. Inserting these values in (5.16) we obtain $g = 0.00299$, which permits use of the approximation (5.17). The 95 per cent confidence limits for ξ are

$$2165.000 + \frac{3000.000 - 2125.277}{0.974561}$$
$$\pm \frac{2.120\sqrt{3179.49}}{0.974561}\sqrt{\left(\frac{1}{1}+\frac{1}{18}\right) + \frac{(3000.000 - 2125.277)^2}{(0.974561)^2 \times 5{,}024{,}850}}$$
$$= 3062.5 \pm 135.2.$$

Thus if we observe a flow rate of 3000 by our new method, we can be 95 per cent confident that the true flow rate is in the interval (2927, 3198).

11.6. The Comparison of Two Regression Lines

We suppose that we have two sets of observations, $(x_{i\nu}, y_{i\nu})$, $i = 1, 2$, $\nu = 1, \ldots, n_i$:

$$(x_{11}, y_{11}), (x_{12}, y_{12}), \ldots, (x_{1n_1}, y_{1n_1})$$

and

$$(x_{21}, y_{21}), (x_{22}, y_{22}), \ldots, (x_{2n_2}, y_{2n_2}).$$

We will discuss the procedure for deciding whether a single common regression line is an adequate fit, or whether separate regression lines

$$\begin{aligned} Y_1 &= a_1 + b_1(x - \bar{x}_1) \\ Y_2 &= a_2 + b_2(x - \bar{x}_2) \end{aligned} \tag{6.1}$$

are necessary.

We start by fitting separate lines, obtaining estimates a_i, b_i, and s_i^2, $i = 1, 2$. If the lines are identical, the s_i^2 will be estimates of a common σ^2, and their ratio will be distributed as F. It is easier to put the larger s_i^2 in the numerator of the variance ratio; a two-sided test will usually be appropriate. If the null hypothesis is rejected, then the lines differ in this regard, but further examination is difficult because the dissimilar variances involve the Behrens–Fisher problem. If the null hypothesis of a common residual variance is accepted, we can form a joint estimate of σ^2,

$$s^2 = \frac{(n_1 - 2)s_1^2 + (n_2 - 2)s_2^2}{n_1 - 2 + n_2 - 2}. \tag{6.2}$$

If the null hypothesis $\beta_1 - \beta_2 = 0$ is true, $(b_1 - b_2)$ will be normally distributed about 0 with a variance

$$V[b_1 - b_2] = V[b_1] + V[b_2] = \frac{\sigma^2}{\sum_\nu^{n_1} (x_{1\nu} - \bar{x}_1)^2} + \frac{\sigma^2}{\sum_\nu^{n_2} (x_{2\nu} - \bar{x}_2)^2} \tag{6.3}$$

where σ^2 will be estimated by (6.2). Thus under the null hypothesis, $\beta_1 - \beta_2 = 0$,

$$\frac{b_1 - b_2}{s\sqrt{\dfrac{1}{\sum_v^{n_1}(x_{1v} - \bar{x}_1)^2} + \dfrac{1}{\sum_v^{n_2}(x_{2v} - \bar{x}_2)^2}}} \sim t(n_1 + n_2 - 4). \quad (6.4)$$

If we reject this null hypothesis, then the lines differ in slope and hence are different. If, on the other hand, we accept this null hypothesis, then we fit a joint estimate of the common slope and proceed to test whether the lines are coincident as well as parallel.

We next need to estimate the common slope. We have two true equations for the two parallel lines,

$$\eta_1 = \alpha_1 + \beta(x - \bar{x}_1), \qquad \eta_2 = \alpha_2 + \beta(x - \bar{x}_2), \quad (6.5)$$

and two estimated equations,

$$Y_1 = a_1 + b(x - \bar{x}_1), \qquad Y_2 = a_2 + b(x - \bar{x}_2). \quad (6.6)$$

The sum of squares of deviations of the observations from the two parallel estimated lines is

$$\begin{aligned} R &= \sum_v^{n_1}(y_{1v} - Y_{1v})^2 + \sum_v^{n_2}(y_{2v} - Y_{2v})^2 \\ &= \sum_v^{n_1}[y_{1v} - a_1 - b(x_{1v} - \bar{x}_1)]^2 + \sum_v^{n_2}[y_{2v} - a_2 - b(x_{2v} - \bar{x}_2)]^2. \quad (6.7) \end{aligned}$$

The least-squares estimates are those which make this a minimum. Differentiating with respect to a_1, a_2, and b and equating to zero gives

$$\frac{\partial R}{\partial a_1} = -2\sum_v^{n_1}[y_{1v} - a_1 - b(x_{1v} - \bar{x}_1)] = 0, \quad (6.8)$$

$$\frac{\partial R}{\partial a_2} = -2\sum_v^{n_2}[y_{2v} - a_2 - b(x_{2v} - \bar{x}_2)] = 0, \quad (6.9)$$

$$\begin{aligned} \frac{\partial R}{\partial b} = &-2\sum_v^{n_1}[y_{1v} - a_1 - b(x_{1v} - \bar{x}_1)](x_{1v} - \bar{x}_1) \\ &-2\sum_v^{n_2}[y_{2v} - a_2 - b(x_{2v} - \bar{x}_2)](x_{2v} - \bar{x}_2) = 0. \quad (6.10) \end{aligned}$$

The first two of these equations give

$$a_1 = \frac{1}{n_1}\sum_v^{n_1} y_{1v}, \qquad a_2 = \frac{1}{n_2}\sum_v^{n_2} y_{2v}, \quad (6.11)$$

and the third gives

$$b = \frac{\sum_{\nu}^{n_1} y_{1\nu}(x_{1\nu} - \bar{x}_1) + \sum_{\nu}^{n_2} y_{2\nu}(x_{2\nu} - \bar{x}_2)}{\sum_{\nu}^{n_1} (x_{1\nu} - \bar{x}_1)^2 + \sum_{\nu}^{n_2} (x_{2\nu} - \bar{x}_2)^2}. \tag{6.12}$$

The same arguments that were used to obtain (2.14) give

$$V[b] = \frac{\sigma^2}{\sum_{i}^{2} \sum_{\nu}^{n_i} (x_{i\nu} - \bar{x}_i)^2}. \tag{6.13}$$

To estimate σ^2 for the model (6.5), the sum of squares of deviations from the two parallel lines is given by (6.7). Inserting the solutions for a_1, a_2, and b, straightforward manipulation leads to

$$R = \left[\sum_{i}^{2} \sum_{\nu}^{n_i} y_{i\nu}^2 - \sum_{i}^{2} \frac{\left(\sum_{\nu}^{n_i} y_{i\nu}\right)^2}{n_i}\right] - \frac{\left[\sum_{i}^{2} \sum_{\nu}^{n_i} y_{i\nu}(x_{i\nu} - \bar{x}_i)\right]^2}{\sum_{i}^{2} \sum_{\nu}^{n_i} (x_{i\nu} - \bar{x}_i)^2}. \tag{6.14}$$

Since we have fitted three parameters to the data, this sum of squares has $(n_1 + n_2 - 3)$ degrees of freedom.

We now proceed to test whether the two parallel lines are identical, i.e., lie on top of each other. If the true lines (6.5) are identical, then $\eta_1 = \eta_2$ for all x, and hence

$$\alpha_1 - \beta\bar{x}_1 = \alpha_2 - \beta\bar{x}_2, \tag{6.15}$$

and

$$(\alpha_1 - \alpha_2) - \beta(\bar{x}_1 - \bar{x}_2) = 0. \tag{6.16}$$

It follows that the quantity

$$(a_1 - a_2) - b(\bar{x}_1 - \bar{x}_2) \tag{6.17}$$

will have expected value zero, and be distributed normally with variance

$$\frac{\sigma^2}{n_1} + \frac{\sigma^2}{n_2} + (\bar{x}_1 - \bar{x}_2)^2\, V[b] = \sigma^2\left[\frac{1}{n_1} + \frac{1}{n_2} + \frac{(\bar{x}_1 - \bar{x}_2)^2}{\sum_{i}^{2} \sum_{\nu}^{n_i} (x_{i\nu} - \bar{x}_i)^2}\right]. \tag{6.18}$$

Thus, if the lines are identical,

$$\frac{(a_1 - a_2) - b(\bar{x}_1 - \bar{x}_2)}{s\sqrt{1/n_1 + 1/n_2 + (\bar{x}_1 - \bar{x}_2)^2 / \sum_{i}^{2} \sum_{\nu}^{n_i} (x_{i\nu} - \bar{x}_i)^2}} \sim t(n_1 + n_2 - 3) \tag{6.19}$$

where s is derived from the sum of squares in (6.14). A numerical example will be discussed in Section 11.8.

11.7. Parallel-Line Biological Assay

An important application of the foregoing section is to a common form of biological assay for assaying vitamins, hormones, etc., in which the "response" of the organism, usually an animal, over a certain range is proportional to the logarithm of the dose. For complicated substances not readily susceptible to chemical analysis this affords a method of assaying the potency of an unknown preparation in terms of a standard: for example, if we require 2 units of the unknown to give the same response as the standard, then the potency of the unknown is $1/2 = 50$ per cent.

Suppose that, if η is the true response and x the true log dose, then, for the standard and unknown, respectively,

$$\eta_1 = \alpha_1 + \beta(x - \bar{x}_1), \tag{7.1}$$

$$\eta_2 = \alpha_2 + \beta(x - \bar{x}_2). \tag{7.2}$$

If the unknown is identical with the standard, then the two lines will be identical, but, if the unknown is more potent, then its line will lie above that for the standard. Let ξ_1 be the value of x_1 when η_1 takes some convenient value, say α_1; substituting α_1 for η_1 and ξ_1 for x in (7.1), we get $\xi_1 = \bar{x}_1$. Let ξ_2 be the value of x_2 when η_2 takes the same value α_1; substituting in (7.2),

$$\alpha_1 = \alpha_2 + \beta(\xi_2 - \bar{x}_2);$$

so

$$\xi_2 = \bar{x}_2 + \frac{\alpha_1 - \alpha_2}{\beta}. \tag{7.3}$$

The horizontal distance between the two lines is of course independent of where we draw the horizontal line since the response lines are parallel. To obtain the same response α_1 with the standard as with the unknown we require a dose $\xi_1 = x_1$ of the standard and a dose $\xi_2 = \bar{x}_2 + (\alpha_1 - \alpha_2)/\beta$ of the unknown. The difference $\xi_1 - \xi_2 = \mu$, say, is the difference in the logarithms of equivalent quantities of standard and unknown, i.e., μ is the logarithm of the potency ratio, and the antilogarithm of μ, say ρ, is the actual potency ratio. We have

$$\mu = \xi_1 - \xi_2 = \bar{x}_1 - \bar{x}_2 - \frac{\alpha_1 - \alpha_2}{\beta}. \tag{7.4}$$

We can estimate μ in terms of the vertical distance between the two parallel lines Ω (see Figure 11.3) and the slope β:

$$\mu = \frac{\Omega}{\beta}. \tag{7.5}$$

The quantity Ω is the difference in response for the same dose of the unknown and standard. Letting x be the same in equations (7.1) and (7.2),

$$\Omega = \eta_2 - \eta_1 = \alpha_2 + \beta(x - \bar{x}_2) - \alpha_1 - \beta(x - \bar{x}_1) = \beta(\bar{x}_1 - \bar{x}_2) - (\alpha_1 - \alpha_2). \tag{7.6}$$

Substituting for Ω in (7.5),

$$\mu = (\bar{x}_1 - \bar{x}_2) - \frac{\alpha_1 - \alpha_2}{\beta}. \tag{7.7}$$

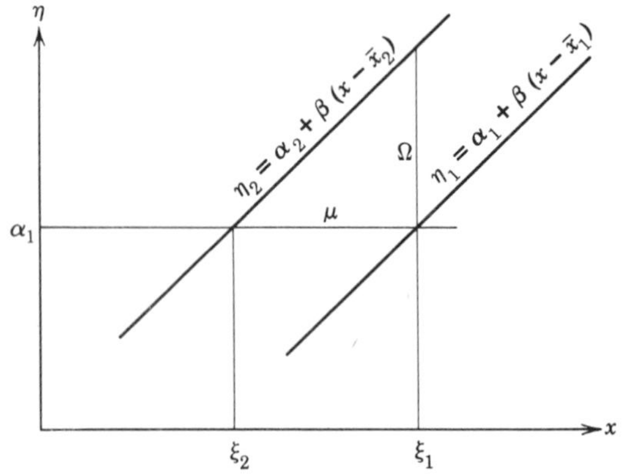

Figure 11.3

In actual practice, of course, we do not know the true lines (7.1) and (7.2); we have estimated lines

$$Y_1 = \bar{y}_1 + b(x - \bar{x}_1), \qquad Y_2 = \bar{y}_2 + b(x - \bar{x}_2), \tag{7.8}$$

an estimated vertical distance between the lines Q, and an estimated logarithm of the potency ratio M,

$$M = \frac{Q}{b} = (\bar{x}_1 - \bar{x}_2) - \frac{\bar{y}_1 - \bar{y}_2}{b}. \tag{7.9}$$

To obtain confidence limits for the logarithm of the potency ratio μ, consider the variable z defined as

$$z = -(\bar{y}_1 - \bar{y}_2) - b[(\xi_1 - \xi_2) - (\bar{x}_1 - \bar{x}_2)]. \tag{7.10}$$

Its expected value is

$$E[z] = -(\alpha_1 - \alpha_2) - \beta[(\xi_1 - \xi_2) - (\bar{x}_1 - \bar{x}_2)] = 0, \tag{7.11}$$

substituting for $(\xi_1 - \xi_2)$ from (7.4). The variance of z is

$$V[z] = V[\bar{y}_1] + V[\bar{y}_2] + [(\xi_1 - \xi_2) - (\bar{x}_1 - \bar{x}_2)]^2 V[b]$$

$$= \sigma^2 \left[\frac{1}{n_1} + \frac{1}{n_2} + \frac{[(\xi_1 - \xi_2) - (\bar{x}_1 - \bar{x}_2)]^2}{\sum_i^2 \sum_\nu^{n_i} (x_{i\nu} - \bar{x}_i)^2} \right]. \tag{7.12}$$

Then, substituting the sample estimate s^2 derived from (6.14) for σ^2,

$$\frac{-(\bar{y}_1 - \bar{y}_2) - b[(\xi_1 - \xi_2) - (\bar{x}_1 - \bar{x}_2)]}{s\sqrt{\dfrac{1}{n_1} + \dfrac{1}{n_2} + \dfrac{[(\xi_1 - \xi_2) - (\bar{x}_1 - \bar{x}_2)]^2}{\sum_i^2 \sum_\nu^{n_i} (x_{i\nu} - \bar{x}_i)^2}}} \sim t(n_1 + n_2 - 3). \tag{7.13}$$

This is similar to (5.5), with a replaced by $(\bar{y}_1 - \bar{y}_2)$, ξ by $(\xi_1 - \xi_2)$, $\bar{x}$ by $(\bar{x}_1 - \bar{x}_2)$, $1/k$ by $(1/n_1 + 1/n_2)$, and $\sum (x_i - \bar{x})^2$ by $\sum_i^2 \sum_\nu^{n_i} (x_{i\nu} - \bar{x}_i)^2$, and with $\bar{y}$ and $1/m$ omitted. Equation (7.13) can thus be handled in the same way as (5.5). If we define g as

$$g = \frac{t^2 s^2}{b^2 \sum_i^2 \sum_\nu^{n_i} (x_{i\nu} - \bar{x}_i)^2}, \tag{7.14}$$

analogous to (5.16), we get as the confidence limits for $(\xi_1 - \xi_2)$,

$$(\bar{x}_1 - \bar{x}_2) + \frac{-(\bar{y}_1 - \bar{y}_2)/b}{1 - g}$$

$$- \frac{ts}{b(1-g)} \sqrt{(1-g)\left(\frac{1}{n_1} + \frac{1}{n_2}\right) + \frac{(\bar{y}_1 - \bar{y}_2)^2}{b^2 \sum_i^k \sum_\nu^{n_i} (x_{i\nu} - \bar{x}_i)^2}}, \tag{7.15}$$

where t takes the probability levels P_2 and P_1 to give $(P_2 - P_1)$ confidence limits.

For a comprehensive review of the statistical problems in biological assay see two books by Finney [5], [6]. The first deals mainly with the awkward situation where the response at each x is not a continuous variable but instead an all-or-none affair, e.g., alive or dead. At each dose we have a proportion h_i of animals surviving. The fitting of a regression line of h on x

is not straightforward since the h_i are binomial variables with variances $\theta_i(1 - \theta_i)/n$ which are not constant but instead a function of θ. In fitting the line the points h_i have to be weighted inversely as their variances. Furthermore, the variances involve the θ_i which are unknown but which can be estimated from a provisional line. This will give a better line, which will give better estimates of the θ_i, which give a still better line. This iterative procedure converges, but a number of theoretical problems are involved, and the calculations in practice are tedious. The second text of Finney is a comprehensive examination of all types of bioassay. See also Emmens [7].

11.8. An Example of Parallel-Line Biological Assay

In an assay of estrogenic hormone [7], three groups of rats received 0.2, 0.3, and 0.4 mg of the standard, and two groups of rats received 1 and 2.5 mg of the unknown. Table 11.5 gives a linear function of the logarithm of the weight of the uteri.

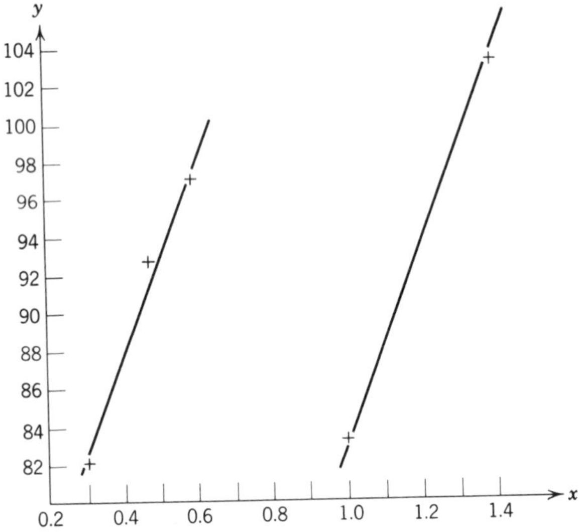

Figure 11.4

If the observations are $(x_{ij\nu}, y_{ij\nu})$, then $i = 1$ for the standard and 2 for the unknown; $j = 1, \ldots, m_i$ corresponding to the number of dosage levels, and actually $m_1 = 3, m_2 = 2$; $\nu = 1, \ldots, n_{ij}$, the number of observations

Table 11.5*

	Standard				Unknown		
Dose, mg	0.2	0.3	0.4		1.0	2.5	
log (dose × 10) = x	0.301	0.477	0.602		1.000	1.398	
i	1	1	1		2	2	
j	1	2	3	$\sum_{j}^{m_1}$	1	2	$\sum_{j}^{m_2}$
Response = $y_{ij\gamma}$	73	77	118		79	101	
	69	93	85		87	86	
	71	116	105		71	105	
	91	78	76		78	111	
	80	87	101		92	102	
	110	86			92	107	
		101				102	
		104				112	
n_{ij}	6	8	5	19	6	8	14
$\sum_{\nu}^{n_{ij}} y_{ij\nu}$	494	742	485	1,721	499	826	1,325
$\sum_{\nu}^{n_{ij}} y^2_{ij\nu}$	41,912	70,100	48,151	160,163	41,863	85,744	127,607
$\sum_{\nu}^{n_{ij}} x_{ij\nu}$	6 × .301	8 × .477	5 × .602	8.632	6 × 1.000	8 × 1.398	17.184
$\sum_{\nu}^{n_{ij}} x^2_{ij\nu}$	6 × .301²	8 × .477²	5 × .602²	4.175858	6 × 1.000²	8 × 1,398²	21.635232
$\sum_{\nu}^{n_{ij}} x_{ij\nu}y_{ij\nu}$	494 × .301	742 × .477	485 × .602	794.598	499 × 1.000	826 × 1.398	1653.748

* Data derived from [7].

at each dose of each preparation. The lower part of Table 11.5 assembles certain sums, sums of squares, and sums of products. We further need

$$\sum_{j}^{m_1}\sum_{v}^{n_{1j}}(x_{1jv}-\bar{x}_{1..})^2=\sum_{j}^{m_1}\sum_{v}^{n_{1j}}x_{1jv}^2-\left(\frac{\sum_{j}^{m_1}\sum_{v}^{n_{1j}}x_{1jv}}{\sum_{j}^{m_1}n_{1j}}\right)^2$$

$$=4.175858-\frac{(8.632)^2}{19}=0.254205,$$

$$\sum_{j}^{m_1}\sum_{v}^{n_{1j}}(y_{1jv}-\bar{y}_{1..})^2=\sum_{j}^{m_1}\sum_{v}^{n_{1j}}y_{1jv}^2-\left(\frac{\sum_{j}^{m_1}\sum_{v}^{n_{1j}}y_{1jv}}{\sum_{j}^{m_1}n_{1j}}\right)^2$$

$$=160{,}163-\frac{(1721)^2}{19}=4276.632,$$

$$\sum_{j}^{m_1}\sum_{v}^{n_{1j}}(x_{1jv}-\bar{x}_{1..})(y_{1jv}-\bar{y}_{1..})=\sum_{j}^{m_1}\sum_{v}^{n_{1j}}x_{1jv}y_{1jv}-\frac{\sum_{j}^{m_1}\sum_{v}^{n_{1j}}x_{1jv}\sum_{j}^{m_1}\sum_{v}^{n_{1j}}y_{1jv}}{\sum_{j}^{m_1}n_{1j}}$$

$$=794.598-\frac{8632\times 1721}{19}=12.720526.$$

The similar quantities for the unknown are 0.543100, 2205.214, and 27.405143. The sum of squares due to regression for the standard is

$$\frac{(12.720526)^2}{0.254205}=636.543$$

and the residual sum of squares about the regression line is (4276.632 − 636.543) = 3640.089; so $s_1^2 = 3640.089/17 = 214.123$. Likewise $s_2^2 = 68.528$. The variance ratio 214.123/68.528 = 3.12 is rather close to $F_{0.975}(17, 12)$, 3.13, but the null hypothesis is acceptable at the two-sided 0.05 level of significance. The joint s^2 (6.2) is (3640.089 + 822.334)/(17 + 12) = 153.877. The next step is to compute $b_1 = 12.720526/0.254204 = 50.041$ and $b_2 = 27.405143/0.543100 = 50.461$. The estimated variance of $(b_1 - b_2)$, using (6.3), is

$$\hat{V}[b_1-b_2]=153.877\left(\frac{1}{0.254204}+\frac{1}{0.543100}\right)=888.660$$

whence the statistic for testing the null hypothesis $\beta_1 = \beta_2$ (6.4) is

$$\frac{50.041-50.461}{\sqrt{888.660}}=-0.014$$

which is distributed as $t(29)$ and is obviously nonsignificant. We therefore form a joint b as given by (6.12),

$$b = \frac{12.720526 + 27.405143}{0.254204 + 0.54310} = \frac{40.125669}{0.797304} = 50.326687,$$

and a new residual sum of squares about the two parallel regression lines as given by (6.14):

$$R = 4276.632 + 2205.214 - \frac{(40.125669)^2}{0.797304} = 4462.454.$$

This has $(19 + 14 - 3) = 30$ degrees of freedom; so the new $s^2 = 4462.454/30 = 148.748$.

The test for whether these two parallel lines can be regarded as a single coincident line is given by (6.19), requiring $\bar{x}_{1\cdot\cdot} = 8.632/19 = 0.454316$, $\bar{x}_{2\cdot\cdot} = 17.184/14 = 1.227429$, $\bar{y}_{1\cdot\cdot} = 1721/19 = 90.578947$, and $\bar{y}_{2\cdot\cdot} = 1325/14 = 94.642857$. The statistic (6.19) has the value

$$\frac{(90.578947 - 94.642857) - 50.326687(0.454316 - 1.227429)}{\sqrt{148.748}\sqrt{1/19 + 1/14 + (0.454316 - 1.227429)^2/0.797304}} = 3.057$$

and is distributed as t with 30 degrees of freedom.

The foregoing concludes our analysis of these data according to the procedures described in Section 11.6. The null hypothesis that the lines are parallel can be accepted, but the null hypothesis that they are coincident must be rejected. We will now apply the methods of Section 11.7 to calculate the potency ratio and its confidence limits.

The logarithm of the potency ratio is given by (7.9):

$$\begin{aligned} M &= (\bar{x}_{1\cdot\cdot} - \bar{x}_{2\cdot\cdot}) - \frac{\bar{y}_{1\cdot\cdot} - \bar{y}_{2\cdot\cdot}}{b} \\ &= (0.454316 - 1.227429) - \frac{90.578947 - 94.642857}{50.3266687} \\ &= -0.773113 - (-0.080751) = -0.692362 = \bar{1}.3076. \end{aligned}$$

The antilogarithm of this, 0.203, is the point estimate of the potency ratio.

The exact confidence limits are given by (7.15). We first calculate g as defined in (7.14) to see if approximate limits would be acceptable. For 95 per cent confidence limits we need $t_{0.975}(30) = 2.042$, and

$$g = \frac{(2.042)^2 \times 148.748}{(50.326687)^2 \times 0.797304} = 0.307144.$$

If g was less than 0.05 we would consider an approximation acceptable, given by putting $g = 0$ in (7.15), but with $g = 0.307$ the exact formula (7.15) must be used:

$$-0.773113 + \frac{-(-0.080751)}{1 - 0.307144}$$

$$\pm \frac{2.042\sqrt{148.748}}{50.326687 \times (1 - 0.30744)} \sqrt{(1 - 0.307144)\left(\frac{1}{19} + \frac{1}{14}\right) + \frac{(-0.080751)^2}{0.797304}}$$

$$= -0.4374 \quad \text{and} \quad -0.8757 = \bar{1}.5626 \quad \text{and} \quad \bar{1}.1243.$$

These are confidence limits for the logarithm of the potency ratio. Their antilogarithms, (0.133, 0.365), are the 95 per cent confidence limits for the potency ratio ρ.

11.9. Regression through the Origin

There are occasions when it appears appropriate for a regression line to pass through the origin, i.e., for the true regression line to be

$$\eta = \beta x. \tag{9.1}$$

In the numerical example considered in Section 11.4, where blood flow rate was measured by a new method y and by a standard method x, it would be reasonable to expect η to equal zero when $x = 0$. We did find in fact that the null hypothesis that the intercept was zero was acceptable. In this section we study the fitting of a line through the origin. We assume that y is distributed normally about η as given by (9.1) with variance σ^2, and that the observations are independent. The estimated regression equation is

$$Y = bx. \tag{9.2}$$

The sum of squares of deviations between the observed values y_i and the predicted values Y_i is

$$R = \sum(y_i - Y_i)^2 = \sum(y_i - bx_i)^2. \tag{9.2}$$

Differentiating with respect to b and equating to zero to make R a minimum gives

$$\frac{dR}{db} = -2\sum(y_i - bx_i)x_i = 0, \tag{9.3}$$

whence

$$b = \frac{\sum x_i y_i}{\sum x_i^2}. \tag{9.4}$$

It is clear that b is a linear function of the y_i, and its variance is

$$V[b] = \frac{\sum x_i^2 V[y_i]}{(\sum x_i^2)^2} = \frac{\sigma^2}{\sum x_i^2}. \tag{9.5}$$

Analogous to (3.1), we write

$$y_i - \eta_i = (y_i - Y_i) + (Y_i - \eta_i) = (y_i - Y_i) + (b - \beta)x_i. \tag{9.6}$$

Squaring and summing over i gives

$$\sum(y_i - \eta_i)^2 = \sum(y_i - Y_i)^2 + (b - \beta)^2 \sum x_i^2, \tag{9.7}$$

the terms being distributed as $\sigma^2\chi^2$ with k, $(k - 1)$, and 1 degrees of freedom, respectively. It follows that s^2 defined as $s^2 = \sum(y_i - Y_i)^2/(k - 1)$ has expected value σ^2 and is independent of b. We have

$$V[Y] = V[bx] = x^2 V[b] = \frac{x^2\sigma^2}{\sum x_i^2}. \tag{9.8}$$

We now write

$$y_i = (y_i - Y_i) + Y_i = (y_i - Y_i) + bx_i$$

and square and sum over i:

$$\begin{aligned} \sum y_i^2 &= \sum(y_i - Y_i)^2 + \sum(bx_i)^2 + 2\sum(y_i - bx_i)bx_i \\ &= \sum(y_i - Y_i)^2 + \frac{(\sum x_i y_i)^2}{\sum x_i^2}. \end{aligned} \tag{9.9}$$

Thus we can calculate $\sum(y_i - Y_i)^2$, which we want as the numerator of s^2, as

$$\sum(y_i - Y_i)^2 = \sum y_i^2 - \frac{(\sum x_i y_i)^2}{\sum x_i^2}. \tag{9.10}$$

To find the expected value of $(\sum x_i y_i)^2/\sum x_i^2$, we note that it can be written as

$$\frac{(\sum x_i y_i)^2}{\sum x_i^2} = \left(\frac{\sum x_i y_i}{\sum x_i^2}\right)^2 \sum x_i^2 = b^2 \sum x_i^2.$$

Also, we note from (9.7) that

$$(b - \beta)^2 \sum x_i^2 = b^2 \sum x_i^2 + \beta^2 \sum x_i^2 - 2b\beta \sum x_i^2$$

has expected value σ^2; so taking expectations

$$\sigma^2 = E\left[\frac{(\sum x_i y_i)^2}{\sum x_i^2}\right] + \beta^2 \sum x_i^2 - 2\beta \sum x_i^2\, E[b].$$

Thus

$$E\left[\frac{(\sum x_i y_i)^2}{\sum x_i^2}\right] = \sigma^2 + \beta^2 \sum x_i^2. \tag{9.11}$$

We can construct a table of analysis of variance (Table 11.6) corresponding to (9.9).

Table 11.6

Source of variance	Sums of squares	Degrees of freedom	E[M.S.]
Due to line	$(\sum x_i y_i)^2/\sum x_i^2$	1	$\sigma^2 + \beta^2 \sum x_i^2$
Residual	$\sum (y_i - Y_i)^2$	$k - 1$	σ^2
Total about origin	$\sum y_i^2$	k	

Applying these results to the data of Table 11.3, we have as the regression coefficient, using (9.4),

$$b = \frac{\sum x_i y_i}{\sum x_i^2} = \frac{87{,}719{,}100}{89{,}394{,}900} = 0.981253,$$

as the sum of squares due to the regression line,

$$\frac{(\sum x_i y_i)^2}{\sum x_i^2} = \frac{(87{,}719{,}100)^2}{89{,}394{,}900} = 86{,}074{,}714.6,$$

and as the residual sum of squares, using (9.10),

$$\begin{aligned}\sum (y_i - Y_i)^2 &= \sum y_i^2 - \frac{(\sum x_i y_i)^2}{\sum x_i^2} \\ &= 86{,}125{,}825.0 - 86{,}074{,}714.6 = 51{,}110.4.\end{aligned}$$

We enter these results in Table 11.7.

Table 11.7

Source of variance	Sum of squares	Degrees of freedom	Mean square	E[M.S.]
Due to line	86,074,714.6	1	86,074,714.6	$\sigma^2 + \beta^2 \sum x_i^2$
Residual	51,110.4	17	3,006.5	σ^2
Total about origin	86,125,825.0	18		

We can combine Tables 11.4 and 11.7 to give a test of whether a line $Y = bx$ through the origin is an adequate fit (Table 11.8.).

Table 11.8

Source of variance	Sum of squares	Degrees of freedom	Mean squares
Remainder using line $Y = bx$	51,110.4	17	
Remainder using line $Y = a + b(x - \bar{x})$	50,871.9	16	3179.5
Difference: attributable to improvement in fit through using two parameters in place of one	238.5	1	238.5

A test of the null hypothesis that there is no improvement in fit when using the two-parameter line in place of the one-parameter line is given by the variance ratio 238.5/3179.5 = 0.075. If this null hypothesis was to be rejected at the α level of significance, this variance ratio would have to be not less than $F_{1-\alpha}(1, 16)$. Clearly the null hypothesis here is acceptable. This test is essentially identical with the test that the intercept of the two-parameter line could be zero. For that test we found $t = 0.2739$; so $[t(16)]^2 = (0.2739)^2 = 0.0750 = F(1, 16)$, as we obtained here.

To revert to Table 11.7, there is clearly no doubt that the null hypothesis $\beta = 0$ has to be rejected. We will be more interested in the null hypothesis $\beta = 1$. Using (9.5),

$$\hat{V}[b] = \frac{s^2}{\sum x_i^2} = \frac{3006.5}{89{,}394{,}900} = 0.3363 \times 10^{-4}$$

and, under the null hypothesis that $\beta = 1$,

$$\frac{b - 1}{\sqrt{\hat{V}[b]}} = \frac{0.981253 - 1}{\sqrt{0.3363 \times 10^{-4}}} = 3.23$$

is distributed as $t(17)$. For the line constrained to pass through the origin we thus have to reject the null hypothesis that $\beta = 1$.

For the unconstrained line $Y = a + b(x - \bar{x})$ we found that the null hypothesis that $\beta = 1$ was acceptable, and that the null hypothesis that the intercept is zero was acceptable. We might have expected on this basis that, if we made the intercept zero, i.e., switched to the line constrained to pass through the origin, then we could continue to accept the null hypothesis that $\beta = 1$. However, the above result shows that this is not the case. We will gain greater insight by constructing a joint confidence region for α and β, and for the intercept and β. This we will proceed to do in Section 11.11.

11.10. The Use of the Regression Line through the Origin in Reverse

Suppose that we observe a new $\bar{y}'$, and we wish to predict the corresponding x and to construct confidence limits for this prediction. We can solve the estimated regression equation (9.2) to obtain a point estimate, $x = \bar{y}'/b$. The expected value of the new $\bar{y}'$ is η. Corresponding to this value of η is a value of x given by solving the true regression equation (9.1) for x, $x = \eta/\beta$. Denote this value of x by ξ, so that $\xi = \eta/\beta$, or $\eta - \beta\xi = 0$. We now define a new variable z,

$$z = \bar{y}' - b\xi. \tag{10.1}$$

This variable will have expected value

$$E[z] = \eta - \xi\, E[b] = \eta - \xi\beta = 0, \qquad (1\ .2)$$

and variance

$$V[z] = V[\bar{y}'] + \xi^2\, V[b] = \frac{\sigma^2}{m} + \xi^2 \frac{\sigma^2}{\sum x^2}. \tag{10.3}$$

Substituting the residual mean square in Table 11.6 as an estimate of σ^2, we have that

$$\frac{\bar{y}' - b\xi}{s\sqrt{1/m + \xi^2/\sum x^2}} \sim t(k-1)\,. \tag{10.4}$$

The subsequent manipulation proceeds along lines similar to Section 11.5, and leads to

$$\frac{b\bar{y}'}{b^2 - t_2^2 s^2/\sum x^2} - \frac{t_2 s}{b^2 - t_2^2 s^2/\sum x^2}\sqrt{\left(b^2 - \frac{t_2^2\, s^2}{\sum x^2}\right)\frac{1}{m} + \frac{\bar{y}'^2}{\sum x^2}} \tag{10.5}$$

as the solution for ξ_2. Use of t_1 in place of t_2 gives ξ_1.

If we define g as

$$g = \left(t_2 \frac{\sqrt{\hat{V}[b]}}{b}\right)^2 = \frac{t_2^2 s^2}{b^2 \sum x_i^2}\,, \tag{10.6}$$

analogous to (5.16), then when g is less than 0.1 b is highly significant and (10.5) can be approximated by

$$\xi_2 = \frac{\bar{y}'}{b} - \frac{t_2 s}{b}\sqrt{\frac{1}{m} + \frac{\bar{y}'^2}{b^2 \sum x^2}}. \tag{10.7}$$

Applying this result to the example of Section 11.4, we will suppose that we observe a single new observation, $y' = 3000$. For 95 per cent confidence limits, $t_{0.975}(17) = 2.110$, and, from Table 11.7, $s^2 = 3006.5$. We have $\sum x_i^2 = 89{,}394{,}900$ and $b = 0.981253$. Thus, using (10.6), the value of g is

$$g = \frac{(2.110)^2 \times 3006.5}{(0.981253)^2 \times 89{,}394{,}900} = 0.000156,$$

which clearly permits us to use the approximation (10.7). The 95 per cent confidence limits are

$$\frac{3000}{0.981253} \pm \frac{2.110 \times \sqrt{3006.5}}{0.981253}\sqrt{\frac{1}{1} + \frac{(3000)^2}{86{,}074{,}714}} = 3057.3 \pm 128.4.$$

The resulting interval (2929, 3186) compares closely with that obtained using the two-parameter line in Section 11.5 (2927, 3198).

11.11. A Joint Confidence Region for α and β

As indicated at the end of Section 11.9, we may have need for a joint confidence region for α, β so that we may know which pairs of values of α and β are compatible with the data.

From Table 11.1 we know that $k(a - \alpha)^2$ is distributed as $\sigma^2\chi^2(1)$ and $(b - \beta)^2 \sum(x_i - \bar{x})^2$ likewise is distributed as $\sigma^2\chi^2(1)$. From (8.3.1) we know that the sum of two independent χ^2's, say $\chi^2(f_1)$ and $\chi^2(f_2)$, is distributed as $\chi^2(f_1 + f_2)$; so

$$k(a - \alpha)^2 + (b - \beta)^2 \sum(x_i - \bar{x})^2 \sim \sigma^2\chi^2(2). \tag{11.1}$$

Thus

$$E[\tfrac{1}{2}\{k(a - \alpha)^2 + (b - \beta)^2 \sum(x_i - \bar{x})^2\}] = \sigma^2. \tag{11.2}$$

Also in Table 11.1, $E[s^2] = \sigma^2$. We thus have two independent mean squares whose expected values are both σ^2; so their ratio has the F distribution:

$$\frac{k(a - \alpha)^2 + (b - \beta)^2 \sum(x_i - \bar{x})^2}{2s^2} \sim F(2, k - 2). \tag{11.3}$$

But

$$\Pr\{F < F_{1-\alpha}\} = 1 - \alpha. \tag{11.4}$$

We replace F by the left-hand side of (11.3):

$$\Pr\left\{\frac{k(a-\alpha)^2 + (b-\beta)^2\sum(x_i-\bar{x})^2}{2s^2} < F_{1-\alpha}(2, k-2)\right\} = 1-\alpha. \qquad (11.5)$$

All pairs of values of (α, β) which satisfy this inequality lie inside the $100(1-\alpha)$ per cent confidence region, and the boundary of the region is given by substituting an equality for the inequality:

$$\frac{k(a-\alpha)^2 + (b-\beta)^2\sum(x_i-\bar{x})^2}{2s^2} = F_{1-\alpha}(2, k-2). \qquad (11.6)$$

To determine the boundary of the confidence region, we have to find those pairs (α, β) which satisfy (11.6).

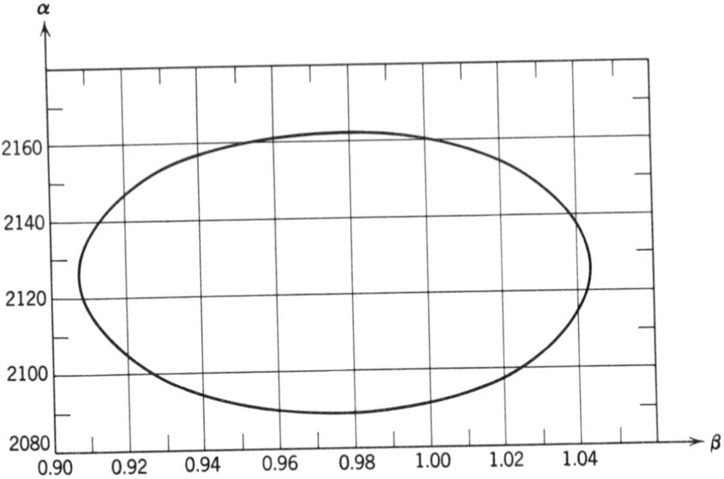

Figure 11.5

For the data of the example in Section 11.4:

$k = 18$, $a = \bar{y} = 2125.277$, $b = 0.974561$,

$\sum(x_i - \bar{x})^2 = 5{,}024{,}950.0$, $s^2 = 3179.49$, $F_{0.95}(2, 16) = 3.63$.

Inserting these values in (11.6) gives the equation

$$18(2125.277 - \alpha)^2 + 5{,}024{,}850 \times (0.974561 - \beta)^2 = 23{,}083.1.$$

When $\beta = 0.974561$, $\alpha = 2089.468$ or 2161.088. When $\alpha = 2125.277$, $\beta = 0.906784$ or 1.042338. Choosing values of β in this range, we get pairs of solutions for α, and, plotting these and connecting them up, we get the ellipse in Figure 11.5. All pairs of values of α, β inside this ellipse are jointly compatible with the data at the 0.05 level of significance.

We are, however, more interested in a joint confidence region for the intercept, say η_0, and β. This is easily obtained, since η_0 is given in terms of α and β by inserting $x = 0$ in (2.1):

$$\eta_0 = \alpha - \beta\bar{x}. \tag{11.7}$$

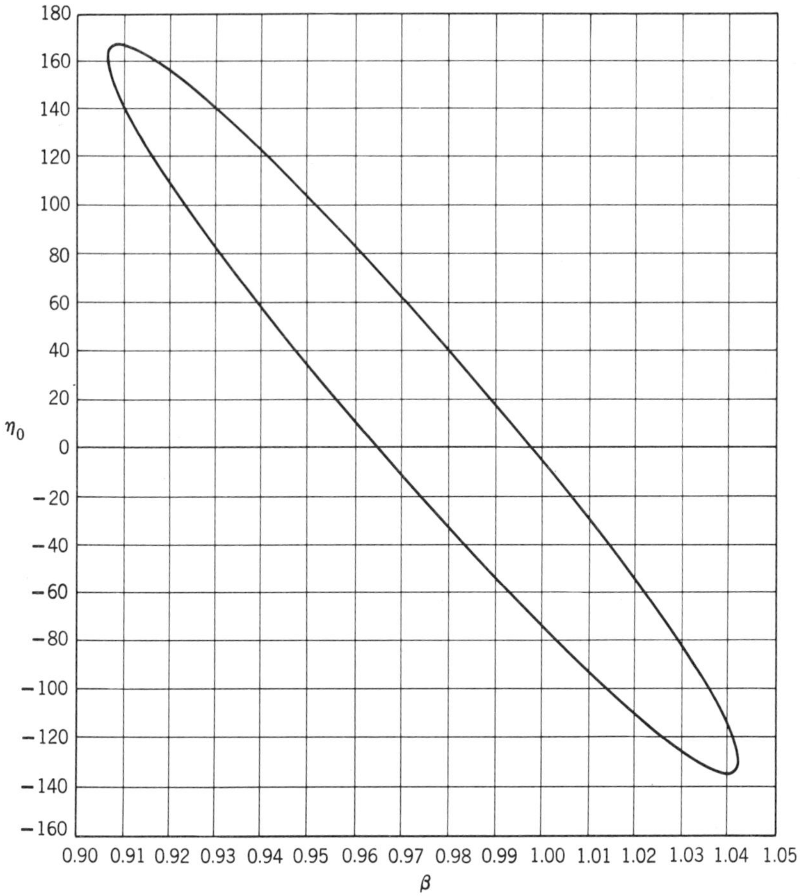

Figure 11.6

Thus, for all our pairs of solutions of α and β we compute η_0, and then plot η_0 against β and again come up with an ellipse (Figure 11.6). This shows that, if we want a large β, say $\beta = 1.03$, then we must have η_0 in the range -122, -87. If we want a zero intercept η_0, we must have β in the range 0.967 to 0.9965, or, if we want $\beta = 1$, we must have an intercept in the range -71 to -9. The ellipse excludes the point $\beta = 1, \eta_0 = 0$. In other words, we can have a zero intercept but not a slope of 1, or we can have a slope of 1 but not a zero intercept; we cannot have a slope of 1 and a zero intercept simultaneously.

11.12. Weighted Linear Regression

Our regression analysis so far has proceeded on the assumption that y is distributed normally about an expected value η with a constant variance σ^2. To consider the example of Section 11.4, we should check whether it appears that our assumption is being satisfied.

If we choose to work with the simpler line, $Y = bx$, from our estimated value of b, 0.981254, for each x_i, we can compute Y_i as in the third column of Table 11.3. In the fourth column we tabulate $d_i = Y_i - y_i$. For the line through the origin, these deviations do not sum to zero, since

$$\sum d_i = \sum(Y_i - y_i) = \sum(bx_i - y_i) = b\sum x_i - \sum y_i = \frac{\sum x_i y_i \sum x_i}{\sum x_i^2} - \sum y_i \quad (12.1)$$

and in general this is not zero. However, for the two-parameter line $Y = a + b(x - \bar{x})$ the deviations do sum to zero, since then

$$\sum(Y_i - y_i) = \sum[a + b(x_i - \bar{x}) - y_i] = n\bar{y} + b\sum(x_i - \bar{x}) - \sum y_i = 0.$$

To resume, the sum of the squares of the deviations tabulated in Table 11.3 is 51,110.6, which checks with the residual sum of squares in Table 11.7. If we take the sums of the squares of the first six, second six, and last six deviations, ordered in terms of increasing x, we get 13,038, 12,974, and 25,097, which suggests that the variance is increasing with x. It is frequently the case that the standard deviation is proportional to what is being measured. Here what is being measured, y, is roughly proportional to x, and so it would be reasonable to assume that $V[y|x] = kx^2$.

The theory of linear regression can be modified to take care of the case where $V[y_i|x_i] = \sigma_i^2$, if the σ_i^2, at least up to a constant of proportionality, are known. In this section we will deal with the two-parameter line $\eta = \alpha + \beta(x - \bar{x})$. In minimizing the sum of squares of deviations, we give each observation a weight $w_i = 1/\sigma_i^2$, and $\bar{x}$ is defined as

$$\bar{x} = \frac{\sum w_i x_i}{\sum w_i} \quad (12.2)$$

and we minimize

$$R = \sum w_i(y_i - Y_i)^2.$$

The subsequent analysis is very similar to that of Section 11.2. Differentiating R with respect to a and b, we get

$$\frac{\partial R}{\partial a} = -2\sum w_i[y_i - a - b(x_i - \bar{x})], \tag{12.3}$$

$$\frac{\partial R}{\partial b} = -2\sum w_i[y_i - a - b(x_i - \bar{x})](x_i - \bar{x}). \tag{12.4}$$

Equating to zero, we obtain

$$a = \frac{\sum w_i y_i}{\sum w_i}, \tag{12.5}$$

$$b = \frac{\sum w_i(x_i - \bar{x})y_i}{\sum w_i(x_i - \bar{x})^2} = \frac{\sum w_i(x_i - \bar{x})(y_i - \bar{y})}{\sum w_i(x_i - \bar{x})^2}. \tag{12.6}$$

The identity (3.1) is unchanged, and here we get on multiplying by the weights w_i, squaring, and summing over i;

$$\sum w_i(y_i - \eta_i)^2 = \sum w_i(y_i - Y_i)^2 + (a - \alpha)^2\sum w_i + (b - \beta)^2\sum w_i(x_i - \bar{x})^2. \tag{12.7}$$

The left-hand side,

$$\sum w_i(y_i - \eta_i)^2 = \sum\left[\frac{(y_i - \eta_i)}{\sigma_i}\right]^2,$$

is distributed as $\chi^2(k)$. The terms on the right-hand side are independent and have χ^2 distributions, whence, by arguments similar to those of Section 11.3,

$$E\left[\frac{\sum w_i(y_i - Y_i)^2}{k - 2}\right] = 1, \tag{12.8}$$

$$V[a] = \frac{1}{\sum w_i}, \tag{12.9}$$

$$V[b] = \frac{1}{\sum w_i(x_i - \bar{x})^2}. \tag{12.10}$$

Corresponding to (3.7), we have

$$\sum w_i(y_i - \bar{y})^2 = \sum w_i(y_i - Y_i)^2 + \sum w_i(Y_i - \bar{y})^2. \tag{12.11}$$

We have just seen, in (12.8), that the expected value of the mean square corresponding to the first term on the right-hand side is 1. The same argument that led to (3.9) gives for the expectation of the second term

$$E[\sum w_i(Y_i - \bar{y})^2] = 1 + \beta^2\sum w_i(x_i - \bar{x})^2. \tag{12.12}$$

Equation (12.11) can be put in a tabular form similar to Table 11.2, with these values for the expectations of the mean squares.

11.13. Regression with $V[y|x]$ a Function of x

The case in which $V[y|x]$ is not a set of arbitrary but known constants but instead a function of x, say $\sigma^2 f(x)$, where σ^2 may be an unknown constant and $f(x)$ is a known function of x, is worth discussing explicitly. If the constant σ^2 is unknown, we may use weights w_i',

$$w_i' = \frac{1}{f(x_i)} = \frac{\sigma^2}{\sigma^2 f(x_i)} = \sigma^2 w_i \tag{13.1}$$

where w_i are the weights of the preceding section, $1/\sigma_i^2$. The analysis proceeds exactly as before, using formulas (12.2) through (12.7) with w_i' in place of w_i; the modified form of (12.7) is

$$\sum w_i'(y_i - \eta_i)^2 = \sum w_i'(y_i - Y_i)^2 + (a - \alpha)^2 \sum w_i' + (b - \beta)^2 \sum w_i'(x_i - \bar{x})^2. \tag{13.2}$$

The left-hand side,

$$\sum w_i'(y_i - \eta_i)^2 = \sum\left(\frac{\sigma^2(y_i - \eta_i)^2}{\sigma^2 f(x_i)}\right) = \sigma^2 \sum\left(\frac{(y_i - \eta_i)^2}{V[y|x_i]}\right) \tag{13.3}$$

is distributed as $\sigma^2\chi^2(k)$, and the terms on the right-hand side will be distributed independently as $\sigma^2\chi^2$ with degrees of freedom $(k - 2)$, 1, and 1, respectively. Analogous to (12.8), (12.12), (12.9), and (12.10), we have

$$E\left[\frac{\sum w_i'(y_i - Y_i)^2}{k - 2}\right] = \sigma^2, \tag{13.4}$$

$$E[\sum w_i'(Y_i - \bar{y})^2] = \sigma^2 + \beta^2 \sum w_i'(x_i - \bar{x})^2, \tag{13.5}$$

$$V[a] = \frac{\sigma^2}{\sum w_i'}, \tag{13.6}$$

$$V[b] = \frac{\sigma^2}{\sum w_i'(x_i - \bar{x})^2}. \tag{13.7}$$

To illustrate these methods, we will analyze the data of Section 11.4 under the assumption that $V[y|x] = \sigma^2 x^2$. We therefore use weights determined by (13.1) as $w_i' = 1/x_i^2$. We will need various sums of squares, etc., which are computed in Tables 11.9 and 11.10. From (12.2),

$$\bar{x} = \frac{\sum w_i' x_i}{\sum w_i'} = \frac{\sum(x_i/x_i^2)}{\sum(1/x_i^2)} = \frac{\sum(1/x_i)}{\sum(1/x_i^2)} \tag{13.8}$$

$$= \frac{88.830899 \times 10^{-4}}{470.773521 \times 10^{-8}} = 1886.913665.$$

Table 11.9

x_i	$10^4/x_i$	$10^8/x_i^2$	y_i	y_i/x_i
1190	8.403361	70.616482	1115	0.936974789
1455	6.872852	47.236098	1425	0.979381443
1550	6.451613	41.623309	1515	0.977419354
1730	5.780347	33.412409	1795	1.037572254
1745	5.730659	32.840453	1715	0.982808022
1770	5.649718	31.919308	1710	0.966101694
1900	5.263158	27.700831	1830	0.963157894
1920	5.208333	27.126736	1920	1.000000000
1960	5.102041	26.030820	1970	1.005102040
2295	4.357298	18.986050	2300	1.002178649
2335	4.282655	18.341136	2280	0.976445396
2490	4.016064	16.128772	2520	1.012048192
2720	3.676471	13.516436	2630	0.966911764
2710	3.690037	13.616372	2740	1.011070110
2530	3.952569	15.622803	2390	0.944664031
2900	3.448276	11.890606	2800	0.965517241
2760	3.623188	13.127494	2630	0.952898550
3010	3.322259	11.037406	2970	0.986710963

Table 11.10

Sum	How formed
$\sum(1/x_i) = 88.830899 \times 10^{-4}$	Sum $\dfrac{10^4}{x_i}$
$\sum(1/x_i^2) = 470.773521 \times 10^{-8}$	Sum $\dfrac{10^8}{x_i^2}$
$\sum(y_i/x_i) = 17.666962386$	Sum $\dfrac{y_i}{x_i}$.
$\sum(y_i/x_i^2) = 870{,}969.264 \times 10^{-8}$	Sum $\dfrac{10^4}{x_i} \times \dfrac{y_i}{x_i}$ or $\dfrac{10^8}{x_i^2} \times y_i$
$\sum(y_i/x_i)^2 = 17.351640$	Sum $\left(\dfrac{y_i}{x_i}\right)^2$

From (12.5),

$$a = \frac{\sum w'_i y_i}{\sum w'_i} = \frac{\sum (y_i/x_i^2)}{\sum (1/x_i^2)} \tag{13.9}$$
$$= \frac{870{,}969.264 \times 10^{-8}}{470.773521 \times 10^{-8}} = 1850.081251.$$

We need

$$\sum w'_i(x_i - \bar{x})(y_i - \bar{y}) = \sum\left(\frac{y_i}{x_i}\right) - \frac{\sum(1/x_i)\sum(y_i/x_i^2)}{\sum(1/x_i^2)} \tag{13.10}$$
$$= 17.666962 - \frac{88.830899 \times 10^{-4} \times 870{,}969.264 \times 10^{-8}}{470.773521 \times 10^{-8}}$$
$$= 1.232524,$$

$$\sum w'_i(x_i - \bar{x})^2 = k - \frac{[\sum(1/x_i)]^2}{\sum(1/x_i^2)} \tag{13.11}$$
$$= 18 - \frac{(88.830899 \times 10^{-4})^2}{470.773521 \times 10^{-8}} = 1.238376,$$

$$\sum w'_i(y_i - \bar{y})^2 = \sum\left(\frac{y_i}{x_i}\right)^2 - \frac{\sum(y_i/x_i^2)}{\sum(1/x_i^2)} \tag{13.12}$$
$$= 17.351640 - \frac{(870{,}969.264 \times 10^{-8})^2}{470.773521 \times 10^{-8}} = 1.238000.$$

We then obtain, from (12.6),

$$b = \frac{\sum w'_i(x_i - \bar{x})(y_i - \bar{y})}{\sum w'_i(x_i - \bar{x})^2} = \frac{1.232524}{1.238376} = 0.995274.$$

The estimated regression line is thus

$$Y = 1850.081 + 0.995274(x - 1886.913).$$

The sum of squares due to regression is

$$\sum w'_i(Y_i - \bar{y})^2 = b^2 \sum w'_i(x_i - \bar{x})^2 = \frac{[\sum w'_i(x_i - \bar{x})(y_i - \bar{y})]^2}{\sum w'_i(x_i - \bar{x})^2} \tag{13.13}$$
$$= \frac{(1.232524)^2}{1.238376} = 1.226699.$$

We can now assemble Table 11.11, the analog of Table 11.4.

The test of the null hypothesis $\beta = 0$ is given by the variance ratio 1.226699/0.000706311 = 1736.8, which will be distributed as $F(1, 16)$. The test of the null hypothesis $\beta = 1$ is obtained by calculating (13.7) as

$$V[b] = \frac{\sigma^2}{k - [\sum(1/x_i)]^2/\sum(1/x_i^2)} \tag{13.14}$$

and

$$\hat{V}[b] = \frac{0.000706311}{1.238376} = 0.000570353.$$

The ratio

$$\frac{b-1}{\sqrt{\hat{V}[b]}} = \frac{0.995274}{2.38821 \times 10^{-2}} = 0.198$$

will be distributed as $t(16)$.

Table 11.11

Source of variance	Sums of squares	Degrees of freedom	Mean squares	E[M.S.]
Due to regression line	1.226699	1	1.226699	$\sigma^2 + \beta^2 \sum w_i'(x_i - \bar{x})^2$
Residual	0.011300	16	0.000706311	σ^2
Total	1.238000	17		

It will be noted that the σ^2 in Table 11.11 is not directly comparable with the σ^2 in Table 11.4, since in the former it is assumed that $V[y|x] = \sigma^2 x^2$, whereas in the latter it is assumed that $V[y|x] = \sigma^2$. If we multiply the residual mean square of Table 11.11 by $\bar{x}^2 = (1886.9)^2$, we get $\sigma^2\bar{x}^2 = 2514$, which is roughly comparable with the remainder mean square of 3179 in Table 11.4. To test whether the weighted line could pass through the origin, we can calculate the intercept by inserting $x = 0$ in the estimated regression equation and obtain $(Y)_{x=0} = -27.915$. In general the variance of a predicted ordinate for a specified value of x is

$$Y[Y] = V[a] + (x - \bar{x})^2\, V[b] = \frac{\sigma^2}{\sum w_i'} + \frac{(x - \bar{x})^2\sigma^2}{\sum w_i'(x_i - \bar{x})^2}. \tag{13.15}$$

For the case $x = 0$, the estimated variance is

$$\hat{V}[(Y)_{x=0}] = s^2\left[\frac{1}{\sum(1/x_i^2)} + \frac{\bar{x}^2}{\sum w_i(x_i - \bar{x})^2}\right]$$

$$= 0.000706311\left[\frac{1}{470.773 \times 10^{-8}} + \frac{(1886.913)^2}{1.238376}\right] = 2180.741.$$

Under the null hypothesis that the intercept is zero, the ratio

$$(-27.915 - 0)/\sqrt{2180.741} = 0.598 \sim t(16).$$

Clearly the null hypothesis is acceptable.

11.14. Weighted Regression through the Origin

The treatment of Section 11.9 readily modifies to the case where $V[y|x_i] = \sigma_i^2$. We shall consider the particular case where $V[y|x_i] = \sigma^2 f(x_i)$. We therefore use weights $w_i' = 1/f(x_i)$, and minimize

$$R = \sum w_i'(y_i - Y_i)^2 = \sum w_i'(y_i - bx_i)^2. \tag{14.1}$$

This leads to the analog of (9.4):

$$b = \frac{\sum w_i' x_i y_i}{\sum w_i' x_i^2}. \tag{14.2}$$

The analog of (9.7) is

$$\sum w_i'(y_i - \eta_i)^2 = \sum w_i'(y_1 - Y_i)^2 + (b - \beta)^2 \sum w_i' x_i^2, \tag{14.3}$$

the left-hand side being distributed as $\sigma^2\chi^2(k)$, and the two terms on the right-hand side being distributed as $\sigma^2\chi^2(k-1)$ and $\sigma^2\chi^2(1)$. It follows that

$$E\left[\frac{\sum w_i'(y_i - Y_i)^2}{k-1}\right] = \sigma^2 \tag{14.4}$$

and

$$V[b] = \frac{\sigma^2}{\sum w_i' x_i^2}. \tag{14.5}$$

The analog of (9.9) is

$$\sum w_i' y_i^2 = \sum w_i'(y_i - Y_i)^2 + \frac{\left(\sum w_i' x_i y_i\right)^2}{\sum w_i' x_i^2}; \tag{14.6}$$

so $\sum w_i'(y_i - Y_i)^2$ is usually calculated from

$$\sum w_i'(y_i - Y_i)^2 = \sum w_i' y_i^2 - \frac{\left(\sum w_i' x_i y_i\right)^2}{\sum w_i' x_i^2}. \tag{14.7}$$

We will apply this procedure to the data of Table 11.3, assuming that $V[y|x] = \sigma^2 x^2$, and using weights $w_i' = 1/x_i^2$. From (14.2),

$$b = \frac{\sum (1/x_i^2) x_i y_i}{\sum (1/x_i^2) x_i^2} = \frac{\sum (y_i/x_i)}{\sum (1)} = \frac{\sum (y_i/x_i)}{k} = \frac{17.666962}{18} = 0.981497. \tag{14.8}$$

The remainder sum of squares (14.7) is

$$\sum\left[\frac{1}{x_i^2}(y_i - Y_i)^2\right] = \sum\left(\frac{y_i}{x_i}\right)^2 - \frac{[\sum(y_i/x_i)]^2}{k} \tag{14.9}$$

$$= 17.351640 - \frac{(17.666962)^2}{18} = 0.011553.$$

Table 11.12 gives the analysis of variance.

Table 11.12

Source of variance	Sum of squares	Degrees of freedom	Mean squares	E[M.S.]
Due to line	17.340087	1	17.340087	$\sigma^2 + \beta^2 \sum w_i' x_i^2$
Residual	0.011553	17	0.000679	σ^2
Total about origin	17.351640	18		

Table 11.13

Source of variance	Sum of squares	Degrees of freedom	Mean squares
Remainder using line $Y = bx$	0.011553	17	
Remainder using line $Y = a + bx$	0.011300	16	0.000706311
Difference attributable to improvement in fit through using two parameters in place of one	0.000252	1	0.000252

The test of whether the weighted line with two parameters is significantly a better fit than the weighted straight line through the origin is given by the analog of Table 11.8, Table 11.13, formed by combining Tables 11.11 and 11.12.

The value of the F statistic is 0.000252/0.000706 = 0.357. The square root of this F, 0.597, will be distributed as $t(16)$, and this checks with the test of Section 11.13 that the intercept could be zero. The straight line through the origin can be accepted as good a fit as the two-parameter line, therefore.

We now test the null hypothesis that the slope of this line could be 1. From (14.5), the estimated variance of b is

$$\hat{V}[b] = \frac{s^2}{\sum(1/x_i^2)x_i^2} = \frac{s^2}{k} = \frac{0.000679}{18} = 0.000037756.$$

The test of the null hypothesis $\beta = 1$ is given by

$$\frac{b-1}{\sqrt{\hat{V}[b]}} = \frac{0.981497 - 1}{0.006144} = -3.01 \sim t(17).$$

It is apparent that the null hypothesis $\beta = 1$ has to be rejected.

11.15. A Joint Confidence Region for α and β Using Weights

The arguments are similar to those of Section 11.11 for the unweighted case. From (13.2), analogous to (11.1),

$$(a-\alpha)^2\sum w_i' + (b-\beta)^2\sum w_i'(x_i - \bar{x})^2 \sim \sigma^2\,\chi^2(2), \tag{15.1}$$

and so, analogous to 11.6,

$$\frac{(a-\alpha)^2\sum w_i' + (b-\beta)^2\sum w_i'(x_i-\bar{x})^2}{2s^2} = F_{1-\alpha}(2, k-2) \tag{15.2}$$

gives the boundary of the $100(1-\alpha)$ joint confidence region for (α, β). For the data of Table 11.3, we are assuming that $w_i = 1/x_i^2$, and, from earlier calculations,

$$\sum w_i' = \sum\left(\frac{1}{x_i^2}\right) = 470.773 \times 10^{-8}, \qquad F_{0.95}(2, 16) = 3.63,$$

$$a = 1850.081, \quad b = 0.995274, \qquad \sum w_i'(x_i - \bar{x})^2 = 1.238376,$$

$$s^2 = 0.00070631175.$$

Substituting in (15.2), we get

$$(1850.081 - \alpha)^2 \times 470.773 \times 10^{-8} + (0.995274 - \beta)^2 \times 1.238376$$
$$= 2 \times 0.000706311 \times 3.63.$$

This equation defines an ellipse, graphed in Figure 11.7, which is a joint 95 per cent confidence region for (α, β). Using (11.7), we derive a joint 95 per cent confidence region for η_0, β, where $\eta_0 = \alpha - \beta\bar{x}$, plotted in Figure 11.8. As in the unweighted case the joint confidence region excludes the point $\beta = 1$, $\eta_0 = 0$, we can either have $\beta = 1$ with an intercept in the interval $(-6, -70)$ or a zero intercept with β in the interval $(0.965, 0.997)$.

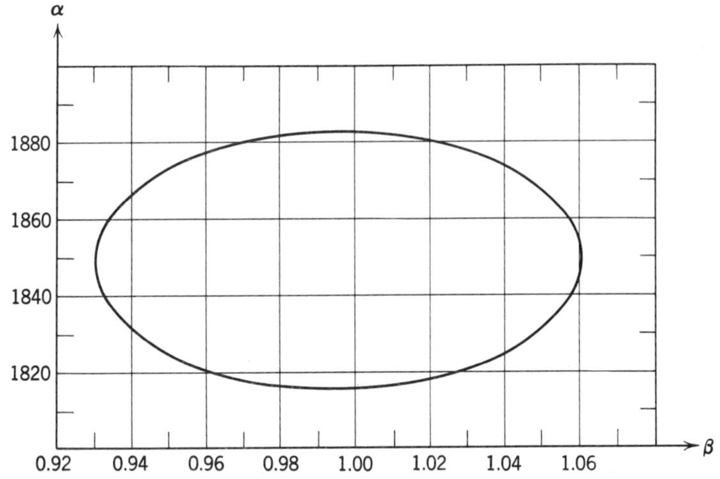

Figure 11.7

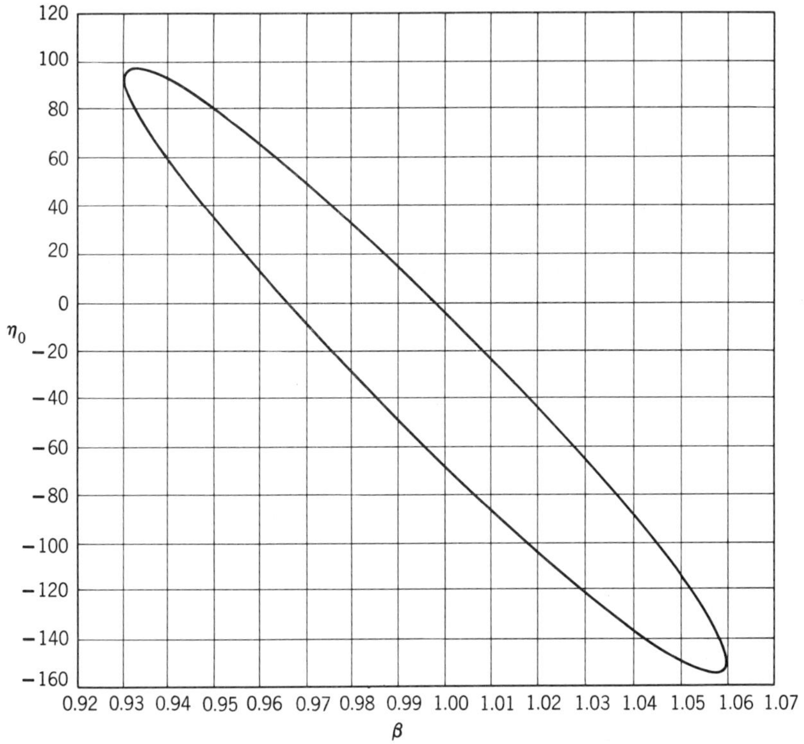

Figure 11.8

11.16. The Use of the Weighted Regression Lines in Reverse

Confidence limits for the ξ corresponding to a newly observed $\bar{y}'$ may be obtained from a two-parameter weighted regression line by the methods of Section 11.5. Defining z as in (5.3), it has expectation zero as before, but its variance is now

$$V[z] = \frac{\sigma^2\xi^2}{m} + \frac{\sigma^2}{\sum(1/x_i^2)} + \frac{(\xi - \bar{x})^2\sigma^2}{k - [\sum(1/x_i)]^2/\sum(1/x_i^2)}. \tag{16.1}$$

This differs from (5.4), among other respects, in that an observation y has a variance of σ^2x^2, when x is a fixed known quantity, and $\sigma^2\xi^2$ in this instance. Similar to (5.5), we have

$$\frac{\bar{y}' - a - b(\xi - \bar{x})}{s\sqrt{\dfrac{\xi^2}{m} + \dfrac{1}{\sum(1/x_i^2)} + \dfrac{(\xi - \bar{x})^2}{k - [\sum(1/x_i)]^2/\sum(1/x_i^2)}}} \sim t(k - 2). \tag{16.2}$$

Putting the left-hand side equal to t_2, where t_2 is the P_2 point of t, will give a quadratic equation for ξ_2, the lower confidence limit. Appreciable algebraic simplification does not seem possible, but the solution can be obtained readily arithmetically for any particular instance. For example, for a single new observation $y' = 3000$, the 95 per cent confidence limits for ξ are 3055.1 ± 184.3.

Confidence limits for the ξ corresponding to a newly observed $\bar{y}'$ may be obtained from a one-parameter weighted regression line by the methods of Section 11.10. Defining z as in (10.1), it has expectation zero as before, but its variance is now

$$V[z] = \frac{\sigma^2\xi^2}{m} + \frac{\xi^2\sigma^2}{k} = \sigma^2\xi^2\left(\frac{1}{m} + \frac{1}{k}\right). \tag{16.3}$$

Similar to (10.4), we have

$$\frac{\bar{y}' - b\xi}{s\xi\sqrt{1/m + 1/k}} \sim t(k - 1). \tag{16.4}$$

Putting the left-hand side of this equal to t_2 will give a linear equation in ξ_2, the solution of which is

$$\xi_2 = \frac{\bar{y}'}{b + t_2 s\sqrt{1/m + 1/k}}. \tag{16.5}$$

For example, for a single new observation $y' = 3000$, the 95 per cent confidence limits for ξ are 3066.8 ± 176.6.

We have analyzed the data of Table 11.3 in four ways, listed in Table 11.14. We have calculated 95 per cent confidence limits for ξ for a new single observation $y' = 3000$, a point at the extreme range of the original observations; these are given in Table 11.14. A similar set for $y' = 2125$, the unweighted mean of the original observations, is also given. As we would anticipate, for $y' = 3000$, the weighted line gives wider limits as it allocates a larger variance to y for large ξ than the unweighted line which assumes a constant variance. Otherwise the results are quite consistent and serve to illustrate the relative uncriticalness of the assumptions in most situations.

Table 11.14. Confidence Limits for ξ for the Data of Table 11.3

	Unweighted		Weighted	
Number of parameters	Two	One	Two	One
$y' = 3000$	3062 ± 135	3057 ± 128	3055 ± 184	3066 ± 177
$y' = 2125$	2165 ± 126	2166 ± 125	2171 ± 127	2173 ± 125

11.17. Linear Regression with Several Observations on y at Each x

In this section we assume that we have observations

$$\begin{array}{ll} y_{11}, \ldots, y_{1n_1} & \text{at } x_1, \\ \vdots & \\ y_{i1}, \ldots, y_{in_i} & \text{at } x_i, \end{array}$$

where $i = 1, \ldots, k$. We define $\bar{x}$ as the mean of the x_i weighted in proportion to the numbers of observations at each point:

$$\bar{x} = \frac{\sum_i^k n_i x_i}{\sum_i^k n_i}. \tag{17.1}$$

We define $\bar{y}_i$ as $\sum_\nu^{n_i} \frac{y_{i\nu}}{n_i}$ and compute the sample variance within each group of replicate observations:

$$s_{1i}^2 = \frac{1}{n_i - 1} \sum_\nu^{n_i} (y_{i\nu} - \bar{y}_i)^2. \tag{17.2}$$

In principle, we might test the null hypothesis that the s_{1i}^2 are drawn from a population with common parameter σ^2 with Bartlett's test. In practice, this will be frequently unrewarding since the n_i are often small and the test will be of low power. Also the s_{1i}^2 are ordered by the magnitude of the x_i from which they were obtained, and Bartlett's test pays no attention to this ordering. If there is a departure from the null hypothesis, it is likely to be that σ^2 increases with x, instead of varying irregularly and it may be more profitable to make a rough graph of s_{1i}^2 against x_i and inspect this with common sense and judgment. Frequently, we must admit, no attempt is made to check this assumption, and one proceeds directly to form a pooled estimate of σ^2, according to (8.3.4):

$$s_1^2 = \frac{\sum_i^k (n_i - 1)s_i^2}{\sum_i^k (n_i - 1)} = \frac{\sum_i^k \sum_\nu^{n_i} (y_{i\nu} - \bar{y}_i)^2}{\sum_i^k n_i - k}. \tag{17.3}$$

The sum of squares of deviations between the observed values $y_{i\nu}$ and the predicted values Y_i is

$$R = \sum_i^k \sum_\nu^{n_i} (y_{i\nu} - Y_i)^2 = \sum_i^k \sum_\nu^{n_i} [y_{i\nu} - a - b(x_i - \bar{x})]^2. \tag{17.4}$$

Partially differentiating R with respect to a and to b, and equating to zero gives

$$\frac{\partial R}{\partial a} = -2 \sum_i^k \sum_\nu^{n_i} [y_{i\nu} - a - b(x_i - \bar{x})] = 0, \tag{17.5}$$

$$\frac{\partial R}{\partial b} = -2 \sum_i^k \sum_\nu^{n_i} [y_{i\nu} - a - b(x_i - \bar{x})](x_i - \bar{x}) = 0. \tag{17.6}$$

Rearranging,

$$a \sum_i^k n_i + b \sum_i^k n_i(x_i - \bar{x}) = \sum_i^k \sum_\nu^{n_i} y_{i\nu}, \tag{17.7}$$

$$a \sum_i^k n_i(x_i - \bar{x}) + b \sum_i^k n_i(x_i - \bar{x})^2 = \sum_i^k n_i(x_i - \bar{x})\bar{y}_i, \tag{17.8}$$

since

$$\sum_i^k \sum_\nu^{n_i} (x_i - \bar{x})y_{i\nu} = \sum_i^k (x_i - \bar{x}) \sum_\nu^{n_i} y_{i\nu} = \sum_i^k n_i(x_i - \bar{x})\bar{y}_i. \tag{17.9}$$

The definition of $\bar{x}$ in (17.1) implies that

$$\sum_i^k n_i(x_i - \bar{x}) = \sum_i^k n_i x_i - \bar{x} \sum_i^k n_i = 0;$$

so (17.7) gives

$$a = \frac{\sum_i^k \sum_\nu^{n_i} y_{i\nu}}{\sum_i^k n_i} = \frac{\sum_i^k n_i \bar{y}_i}{\sum_i^k n_i} = \bar{y}, \tag{17.10}$$

and (17.8) gives

$$b = \frac{\sum_i^k n_i(x_i - \bar{x})\bar{y}_i}{\sum_i^k n_i(x_i - \bar{x})^2} = \frac{\sum_i^k n_i(x_i - \bar{x})\bar{y}_i - \sum_i^k n_i(x_i - \bar{x})\bar{y}}{\sum_i^k n_i(x_i - \bar{x})^2}$$

$$= \frac{\sum_i^k n_i(x_i - \bar{x})(\bar{y}_i - \bar{y})}{\sum_i^k n_i(x_i - \bar{x})^2}. \tag{17.11}$$

We will now consider an analysis of variance representation. The deviation of an observation $y_{i\nu}$ from the value η_i predicted by the true regression equation (2.1) can be written as

$$y_{i\nu} - \eta_i = (y_{i\nu} - \bar{y}_i) + (\bar{y}_i - \eta_i) = (y_{i\nu} - \bar{y}_i) + (\bar{y}_i - Y_i) + (Y_i - \eta_i)$$
$$= (y_{i\nu} - \bar{y}_i) + (\bar{y}_i - Y_i) + (a - \alpha) + (b - \beta)(x_i - \bar{x}). \tag{17.12}$$

This equation is represented in Figure 11.9; various points in this figure are:

$(x_i, y_{i\nu})$: an individual observation on y at x_i.
$(x_i, \bar{y}_i)$: the mean of n_i observations on y at x_i.
(x_i, Y_i): the point on the estimated line at x_i.
(x_i, η_i): the point on the true regression line at x_i.

In (17.12), the terms on the right-hand side are:

$(y_{i\nu} - \bar{y}_i)$: the deviation of an individual $y_{i\nu}$ from the mean $\bar{y}_i$ of the n_i observations at x_i.

$(\bar{y}_i - Y_i)$: the deviation of the mean $\bar{y}_i$ of the n_i observations at x_i from the value Y_i predicted by the estimated equation.

$(Y_i - \eta_i)$: the deviation of the value Y_i predicted by the estimated equation from the value η_i predicted by the true equation, split into two parts:

$(a - \alpha)$: the deviation of the sample estimate a from the true value α.

$(b - \beta)(x_i - \bar{x})$: the distance in the y direction due to the deviation of the sample estimate b from the true value β.

Squaring and summing (17.12) over i and ν gives an equation which is written in tabular form in the second column of Table 11.15. The various cross products are easily shown to be equal to zero.

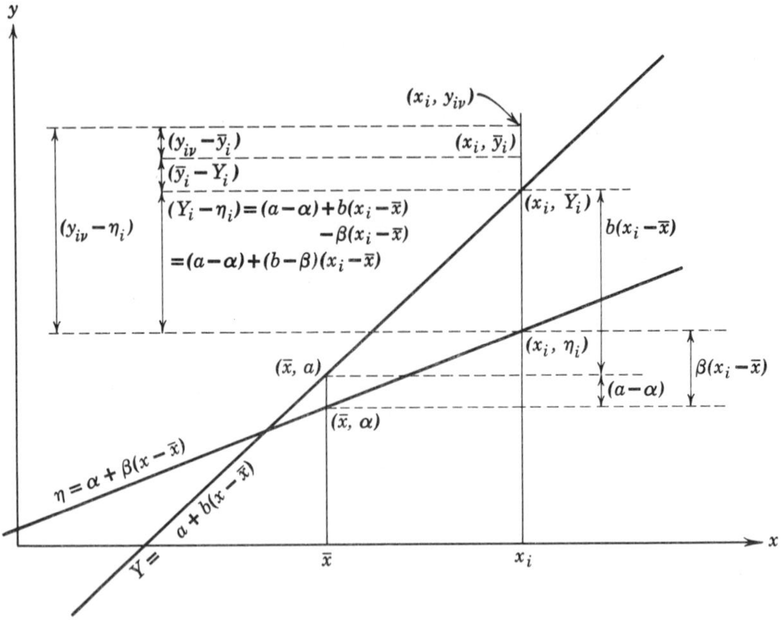

Figure 11.9

Table 11.15

Source of variation	Degrees of freedom	Sums of squares	Mean squares
Deviation of a from α	1	$(a - \alpha)^2 \sum_i^k n_i$	s_4^2
Deviation of b from β	1	$(b - \beta)^2 \sum_i^k n_i(x_i - \bar{x})^2$	s_3^2
Sample group means	$k - 2$	$\sum_i^k n_i(\bar{y}_i - Y_i)^2$	s_2^2
Within groups	$\sum_i^k n_i - k$	$\sum_i^k \sum_\nu^{n_i} (y_{i\nu} - \bar{y}_i)^2$	s_1^2
About theoretical line	$\sum_i^k n_i$	$\sum_i^k \sum_\nu^{n_i} (y_{i\nu} - \eta_i)^2$	

In this equation, we have partitioned a sum of squares with $\sum_i^k n_i$ degrees of freedom into four sums of squares. The numbers of degrees of freedom for these four sums of squares are as follows. The first and second components each involve only one variable, a and b, respectively, and these each have one degree of freedom. The third component involves k variables but equating (17.5) and (17.6) to zero imposed two restrictions, and so the degrees of freedom are $(k - 2)$. The fourth component is the numerator of (17.3) which we know to have $[(\sum_i^k n_i) - k]$ degrees of freedom. Thus the sum of the sums of squares equals the sum of squares on the left-hand side, and the sum of the degrees of freedom, likewise; so, by Cochran's theorem, the sums of squares are distributed as $\sigma^2\chi^2$ and are independent.

We can readily make some useful inferences from Table 11.15. If $(a - \alpha)^2 \sum_i^k n_i$ is distributed as $\sigma^2\chi^2$ with one degree of freedom, analogously to (3.3),

$$V[a] = E[(a - \alpha)^2] = \frac{\sigma^2}{\sum_i^k n_i}. \tag{17.13}$$

Likewise,

$$V[b] = E[(b - E[b])^2] = \frac{\sigma^2}{\sum_i^k n_i(x_i - \bar{x})^2}. \tag{17.14}$$

Since a and b are independent,

$$\begin{aligned} V[Y] = V[a + b(x - \bar{x})] &= V[a] + (x - \bar{x})^2\, V[b] \\ &= \sigma^2\left[\frac{1}{\sum_i^k n_i} + \frac{(x - \bar{x})^2}{\sum_i^k n_i(x_i - \bar{x})^2}\right]. \end{aligned} \tag{17.15}$$

We now write

$$y_{i\nu} - \bar{y} = (y_{i\nu} - \bar{y}_i) + (\bar{y}_i - Y_i) + (Y_i - \bar{y}),$$

and square and sum over i and ν:

$$\sum_i^k \sum_\nu^{n_i} (y_{i\nu} - \bar{y})^2 = \sum_i^k \sum_\nu^{n_i} (y_{i\nu} - \bar{y}_i)^2 + \sum_i^k n_i(\bar{y}_i - Y_i)^2 + \sum_i^k n_i(Y_i - \bar{y})^2. \tag{17.16}$$

The first item on the right-hand side is the numerator of s_1^2 in (17.3), and we know it to be distributed as $\sigma^2\chi^2$ with $[(\sum_i^k n_i) - k]$ degrees of freedom, and the corresponding mean square has expected value σ^2. The second item is the numerator of s_2^2 in Table 11.15, and we know that, if the η_i really lie on the regression line $\alpha + \beta(x_i - \bar{x})$, then this sum of squares is distributed as $\sigma^2\chi^2$ with $(k - 2)$ degrees of freedom. It is possible, however, that the η_i do not lie on this line. Even if the η_i do not lie on a straight line, it will be possible to fit a least-squares line to the points (x_i, η_i), and the parameters will be, by analogy with (17.9) and (17.10),

$$\alpha = \bar{\eta} = \frac{\sum_i^k n_i\eta_i}{\sum_i^k n_i}, \qquad \beta = \frac{\sum_i^k n_i(x_i - \bar{x})\eta_i}{\sum_i^k n_i(x_i - \bar{x})^2}.$$

We can write

$$\begin{aligned}\bar{y}_i - \eta_i &= (\bar{y}_i - Y_i) + (Y_i - \eta_i)\\ &= (\bar{y}_i - Y_i) + [a + b(x_i - \bar{x}) - \bar{\eta} - \beta(x_i - \bar{x})] - [\eta_i - \bar{\eta} - \beta(x_i - \bar{x})]\\ &= (\bar{y}_i - Y_i) - [\eta_i - \bar{\eta} - \beta(x_i - \bar{x})] + (a - \bar{\eta}) + (b - \beta)(x_i - \bar{x}).\end{aligned}$$

Square and sum over i and ν:

$$\begin{aligned}\sum_i^k n_i(\bar{y}_i - \eta_i)^2 &= \sum_i^k n_i\{(\bar{y}_i - Y_i) - [\eta_i - \bar{\eta} - \beta(x_i - \bar{x})]\}^2\\ &\quad + (a - \bar{\eta})^2\sum_i^k n_i + (b - \beta)^2\sum_i^k n_i(x_i - \bar{x})^2. \qquad (17.17)\end{aligned}$$

The left-hand side will be distributed as $\sigma^2\chi^2$ with k degrees of freedom. The terms on the right-hand side will be distributed $\sigma^2\chi^2$ with degrees of freedom $(k - 2)$, 1, and 1, respectively; so, considering the first term,

$$\begin{aligned}E[\sum_i^k n_i\{(\bar{y}_i - Y_i) + [\eta_i - \bar{\eta} - \beta(x_i - \bar{x})]\}^2] &= (k - 2)\sigma^2\\ = E[\sum_i^k n_i(\bar{y}_i - Y_i)^2] &+ E[\sum_i^k n_i\{\eta_i - \bar{\eta} - \beta(x_i - \bar{x})\}^2]\\ &-2E[\sum_i^k n_i(\bar{y}_i - Y_i)\{\eta_i - \bar{\eta} - \beta(x_i - \bar{x})\}]. \qquad (17.18)\end{aligned}$$

The last term here can be written as

$$\begin{aligned}&-2\sum_i^k n_i\{\eta_i - \bar{\eta} - \beta(x_i - \bar{x})\}\,E[\bar{y}_i - Y_i]\\ &\qquad = -2\sum_i^k n_i\{\eta_i - \bar{\eta} - \beta(x_i - \bar{x})\}\{\eta_i - \alpha - \beta(x_i - \bar{x}_i)\}\\ &\qquad = -2\sum_i^k n_i\{\eta_i - \bar{\eta} - \beta(x_i - \bar{x})\}^2,\end{aligned}$$

since $\alpha = \bar{\eta}$. Then (17.18) can be rearranged to give

$$E[\sum_i^k n_i(\bar{y}_i - Y_i)^2] = (k-2)\sigma^2 + \sum_i^k n_i\{\eta_i - \bar{\eta} - \beta(x_i - \bar{x})\}^2. \qquad (17.19)$$

The same arguments that gave (3.9) here give

$$E[\sum_i^k n_i(Y_i - \bar{y})^2] = \sigma^2 + \beta^2 \sum_i^k n_i(x_i - \bar{x})^2. \qquad (17.20)$$

We can now put (17.16) in a tabular form (Table 11.16) and enter the expectations of the mean squares which we have just found. All the sums of squares can be calculated, though the forms in Table 11.16 are not the most convenient for computation.

Table 11.16

Source of variance	Sum of squares	Degrees of freedom	Mean squares	E[M.S.]
Slope of line	$\sum_i^k n_i(Y_i - \bar{y})^2$	1	s_3^2	$\sigma^2 + \beta^2 \sum_i^k n_i(x_i - \bar{x})^2$
Variation of true group means about line	$\sum_i^k n_i(\bar{y}_i - Y_i)^2$	$k-2$	s_2^2	$\sigma^2 + \dfrac{\sum_i^k n_i(\eta_i - \bar{\eta} - \beta(x_i - \bar{x}))^2}{k-2}$
Within groups	$\sum_i^k \sum_\nu^{n_i} (y_{i\nu} - \bar{y}_i)^2$	$\left(\sum_i^k n_i\right) - k$	s_1^2	σ^2
Total	$\sum_i^k \sum_\nu^{n_i} (y_{i\nu} - \bar{y})^2$	$\left(\sum_i^k n_i\right) - 1$		

A test of the null hypothesis that the η_i do lie on a straight line is given by the variance ratio s_2^2/s_1^2, since under the null hypothesis the expected value of s_2^2 is σ^2, and s_2^2 is independent of s_1^2. Also a test of the null hypothesis that $\beta = 0$ is given by the variance ratio s_3^2/s_1^2, for the same reasons.

11.18. An Example of Linear Regression with Several Observations on y at Each x

The data of Table 11.17 give the square root of the stopping distance in feet y of an automobile when traveling on a road with a certain surface at a number of speeds in miles per hour x. The results are only directly applicable to that automobile on that road; if we want to make a general inference about other automobiles of the same model or about other roads,

Table 11.17

x_i	20.5	30.5	40.5	48.8	57.8	
y_{iv}	3.92 3.65	5.82 5.20	8.55	10.63	11.94	
n_i	2	2	1	1	1	$\sum_i^k n_i = 7$
$\sum_v^{n_i} y_{iv}$	7.57	11.02	8.55	10.63	11.94	$\sum_i^k \sum_v^{n_i} y_{iv} = 49.71$

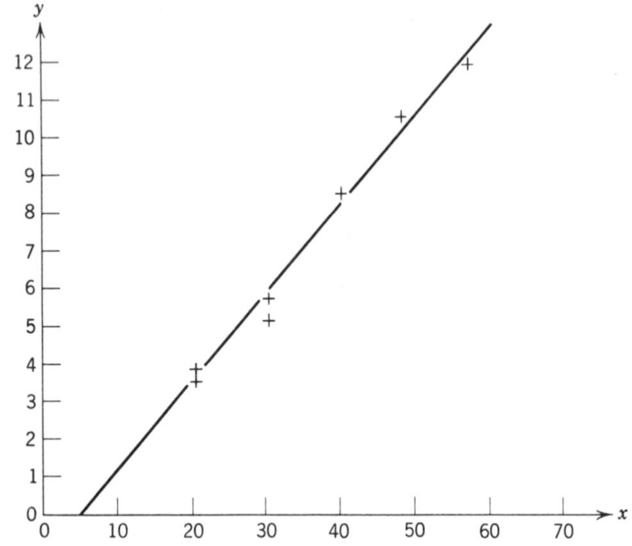

Figure 11.10

we can only do it with data either from a sample of automobiles and from a sample of roads, or from a substantial body of experience that tells us that the variation between automobiles of a certain model and between roads is very slight.

The reasons for choosing the square root of the stopping distance as the dependent variable are that a plot of the distance itself against speed showed obvious signs of curvature, whereas the square root appears to be linear (Figure 11.10). Since the energy of a moving object is proportional to the square of its velocity, this is reasonable. We could have chosen the stopping distance as the dependent variable, and the square of the speed as the independent variable, and this would have come to almost the same thing. However, one of the assumptions of the regression analysis is that the variance of the dependent variable, given the independent variable, is constant, and this is much more likely to be so when we use the square root than the stopping distance itself. It is comparatively rarely that we have sufficient data to discriminate objectively between different possible models, and usually all we can do is to make plausible guesses based on previous experience in similar fields.

Table 11.16 involves four sums of squares which we will now compute. The general procedure is to convert averages into sums over the appropriate index.

The total sum of squares is

$$\sum_i^k \sum_\nu^{n_i} (y_{i\nu} - \bar{y})^2 = \sum_i^k \sum_\nu^{n_i} y_{i\nu}^2 - \frac{\left(\sum_i^k \sum_\nu^{n_i} y_{i\nu}\right)^2}{\sum_i^k n_i} \tag{18.1}$$

$$= (3.92)^2 + \cdots + (11.94)^2 - \frac{(49.71)^2}{7}$$

$$= 418.2643 - 353.012014 = 65.252286.$$

The within-groups sum of squares is, analogous to (10.2.19),

$$\sum_i^k \sum_\nu^{n_i} (y_{i\nu} - \bar{y}_i)^2 = \sum_i^k \sum_\nu^{n_i} y_{i\nu}^2 - \sum_i^k \frac{\left(\sum_\nu^{n_i} y_{i\nu}\right)^2}{n_i} \tag{18.2}$$

$$= 418.2643 - \left[\frac{(7.57)^2}{2} + \frac{(11.02)^2}{2} + \cdots + \frac{(11.94)^2}{1}\right]$$

$$= 418.2643 - 418.035650 = 0.228650.$$

The sum of squares for the slope of the line is, by (17.20),

$$\sum_i^k n_i(Y_i - \bar{y})^2 = b^2 \sum_i^k n_i(x_i - \bar{x})^2 = \frac{\left[\sum_i^k n_i(x_i - \bar{x})(\bar{y}_i - \bar{y})\right]^2}{\sum_i^k n_i(x_i - \bar{x})^2}. \tag{18.3}$$

For this we need

$$\sum_i^k n_i(x_i - \bar{x})^2 = \sum_i^k n_i x_i^2 - \frac{(\sum_i^k n_i x_i)^2}{\sum_i^k n_i} \tag{18.4}$$

$$= [2 \times (20.5)^2 + 2 \times (30.5)^2 + \cdots + 1 \times (57.8)^2] - \frac{(2 \times 20.5 + 2 \times 30.5 + \cdots + 1 \times 57.8)^2}{7}$$

$$= 1199.128572$$

and

$$\sum_i^k n_i(x_i - \bar{x})(\bar{y}_i - \bar{y}) = \sum_i^k x_i \sum_v^{n_i} y_{iv} - \frac{(\sum_i^k \sum_v^{n_i} y_{iv})(\sum_i^k n_i x_i)}{\sum_i^k n_i} \tag{18.5}$$

$$= (20.5 \times 7.57 + 30.5 \times 11.02 + \cdots + 57.8 \times 11.94) - \frac{49.71 \times 249.1}{7}$$

$$= 277.480143,$$

whence, substituting in (18.3),

$$\sum_i^k n_i(Y_i - \bar{y})^2 = \frac{(277.480143)^2}{1199.128572} = 64.209320.$$

Finally we want the sum of squares for the variation of the true group means about the true line:

$$\sum_i^k n_i(\bar{y}_i - Y_i)^2 = \sum_i^k n_i[\bar{y}_i - \bar{y} - b(x_i - \bar{x})]^2$$

$$= \left[\sum_i^k \frac{(\sum_v^{n_i} y_{iv})^2}{n_i} - \frac{(\sum_i^k \sum_v^{n_i} y_{iv})^2}{\sum_i^k n_i}\right] - \frac{[\sum_i^k n_i(x_i - x)(\bar{y}_i - y)]^2}{\sum_i^k n_i(x_i - \bar{x})^2} \tag{18.6}$$

$$= (418.035650 - 353.012014) - 64.209320 = 0.814316.$$

We now have the numerical values of all the mean squares, and can enter them in Table 11.18 which corresponds to Table 11.16.

The test of linearity is given by 0.271439/0.114325 = 2.37 which under the null hypothesis is distributed as F with degrees of freedom 3 and 2. The 0.90 point is 9.16; so obviously the null hypothesis is acceptable. The test of the null hypothesis $\beta = 0$ is given by 64.209320/0.114325 = 562, which is distributed as F with degrees of freedom 1 and 2. The 0.995 point is 199; so obviously we reject the null hypothesis. However, many would take a point of view that either the true regression is linear or it is not. If it is, then the expected value of s_2^2 is σ^2, and they would pool the sums of squares and degrees of freedom of s_2^2 and s_1^2 to get a new estimate of σ^2, say $s_1'^2$, with degrees of freedom $[(\sum_i^k n_i) - 2] = 5$. On the other hand, if the test of linearity leads to the rejection of the null hypothesis, then there is little point to a test of the null hypothesis $\beta = 0$. Deviation from

Table 11.18

Source of variance	Sum of squares	Degrees of freedom	Mean squares
Slope of line	64.209320	1	64.209320
Variation of true group means about the line	0.814316	3	0.271439
Within groups	0.228650	2	0.114325
Total	65.252286	6	

linearity could be of two types. The η_i could lie erratically on either side of a line, the deviation having no systematic pattern, or η_i could lie on some more complicated curve such as a parabola. One would plot the points and inspect them to decide what the situation was.

The estimates of the parameters for the regression line are

$$a = \bar{y} = \frac{\sum_i^k \sum_v^{n_i} y_{iv}}{\sum_i^k n_i} = \frac{49.71}{7} = 7.101429,$$

$$b = \frac{\sum_i^k n_i(x_i - \bar{x})(\bar{y}_i - \bar{y})}{\sum_i^k n_i(x_i - \bar{x})^2} = \frac{277.480143}{1{,}199.128572} = 0.231401,$$

$$\bar{x} = \frac{\sum_i^k n_i x}{\sum_i^k n_i} = \frac{249.7}{7} = 35.585714;$$

so the estimated line is

$$Y = 7.101429 + 0.231401(x - 35.585714) = -1.133141 + 0.231401x.$$

The pooled estimate $s_1'^2$ of σ^2 is

$$s_1'^2 = \frac{0.814316 + 0.228650}{3 + 2} = 0.208593.$$

A test of the null hypothesis $\beta = 0$ equivalent to the one above can be made by substituting $s_1'^2$ for σ^2 in (17.14) which gives the estimated variance of b as

$$\hat{V}[b] = \frac{0.208593}{1199.128} = 0.0001740.$$

Then

$$\frac{b - \beta}{\sqrt{\hat{V}[b]}} \sim t\left(\sum_i^k n_i - 2\right). \qquad (18.7)$$

Putting $\beta = 0$, we have $(0.2314 - 0)/\sqrt{0.0001740} = 17.5$, which is a very large value for t. Confidence limits for β follow in the usual way:

$$\Pr\{b - t_2\sqrt{\hat{V}[b]} < \beta < b - t_1\sqrt{\hat{V}[b]}\} = P_2 - P_1;$$

so 95 per cent confidence limits are $0.2314 \pm 2.571 \times 0.1319$ or (0.1975, 0.2653).

We might ask what is the predicted square-root stopping distance when $x = 50$:

$$Y = -1.133141 + 0.231401 \times 50 = 10.437.$$

Using $s'^2 = 0.208593$ with 5 degrees of freedom in place of σ^2 in (17.15).

$$\hat{V}[Y] = 0.208593\left[\frac{1}{7} + \frac{(50 - 35.5857)^2}{1199.128}\right] = 0.065942,$$

whence 95 per cent confidence limits for η at $x = 50$ are $\pm 2.571 \times \sqrt{0.065942} = \pm 0.660$ on either side of Y, i.e., (9.777, 11.097).

In this case, if we are interested in not hitting something, a one-sided confidence limit might be more reasonable; for example, using $t_{0.01}(5) = -3.365$ to get an upper confidence limit.

$$10.437 - (-3.365) \times \sqrt{0.065942} = 11.301.$$

Thus we are 99 per cent confident that $\eta < 11.301$. However, we are probably more interested in a confidence limit for an individual observation, for which we use the equivalent of (3.6), which gives $\hat{V}[y - Y] = 0.274535$. The one-sided 99 per cent confidence limit is now $10.437 + 3.365\sqrt{0.274575} = 12.200$.

11.19. The Comparison of Several Regression Lines: Simple Analysis of Covariance

The comparison of two regression lines (Section 11.6) fell into three parts; first, testing that the variance around the separate lines could be regarded as homogeneous; second, testing whether parallel lines through the respective means could be regarded as an acceptable fit; and third, testing whether these separate parallel lines could be regarded as coincident, i.e., as a single line.

This last operation is subject to a slightly different interpretation. Suppose that the two estimated parallel lines are

$$Y_1 = \bar{y}_1 + b(x - \bar{x}_1), \qquad Y_2 = \bar{y}_2 + b(x - \bar{x}_2). \tag{19.1}$$

The observed averages of the y's of the two samples are $\bar{y}_1$ and $\bar{y}_2$. However, the x averages of the two samples were in general different, being $\bar{x}_1$ and $\bar{x}_2$. We might ask what the y averages would have been if the x averages had been the same, say equal to the weighted mean for the two samples,

$$\bar{x} = \frac{n_1\bar{x}_1 + n_2\bar{x}_2}{n_1 + n_2} = \frac{\sum_{\nu}^{n_1} x_{1\nu} + \sum_{\nu}^{n_2} x_{2\nu}}{n_1 + n_2}. \tag{19.2}$$

Inserting this value of x in the two equations (19.1),

$$Y_{1(\bar{x})} = \bar{y}_1 + b(\bar{x} - \bar{x}_1), \qquad Y_{2(\bar{x})} = \bar{y}_2 + b(\bar{x} - \bar{x}_1);$$

so

$$Y_{1(\bar{x})} - Y_{2(\bar{x})} = (\bar{y}_1 - \bar{y}_2) - b(\bar{x}_1 - \bar{x}_2) \tag{19.3}$$

is the difference between the y averages, adjusted for differences in the x averages. But this is precisely the same quantity as (6.17), which we developed for testing whether the lines are identical. In other words, the test that the true lines are identical is the same as a test of whether the η averages are the same after adjustment for differences in the x averages. A test of whether a group of population means is identical is known as the analysis of variance. Here we are making an analysis of variance with adjustment for variation in x; this is called, perhaps not very felicitously, the analysis of covariance, the variable x being called the covariate or concomitant variable.

An example suitable for covariance analysis is a study of the marketable weight of hogs fed different rations; it might be appropriate to use covariance on the weight of each hog at the start of the feeding trial. It would be most inappropriate to use as a covariate the amount of ration consumed per day, because this might be influenced by the ration itself. In pharmacological experiments, some initial measurement on each experimental subject might be used as a covariate. In experiments on performance of tests by human subjects after taking drugs, or after receiving instruction, measurements made on the same or similar tests before the administration of the treatment might be good covariates. All that is required of a covariate is that it be independent of the treatments under study, and that it be correlated with the variable we are analyzing. If the covariate x selected is actually uncorrelated with y, then there is no significant loss in precision compared with a simple analysis of variance of y. The only consequence is the wasted effort that goes into the additional arithmetic.

We assume that we have k groups of observations $(x_{i\nu}, y_{i\nu})$, $i = 1, \ldots, k$, $\nu = 1, \ldots, n_i$. A separate line can be fitted to each group, $Y = \bar{y}_{i\cdot} + b_i(x - \bar{x}_{i\cdot})$, and a sum of squares for variation about each line s_{i1}^2 will be obtained. These may be tested for heterogeneity by Bartlett's test, and, if the null hypothesis is acceptable, pooled to give

$$s_1^2 = \frac{\sum_i^k (n_i - 2)s_{i1}^2}{\sum_i^k (n_i - 2)}. \tag{19.4}$$

There are four sets of lines to be considered:

1. The k individual lines,

$$Y = \bar{y}_{i\cdot} + b_i(x - \bar{x}_{i\cdot}), \tag{19.5}$$

where b_i is, of course,

$$b_i = \frac{\sum_\nu^{n_i} (x_{i\nu} - \bar{x}_{i\cdot})y_{i\nu}}{\sum_\nu^{n_i}(x_{i\nu} - \bar{x}_{i\cdot})^2}. \tag{19.6}$$

2. The k parallel lines with an average slope $\bar{b}$;

$$Y = \bar{y}_{i\cdot} + \bar{b}(x - \bar{x}_{i\cdot}), \tag{19.7}$$

where, by analogy with (6.12),

$$\bar{b} = \frac{\sum_i^k \sum_\nu^{n_i} (x_{i\nu} - \bar{x}_{i\cdot})y_{i\nu}}{\sum_i^k \sum_\nu^{n_i} (x_{i\nu} - \bar{x}_{i\cdot})^2}. \tag{19.8}$$

3. The least-squares line for the group means $(\bar{x}_{i\cdot}, \bar{y}_{i\cdot})$,

$$Y = \bar{y}_{\cdot\cdot} + \hat{b}(x - \bar{x}_{\cdot\cdot}), \tag{19.9}$$

where

$$\hat{b} = \frac{\sum_i^k n_i(\bar{x}_{i\cdot} - \bar{x}_{\cdot\cdot})\bar{y}_{i\cdot}}{\sum_i^k n_i(\bar{x}_{i\cdot} - \bar{x}_{\cdot\cdot})^2}. \tag{19.10}$$

4. The over-all regression line which assumes that all observations come from a single population,

$$Y = \bar{y}_{\cdot\cdot} + b(x - \bar{x}_{\cdot\cdot}), \tag{19.11}$$

where

$$b = \frac{\sum_i^k \sum_\nu^{n_i} (x_{i\nu} - \bar{x}_{\cdot\cdot})y_{i\nu}}{\sum_i^k \sum_\nu^{n_i} (x_{i\nu} - \bar{x}_{\cdot\cdot})^2}. \tag{19.12}$$

In this formula, the numerator can be written as

$$\sum_i^k \sum_\nu^{n_i} (x_{i\nu} - \bar{x}_{\cdot\cdot})y_{i\nu} = \sum_i^k \sum_\nu^{n_i} x_{i\nu}y_{i\nu} - \frac{(\sum_i^k \sum_\nu^{n_i} x_{i\nu})(\sum_i^k \sum_\nu^{n_i} y_{i\nu})}{\sum_i^k n_i}. \tag{19.13}$$

The numerator of $\bar{b}$, (19.8), is equal to

$$\sum_i^k \sum_\nu^{n_i} (x_{i\nu} - \bar{x}_{i\cdot})(y_{i\nu} - \bar{y}_{i\cdot}) = \sum_i^k \sum_\nu^{n_i} x_{i\nu}y_{i\nu} - \sum_i^k \frac{(\sum_\nu^{n_i} x_{i\nu} \sum_\nu^{n_i} y_{i\nu})}{n_i}, \tag{19.14}$$

and the numerator of $\hat{b}$, (19.10), is equal to

$$\sum_i^k n_i(\bar{x}_{i\cdot} - \bar{x}_{\cdot\cdot})(\bar{y}_{i\cdot} - \bar{y}_{\cdot\cdot})$$
$$= \sum_i^k \left(\frac{\sum_\nu^{n_i} x_{i\nu} \sum_\nu^{n_i} y_{\nu i}}{n_i}\right) - \frac{(\sum_i^k \sum_\nu^{n_i} x_{i\nu})(\sum_i^k \sum_\nu^{n_i} y_{i\nu})}{\sum_1^k n_i}; \tag{19.15}$$

so the numerator of (19.12), which is (19.13), equals the sum of (19.14) and (19.15). Also the denominator of b (19.12) is

$$\sum_i^k \sum_\nu^{n_i} (x_{i\nu} - \bar{x}_{..})^2 = \sum_i^k \sum_\nu^{n_i} (x_{i\nu} - \bar{x}_{i.})^2 + \sum_i^k n_i(\bar{x}_{i.} - \bar{x}_{..})^2. \tag{19.16}$$

Making these substitutions in (19.12) we get

$$b \doteq \frac{\sum_i^k \sum_\nu^{n_i} (x_{i\nu} - \bar{x}_{i.})(y_{i\nu} - \bar{y}_{i.}) + \sum_i^k n_i(\bar{x}_{i.} - \bar{x}_{..})(\bar{y}_{i.} - \bar{y}_{..})}{\sum_i^k \sum_\nu^{n_i} (x_{i\nu} - \bar{x}_{i.})^2 + \sum_i^k n_i(\bar{x}_{i.} - \bar{x}_{..})^2}$$

$$= \frac{\bar{b} \sum_i^k \sum_\nu^{n_i} (x_{i\nu} - \bar{x}_{i.})^2 + \hat{b} \sum_i^k n_i(\bar{x}_{i.} - \bar{x}_{..})^2}{\sum_i^k \sum_\nu^{n_i} (x_{i\nu} - \bar{x}_{i.})^2 + \sum_i^k n_i(\bar{x}_{i.} - \bar{x}_{..})^2}, \tag{19.17}$$

which shows that b is a weighted average of $\bar{b}$ and $\hat{b}$.

We can write the deviation of an observation $y_{i\nu}$ at $x_{i\nu}$ from the value predicted by the line (4) as the sum of four components:

(i) The deviation between $y_{i\nu}$ and the value predicted by the individual regression line (1):

$$y_{i\nu} - [\bar{y}_{i.} + b_i(x_{i\nu} - \bar{x}_{i.})]. \tag{19.18}$$

(ii) The deviation between the slope of the individual lines (1) and the slope of the parallel lines (2), weighted by the deviation of $x_{i\nu}$ from $\bar{x}_{i.}$:

$$(b_i - \bar{b})(x_{i\nu} - \bar{x}_{i.}). \tag{19.19}$$

(iii) The deviation of the mean of the ith group $\bar{y}_{i.}$ from the value predicted by the regression line for group means, line (4):

$$\bar{y}_{i.} - [\bar{y}_{..} + \hat{b}(\bar{x}_{i.} - \bar{x}_{..})]. \tag{19.20}$$

(iv) The nature of the fourth component,

$$(\bar{b} - \hat{b})(x_{i\nu} - \bar{x}_{i.}) + (\hat{b} - b)(x_{i\nu} - \bar{x}_{..}), \tag{19.21}$$

is not immediately obvious. We will see, however, that it is related to the difference between $\bar{b}$ and $\hat{b}$.

We thus have an identity

$$\begin{aligned} y_{i\nu} - [\bar{y}_{..} + b(x_{i\nu} - \bar{x}_{..})] = {} & \{y_{i\nu} - [\bar{y}_{i.} + b_i(x_{i\nu} - \bar{x}_{i.})]\} + (b_i - \bar{b})(x_{i\nu} - \bar{x}_{i.}) \\ & + \{\bar{y}_{i.} - [\bar{y}_{..} + \hat{b}(\bar{x}_{i.} - \bar{x}_{..})]\} \\ & + [(\bar{b} - \hat{b})(x_{i\nu} - \bar{x}_{i.}) + (\hat{b} - b)(x_{i\nu} - \bar{x}_{..})] \end{aligned} \tag{19.22}$$

which we square and sum over i and ν. The sums of squares are entered in Table 11.19, but, for the sum of squares arising from the last item (iv) (19.21), we use the following identity:

$$\sum_i^k \sum_\nu^{n_i} [(\bar{b} - \hat{b})(x_{i\nu} - \bar{x}_{i\cdot}) + (\hat{b} - b)(x_{i\nu} - \bar{x}_{\cdot\cdot})]^2 = \frac{(\hat{b} - \bar{b})^2}{\dfrac{1}{\sum_i^k n_i(\bar{x}_{i\cdot} - \bar{x}_{\cdot\cdot})^2} + \dfrac{1}{\sum_i^k \sum_\nu^{n_i} (x_{i\nu} - \bar{x}_{i\cdot})^2}}. \quad (19.23)$$

This identity can be proved as follows: Substituting from (19.17) for b, (19.21) can be written as

$$(\bar{b} - \hat{b})(x_{i\nu} - \bar{x}_{i\cdot}) + (\hat{b} - b)(x_{i\nu} - \bar{x}_{\cdot\cdot}) = (\bar{b} - \hat{b})(x_{i\nu} - \bar{x}_{i\cdot})$$
$$+ \left[\hat{b} - \frac{\bar{b} \sum_i^k \sum_\nu^{n_i} (x_{i\nu} - \bar{x}_{i\cdot})^2 + \hat{b} \sum_i^k n_i(\bar{x}_{i\cdot} - \bar{x}_{\cdot\cdot})^2}{\sum_i^k \sum_\nu^{n_i}(x_{i\nu} - \bar{x}_{i\cdot})^2 + \sum_i^k n_i(\bar{x}_{i\cdot} - \bar{x}_{\cdot\cdot})^2}\right](x_{i\nu} - \bar{x}_{\cdot\cdot})$$
$$= \frac{(\bar{b} - \hat{b})}{\sum_i^k \sum_\nu^{n_i} (x_{i\nu} - \bar{x}_{i\cdot})^2 + \sum_i^k n_i(\bar{x}_{i\cdot} - \bar{x}_{\cdot\cdot})^2} \quad (19.24)$$
$$\times [(x_{i\nu} - \bar{x}_{i\cdot}) \sum_i^k n_i(\bar{x}_{i\cdot} - \bar{x}_{\cdot\cdot})^2 - (\bar{x}_{i\cdot} - \bar{x}_{\cdot\cdot}) \sum_i^k \sum_\nu^{n_i} (x_{i\nu} - \bar{x}_{i\cdot})^2].$$

If we denote the part in [ ] by P, and let $Q = \sum_i^k \sum_\nu^{n_i} P^2$, then

$$Q = \sum_i^k \sum_\nu^{n_i} [(x_{i\nu} - \bar{x}_{i\cdot})^2 \{\sum_i^k n_i(\bar{x}_{i\cdot} - \bar{x}_{\cdot\cdot})^2\}^2$$
$$+ (\bar{x}_{i\cdot} - \bar{x}_{\cdot\cdot})^2 \{\sum_i^k \sum_\nu^{n_i} (x_{i\nu} - \bar{x}_{i\cdot})^2\}^2$$
$$- 2(x_{i\nu} - \bar{x}_{i\cdot})(\bar{x}_{i\cdot} - \bar{x}_{\cdot\cdot}) \sum_i^k n_i(\bar{x}_{i\cdot} - \bar{x}_{\cdot\cdot})^2 \sum_i^k \sum_\nu^{n_i} (x_{i\nu} - \bar{x}_{i\cdot})^2].$$

Since the cross-product term sums to zero,

$$Q = \sum_i^k n_i(\bar{x}_{i\cdot} - \bar{x}_{\cdot\cdot})^2 \sum_i^k \sum_\nu^{n_i} (x_{i\nu} - \bar{x}_{i\cdot})^2 [\sum_i^k n_i(\bar{x}_{i\cdot} - \bar{x}_{\cdot\cdot})^2 + \sum_i^k \sum_\nu^{n_i} (x_{i\nu} - \bar{x}_{i\cdot})^2]. \quad (19.25)$$

Squaring and summing (19.24) over i and ν then gives the identity (19.23).

We need computing forms for the sums of squares in Table 11.19. The sums of squares for s_4^2 is satisfactory as it stands. The sum of squares for s_3^2 is

$$\sum_i^k n_i[\bar{y}_{i\cdot} - \{\bar{y}_{\cdot\cdot} + \bar{b}(\bar{x}_{i\cdot} - \bar{x}_{\cdot\cdot})\}]^2$$

$$= \sum_i^k n_i(\bar{y}_{i\cdot} - \bar{y}_{\cdot\cdot})^2 - \frac{[\sum_i^k n_i(\bar{x}_{i\cdot} - \bar{x}_{\cdot\cdot})(\bar{y}_{i\cdot} - \bar{y}_{\cdot\cdot})]^2}{\sum_i^k n_i(\bar{x}_{i\cdot} - \bar{x}_{\cdot\cdot})^2}. \tag{19.26}$$

The sum of squares for s_2^2 is

$$\sum_i^k (b_i - \bar{b})^2 \sum_\nu^{n_i} (x_{i\nu} - \bar{x}_{i\cdot})^2$$

$$= \sum_i^k \frac{[\sum_\nu^{n_i} (x_{i\nu} - \bar{x}_{i\cdot})(y_{i\nu} - \bar{y}_{i\cdot})]^2}{\sum_\nu^{n_i} (x_{i\nu} - \bar{x}_{i\cdot})^2} - \frac{[\sum_i^k \sum_\nu^{n_i} (x_{i\nu} - x_{i\cdot})(y_{i\nu} - \bar{y}_{i\cdot})]^2}{\sum_i^k \sum_\nu^{n_i} (x_{i\nu} - \bar{x}_{i\cdot})^2}. \tag{19.27}$$

The sum of squares for s_1^2 is the sum of the sums of squares of deviations about the separate lines: Each of these sums of squares is

$$\sum_\nu^{n_i} (y_{i\nu} - \bar{y}_{i\cdot})^2 - \frac{[\sum_\nu^{n_i} (x_{i\nu} - \bar{x}_{i\cdot})(y_{i\nu} - \bar{y}_{i\cdot})]^2}{\sum_\nu^{n_i} (x_{i\nu} - \bar{x}_{i\cdot})^2}; \tag{19.28}$$

so the sum over i is

$$\sum_i^k \sum_\nu^{n_i} (y_{i\nu} - \bar{y}_{i\cdot})^2 - \sum_i^k \left\{ \frac{[\sum_\nu^{n_i} (x_{i\nu} - x_{i\cdot})(y_{i\nu} - \bar{y}_{i\cdot})^2]}{\sum_\nu^{n_i} (x_{i\nu} - \bar{x}_{i\cdot})^2} \right\}. \tag{19.29}$$

The sum of squares about the over-all line is

$$\sum_i^k \sum_\nu^{n_i} (y_{i\nu} - \bar{y}_{\cdot\cdot})^2 - \frac{[\sum_i^k \sum_\nu^{n_i} (y_{i\nu} - \bar{y}_{\cdot\cdot})(x_{i\nu} - \bar{x}_{\cdot\cdot})]^2}{\sum_i^k \sum_\nu^{n_i} (x_{i\nu} - \bar{x}_{\cdot\cdot})^2}. \tag{19.30}$$

Table 11.19

Source of variance	Sum of squares	Degrees of freedom	Mean squares
Between $\hat{b}$ and $\bar{b}$	$(\hat{b} - \bar{b})^2 \bigg/ \left[\frac{1}{\sum_i^k n_i(\bar{x}_{i\cdot} - \bar{x}_{\cdot\cdot})^2} + \frac{1}{\sum_i^k \sum_\nu^{n_i} (x_{i\nu} - \bar{x}_{i\cdot})^2}\right]$	1	s_4^2
Deviations of the group means about their regression line	$\sum_i^k n_i[\bar{y}_{i\cdot} - \{\bar{y}_{\cdot\cdot} + \hat{b}(\bar{x}_{i\cdot} - \bar{x}_{\cdot\cdot})\}]^2$	$k - 2$	s_3^2
Between the individual slopes b_i	$\sum_i^k (b_i - \bar{b})^2 \sum_\nu^{n_i} (x_{i\nu} - \bar{x}_{i\cdot})^2$	$k - 1$	s_2^2
About the individual lines	$\sum_i^k \sum_\nu^{n_i} \{y_{i\nu} - [\bar{y}_{i\cdot} + b_i(x_{i\nu} - \bar{x}_{i\cdot})]\}^2$	$\sum_i^k n_i - 2k$	s_1^2
About the over-all line	$\sum_i^k \sum_\nu^{n_i} \{y_{i\nu} - [\bar{y}_{\cdot\cdot} + b(x_{i\nu} - \bar{x}_{\cdot\cdot})]\}^2$	$\sum_i^k n_i - 2$	

Table 11.20

1	2	3	4	5	6	7	8	9	10	11
i	n_i	$\sum_{\nu}^{n_i} y_{i\nu}$	$\bar{y}_{i.}$	$\sum_{\nu}^{n_i} x_{i\nu}$	$\bar{x}_{i.}$	$\sum_{\nu}^{n_i} y_{i\nu}^2$	$\sum_{\nu}^{n_i} x_{i\nu}^2$	$\sum_{\nu}^{n_i} y_{i\nu}x_{i\nu}$	$\left(\sum_{\nu}^{n_i} y_{i\nu}\right)^2 / n_i$	[7] − [10] = $\sum_{\nu}^{n_i} (y_{i\nu}-\bar{y}_{i.})^2$
1	30	2123	70.767	2223	74.100	159,813	176,675	162,518	150,237.633	9,575.367
2	45	3147	69.933	3138	69.733	232,975	233,698	227,882	220,080.200	12,894.800
3	37	2942	79.514	2462	66.541	247,854	175,194	204,100	233,928.757	13,925.243
	$\sum_{i}^{k} n_i = 112$	$\sum_{i}^{k}\sum_{\nu}^{n_i} y_{i\nu} = 8212$		$\sum_{i}^{k}\sum_{\nu}^{n_i} x_{i\nu} = 7823$		$\sum_{i}^{k}\sum_{\nu}^{n_i} y_{i\nu}^2 = 640,642$	$\sum_{i}^{k}\sum_{\nu}^{n_i} x_{i\nu}^2 = 585,567$	$\sum_{i}^{k}\sum_{\nu}^{n_i} y_{i\nu}x_{i\nu} = 594,500$	$\sum_{i}^{k}\frac{\left(\sum_{\nu}^{n_i} y_{i\nu}\right)^2}{n_i} = 604,246.590$	$\sum_{i}^{k}\sum_{\nu}^{n_i} (y_{i\nu}-\bar{y}_{i.})^2 = 36,395.410$

Table 11.20 (continued)

1	12	13	14	15	16	17
		[8] − [12] =		[9] − [14] =	[15]²/[13] =	[11] − [16]
i	$(\sum_{\nu}^{n_i} x_{i\nu})^2/n_i$	$\sum_{\nu}^{n_i} (x_{i\nu}-\bar{x}_{i.})^2$	$\sum_{\nu}^{n_i} x_{i\nu} \sum_{\nu}^{n_i} y_{i\nu}/n_i$	$\sum_{\nu}^{n_i} (x_{i\nu}-\bar{x}_{i.})(y_{i\nu}-\bar{y}_{i.})$	$\frac{[\sum_{\nu}^{n_i} (x_{i\nu}-\bar{x}_{i.})(y_{i\nu}-\bar{y}_{i.})]^2}{\sum_{\nu}^{n_i} (x_{i\nu}-\bar{x}_{i.})^2}$	
1	164,724.300	11,950.700	157,314.300	5203.700	2265.850	7309.517
2	218,823.200	14,874.800	219,450.800	8431.200	4778.897	8115.903
3	163,822.811	11,371.189	195,762.270	8337.730	6113.498	7811.645
	$\sum_{i}^{k} \frac{(\sum_{\nu}^{n_i} x_{i\nu})^2}{n_i}$	$\sum_{i}^{k} \sum_{\nu}^{n_i} (x_{i\nu}-\bar{x}_{i.})^2$	$\sum_{i}^{k} \frac{\sum_{\nu}^{n_i} x_{i\nu} \sum_{\nu}^{n_i} y_{i\nu}}{n_i}$	$\sum_{i}^{k} \sum_{\nu}^{n_i} (x_{i\nu}-\bar{x}_{i.})(y_{i\nu}-\bar{y}_{i.})$	$\sum_{i}^{k} \frac{[\sum_{\nu}^{n_i} (x_{i\nu}-\bar{x}_{i.})(y_{i\nu}-\bar{y}_{i.})]^2}{\sum_{\nu}^{n_i} (x_{i\nu}-\bar{x}_{i.})^2}$	Sum of squares for s_1^2
	= 547,370.311	= 38,196.689	= 572,527.370	= 21,972.630	= 13,158.245	= 23,237.165

We might add two items to Table 11.19: first, the sum of squares due to the over-all line,

$$\frac{\left[\sum_{i}^{k}\sum_{\nu}^{n_i}(y_{i\nu}-\bar{y}_{..})(x_{i\nu}-\bar{x}_{..})\right]^2}{\sum_{i}^{k}\sum_{\nu}^{n_i}(x_{i\nu}-\bar{x}_{..})^2}, \tag{19.31}$$

and second, the total sum of squares about the grand mean,

$$\sum_{i}^{k}\sum_{\nu}^{n_i}(y_{i\nu}-\bar{y}_{..})^2. \tag{19.32}$$

Table 11.20 gives the results of observations on three lime kilns. The variables x and y were daily observations on the tons of lime made per day x and a measure of the quality of the lime y. The mean qualities $\bar{y}_{1\cdot}$, $\bar{y}_{2\cdot}$, $\bar{y}_{3\cdot}$ (column 4) were 70.767, 69.933, and 79.514. A simple analysis of variance could be made on $y_{i\nu}$ to test the null hypothesis that there was no difference between the kilns as regards quality, but it was known that y was roughly linearly related to x, and the tonnage means $\bar{x}_{1\cdot}$, $\bar{x}_{2\cdot}$, and $\bar{x}_{3\cdot}$ (column 6) were 74.100, 69.733, and 66.541. We therefore want to compare the y means adjusted for variation in the x means. We need the sums of squares and products of $x_{i\nu}$ and $y_{i\nu}$, and these are given in columns 7, 8, and 9. We next calculate $\sum_{\nu}^{n_i}(y_{i\nu}-\bar{y}_{i\cdot})^2$, etc., in columns 10 through 15 of Table 11.20. The total of column 17 is (19.29), the sums of squares for s_1^2.

To calculate the other sums of squares we need certain identities. Taking them in the order in which they first appear in Table 11.19, for $\hat{b}$ as defined in (19.10) we use (19.15)

$$\sum_{i}^{k} n_i(\bar{x}_{i\cdot}-\bar{x}_{..})(\bar{y}_{i\cdot}-\bar{y}_{..})$$
$$=[14]-\frac{[5][3]}{[2]}=572{,}527.370-\frac{7823\times 8212}{112}=-1066.166,$$

where the numbers in square brackets [ ] are the column totals from Table 11.20, and

$$\sum_{i}^{k} n_i(\bar{x}_{i\cdot}-\bar{x}_{..})^2=\sum_{i}^{k}\frac{\left(\sum_{\nu}^{n_i}x_{i\nu}\right)^2}{n_i}-\frac{\left(\sum_{i}^{k}\sum_{\nu}^{n_i}x_{i\nu}\right)^2}{\sum_{i}^{k}n_i}$$
$$=[12]-\frac{[5]^2}{[2]}=547{,}370.311-\frac{(7823)^2}{112}=947.731.$$

Substituting in (19.10) gives

$$\hat{b} = \frac{-1066.166}{947.731} = -1.24967.$$

For $\bar{b}$, as defined in (19.8), we already have the necessary numbers:

$$\bar{b} = \frac{[15]}{[13]} = \frac{21{,}972.630}{38{,}196.689} = 0.575250.$$

We can now calculate the sum of squares for s_4^2 as

$$(-1.124967 - 0.575250)^2\left(\frac{1}{947.731} + \frac{1}{38{,}196.689}\right)^{-1} = 2673.310.$$

For the sum of squares for s_3^2 (19.26), we need

$$\sum_i^k n_i(\bar{y}_{i\cdot} - \bar{y}_{\cdot\cdot})^2 = \sum_i^k \frac{(\sum_\nu^{n_i} y_{i\nu})^2}{n_i} - \frac{(\sum_i^k \sum_\nu^{n_i} y_{i\nu})^2}{\sum_i^k n_i}$$

$$= [10] - \frac{[3]^2}{[2]} = 604{,}246.590 - \frac{(8212)^2}{112} = 2131.019$$

and (19.26) takes the value

$$2131.019 - \frac{(-1066.166)^2}{947.731} = 931.618.$$

The sum of squares for s_2^2 is given by (19.27):

$$[16] - \frac{[15]^2}{[13]} = 13{,}158.245 - \frac{(21{,}972.630)^2}{38{,}196.689} = 518.498.$$

The sum of squares about the over-all line (19.30) involves

$$\sum_i^k \sum_\nu^{n_i} (y_{i\nu} - \bar{y}_{\cdot\cdot})^2 = \frac{\sum_i^k \sum_\nu^{n_i} y_{i\nu}^2 - (\sum_i^k \sum_\nu^{n_i} y_{i\nu})^2}{\sum_i^k n_i}$$

$$= [7] - \frac{[3]^2}{[2]} = 640{,}642 - \frac{(8212)^2}{112} = 38{,}526.429,$$

$$\sum_i^k \sum_\nu^{n_i} (y_{i\nu} - \bar{y}_{\cdot\cdot})(x_{i\nu} - \bar{x}_{\cdot\cdot}) = \sum_i^k \sum_\nu^{n_i} x_{i\nu}y_{i\nu} - \frac{\sum_i^k \sum_\nu^{n_i} x_{i\nu} \sum_i^k \sum_\nu^{n_i} y_{i\nu}}{\sum_i^k n_i}$$

$$= [9] - \frac{[5][3]}{[2]} = 594{,}500 - \frac{7823 \times 8212}{112} = 20{,}906.464,$$

and

$$\sum_i^k \sum_v^{n_i} (x_{iv} - \bar{x}_{..})^2 = \sum_i^k \sum_v^{n_i} x_{iv}^2 - \frac{\left(\sum_i^k \sum_v^{n_i} x_{iv}\right)^2}{\sum_i^k n_i}$$

$$= [8] - \frac{[5]^2}{[2]} = 585{,}567 - \frac{(7823)^2}{112} = 39{,}144.420,$$

which we substitute in (19.30) to get

$$38{,}526.429 - \frac{(20{,}906.464)^2}{39{,}144.420} = 27{,}360.591$$

as the sum of squares about the over-all line. The sum of squares due to the over-all regression (19.31) is

$$\frac{(20{,}906.464)^2}{39{,}144.420} = 11{,}165.838.$$

Finally the total sum of squares (19.32) is $\sum_i^k \sum_v^{n_i} (y_{iv} - \bar{y}_{..})^2 = 38{,}526.429$.

We now assemble all these sums of squares in Table 11.21.

Table 11.21

Source of variance	Sums of squares	Degrees of freedom	Mean squares
Between $\hat{b}$ and $\bar{b}$	2,673,310	1	$2673.310 = s_4^2$
Deviations of the group means about their regression line	931.618	1	$931.618 = s_3^2$
Between the individual slopes	518.498	2	$259.249 = s_2^2$
About the individual lines	23,237.165	106	$219.219 = s_1^2$
About the over-all line	27,360.591	110	
Due to the over-all line	11,165.838	1	
Total	38,526.429	111	

The interpretation of Table 11.21 is as follows. We first check that the lines for the separate groups of points can be regarded as parallel with the variance ratio $s_2^2/s_1^2 = 259.249/219.219 = 1.18$. Under the null hypothesis that the lines are parallel, this is distributed as $F(2, 106)$. Clearly the null hypothesis is acceptable.

In this form of analysis the test for identity of the adjusted y means is broken into two parts. The variance ratio s_3^2/s_1^2 tests that the group means do not depart significantly from the least-squares line through them; that is, it is a test of linearity of the relationship between group means. To reject this null hypothesis is to conclude that the adjusted means do differ. On the other hand, if we accept this null hypothesis we then go on to test the further null hypothesis that this line is parallel to the individual lines with the variance ratio s_4^2/s_1^2: if this line is parallel to the individual lines, then all lines must coalesce into a single line, and the null hypothesis that the adjusted group means are identical is acceptable. Here the first test does reach the 5 per cent level of significance, and the second test is overwhelmingly significant. In some forms of analysis of covariance, the sums of squares for s_4^2 and s_3^2 are pooled and tested in this form, as discussed in the next section.

If we accept the null hypothesis that the individual lines are parallel, we can construct the adjusted means as follows. The individual lines with common slope (19.7) are

$$Y_i = \bar{y}_{i\cdot} + \bar{b}(x - \bar{x}_{i\cdot})$$

and the y mean adjusted for x equal to $\bar{x}_{\cdot\cdot}$ is

$$Y_{i(\text{adj})} = \bar{y}_{i\cdot} + \bar{b}(\bar{x}_{\cdot\cdot} - \bar{x}_{i\cdot}). \tag{19.33}$$

For example, $\bar{x}_{\cdot\cdot} = \dfrac{7823}{112} = 69.848$

and $Y_{1(\text{adj})} = 70.767 + 0.57525(69.848 - 74.100) = 68.321.$

The variance between two adjusted means is

$$\begin{aligned} V[Y_{i(\text{adj})} - Y_{i'(\text{adj})}] &= V[\bar{y}_{i\cdot} + \bar{b}(\bar{x}_{\cdot\cdot} - \bar{x}_{i\cdot}) - \bar{y}_{i'\cdot} - \bar{b}(\bar{x}_{\cdot\cdot} - \bar{x}_{i'\cdot})] \\ &= V[\bar{y}_{i\cdot}] + V[\bar{y}_{i'\cdot}] + (\bar{x}_{i\cdot} - \bar{x}_{i'\cdot})^2\, V[\bar{b}] \\ &= \sigma^2\left[\frac{1}{n_i} + \frac{1}{n_{i'}} + \frac{(\bar{x}_{i\cdot} - \bar{x}_{i'\cdot})^2}{\sum_i^k \sum_\nu^{n_i} (x_{i\nu} - \bar{x}_{i\cdot})^2}\right]. \end{aligned}$$

For example, the estimated variance between the adjusted means for kilns 1 and 2 is

$$\hat{V}[Y_{1(\text{adj})} - Y_{2(\text{adj})}] = 219.219\left[\frac{1}{30} + \frac{1}{45} + \frac{(74.100 - 69.733)^2}{38{,}196.689}\right] = 12.29,$$

and the confidence limits can be immediately constructed.

It is natural to inquire whether the analysis of covariance of these data has achieved any advantages over a simple analysis of variance of y. From the calculations given, we can readily assemble Table 11.22. The variance ratio is 3.191, which can be compared with 8.222 obtained from Table 11.21 by pooling s_4^2 and s_3^2. We can also compute the variances between the unadjusted means as

$$\hat{V}[Y_1 - Y_2] = 333.903(\tfrac{1}{30} + \tfrac{1}{45}) = 18.550$$

which is some 50 per cent larger than the variance between the adjusted means.

Table 11.22

Source of variance	Sums of squares	Degrees of freedom	Mean squares
Between kilns	2,131.019	2	1065.509
Within kilns	36,395.410	109	333.903
Total	38,526.429	111	

11.20. Simple Analysis of Covariance

Quite frequently the analysis of the previous section is simplified. Two changes are made:

1. The sums of squares and degrees of freedom for s_4^2 and s_3^2 in Table 11.21 are combined into a single line measuring differences between the adjusted y means.
2. The test for parallelism of the individual slopes involving s_2^2 is omitted.

The effect of these two changes is to simplify the arithmetic considerably. This modified analysis starts from a table of sums of squares and products (Table 11.23).

To pool s_4^2 and s_3^2 in Table 11.21 involves pooling the degrees of freedom, $1 + (k - 2) = k - 1$, and the corresponding sums of squares. Call the pooled mean square s_6^2. Then the corresponding sums of squares will be $(k - 1)s_6^2$. Straightforward manipulation gives for the sum of squares for the adjusted y means

$$(k - 1)s_6^2 = T_{yy} - \frac{(E_{xy} + T_{xy})^2}{E_{xx} + T_{xx}} + \frac{E_{xy}^2}{E_{xx}}, \qquad (20.1)$$

changing from the notation of Table 11.21 to that of Table 11.23.

To dispense with the test for parallelism of the individual lines amounts to assuming that the individual lines are parallel, when s_2^2 of Table 11.21 will have expected value σ^2. Pooling the degrees of freedom of s_2^2 and s_1^2 gives

$$(k-1)+\left(\sum_i^k n_i - 2k\right) = \sum_i^k n_i - k - 1.$$

Straightforward manipulation gives the error sum of squares as

$$\left(\sum_i^k n_i - k - 1\right)s_5^2 = \left(E_{yy} - \frac{E_{xy}^2}{E_{xx}}\right) \tag{20.2}$$

changing from the notation of Table 11.21 to that of Table 11.23.

Table 11.23

Source of variance	Degrees of freedom	Sums of squares and products		
		for x^2	for xy	for y^2
Groups	$k-1$	$\sum_i^k n_i(\bar{x}_{i\cdot}-\bar{x}_{\cdot\cdot})^2 = T_{xx}$	$\sum_i^k n_i(\bar{x}_{i\cdot}-\bar{x}_{\cdot\cdot})(\bar{y}_{i\cdot}-\bar{y}_{\cdot\cdot}) = T_{xy}$	$\sum_i^k n_i(\bar{y}_{i\cdot}-\bar{y}_{\cdot\cdot})^2 = T_{yy}$
Error	$\sum_i^k n_i-k$	$\sum_i^k\sum_\nu^{n_i}(x_{i\nu}-\bar{x}_{i\cdot})^2 = E_{xx}$	$\sum_i^k\sum_\nu^{n_i}(x_{i\nu}-\bar{x}_{i\cdot})(\bar{y}_{i\nu}-\bar{y}_{i\cdot}) = E_{xy}$	$\sum_i^k\sum_\nu^{n_i}(y_{i\nu}-\bar{y}_{i\cdot})^2 = E_{yy}$
Total	$\sum_i^k n_i-1$	$\sum_i^k\sum_\nu^{n_i}(x_{i\nu}-\bar{x}_{\cdot\cdot})^2 = S_{xx}$	$\sum_i^k\sum_\nu^{n_i}(x_{i\nu}-\bar{x}_{\cdot\cdot})(y_{i\nu}-\bar{y}_{\cdot\cdot}) = S_{xy}$	$\sum_i^k\sum_\nu^{n_i}(y_{i\nu}-\bar{y}_{\cdot\cdot})^2 = S_{yy}$

Under the null hypothesis that the adjusted means are equal, s_6^2/s_5^2 will be distributed as $F(k-1, \sum_i^k n_i - k - 1)$.

To apply this simplified procedure to the data of the example of the previous section, Table 11.24 gives the numerical values corresponding to the data of Table 11.20.

The T's and the S's have been calculated earlier, the E's are most easily obtained by difference. Using (20.1), the sum of squares for adjusted y means is

$$2s_6^2 = 2131.019 - \frac{(20{,}906.464)^2}{39{,}144.420} + \frac{(21{,}972.630)^2}{38{,}196.689} = 3604.927;$$

so $s_6^2 = 1802.463$. It will be noted that, as a check, the sum of the sums of squares for s_4^2 and s_3^2 in Table 11.21 is $2673.310 + 931.618 = 3604.928$. Using (20.2), the sum of squares for error is

$$(112 - 3 - 1)s_5^2 = 36{,}395.410 - \frac{(21{,}972.630)^2}{38{,}196.689} = 23{,}755.664;$$

so $s_5^2 = 219.960$. It will be noted, as a check, that the sum of squares for s_2^2 and s_1^2 in Table 11.21 is $518.498 + 23{,}237.165 = 23{,}755.663$.

Table 11.24

Source of variance	Degrees of freedom	Sums of squares and sum of products of deviations		
		for x^2	for xy	for y^2
Groups	2	$T_{xx} = 947.731$	$T_{xy} = -1{,}066.166$	$T_{yy} = 2{,}131.019$
Error	109	$E_{xx} = 38{,}196.689$	$E_{xy} = 21{,}972.630$	$E_{yy} = 36{,}395.410$
Total	111	$S_{xx} = 39{,}144.420$	$S_{xy} = 20{,}906.464$	$S_{yy} = 38{,}526.429$

Hence the test of the null hypothesis of equality of the adjusted means is

$$\frac{s_6^2}{s_5^2} = \frac{1802.463}{219.960} = 8.19 \sim F(2, 108).$$

The arithmetic necessary for this simplified analysis of covariance is substantially less complex than in the full analysis of the previous section. Nevertheless, the full analysis would ordinarily be indicated except in routine applications where a substantial body of previous experience had established that the separate lines, if not truly parallel, at least must be very nearly so. Nonparallelism of the lines is an important feature and should not be overlooked.

The interpretation of an analysis of covariance can prove remarkably tricky, and a paper by Fairfield Smith [8] should be studied in this context. For a general discussion see Cochran [9].

11.21. Exponential Regression

Suppose that our model is

$$\eta = \alpha e^{\beta x}. \tag{21.1}$$

The sum of squares of deviations between the observations y_i and the predictions Y_i given by the estimated equation $Y = ae^{bx}$ is

$$R = \sum(y_i - Y_i)^2 = \sum(y_i - ae^{bx_i})^2. \tag{21.2}$$

Differentiating this with respect to a and b and equating to zero gives

$$\frac{\partial R}{\partial a} = -2\sum y_i e^{bx_i} + 2a\sum e^{2bx_i} = 0,$$

$$\frac{\partial R}{\partial b} = -2a\sum x_i y_i e^{bx_i} + 2a^2\sum x_i e^{2bx_i} = 0,$$

whence we have the two simultaneous equations

$$\begin{aligned} \sum y_i e^{bx_i} &= a\sum e^{2bx_i}, \\ \sum x_i y_i e^{bx_i} &= a\sum x_i e^{2bx_i}, \end{aligned} \tag{21.3}$$

in the two unknowns a and b. An exact solution can only be approximated to by a tedious iterative procedure.

An alternative approach is to take logarithms of (21.1):

$$\log \eta = \log \alpha + \beta x, \tag{21.4}$$

and obtain a least-squares solution for $\log \alpha$ and β by minimizing

$$R = \sum(\log y_i - \log Y_i)^2 \tag{21.5}$$

in the usual way, i.e., handle the problem as if it was to regress $\log y$ on x. The use of $\log y$ in place of y means that we are minimizing the sums of squares of deviations of $\log y$ from $\log Y$ instead of y from Y; so we will obtain a different solution. Also, if $V[y|x] = \sigma^2$, a constant, then $V[\log y|x]$ will not be a constant, and the least-squares analysis based on $\log y$ will be incorrect. Quite often, however, $V[y|x] = k^2\eta^2$; i.e., the standard deviation is proportional to the mean, and then, as discussed in Section 3.4, $\log y$ will have a constant variance. In these circumstances, then, we will be correct in regressing $\log y$ on x.

REFERENCES

1. Wallis, W. Allen, and Harry V. Roberts, *Statistics: a New Approach.* Glencoe, Illinois: The Free Press, 1956.
2. Acton, Forman S., *Analysis of Straight-Line Data.* New York: John Wiley & Sons, 1959.
3. David, F. N., and J. Neyman, "Extension of the Markov theorem of least squares," *Statistical Research Memoirs*, 2(1938), 105–116.
4. Plackett, R. L., "A historical note on least squares," *Biometrika*, 36(1949), 458–460.
5. Finney, D. J., *Probit Analysis.* 2d ed.; Cambridge, England: University Press, 1952.
6. ——— *Statistical Methods in Biological Assay.* New York: Hafner Publishing Co., 1952.

7. Emmens, C. W., *Principles of Biological Assay*. London: Chapman & Hall, 1948.
8. Smith, H. Fairfield, "Interpretation of adjusted treatment means and regressions in analysis of covariance," *Biometrics*, 13(1957), 282–308.
9. Cochran, William G., "Analysis of covariance: its nature and uses." *Biometrics*, 13(1957), 261–281.

EXERCISES

11.1. The solubility of nitrous oxide in nitrogen dioxide was determined with results as below for temperature ranging from 263 to 283 degrees absolute. The reciprocal temperature is expressed as $(1000/T)$. A number of independent determinations were made at each temperature. [Data from W. Arthur Rocker, "Solubility and freezing point depression of nitrous oxide in liquid nitrogen dioxide," *Analytical Chemistry*, 24(1952), 1322–1324.]

Reciprocal temperature	3.801	3.731	3.662	3.593	3.533
Solubility, % by weight	1.28	1.21	1.11	0.81	0.65
	1.33	1.27	1.04	0.82	0.59
	1.52				0.63

(*a*) Fit a straight line of the regression of solubility on reciprocal temperature.

(*b*) Test this line for deviations from linearity.

(*c*) If the hypothesis of linearity is acceptable, form a pooled estimate of the variance of the solubility measurements.

(*d*) What is your estimate of the true solubility for a reciprocal temperature of 3.78?

(*e*) What are the 95 per cent confidence limits for this estimate?

(*f*) What are the 95 per cent confidence limits for the slope of the line?

(*g*) Suppose you took a sample and found its solubility to be 1.30. Between what limits would you have 95 per cent confidence that the reciprocal temperature lay (assuming the sample to be saturated)? Use (i) an exact method, (ii) an approximate method.

11.2. The data below are similar to those of Table 11.17 but on a sample of a different make of automobile.

x_i	19.65	31.15	35.95	50.15	59.65
y_i	3.44	4.98	6.40	8.88	11.22
	3.93	5.45			

I. (*a*) Obtain the regression line of y on x.

(*b*) Test the null hypothesis of linearity for this line.

(*c*) Extrapolate the line to $x = 0$, and construct 95 per cent confidence limits for η at this value of x.

II. Compare this line with that for the data of Table 11.3.
(*a*) Compare the variances about the regression lines.
(*b*) Compare the slopes.
(*c*) Test whether the lines can be regarded as coincident.

11.3. In a comparison of a new method of gas analysis with a standard method, the following results were obtained on a series of samples:

Standard method (x):	2.97	3.56	6.45	1.12	6.66	1.37	6.80
New method (y):	2.94	3.54	6.48	1.08	6.73	1.33	6.86

[Data from Jere Mead, "A critical orifice CO_2 analysis suitable for student use," *Science*, 121(1955), 103–104.]

Fit the line $y = a + b(x - \bar{x})$, and test at the level of significance $\alpha = 0.05$ the null hypotheses
(*a*) $\beta = 1$.
(*b*) The intercept on the y axis equals zero.
(*c*) Items (*a*) and (*b*) jointly.

11.4. In an assay of a preparation of insulin of unknown potency against a standard, three doses of the unknown and three doses of the standard were injected into rabbits, and the percentage fall in blood sugar after a certain period was observed; these are the data below. In insulin assay of this type, it is usually assumed that the plot of the above variable against log dose is a straight line.
(*a*) Test the parallelism of the two lines.
(*b*) Calculate the point estimate of the potency ratio.
(*c*) Calculate 95 per cent confidence limits for the potency ratio.

Preparation					
Standard log dose			Unknown log dose		
0.36	0.56	0.76	0.36	0.56	0.76
17	64	62	33	41	56
21	48	72	37	64	62
49	34	61	40	34	57
54	63	91	16	64	72
			21	48	73
			18	34	72
			25		81
					60

11.5. A sample of 56 subjects were given a test involving mental addition, x. They were divided into four groups randomly, and each group drank one of four beverages, which could not be distinguished by the subject. After a short time interval to allow the drugs in the beverages to act, the subjects were retested by a replicate of the first test, y. The scores are as below (data from H. Nash).

Drug A		Drug B		Drug C		Drug D	
x	y	x	y	x	y	x	y
24	24	23	18	27	35	27	28
28	30	33	32	27	31	44	40
38	39	39	33	44	55	39	34
42	41	36	35	38	43	27	27
24	27	18	19	32	44	59	47
39	46	28	28	32	28	36	30
45	56	43	41	24	33	19	24
19	25	37	37	13	13	34	28
19	18	30	33	39	39	22	21
22	25	49	39	52	58	28	28
34	31	37	38	17	18	39	39
52	52	40	41	20	17	29	26
27	38	36	38	49	41	55	46
42	45	41	36	29	25	49	42

I. Make a simple analysis of variance on the y's.

II. Make a simple analysis of variance on the differences $(y - x)$.

III. (*a*) Make an analysis of covariance of y, including a test for the parallelism of the separate regression lines.

(*b*) Discuss the difference between I, II, and III*a*.

(*c*) Construct a simple (nonmultiple) comparison 95 per cent confidence interval for the difference between the adjusted means for drugs A and B.

(*d*) B is a placebo and C and D are two levels of a certain drug, where the level of D is twice the level of C. The contrast $(B - 2C + D)$ will measure the linearity of response. Construct a 95 per cent multiple-comparison confidence interval for this contrast.

Certain sums and sums of squares and products which may be useful are below.

i	n_i	$\sum_{\nu}^{n_i} y_{i\nu}$	$\sum_{\nu}^{n_i} x_{i\nu}$	$\sum_{\nu}^{n_i} y_{i\nu}^2$	$\sum_{\nu}^{n_i} x_{i\nu}^2$	$\sum_{\nu}^{n_i} x_{i\nu}y_{i\nu}$
1	14	497	455	19,367	16,249	17,623
2	14	468	490	16,332	18,008	17,066
3	14	480	443	18,842	15,787	17,018
4	14	460	507	16,040	20,265	17,941
$\sum_{i}^{k}$	56	1905	1895	70,581	70,309	69,648

CHAPTER 12

The Bivariate Normal Distribution and the Correlation Coefficient

12.1. Introduction

In the preceding chapter we supposed that we observed y at a number of selected values of x. Ths distribution of x was what we cared to make it, and x was not a random variable. In this chapter we discuss the case where both x and y are random variables, drawn from some hypothetical population. For example, x could be the girth of a hog and y its marketable weight; or x could be the "intelligence" of a brother and y the "intelligence" of his sister; or x could be the grade average of members of a class and y their income in dollars after Federal income taxes, 10 years later. In every case care should be taken to define quite precisely the population from which the sample is taken, and to recognize that any inferences possible are strictly applicable only to that population.

12.2. Transformations of Bivariate Distributions

In Section 1.11 we saw how to obtain the distribution of a function of x, given the distribution of x. In this section we do the analogous thing for a bivariate distribution.

We are given a bivariate distribution with the probability density determined by the function $p_x(x_1, x_2)$. We are also given that y_1 is some function of x_1, x_2, namely, $y_1 = f_1(x_1, x_2)$, and likewise y_2 is another function of x_1, x_2, namely, $y_2 = f_2(x_1, x_2)$. We assume that these functions have continuous first partial derivatives, and that in both of them y_i increases (or decreases) monotonically with x_i, so that to each point in the (x_1, x_2) plane there is one and only one point in the (y_1, y_2) plane and vice versa. Let the inverse functions expressing x_i as functions of y_i be $x_1 = g_1(y_1, y_2)$, $x_2 = g_2(y_1, y_2)$.

Now, if x_1', x_2' are random variables, then y_1', y_2' will be random variables. Our problem is to determine

$$\Pr\{y_1 < y_1' < y_1 + dy_1, y_2 < y_2' < y_2 + dy_2\} = p_y(y_1, y_2)\, dy_1\, dy_2 \qquad (2.1)$$

where $p_y(y_1, y_2)$ is the joint probability density function of y_1, y_2, given that we know $p_x(x_1, x_2)$ and the functions f_1 and f_2.

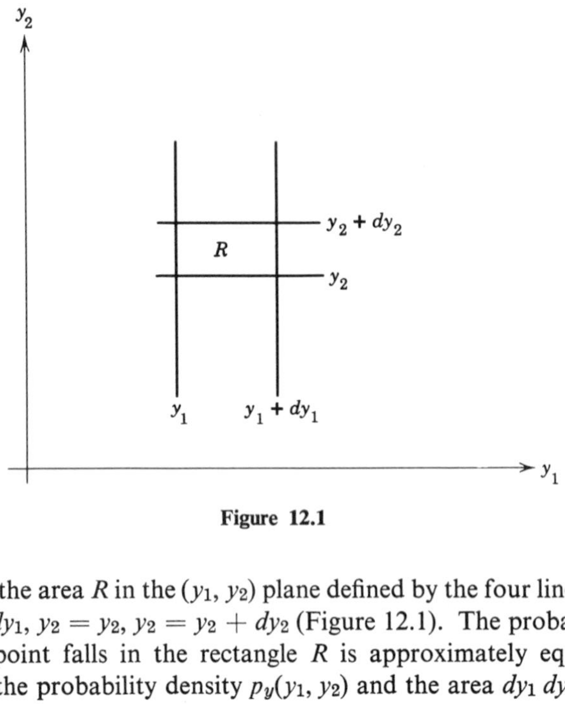

Figure 12.1

Consider the area R in the (y_1, y_2) plane defined by the four lines $y_1 = y_1$, $y_1 = y_1 + dy_1$, $y_2 = y_2$, $y_2 = y_2 + dy_2$ (Figure 12.1). The probability that a random point falls in the rectangle R is approximately equal to the product of the probability density $p_y(y_1, y_2)$ and the area $dy_1\, dy_2$:

$$p_y(y_1, y_2)\, dy_1\, dy_2\,. \qquad (2.2)$$

Now, for y_1 equal to some constant, the equation $y_1 = f_1(x_1, x_2)$ will determine a line in the (x_1, x_2) plane, say A. Similarly the equations $y_1 + dy_1 = f_1(x_1, x_2)$, $y_2 = f_2(x_1, x_2)$, $y_2 + dy_2 = f_2(x_1, x_2)$ will determine three more lines B, C, and D (Figure 12.2). These four lines will enclose an area S. Now, because of the one-to-one correspondence of points (y_1, y_2) with points (x_1, x_2), whenever a random point (y_1, y_2) falls inside the rectangle R in Figure 12.1, the corresponding point (x_1, x_2) falls inside the figure S in Figure 12.2. The probability of (x_1, x_2) falling inside S is approximately equal to the product of the probability density $p_x(x_1, x_2)$ times the area of S; hence

$$p_y(y_1, y_2)\, dy_1\, dy_2 = p_x(x_1, x_2)(\text{area of } S). \tag{2.3}$$

We therefore need to find the area of S. S is approximately a parallelogram. It is known from coordinate geometry that, if (x_1, x_2), (x_1', x_2'), and (x_1'', x_2'')

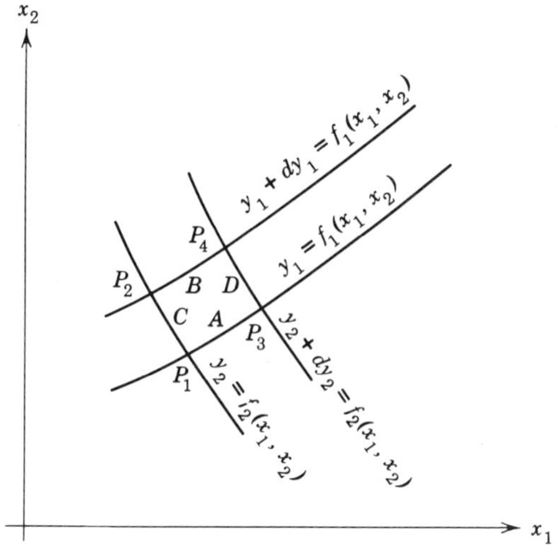

Figure 12.2

are three of the vertices of a parallelogram, then the area of the parallelogram is given by the absolute value of the determinant

$$\begin{vmatrix} 1 & x_1 & x_2 \\ 1 & x_1' & x_2' \\ 1 & x_1'' & x_2'' \end{vmatrix}. \tag{2.4}$$

We therefore need the coordinates of three of the vertices of S. The coordinates of P_1 in Figure 12.2 are $(g_1(y_1, y_2), g_2(y_1, y_2))$. The coordinates of P_2 are $(g_1(y_1 + dy_1, y_2), g_2(y_1 + dy_1, y_2))$. But, by Taylor series,

$$g_1(y_1 + dy_1, y_2) = g_1(y_1, y_2) + \frac{\partial g_1}{\partial y_1} dy_1 + \text{higher order terms},$$

$$g_2(y_1 + dy_1, y_2) = g_2(y_1, y_2) + \frac{\partial g_2}{\partial y_1} dy_1 + \text{higher order terms};$$

so the coordinates of P_2 can be written, ignoring the higher-order terms, as approximately

$$\left(g_1(y_1, y_2) + \frac{\partial g_1}{\partial y_1} dy_1, g_2(y_1, y_2) + \frac{\partial g_2}{\partial y_1} dy_1\right).$$

Similarly the coordinates of P_3 are approximately

$$\left(g_1(y_1, y_2) + \frac{\partial g_1}{\partial y_2} dy_2, g_2(y_1, y_2) + \frac{\partial g_2}{\partial y_2} dy_2\right).$$

Substituting these three coordinates in (2.4), we get for the area of S:

$$\begin{vmatrix} 1 & g_1(y_1, y_2) & g_2(y_1, y_2) \\ 1 & g_1(y_1, y_2) + \dfrac{\partial g_1}{\partial y_1} dy_1 & g_2(y_1, y_2) + \dfrac{\partial g_2}{\partial y_1} dy_1 \\ 1 & g_1(y_1, y_2) + \dfrac{\partial g_1}{\partial y_2} dy_2 & g_2(y_1, y_2) + \dfrac{\partial g_2}{\partial y_2} dy_2 \end{vmatrix}.$$

Expanding this determinant gives

$$\left(\frac{\partial g_1}{\partial y_1}\frac{\partial g_2}{\partial y_2} - \frac{\partial g_1}{\partial y_2}\frac{\partial g_2}{\partial y_1}\right) dy_1\, dy_2 = \begin{vmatrix} \dfrac{\partial g_1}{\partial y_1} & \dfrac{\partial g_2}{\partial y_1} \\ \dfrac{\partial g_1}{\partial y_2} & \dfrac{\partial g_2}{\partial y_2} \end{vmatrix} dy_1\, dy_2 . \qquad (2.5)$$

Substituting this for the area of S in (2.3) gives

$$p_y(y_1, y_2)\, dy_1\, dy_2 = p_x(x_1, x_2) \begin{vmatrix} \dfrac{\partial g_1}{\partial y_1} & \dfrac{\partial g_2}{\partial y_1} \\ \dfrac{\partial g_1}{\partial y_2} & \dfrac{\partial g_2}{\partial y_2} \end{vmatrix} dy_1\, dy_2$$

and

$$p_y(y_1, y_2) = p_x(g_1(y_1, y_2), g_2(y_1, y_2)) \begin{vmatrix} \dfrac{\partial g_1}{\partial y_1} & \dfrac{\partial g_2}{\partial y_1} \\ \dfrac{\partial g_1}{\partial y_2} & \dfrac{\partial g_2}{\partial y_2} \end{vmatrix} \qquad (2.6)$$

where the absolute value of the determinant is used.

12.3. The Bivariate Normal Distribution

In this section we shall postulate a certain model which will lead us to the bivariate normal distribution.

Let x_1, x_2 be independent normally distributed variables with zero means and unit variances. Let y'_1, y'_2 be linear functions of x_1, x_2 defined by constants η_i, l_{ij}:

$$\begin{aligned} y'_1 &= \eta_1 + l_{11}x_1 + l_{12}x_2 , \\ y'_2 &= \eta_2 + l_{21}x_1 + l_{22}x_2 . \end{aligned} \tag{3.1}$$

It will be more convenient to deal with $y_1 = y'_1 - \eta_1$, $y_2 = y'_2 - \eta_2$, since these new variables will have expected values zero. Thus y_1 and y_2 are functions of x_1 and x_2:

$$\begin{aligned} y_1 &= f_1(x_1, x_2) = l_{11}x_1 + l_{12}x_2 , \\ y_2 &= f_2(x_1, x_2) = l_{21}x_1 + l_{22}x_2 . \end{aligned} \tag{3.2}$$

The variables y_1, y_2 will be normally distributed with expectations zero, and

$$V[y_1] = l_{11}^2 + l_{12}^2, \qquad V[y_2] = l_{21}^2 + l_{22}^2 , \tag{3.3}$$

$$\begin{aligned} \text{Cov}[y_1, y_2] &= E[y_1y_2] - E[y_1]\,E[y_2] \\ &= E[l_{11}l_{21}x_1^2 + l_{12}l_{22}x_2^2 + l_{11}l_{22}x_1x_2 + l_{12}l_{21}x_1x_2] \\ &= l_{11}l_{21} + l_{12}l_{22} , \end{aligned} \tag{3.4}$$

since $E[x_i^2] = 1$, and since x_1, x_2 are independent, $E[x_1x_2] = E[x_1]\,E[x_2] = 0$.

We can solve the equations (3.2) to give the inverse functions of x in terms of y_1, y_2:

$$x_1 = g_1(y_1, y_2) = \frac{l_{22}y_1 - l_{12}y_2}{l_{11}l_{22} - l_{12}l_{21}} = \frac{l_{22}y_1 - l_{12}y_2}{\lambda} , \tag{3.5}$$

$$x_2 = g_2(y_1, y_2) = \frac{-l_{21}y_1 + l_{11}y_2}{l_{11}l_{22} - l_{12}l_{21}} = \frac{-l_{21}y_1 + l_{11}y_2}{\lambda} , \tag{3.6}$$

if we define

$$\lambda = l_{11}l_{22} - l_{12}l_{21} . \tag{3.7}$$

The random variables x_1, x_2 by definition are independent and $N(0, 1)$; so

$$\begin{aligned} p\{x_1, x_2\} = p\{x_1\}\,p\{x_2\} &= \frac{1}{\sqrt{2\pi}} \exp\left(\frac{-x_1^2}{2}\right) \cdot \frac{1}{\sqrt{2\pi}} \exp\left(\frac{-x_2^2}{2}\right) \\ &= \frac{1}{2\pi} \exp\left(-\frac{1}{2}(x_1^2 + x_2^2)\right). \end{aligned} \tag{3.8}$$

To get the distribution of (y_1, y_2) we use the result of the previous section (2.6). We need

$$\frac{\partial g_1}{\partial y_1} = \frac{l_{22}}{\lambda}, \qquad \frac{\partial g_2}{\partial y_1} = -\frac{l_{21}}{\lambda},$$
$$\frac{\partial g_1}{\partial y_2} = -\frac{l_{12}}{\lambda}, \qquad \frac{\partial g_2}{\partial y_2} = \frac{l_{11}}{\lambda};$$

so

$$\begin{vmatrix} \dfrac{\partial g_1}{\partial y_1} & \dfrac{\partial g_2}{\partial y_1} \\ \dfrac{\partial g_1}{\partial y_2} & \dfrac{\partial g_2}{\partial y_2} \end{vmatrix} = \frac{l_{22}}{\lambda}\cdot\frac{l_{11}}{\lambda} - \frac{(-l_{12})}{\lambda}\cdot\frac{(-l_{21})}{\lambda} = \frac{1}{\lambda}, \tag{3.9}$$

We now use (2.6):

$$p(y_1, y_2) = \frac{1}{2\pi}\exp\left\{-\frac{1}{2}\left[\left(\frac{l_{22}y_1 - l_{12}y_2}{\lambda}\right)^2 + \left(\frac{-l_{21}y_1 + l_{11}y_2}{\lambda}\right)^2\right]\right\}\frac{1}{\lambda}. \tag{3.10}$$

Define ρ as the correlation coefficient between y_1 and y_2:

$$\rho = \frac{\mathrm{Cov}[y_1, y_2]}{\sqrt{V[y_1]\,V[y_2]}} = \frac{l_{11}l_{21} + l_{12}l_{22}}{\sqrt{(l_{11}^2 + l_{12}^2)(l_{21}^2 + l_{22}^2)}}. \tag{3.11}$$

Let $V[y_1] = \sigma_1^2$, $V[y_2] = \sigma_2^2$: Then

$$\begin{aligned}\sigma_1^2\sigma_2^2(1-\rho^2) &= (l_{11}^2 + l_{12}^2)(l_{21}^2 + l_{22}^2)\left[1 - \frac{(l_{11}l_{21} + l_{12}l_{22})^2}{(l_{11}^2 + l_{12}^2)(l_{21}^2 + l_{22}^2)}\right] \\ &= (l_{11}l_{22} - l_{12}l_{21})^2 = \lambda^2,\end{aligned} \tag{3.12}$$

and the constant part of (3.10) outside the exponent is

$$\frac{1}{2\pi\lambda} = \frac{1}{2\pi\sigma_1\sigma_2\sqrt{1-\rho^2}}. \tag{3.13}$$

The exponent of (3.10) is

$$\begin{aligned}-\frac{1}{2\lambda^2}&\{(l_{22}^2 + l_{21}^2)y_1^2 - 2(l_{11}l_{21} + l_{12}l_{22})y_1y_2 + (l_{11}^2 + l_{12}^2)y_2^2\} \\ &= -\frac{1}{2\sigma_1^2\sigma_2^2(1-\rho^2)}(\sigma_2^2y_1^2 - 2\rho\sigma_1\sigma_2y_1y_2 + \sigma_1^2y_2^2) \\ &= -\frac{1}{2(1-\rho^2)}\left(\frac{y_1^2}{\sigma_1^2} - \frac{2\rho y_1y_2}{\sigma_1\sigma_2} + \frac{y_2^2}{\sigma_2^2}\right).\end{aligned} \tag{3.14}$$

Substituting in (3.10),

$$p(y_1, y_2) = \frac{1}{2\pi\sigma_1\sigma_2\sqrt{1-\rho^2}} \exp\left\{-\frac{1}{2(1-\rho^2)}\left[\left(\frac{y_1}{\sigma_1}\right)^2 - 2\rho\left(\frac{y_1}{\sigma_1}\right)\left(\frac{y_2}{\sigma_2}\right) + \left(\frac{y_2}{\sigma_2}\right)^2\right]\right\}. \quad (3.15)$$

Finally, we may make the further transformation back to y_1', y_2' which is very simple since the determinant is merely 1:

$$p(y_1', y_2') = \frac{1}{2\pi\sigma_1\sigma_2\sqrt{1-\rho^2}} \exp\left\{-\frac{1}{2(1-\rho^2)}\left[\left(\frac{y_1'-\eta_1}{\sigma_1}\right)^2 - 2\rho\left(\frac{y_1'-\eta_1}{\sigma_1}\right)\left(\frac{y_2'-\eta_2}{\sigma_2}\right) + \left(\frac{y_2'-\eta_2}{\sigma_2}\right)^2\right]\right\}, \quad (3.16)$$

and this is the general form for the bivariate normal distribution.

We can note at once an important result. If the covariance of y_1', y_2' is zero, then $\rho = 0$, and (3.16) becomes

$$\begin{aligned} p(y_1', y_2') &= \frac{1}{2\pi\sigma_1\sigma_2} \exp\left\{-\frac{1}{2}\left[\left(\frac{y_1'-\eta_1}{\sigma_1}\right)^2 + \left(\frac{y_2'-\eta_2}{\sigma_2}\right)^2\right]\right\} \\ &= \frac{1}{\sqrt{2\pi}\,\sigma_1} \exp\left[-\frac{1}{2}\left(\frac{y_1'-\eta_1}{\sigma_1}\right)^2\right] \cdot \frac{1}{\sqrt{2\pi}\,\sigma_2} \exp\left[-\frac{1}{2}\left(\frac{y_2'-\eta_2}{\sigma_2}\right)^2\right] \\ &= p\{y_1'\}\, p\{y_2'\}; \end{aligned} \quad (3.17)$$

so under this circumstance y_1' and y_2' are independent. This is the result which was assumed several times in the discussion in Sections 8.4 and 8.5.

12.4. Some Properties of the Bivariate Normal Distribution

The general form is given in (3.16). Just as with the univariate normal distribution we found it convenient to have a standardized form, so it will be here. We define new variables

$$u_1 = f_1(y_1', y_2') = \frac{y_1' - \eta_1}{\sigma_1}, \qquad u_2 = f_2(y_1', y_2') = \frac{y_2' - \eta_2}{\sigma_2},$$

with inverse functions

$$y_1' = g_1(u_1, u_2) = u_1\sigma_1 + \eta_1, \qquad y_2' = g_2(u_1, u_2) = u_2\sigma_2 + \eta_2,$$

so that

$$\frac{\partial g_1}{\partial u_1} = \sigma_1, \qquad \frac{\partial g_1}{\partial u_2} = 0, \qquad \frac{\partial g_2}{\partial u_1} = 0, \qquad \frac{\partial g_2}{\partial u_2} = \sigma_2.$$

The probability density of (u_1, u_2) will be, using (2.6),

$$p(u_1, u_2) = \frac{1}{2\pi\sigma_1\sigma_2\sqrt{1-\rho^2}} \exp\left[-\frac{1}{2(1-\rho^2)}(u_1^2 - 2\rho u_1 u_2 + u_2^2)\right]\sigma_1\sigma_2$$
$$= \frac{1}{2\pi\sqrt{1-\rho^2}} \exp\left[-\frac{1}{2(1-\rho^2)}(u_1^2 - 2\rho u_1 u_2 + u_2^2)\right]. \tag{4.1}$$

It will be convenient to use the symbol $\phi(u_1, u_2)$ for this standardized form. Of course, $\phi(u_1, u_2)$ is a function of ρ.

In studying the properties of the standardized bivariate normal distribution (4.1), it will be convenient to make a further pair of transformations. We define new variables

$$u_1' = f_1(u_1, u_2) = u_1 ,$$
$$u_2' = u_{2.1} = f_2(u_1, u_2) = \frac{u_2 - \rho u_1}{\sqrt{1-\rho^2}} .$$

The inverse functions are

$$u_1 = g_1(u_1', u_2') = u_1' ,$$
$$u_2 = g_2(u_1', u_2') = \rho u_1' + \sqrt{1-\rho^2}\,u_2' ,$$

so that

$$\frac{\partial g_1}{\partial u_1} = 1, \qquad \frac{\partial g_1}{\partial u_2} = 0, \qquad \frac{\partial g_2}{\partial u_1} = \rho, \qquad \frac{\partial g_2}{\partial u_2} = \sqrt{1-\rho^2},$$

and the determinant is

$$\begin{vmatrix} \dfrac{\partial g_1}{\partial u_1'} & \dfrac{\partial g_2}{\partial u_1'} \\ \dfrac{\partial g_1}{\partial u_2'} & \dfrac{\partial g_2}{\partial u_2'} \end{vmatrix} = \begin{vmatrix} 1 & \rho \\ 0 & \sqrt{1-\rho^2} \end{vmatrix} = \sqrt{1-\rho^2}. \tag{4.2}$$

Also

$$u_1^2 - 2\rho u_1 u_2 + u_2^2 = u_1'^2 - 2\rho u_1'(\rho u_1' + \sqrt{1-\rho^2}\,u_2') + (\rho u_1' + \sqrt{1-\rho^2}\,u_2')^2$$
$$= (1-\rho^2)(u_1'^2 + u_2'^2). \tag{4.3}$$

We now write down the probability density of (u_1', u_2'), using (2.6) again:

$$p\{u_1', u_2'\} = \frac{1}{2\pi\sqrt{1-\rho^2}} \exp\left[-\frac{1}{2}(u_1'^2 + u_2'^2)\right]\sqrt{1-\rho^2}$$
$$= \frac{1}{\sqrt{2\pi}} \exp\left(-\frac{u_1'^2}{2}\right) \frac{1}{\sqrt{2\pi}} \exp\left(-\frac{u_2'^2}{2}\right). \tag{4.4}$$

Thus u_1', u_2' are independent. We get the marginal distribution of u_1' by integrating $p\{u_1', u_2'\}$ over u_2':

$$p\{u_1'\} = \int_{-\infty}^{\infty} p\{u_1', u_2'\}\, du_2'$$
$$= \frac{1}{\sqrt{2\pi}} \exp\left(-\frac{u_1'^2}{2}\right) \int_{-\infty}^{\infty} \frac{1}{\sqrt{2\pi}} \exp\left(-\frac{u_2'^2}{2}\right) du_2' = \frac{1}{\sqrt{2\pi}} \exp\left(-\frac{u_1'^2}{2}\right), \tag{4.5}$$

since the integral is just the integral of a unit normal distribution which must equal 1. Hence the marginal distribution of $u_1' = u_1$ is a unit normal distribution, and so the marginal distribution of y_1' will be a normal distribution with mean η_1 and variance σ_1^2. The same argument shows that the marginal distribution of y_2' is normal with mean η_2 and variance σ_2^2.

The conditional distribution of u_2, given u_1, is

$$p\{u_2|u_1\} = \frac{p\{u_1, u_2\}}{p\{u_1\}} = \frac{\dfrac{1}{2\pi\sqrt{1-\rho^2}} \exp\left[-\dfrac{1}{2(1-\rho^2)}(u_1^2 - 2\rho u_1 u_2 + u_2^2)\right]}{\dfrac{1}{\sqrt{2\pi}} \exp\left(-\dfrac{u_1^2}{2}\right)}$$
$$= \frac{1}{\sqrt{2\pi}\sqrt{1-\rho^2}} \exp\left[-\frac{1}{2}\left(\frac{u_2 - \rho u_1}{\sqrt{1-\rho^2}}\right)^2\right], \tag{4.6}$$

which can be regarded as a normal distribution of u_2 with mean ρu_1 and variance $(1 - \rho^2)$. We now transform this by defining $x_2 = f_2(u_1, u_2) = u_2\sigma_2 + \xi_2$, so that the inverse function is $u_2 = g_2(x_1, x_2) = (x_2 - \xi_2)/\sigma_2$, and $dg_2/dx_2 = 1/\sigma_2$. We also define $x_1 = u_1\sigma_1 + \xi_1$. Then (4.6) becomes

$$p\{x_2|x_1\} = \frac{1}{\sqrt{2\pi}\sqrt{1-\rho^2}} \exp\left\{-\frac{1}{2}\left[\frac{\dfrac{x_2 - \xi_2}{\sigma_2} - \rho\left(\dfrac{x_1 - \xi_1}{\sigma_1}\right)}{\sqrt{1-\rho^2}}\right]^2\right\} \frac{1}{\sigma_2}$$
$$= \frac{1}{\sqrt{2\pi}\,\sigma_2\sqrt{1-\rho^2}} \exp\left[-\frac{1}{2}\left\{\frac{x_2 - \left[\xi_2 + \rho\left(\dfrac{\sigma_2}{\sigma_1}\right)(x_1 - \xi_1)\right]}{\sigma_2\sqrt{1-\rho^2}}\right\}^2\right], \tag{4.7}$$

which can be regarded as a normal distribution of a random variable x_2 with mean

$$E[x_2|x_1] = \xi_2 + \rho\left(\frac{\sigma_2}{\sigma_1}\right)(x_1 - \xi_1), \tag{4.8}$$

and variance

$$V[x_2|x_1] = \sigma_2^2(1 - \rho^2). \tag{4.9}$$

The system is, of course, symmetric in x_1 and x_2, and so we have

$$E[x_1|x_2] = \xi_1 + \rho\left(\frac{\sigma_1}{\sigma_2}\right)(x_2 - \xi_2), \tag{4.10}$$

$$V[x_1|x_2] = \sigma_1^2(1 - \rho^2). \tag{4.11}$$

Thus the means of the conditional distributions are linear functions of the other variable, and the variances are constants. We recall that in Section 11.2 our model for linear regression was that y was normally distributed around its expected value with a constant variance, and this expected value was a simple linear function of another variable x. Therefore the conditions for a conditional regression analysis of x_1 on x_2, and for a conditional regression analysis of x_2 on x_1, are both satisfied. Here there are two true regression lines, (4.8) and (4.10), with regression coefficients

$$\beta_{x_2|x_1} = \rho\left(\frac{\sigma_2}{\sigma_1}\right), \qquad \beta_{x_1|x_2} = \rho\left(\frac{\sigma_1}{\sigma_2}\right). \tag{4.12}$$

The product of the two regression coefficients is ρ^2. To find the point of intersection of the two regression lines, we can substitute x_2 from (4.8) into (4.10) which gives $x_1 - \xi_1 = \rho^2(x_1 - \xi_1)$, which is only true if $x_1 = \xi_1$, and similarly we obtain $x_2 = \xi_2$. The point of intersection is therefore (ξ_1, ξ_2).

We find the angle between the two regression lines as follows. In Figure 12.3,

$$\beta_{x_1|x_2} = \tan A, \qquad \beta_{x_2|x_1} = \tan C, \tag{4.13}$$

and B is the angle between the two regression lines. For three angles, say A, $(B + 90°)$, and C, whose sum is 180°,

$$\tan A + \tan(B + 90°) + \tan C = \tan A \tan(B + 90°) \tan C,$$

whence

$$\tan(B + 90°) = \frac{\tan A + \tan C}{\tan A \tan C - 1}$$

$$= \frac{\rho(\sigma_1/\sigma_2) + \rho(\sigma_2/\sigma_1)}{\rho(\sigma_1/\sigma_2)\rho(\sigma_2/\sigma_1) - 1} = \frac{\rho}{\rho^2 - 1}\,\frac{\sigma_1^2 + \sigma_2^2}{\sigma_1\sigma_2};$$

so

$$\tan B = -\frac{1}{\tan(B + 90°)} = \frac{1 - \rho^2}{\rho}\,\frac{\sigma_1\sigma_2}{\sigma_1^2 + \sigma_2^2}. \tag{4.14}$$

When $\rho = 1$, $\tan B = 0$, and so the two regression lines are identical. When $\rho = 0$, $\tan B = \infty$, and so the lines are at right angles to each other.

We can write (4.9) and (4.11) as

$$\frac{V[x_2|x_1]}{V[x_2]} = 1 - \rho^2 = \frac{V[x_1|x_2]}{V[x_1]}. \tag{4.15}$$

Thus, when $\rho = 1$, the conditional variance $V[x_2|x_1] = 0$, and, when $\rho = 0$, the conditional variance equals the unconditional variance. Thus ρ^2 can be regarded as measuring the fraction of the variance of x_2 "explained" by the regression on x_1, and vice versa. This is one of the most useful interpretations of the correlation coefficient.

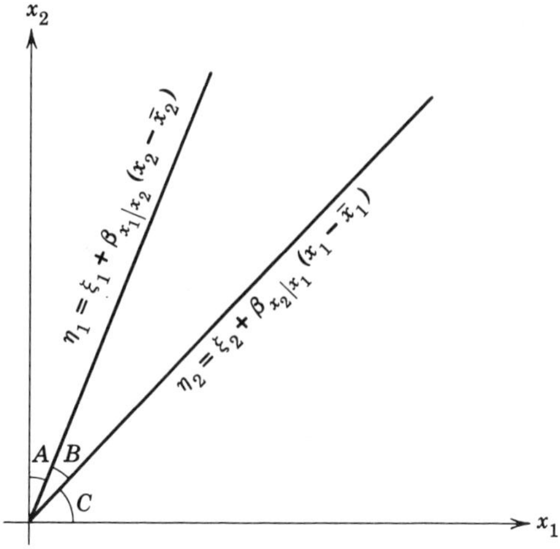

Figure 12.3

The nature of the surface generated by the bivariate normal distribution can be seen from the equation for its probability density (3.16). If we place this equal to a constant, this implies

$$\left(\frac{y_1 - \eta_1}{\sigma_1}\right)^2 - 2\rho\left(\frac{y_1 - \eta_1}{\sigma_1}\right)\left(\frac{y_2 - \eta_2}{\sigma_2}\right) + \left(\frac{y_2 - \eta_2}{\sigma_2}\right)^2 = \text{constant}, \tag{4.16}$$

dropping the primes from the y's. This equation defines ellipses, for different values of the constant, at an angle to the axes. When $\rho = 0$, this equation becomes

$$\left(\frac{y_1 - \eta_1}{\sigma_1}\right)^2 + \left(\frac{y_2 - \eta_2}{\sigma_2}\right)^2 = \text{constant}, \tag{4.17}$$

which defines ellipses whose principal axes are parallel to the (y_1, y_2) axes.

We can use the results of this section to indicate the proof of an important theorem we assumed in Section 1.22, namely, that any linear combination of independent random normal variables is itself normally distributed. To prove this for n random variables, it will be sufficient to prove it for two random variables. The proof is along the following lines.

In (3.2) we defined y_1 as $(l_{11}x_1 + l_{12}x_2)$ where l_{11} and l_{12} are constants and x_1 and x_2 are independent random variables normally distributed with means zero and unit variances. In (3.15) we found the joint density function $p\{y_1, y_2\}$, where y_2 was another linear combination $(l_{21}x_1 + l_{22}x_2)$. We defined u_1 as $(y_1' - \eta_1)/\sigma_1$, which is equal to y_1/σ_1. We subsequently defined u_1' as u_1, and found in (4.5) that u_1' was normally distributed with mean zero and unit variance. It follows that the linear combination $l_{11}x_1 + l_{12}x_2 = y_1 = u_1\sigma_1$ will be normally distributed, with zero mean and variance $\sigma_1^2 = l_{11}^2 + l_{12}^2$. The arguments are changed only in detail if, instead of being distributed $N(0, 1)$, the x_i are distributed $N(\xi_i, \sigma_{x_i}^2)$.

12.5. Estimation of the Parameters of the Bivariate Normal Distribution

In this section we will use the method of maximum likelihood to estimate the parameters of the bivariate normal distribution. We saw in (2.3.9) that the maximum likelihood estimator $\hat{\sigma}^2$ of the variance of a univariate normal distribution was $\sum_i^n (x_i - \bar{x})^2/n$. In an expectation of the same result for the bivariate case we will define

$$s_i^2 = \frac{1}{n}\sum_\nu^n (x_{i\nu} - \bar{x}_i)^2, \qquad i = 1, 2, \tag{5.1}$$

and

$$s_{12} = \frac{1}{n}\sum_\nu^n (x_{1\nu} - \bar{x}_1)(x_{2\nu} - \bar{x}_2). \tag{5.2}$$

The likelihood, $L = \prod_i^n p\{x_{1\nu}, x_{2\nu}\}$, where

$$p\{x_{1\nu}, x_{2\nu}\} = \frac{1}{2\pi\sigma_1\sigma_2\sqrt{1-\rho^2}} \exp\left\{-\frac{1}{2(1-\rho^2)}\left[\left(\frac{x_{1\nu}-\xi_1}{\sigma_1}\right)^2 - 2\rho\left(\frac{x_{1\nu}-\xi_1}{\sigma_1}\right)\left(\frac{x_{2\nu}-\xi_2}{\sigma_2}\right) + \left(\frac{x_{2\nu}-\xi_2}{\sigma_2}\right)^2\right]\right\} \tag{5.3}$$

is

$$L = \left(\frac{1}{2\pi\sigma_1\sigma_2\sqrt{1-\rho^2}}\right)^n \exp\left\{-\frac{1}{2(1-\rho^2)}\sum_\nu^n\left[\left(\frac{x_{1\nu}-\xi_1}{\sigma_1}\right)^2 - 2\rho\left(\frac{x_{1\nu}-\xi_1}{\sigma_1}\right)\left(\frac{x_{2\nu}-\xi_2}{\sigma_2}\right) + \left(\frac{x_{2\nu}-\xi_2}{\sigma_2}\right)^2\right]\right\}. \tag{5.4}$$

As is usually the case, it is easier to maximize the logarithm of the likelihood:

$$\log L = -n \log(2\pi\sigma_1\sigma_2\sqrt{1-\rho^2}) - \frac{1}{2(1-\rho^2)}$$

$$\sum_\nu^n \left[\frac{(x_{1\nu}-\xi_1)^2}{\sigma_1^2} - 2\rho\frac{(x_{1\nu}-\xi_1)(x_{2\nu}-\xi_2)}{\sigma_1\sigma_2} + \frac{(x_{2\nu}-\xi_2)^2}{\sigma_2^2}\right]. \tag{5.5}$$

Differentiating with respect to ξ_1 gives

$$\frac{\partial \log L}{\partial \xi_1} = \frac{1}{2(1-\rho^2)}$$

$$\left\{\frac{1}{\sigma_1^2}\sum_\nu^n (x_{1\nu}-\xi_1)\cdot 2\cdot(-1) - \frac{2\rho}{\sigma_1\sigma_2}\sum_\nu^n (x_{2\nu}-\xi_2)\cdot(-1)\right\},$$

and we get a similar expression on differentiating with respect to ξ_2. Equating to zero gives two simultaneous equations,

$$-\frac{1}{\sigma_1^2}\sum_\nu^n (x_{1\nu}-\hat{\xi}_1) + \frac{\rho}{\sigma_1\sigma_2}\sum_\nu^n (x_{2\nu}-\hat{\xi}_2) = 0$$

$$\frac{\rho}{\sigma_1\sigma_2}\sum_\nu^n (x_{1\nu}-\hat{\xi}_1) - \frac{1}{\sigma_2^2}\sum_\nu^n (x_{2\nu}-\hat{\xi}_2) = 0$$

which lead to the solutions

$$\hat{\xi}_i = \frac{1}{n}\sum_\nu^n x_{i\nu} = \bar{x}_i, \qquad i = 1, 2. \tag{5.6}$$

We next differentiate $\log L$ with respect to σ_1:

$$\frac{\partial \log L}{\partial \sigma_1} = -\frac{n}{\sigma_1} - \frac{1}{2(1-\rho^2)}$$

$$\left[\frac{\sum_\nu^n (x_{1\nu}-\xi_1)^2(-2)}{\sigma_1^3} - 2\rho\frac{\sum_\nu^n (x_{1\nu}-\xi_1)(x_{2\nu}-\xi_2)(-1)}{\sigma_1^2\sigma_2}\right]. \tag{5.7}$$

Equating to zero to get the maximum-likelihood estimators gives

$$\frac{\sum_\nu^n (x_{1\nu}-\hat{\xi}_1)^2}{\hat{\sigma}_1^2} = \frac{\sum_\nu^n (x_{1\nu}-\hat{\xi}_1)(x_{2\nu}-\hat{\xi}_2)}{\hat{\sigma}_1\hat{\sigma}_2} + n(1-\hat{\rho}^2). \tag{5.8}$$

We now substitute $\bar{x}_1$ for $\hat{\xi}_1$, $\bar{x}_2$ for $\hat{\xi}_2$, and introduce the definitions (5.1) and (5.2) to get

$$\frac{s_1^2}{\hat{\sigma}_1^2} = \frac{\hat{\rho} s_{12}}{\hat{\sigma}_1 \hat{\sigma}_2} + (1 - \hat{\rho}^2). \tag{5.9}$$

Obviously, by differentiating log L with respect to σ_2 and proceeding similarly we will get

$$\frac{s_2^2}{\hat{\sigma}_2^2} = \frac{\hat{\rho} s_{12}}{\hat{\sigma}_1 \hat{\sigma}_2} + (1 - \hat{\rho}^2). \tag{5.10}$$

Combining (5.9) with (5.10) we get $\hat{\sigma}_2 = \hat{\sigma}_1(s_2/s_1)$: Substituting this in (5.9) and solving for $\hat{\sigma}_1^2$ gives

$$\hat{\sigma}_1^2 = \frac{s_1}{s_2} \cdot \frac{s_1 s_2 - \hat{\rho} s_{12}}{1 - \hat{\rho}^2}. \tag{5.11}$$

Similarly,

$$\hat{\sigma}_2^2 = \frac{s_2}{s_1} \cdot \frac{s_1 s_2 - \hat{\rho} s_{12}}{1 - \hat{\rho}^2}. \tag{5.12}$$

However, these solutions for $\hat{\sigma}_1^2$ and $\hat{\sigma}_2^2$ still contain $\hat{\rho}^2$ whose solution has not yet been obtained. We now differentiate log L with respect to ρ:

$$\frac{\partial \log L}{\partial \rho} = \frac{n\rho}{1 - \rho^2} + \frac{1}{1 - \rho^2} \frac{\sum_\nu^n (x_{1\nu} - \xi_1)(x_{2\nu} - \xi_2)}{\sigma_1 \sigma_2}$$
$$- \frac{\rho}{(1 - \rho^2)^2} \left[\frac{\sum_\nu^n (x_{1\nu} - \xi_1)^2}{\sigma_1^2} - 2\rho \frac{\sum_\nu^n (x_{1\nu} - \xi_1)(x_{2\nu} - \xi_2)}{\sigma_1 \sigma_2} + \frac{\sum_\nu^n (x_{2\nu} - \xi_2)^2}{\sigma_2^2} \right]. \tag{5.13}$$

Equating to zero to give the maximum-likelihood solutions, substituting $\bar{x}_1$ for $\hat{\xi}_1$ and $\bar{x}_2$ for $\hat{\xi}_2$, and introducing the definitions (5.1) and (5.2), we get, on multiplying by $(1 - \hat{\rho}^2)/n$,

$$\hat{\rho} + \frac{s_{12}}{\hat{\sigma}_1 \hat{\sigma}_2} - \frac{\hat{\rho}}{1 - \hat{\rho}^2} \left(\frac{s_1^2}{\hat{\sigma}_1^2} - 2\hat{\rho} \frac{s_1 s_2}{\hat{\sigma}_1 \hat{\sigma}_2} + \frac{s_2^2}{\hat{\sigma}_2^2} \right) = 0. \tag{5.14}$$

Substituting for $\hat{\sigma}_1$ and $\hat{\sigma}_2$ from (5.11) and (5.12) gives the maximum-likelihood solution for ρ:

$$\hat{\rho} = \frac{s_{12}}{\sqrt{s_1^2 s_2^2}}. \tag{5.15}$$

Substituting this value of $\hat{\rho}$ in (5.11) and (5.12) gives the maximum-likelihood solutions for σ_1^2 and σ_2^2:

$$\hat{\sigma}_1^2 = s_1^2, \qquad \hat{\sigma}_2^2 = s_2^2. \tag{5.16}$$

We know that the bivariate normal distribution (5.3) when integrated over x_2 gives a marginal distribution in x_1 which is normal with parameters ξ_1, σ_1^2, and we further know that (5.1) is a biased estimator of σ_i^2, s_i^2 having an expected value $(n-1)\,\sigma_i^2/n$. The unbiased estimator, say $s_i'^2$, is

$$s_i'^2 = \frac{1}{n-1}\sum_{\nu}^{n}(x_{i\nu} - \bar{x}_i)^2 \cdot \tag{5.17}$$

In the same way we might expect that s_{12} as defined in (5.2) is a biased estimator of the covariance. To check on this we note that

$$\begin{aligned} ns_{12} &= \sum_{\nu}^{n}(x_{1\nu} - \bar{x}_1)(x_{2\nu} - \bar{x}_2) \\ &= \sum_{\nu}^{n}[(x_{1\nu} - \xi_1) - (\bar{x}_1 - \xi_1)][(x_{2\nu} - \xi_2) - (\bar{x}_2 - \xi_2)] \\ &= \sum_{\nu}^{n}(x_{1\nu} - \xi_1)(x_{2\nu} - \xi_2) - n(\bar{x}_1 - \xi_1)(\bar{x}_2 - \xi_2); \end{aligned}$$

so

$$\begin{aligned} E[ns_{12}] &= \sum_{\nu}^{n}E[(x_{1\nu} - \xi_1)(x_{2\nu} - \xi_2)] - nE[(\bar{x}_1 - \xi_1)(\bar{x}_2 - \xi_2)] \\ &= n\,\mathrm{Cov}[x_1, x_2] - n\,\mathrm{Cov}[\bar{x}_1, \bar{x}_2]. \end{aligned} \tag{5.18}$$

Now

$$\begin{aligned} \mathrm{Cov}[\bar{x}_1, \bar{x}_2] &= E[\bar{x}_1\bar{x}_2] - E[\bar{x}_1]\,E[\bar{x}_2] \\ &= E\left[\left(\frac{1}{n}\sum_{i}^{n}x_{1i}\right)\left(\frac{1}{n}\sum_{j}^{n}x_{2j}\right)\right] - E\left[\frac{1}{n}\sum_{i}^{n}x_{1i}\right]E\left[\frac{1}{n}\sum_{j}^{n}x_{2j}\right] \\ &= \frac{1}{n^2}E\left[\sum_{i}^{n}x_{1i}x_{2i}\right] + \frac{1}{n^2}E\left[\sum_{i}^{n}\sum_{\substack{j \\ i\neq j}}^{n}x_{1i}x_{2j}\right] - \frac{1}{n^2}\left(\sum_{i}^{n}E[x_{1i}]\right)\left(\sum_{j}^{n}E[x_{2j}]\right) \\ &= \frac{1}{n^2}\sum_{i}^{n}E[x_{1i}x_{2i}] + \frac{1}{n^2}\sum_{i}^{n}\sum_{\substack{j \\ i\neq j}}^{n}E[x_{1i}]\,E[x_{2j}] \\ &\qquad - \frac{1}{n^2}\sum_{i}^{n}E[x_{1i}]\,E[x_{2i}] - \frac{1}{n^2}\sum_{i}^{n}\sum_{\substack{j \\ i\neq j}}^{n}E[x_{1i}]\,E[x_{2j}] \\ &= \frac{1}{n}\{E[x_{1i}x_{2i}] - E[x_{1i}]\,E[x_{2i}]\} = \frac{1}{n}\mathrm{Cov}[x_1, x_2]. \end{aligned} \tag{5.19}$$

Substituting this in (5.18), we get

$$E[s_{12}] = \frac{n-1}{n}\mathrm{Cov}[x_1, x_2]\,. \tag{5.20}$$

Thus s_{12} as defined in (5.2) is a biased estimator of the covariance, but we can define s'_{12} as

$$s'_{12} = \frac{1}{n-1}\sum_{\nu}^{n}(x_{1\nu} - \bar{x}_1)(x_{2\nu} - \bar{x}_2)\,, \tag{5.21}$$

and this will be an unbiased estimator.

As far as ρ is concerned, it makes no difference whether we use s_{12}, s_i^2, or s'_{12}, $s_i'^2$ in (5.15) as the denominators, n and $(n-1)$, respectively, cancel out, and in both cases we get as the maximum-likelihood estimator for ρ, usually denoted by r,

$$r = \frac{\sum_{\nu}^{n}(x_{1\nu} - \bar{x}_1)(x_{2\nu} - \bar{x}_2)}{\sqrt{\sum_{\nu}^{n}(x_{1\nu} - \bar{x}_1)^2 \sum_{\nu}^{n}(x_{2\nu} - \bar{x}_2)^2}}\,. \tag{5.22}$$

However, it can be shown that

$$E[r] = \rho - \frac{\rho(1-\rho^2)}{2n} + \cdots,$$

i.e., r is a biased estimator of ρ except when $\rho = 0$.

The estimated regression coefficients can be obtained by the standard regression techniques. Alternatively, and it comes to the same thing, we can estimate $\beta_{x_2|x_1}$ as $b_{x_2|x_1} = r\left(\frac{s_2}{s_1}\right)$. Substituting from (5.22) for r and from (5.17) for s_1^2 and s_2^2 gives

$$b_{x_2|x_1} = \frac{\sum_{\nu}^{n}(x_{1\nu} - \bar{x}_1)(x_{2\nu} - \bar{x}_2)}{\sum_{\nu}^{n}(x_{1\nu} - \bar{x}_1)^2} \tag{5.23}$$

which is identical with (11.2.11).

The usual regression estimate for the residual variance about the regression line is

$$s^2_{x_2|x_1} = \frac{1}{n-2}\left\{\sum_{\nu}^{n}(x_{2\nu} - \bar{x}_2)^2 - \frac{[\sum_{\nu}^{n}(x_{2\nu} - \bar{x}_2)(x_{1\nu} - \bar{x}_1)]^2}{\sum_{\nu}^{n}(x_{1\nu} - \bar{x}_1)^2}\right\}$$

$$= \frac{n-1}{n-2}\left[\frac{\sum_{\nu}^{n}(x_{2\nu} - \bar{x}_2)^2}{n-1}\right]\left\{1 - \left[\frac{\sum_{\nu}^{n}(x_{1\nu} - \bar{x}_1)(x_{2\nu} - \bar{x}_2)}{\sqrt{\sum_{\nu}^{n}(x_{1\nu} - \bar{x}_1)^2 \sum_{\nu}^{n}(x_{2\nu} - \bar{x}_2)^2}}\right]^2\right\}$$

$$= \frac{n-1}{n-2}\, s_2^2(1 - r^2); \tag{5.24}$$

so the insertion of sample estimators into (4.9), $V[x_2|x_1] = \sigma_2^2(1 - \rho^2)$ would give a biased estimator for $V[x_2|x_1]$.

12.6. Tests of Significance for the Correlation Coefficient

We know that b is normally distributed around β with a variance given by (11.2.14), and so, conditionally on the observed values of x_1,

$$\frac{b_{x_2|x_1} - \beta_{x_2|x_1}}{s_{x_2|x_1} \Big/ \sqrt{\sum_{\nu}^{n} (x_{1\nu} - \bar{x}_1)^2}} \sim t(n-2) .$$

The null hypothesis that $\beta_{x_2|x_1} = 0$ is therefore tested by calculating

$$\frac{b_{x_2|x_1}}{s_{x_2|x_1} \Big/ \sqrt{\sum_{\nu}^{n} (x_{1\nu} - \bar{x}_1)^2}} = \frac{r(s_2/s_1)}{\sqrt{\left(\frac{n-1}{n-2}\right) s_2^2(1 - r^2)/(n-1)s_1^2}} = \frac{r\sqrt{n-2}}{\sqrt{1-r^2}} . \tag{6.1}$$

Under the null hypothesis that $\beta_{x_2|x_1} = 0$, this will be distributed as $t(n-2)$. But the null hypothesis that $\beta_{x_2|x_1} = 0$ is the same as the null hypothesis that $\rho = 0$. Thus (6.1) referred to the t table with $(n - 2)$ degrees of freedom is a test of the null hypothesis that $\rho = 0$.

Alternatively we can use a very good approximation due to Fisher:

$$z = \frac{1}{2} \log_e \left(\frac{1+r}{1-r}\right) = 1.1513 \log_{10} \left(\frac{1+r}{1-r}\right) \tag{6.2}$$

is approximately normally distributed about

$$\zeta = \frac{1}{2} \log_e \left(\frac{1+\rho}{1-\rho}\right)$$

with variance

$$V[z] \simeq \frac{1}{n-3} . \tag{6.3}$$

Thus, under the null hypothesis that $\rho = 0$, $z\sqrt{n-3}$ is a unit normal deviate. Also, the null hypothesis that two independent sample correlation coefficients come from the same population ρ can be tested by referring

$$\frac{z_1 - z_2}{\sqrt{1/(n_1 - 3) + 1/(n_2 - 3)}} .$$

to tables of the normal distribution.

12.7. The Effects of Errors of Measurement

The conditional variances $V[x_2|x_1]$ and $V[x_1|x_2]$, being equal to $(1 - \rho^2)\, V[x_2]$ and $(1 - \rho^2)\, V[x_1]$, are an essential part of the nature of a bivariate normal distribution and represent a property of the population under study. For example, if u, v are the girth and weight of a hog, the variation of u about its regression line on v is a property of this population of hogs. However, u, v are not directly observable: We can only measure them with a certain degree of accuracy; i.e., we observe x', y' defined as

$$x' = u + d \tag{7.1}$$

$$y' = v + e \tag{7.2}$$

where d, e are normally distributed about zero with variance σ_d^2, σ_e^2. We assume that the errors of measurement are independent of each other and of u and v; i.e.,

$$\text{Cov}[d, e] = \text{Cov}[d, u] = \text{Cov}[d, v] = \text{Cov}[e, u] = \text{Cov}[e, v] = 0. \tag{7.3}$$

For convenience, suppose that u, v both have expected values zero. Then the expected values of the observed variables x', y' are both zero, and

$$\begin{aligned} V[x'] &= V[u] + V[d] \\ V[y'] &= V[v] + V[e] \\ \text{Cov}[x', y'] &= E[x'y'] - E[x']\, E[y'] \\ &= E[uv] + E[de] + E[ue] + E[vd] \\ &= E[uv] - E[u]\, E[v] = \text{Cov}[u, v]. \end{aligned} \tag{7.4}$$

The correlation coefficient between the observed variables x', y' is

$$\begin{aligned} \rho_{x'y'} &= \frac{\text{Cov}[x', y']}{\sqrt{V[x']\, V[y']}} = \frac{\text{Cov}[u, v]}{\sqrt{(V[u] + V[d])(V[v] + V[e])}} \\ &= \frac{\rho_{uv}}{\sqrt{(1 + V[d]/V[u])(1 + V[e]/V[v])}} \end{aligned} \tag{7.5}$$

since $\rho_{uv} = \text{Cov}[u, v]/\sqrt{V[u]\, V[v]}$. We see from (7.5) that, if there are no errors of measurement, then of course $\rho_{x'y'} = \rho_{uv}$ since $x' = u$, $y' = v$. However, as the errors of measurement become appreciable, the correlation between the observed variables becomes smaller than it would have been in the absence of errors of measurement: i.e., $\rho_{x'y'} < \rho_{uv}$.

The regression coefficients are also affected. From (4.12),

$$\beta_{u|v} = \rho_{uv} \sqrt{\frac{V[u]}{V[v]}}, \tag{7.6}$$

$$\text{and} \quad \beta_{x'|y'} = \rho_{x'y'}\sqrt{\frac{V[x']}{V[y']}} = \rho_{uv} \cdot \frac{\sqrt{V[x']/V[v']}}{\sqrt{(1 + V[d]/V[u])(1 + V[e]/V[v])}}$$

$$= \frac{\beta_{u|v}}{(1 + V[e]/V[v])}. \tag{7.7}$$

Therefore, if $y' = v + e$ is measured with an appreciable error, then the regression coefficient of the observed variables x' on y' is a biased estimate of the regression coefficient of the true variables u on v. Note, however, that, if v is measured without error, then

$$\beta_{x'|y'=v} = \beta_{u|y'=v}; \tag{7.8}$$

i.e., the presence of error in $u = x' - d$ does not lead to a bias in this regression coefficient. The additional variance in x' as compared with u will increase the variance of the sample estimate, of course, but no bias is introduced.

12.8. The Berkson Model for Linear Regression

Berkson [1] pointed out a situation in which an unbiased estimate of a regression coefficient can be obtained even in the presence of errors in the independent variable. His model was reviewed by Lindley [2]. Suppose that there is a true linear relation

$$v = \alpha + \beta u, \tag{8.1}$$

where α and β are constants. As in the previous section, we can only observe

$$x' = u + d \tag{8.2}$$

$$y' = v + e; \tag{8.3}$$

so $v = y' - e$, $u = x' - d$. Substituting in (8.1),

$$y' - e = \alpha + \beta(x' - d)$$

or

$$y' = \alpha + \beta x' + (e - \beta d). \tag{8.4}$$

This appears at first sight to be a standard regression model, y' being given by a linear equation $(\alpha + \beta x')$ plus a random error $(e - \beta d)$. Unfortunately the random error $(e - \beta d)$ is not independent of the independent variable x', since $x' = u + d$; and, since they both contain the random variable d, they cannot be independent.

Berkson pointed out that, if we are in an experimental situation, and deliberately set the independent variable to a selected value X', then it is true that in actuality we get not X', but

$$u = X' - d, \tag{8.5}$$

where d is a random error. If we substitute this value of u in (8.1), and v from (8.3), we get

$$y' - e = \alpha + \beta(X' - d)$$

or

$$y' = \alpha + \beta X' + (e - \beta d). \tag{8.6}$$

This is a standard linear regression situation, since X' is a fixed, chosen variable and the error term $(e - \beta d)$ is independent of X'. Hence our sample estimate of β will be unbiased.

The result illustrates one of the many advantages that accrue from experimental as distinct from observational work.

For a generalization of Berkson's model, see Scheffé [3].

REFERENCES

1. Berkson, J., "Are there two regressions?" *Journal of the American Statistical Association*, 45(1950), 164–180.
2. Lindley, D. V., "Estimation of a functional relationship," *Biometrika*, 40(1953), 47–49.
3. Scheffé, H., "Fitting straight lines when one variable is controlled," *Journal of the American Statistical Association*, 53(1958), 106–117.

EXERCISES

12.1. For a number of storms, the amounts of rain falling at two sites were observed. The amounts, transformed in a certain way to give better bivariate normality, were as follows:

x_1	1.05	1.40	0.69	1.41	0.51	1.49	1.38	2.00	0.96	1.31	2.07	1.02	0.89	1.51
x_2	0.66	1.16	0.64	1.07	0.33	1.59	1.11	1.33	0.96	1.40	1.71	0.75	0.75	0.92

For these data, $n = 14$, $\Sigma x_1 = 1769$, $\Sigma x_2 = 1438$, $\Sigma x_1^2 = 249{,}465$, $\Sigma x_2^2 = 167{,}508$, $\Sigma x_1 x_2 = 201{,}135$.

(*a*) Obtain estimates of (i) ρ, (ii) $V[x_2]$, (iii) $V[x_2|x_1]$.

(*b*) Test the null hypothesis that $\rho = 0$.

(*c*) Obtain the regression equation of x_2 on x_1.

(*d*) Obtain the regression equation of x_1 on x_2.

(*e*) If we observe $x_1 = 1.4$, what is the predicted value of x_2?

(*f*) If we observe $x_2 = 1.13$, what is the predicted value of x_1?

(*g*) Another set of 18 storms gave a sample correlation coefficient between another pair of sites of 0.703. Test the null hypothesis that the correlations between the two sites in each pair are equal.

12.2. In a standardization of the speedometer of an automobile, the driver adjusted his setting of the accelerator so that the speedometer read a series of selected values: 20, 30, etc., mph. The speed being kept steady at these values, an assistant read the speed as recorded by an accurately calibrated fifth wheel. The observations were as follows:

Speedometer	20	30	40	50	60	70	80	90
Fifth wheel	20.5	30.5	40.5	48.8	57.9	68.2	75.8	86.3

The purpose of this operation is so that the driver will be able to infer his true speed from his reading of the speedometer.

State carefully an appropriate model for the relationship between these two sets of numbers, assuming the relationship to be some form of straight line.

(*a*) Test the null hypotheses (i) that the line has a slope of 1, (ii) that the line has a zero intercept, (iii) that the line has a slope of 1 and a zero intercept.

(*b*) Predict the true speed for a speedometer reading of 63. Give a 95 per cent confidence interval for the true speed, given that the speedometer reads 63.

CHAPTER 13

Two-Way Analysis of Variance

13.1. Introduction: the Model for Model I Analysis

In Chapter 10 we considered the analysis of variance where the data were classified in one way. In this chapter we will discuss the analysis of two-way tables, first when both classifications are model I, then when both are model II, and finally the mixed case where one classification is model I and the other model II.

We suppose that the data are in the form of Table 13.1. For example, rows could correspond to varieties of corn, and columns to quantity of some fertilizer, and we have n independent estimates $x_{ij\nu}$ for each row $\times$ column combination. We assume that the rt sets of n observations are random samples from rt separate populations, each normally distributed about means ξ_{ij} but all with the same variance σ^2. The model is

$$x_{ij\nu} = \xi_{ij} + z_{ij\nu}: \qquad z_{ij\nu} \sim N(0, \sigma^2), \tag{1.1}$$

$$i = 1, \ldots, r: \quad j = 1, \ldots, t: \quad \nu = 1, \ldots, n.$$

Table 13.1

$j =$	1	2 $\cdots$	t	
$i =$				
1	$x_{11\nu}$	$x_{12\nu}$	$x_{1t\nu}$	$\bar{x}_{1\cdot\cdot}$
2	$x_{21\nu}$	$x_{22\nu}$	$x_{2t\nu}$	$\bar{x}_{2\cdot\cdot}$
$\vdots$				
r	$x_{r1\nu}$	$x_{r2\nu}$	$x_{rt\nu}$	$\bar{x}_{r\cdot\cdot}$
Averages	$\bar{x}_{\cdot 1\cdot}$	$\bar{x}_{\cdot 2\cdot}$	$\bar{x}_{\cdot t\cdot}$	$\bar{x}_{\cdot\cdot\cdot}$

The means of the sample observations in each cell are $\bar{x}_{ij\cdot} = \frac{1}{n}\sum_{\nu}^{n} x_{ij\nu}$. The mean of the sample means in the ith row is

$$\bar{x}_{i\cdot\cdot} = \frac{1}{t}\sum_{j}^{t} \bar{x}_{ij\cdot} = \frac{1}{tn}\sum_{j}^{t}\sum_{\nu}^{n} x_{ij\nu},$$

and the mean of the sample means in the jth column is

$$\bar{x}_{\cdot j\cdot} = \frac{1}{r}\sum_{i}^{r} \bar{x}_{ij\cdot} = \frac{1}{rn}\sum_{i}^{r}\sum_{\nu}^{n} x_{ij\nu}.$$

Table 13.2

$i=$ \ $j=$	1	$2 \cdots$	t	Means	Deviations
1	ξ_{11}	$\xi_{12} \cdots$	ξ_{1t}	$\xi_{1\cdot}$	$\xi_{1\cdot} - \xi = \eta_1$
2	ξ_{21}	ξ_{22}	ξ_{2t}	$\xi_{2\cdot}$	$\xi_{2\cdot} - \xi = \eta_2$
$\vdots$					
r	ξ_{r1}	ξ_{r2}	ξ_{rt}	$\xi_{r\cdot}$	$\xi_{r\cdot} - \xi = \eta_r$
Means	$\xi_{\cdot 1}$	$\xi_{\cdot 2}$	$\xi_{\cdot t}$	ξ	
Deviation	$\xi_{\cdot 1} - \xi = \zeta_1$	$\xi_{\cdot 2} - \xi = \zeta_2$	$\xi_{\cdot t} - \xi = \zeta_t$		

Table 13.2 gives the population means ξ_{ij} for each cell, the row and column means, defined as $\xi_{i\cdot} = \frac{1}{t}\sum_{j}^{t} \xi_{ij}$, $\xi_{\cdot j} = \frac{1}{r}\sum_{i}^{r} \xi_{ij}$, and the grand mean defined as

$$\xi = \frac{1}{r}\sum_{i}^{r} \xi_{i\cdot} = \frac{1}{rt}\sum_{i}^{r}\sum_{j}^{t} \xi_{j} = \frac{1}{t}\sum_{j}^{t} \xi_{\cdot j}. \tag{1.2}$$

The deviations of each row mean from the grand mean are denoted by η_i,

$$\eta_i = \xi_{i\cdot} - \xi, \tag{1.3}$$

and the deviations of each column mean from the grand mean by ζ_j:

$$\zeta_j = \xi_{\cdot j} - \xi. \tag{1.4}$$

Clearly, both these sets of deviations sum to zero:

$$\sum_{i}^{r} \eta_i = 0 = \sum_{j}^{t} \zeta_j. \tag{1.5}$$

We define quantities θ_{ij} as the difference between the true mean for the ijth cell, ξ_{ij}, and what we would expect on the basis of an additive model,

$$\text{Grand mean} + \text{row effect} + \text{column effect} = \xi + \eta_i + \zeta_j; \quad (1.6)$$

i.e.

$$\theta_{ij} = \xi_{ij} - (\xi + \eta_i + \zeta_j). \quad (1.7)$$

Thus, if the true cell mean is equal to the prediction (1.6), then the additive model holds and $\theta_{ij} = 0$. In other words,

$$\xi_{ij} = \xi + \eta_i + \zeta_j + \theta_{ij}, \quad (1.8)$$

the θ_{ij} measuring the departure from the additive model (1.6). The θ_{ij} are known as the *interaction* constants. When we say that we have zero interaction, we mean that we have an additive model as in (1.6). The θ_{ij} sum to zero over each suffix, for each value of the other suffix; for the sum over i,

$$\sum_i^r \theta_{ij} = \sum_i^r \xi_{ij} - r\xi - \sum_i^r \eta_i - r\zeta_j .$$

But $\sum_i^r \eta_i = 0$, from (1.5), and, from (1.4),

$$r\zeta_j = r\xi_{.j} - r\xi = \sum_i^r \xi_{ij} - r\xi;$$

so

$$\sum_i^r \theta_{ij} = \sum_i^r \xi_{ij} - r\xi - 0 - \sum_i^r \xi_{ij} + r\xi = 0. \quad (1.9)$$

Likewise,

$$\sum_j^t \theta_{ij} = 0. \quad (1.10)$$

Specifically, we have t relations,

$$\sum_i^r \theta_{i1} = \sum_i^r \theta_{i2} = \cdots = \sum_i^r \theta_{it} = 0, \quad (1.11)$$

and r relations,

$$\sum_j^t \theta_{1j} = \sum_j^t \theta_{2j} = \cdots = \sum_j^t \theta_{rj} = 0. \quad (1.12)$$

However, effectively there are only $(r + t - 1)$ independent restrictions on the θ_{ij}. This is because we have, say, the t restrictions (1.11), which when summed determine the relation $\sum_j^t (\sum_i^r \theta_{ij}) = 0$. But then the $\sum_j^t \theta_{ij}$ (1.12), whose sum is $\sum_i^r (\sum_j^t \theta_{ij}) = \sum_j^t \sum_i^r \theta_{ij}$, must also sum to zero. In other words, only $(r - 1)$ of the r relations (1.12) will be independent.

Thus the total number of independent restrictions on the θ_{ij} is $(r + t - 1)$. Since the number of the θ_{ij} is rt, the number of independent constants in this group is

$$rt - (r + t - 1) = (r - 1)(t - 1).$$

We now rewrite the original model (1.1) as

$$x_{ij\nu} = \xi + \eta_i + \zeta_j + \theta_{ij} + z_{ij\nu}\,. \tag{1.13}$$

The original model involved rt independent cell means ξ_{ij}; this model involves the grand mean ξ, $(r - 1)$ independent row constants η_i, $(t - 1)$ independent column constants ζ_j, and $(r - 1)(t - 1)$ independent interaction constants θ_{ij}. The total number of independent parameters in the new model (1.13) is

$$1 + (r - 1) + (t - 1) + (r - 1)(t - 1) = rt,$$

the same as the original model (1.1). If the full number of parameters are needed, very little will be gained by the change in the model. However, if the null hypothesis of additivity can be accepted, we can regard the interaction constants θ_{ij} as zero, and then we have only to consider the grand mean and row and column parameters, a very substantial reduction in the number of parameters. Furthermore, it may happen that either the row or column parameters, or both, can be regarded as zero, which would allow further reduction in the number of parameters necessary to describe the situation. In fact, if both were zero, the only parameter left is the grand mean ξ.

Corresponding to the population parameters ξ, η_i, ζ_j, and θ_{ij}, we will have sample analogs. The sample analog of ξ (1.2) is

$$\bar{x}_{...} = \sum_i^r \sum_j^t \sum_\nu^n x_{ij\nu}/rtn,$$

of η_i(1.3) is $(\bar{x}_{i..} - \bar{x}_{...})$, of ζ_j (1.4) is $(\bar{x}_{.j.} - \bar{x}_{...})$, and of θ_{ij} (1.7), is

$$\bar{x}_{ij.} - [\bar{x}_{...} + (\bar{x}_{i..} - \bar{x}_{...}) + (\bar{x}_{.j.} - \bar{x}_{...})] = \bar{x}_{ij.} - \bar{x}_{i..} - \bar{x}_{.j.} + \bar{x}_{...}\,. \tag{1.14}$$

Using these expressions we can write an identity analogous to (1.8):

$$\bar{x}_{ij.} = \bar{x}_{...} + (\bar{x}_{i..} - \bar{x}_{...}) + (\bar{x}_{.j.} - \bar{x}_{...}) + (\bar{x}_{ij.} - \bar{x}_{i..} - \bar{x}_{.j.} + \bar{x}_{...}). \tag{1.15}$$

If we subtract this from (1.8), we get an expression for the deviation of the sample mean for the ijth cell from the true value for the mean of that cell:

$$\begin{aligned}\bar{x}_{ij.} - \xi_{ij} = {} & (\bar{x}_{ij.} - \bar{x}_{i..} - \bar{x}_{.j.} + \bar{x}_{...} - \theta_{ij}) \\ & + (\bar{x}_{i..} - \bar{x}_{...} - \eta_i) + (\bar{x}_{.j.} - \bar{x}_{...} - \zeta_j) + (\bar{x}_{...} - \xi). \end{aligned} \tag{1.16}$$

This identity will be used in the following section.

13.2. The Analysis of Variance

We start with an identity expressing the deviation of the νth observation in the ijth cell from the true mean for that cell as the sum of the deviation of the νth observation from the sample mean of the ijth cell plus the deviation of the sample mean for the cell from the true mean:

$$x_{ij\nu} - \xi_{ij} = (x_{ij\nu} - \bar{x}_{ij.}) + (\bar{x}_{ij.} - \xi_{ij}). \tag{2.1}$$

We square this and then sum over ν:

$$\sum_{\nu}^{n} (x_{ij\nu} - \xi_{ij})^2 = \sum_{\nu}^{n} (x_{ij\nu} - \bar{x}_{ij.})^2 + n(\bar{x}_{ij.} - \xi_{ij})^2. \tag{2.2}$$

The left-hand side is distributed as $\sigma^2\chi^2(n)$, and the two terms on the right-hand side are distributed as $\sigma^2\chi^2(n - 1)$ and $\sigma^2\chi^2(1)$. Now sum over i and j.

$$\sum_{i}^{r}\sum_{j}^{t}\sum_{\nu}^{n} (x_{ij\nu} - \xi_{ij})^2 = \sum_{i}^{r}\sum_{j}^{t}\sum_{\nu}^{n} (x_{ij\nu} - \bar{x}_{ij.})^2 + n\sum_{i}^{r}\sum_{j}^{t} (\bar{x}_{ij.} - \xi_{ij})^2. \tag{2.3}$$

By the additivity of χ^2's, the left-hand side will be distributed as $\sigma^2\chi^2(rtn)$, and the two terms on the right-hand side as $\sigma^2\chi^2(rt(n - 1))$ and $\sigma^2\chi^2(rt)$. If we define

$$s_1^2 = \frac{1}{rt(n-1)}\sum_{i}^{r}\sum_{j}^{t}\sum_{\nu}^{n} (x_{ij\nu} - \bar{x}_{ij.})^2, \tag{2.4}$$

it will have expected value σ^2 and be independent of the other term on the right-hand side of (2.3).

Now consider this other term. If we square the identity (1.16) and sum over i, j, and ν (summing over ν amounts to multiplication by n), we get

$$n\sum_{i}^{r}\sum_{j}^{t} (\bar{x}_{ij.} - \xi_{ij})^2 = n\sum_{i}^{r}\sum_{j}^{t} (\bar{x}_{ij.} - \bar{x}_{i..} - \bar{x}_{.j.} + \bar{x}_{...} - \theta_{ij})^2$$
$$+ nt\sum_{i}^{r} (\bar{x}_{i..} - \bar{x}_{...} - \eta_i)^2 + nr\sum_{j}^{t} (\bar{x}_{.j.} - \bar{x}_{...} - \zeta_j)^2 + ntr(\bar{x}_{...} - \xi)^2. \tag{2.5}$$

The left-hand side is distributed as $\sigma^2\chi^2(rt)$. The degrees of freedom for the first term on the right-hand side follow from the fact that the random variables $(\bar{x}_{ij.} - \bar{x}_{i..} - \bar{x}_{.j.} + \bar{x}_{...})$ are subject to the conditions

$$\sum_{i}^{r} (\bar{x}_{ij.} - \bar{x}_{i..} - \bar{x}_{.j.} + \bar{x}_{...}) = 0 \text{ for each } j,$$

$$\sum_{j}^{t} (\bar{x}_{ij.} - \bar{x}_{i..} - \bar{x}_{.j.} + \bar{x}_{...}) = 0 \text{ for each } i,$$

and, similar to the argument for the analogous θ_{ij}, those form only $(r + t - 1)$ independent relations. The degrees of freedom for this term are therefore

$$rt - (r + t - 1) = (r - 1)(t - 1).$$

For the second and third terms we have the conditions

$$\sum_i^r (\bar{x}_{i\cdot\cdot} - \bar{x}_{\cdot\cdot\cdot}) = 0 = \sum_j^t (\bar{x}_{\cdot j\cdot} - \bar{x}_{\cdot\cdot\cdot})$$

and so the degrees of freedom are $(r - 1)$ and $(t - 1)$, respectively. The last term involving the single random variable $\bar{x}_{\cdot\cdot\cdot}$ has 1 degree of freedom. Hence, by Cochran's theorem, these sums of squares will be distributed as $\sigma^2\chi^2$ and be independent.

The terms in (2.5) cannot be computed as they involve the usually unknown true parameters. However, we can write the identity

$$x_{ij\nu} - \bar{x}_{\cdot\cdot\cdot} = (\bar{x}_{ij\cdot} - \bar{x}_{i\cdot\cdot} - \bar{x}_{\cdot j\cdot} + \bar{x}_{\cdot\cdot\cdot}) + (\bar{x}_{i\cdot\cdot} - \bar{x}_{\cdot\cdot\cdot}) + (\bar{x}_{\cdot j\cdot} - \bar{x}_{\cdot\cdot\cdot}) + (x_{ij\nu} - \bar{x}_{ij\cdot}),$$

and square and sum over i, j, and ν:

$$\sum_i^r \sum_j^t \sum_\nu^n (x_{ij\nu} - \bar{x}_{\cdot\cdot\cdot})^2 = n \sum_i^r \sum_j^t (\bar{x}_{ij\cdot} - \bar{x}_{i\cdot\cdot} - \bar{x}_{\cdot j\cdot} + \bar{x}_{\cdot\cdot\cdot})^2$$
$$+ nt \sum_i^r (\bar{x}_{i\cdot\cdot} - \bar{x}_{\cdot\cdot\cdot})^2 + nr \sum_j^t (\bar{x}_{\cdot j\cdot} - \bar{x}_{\cdot\cdot\cdot})^2 + \sum_i^r \sum_j^t \sum_\nu^n (x_{ij\nu} - \bar{x}_{ij\cdot})^2. \quad (2.6)$$

The left-hand side is the total sum of squares about the observed mean. On the right-hand side, the last term is the numerator sum of squares for s_1^2 as defined in (2.4). We now find the expected values of the other components on the right-hand side. We have the identity

$$n \sum_i^r \sum_j^t (\bar{x}_{ij\cdot} - \bar{x}_{i\cdot\cdot} - \bar{x}_{\cdot j\cdot} + \bar{x}_{\cdot\cdot\cdot} - \theta_{ij})^2$$
$$= n \sum_i^r \sum_j^t (\bar{x}_{ij\cdot} - \bar{x}_{i\cdot\cdot} - \bar{x}_{\cdot j\cdot} + \bar{x}_{\cdot\cdot\cdot})^2 + n \sum_i^r \sum_j^t \theta_{ij}^2$$
$$- 2n \sum_i^r \sum_j^t \theta_{ij}(\bar{x}_{ij\cdot} - \bar{x}_{i\cdot\cdot} - \bar{x}_{\cdot j\cdot} + \bar{x}_{\cdot\cdot\cdot}). \quad (2.7)$$

When we take expected values, we know from (2.5) that the expected value of the left-hand side is

$$E[\sigma^2\chi^2((r - 1)(t - 1))] = (r - 1)(t - 1)\sigma^2.$$

Also, $E[\bar{x}_{ij\cdot} - \bar{x}_{i\cdot\cdot} - \bar{x}_{\cdot j\cdot} + \bar{x}_{\cdot\cdot\cdot}] = \theta_{ij}$. We therefore have

$$(r - 1)(t - 1)\sigma^2 = E[n \sum_i^r \sum_j^t (\bar{x}_{ij\cdot} - \bar{x}_{i\cdot\cdot} - \bar{x}_{\cdot j\cdot} + \bar{x}_{\cdot\cdot\cdot})^2] - n \sum_i^r \sum_j^t \theta_{ij}^2;$$

so, if we define s_2^2 as

$$s_2^2 = \frac{n \sum_i^r \sum_j^t (\bar{x}_{ij.} - \bar{x}_{i..} - \bar{x}_{.j.} + \bar{x}_{...})^2}{(r-1)(t-1)}, \tag{2.8}$$

it will have expected value

$$E[s_2^2] = \sigma^2 + \frac{n \sum_i^r \sum_j^t \theta_{ij}^2}{(r-1)(t-1)}. \tag{2.9}$$

Similarly we have the identity

$$nt \sum_i^r (\bar{x}_{i..} - \bar{x}_{...} - \eta_i)^2$$
$$= nt \sum_i^r (\bar{x}_{i..} - \bar{x}_{...})^2 + nt \sum_i^r \eta_i^2 - 2nt \sum_i^r \eta_i(\bar{x}_{i..} - \bar{x}_{...}),$$

and the expected value of the left-hand side is

$$E[\sigma^2\chi^2(r-1)] = (r-1)\sigma^2 \qquad \text{and} \qquad E[(\bar{x}_{i..} - \bar{x}_{...})] = \eta_i;$$

thus $$(r-1)\sigma^2 = E[nt \sum_i^r (\bar{x}_{i..} - \bar{x}_{...})^2] - nt \sum_i^r \eta_i^2;$$

so, if we define s_4^2 as

$$s_4^2 = \frac{nt \sum_i^r (\bar{x}_{i..} - \bar{x}_{...})^2}{r-1}, \tag{2.10}$$

it will have expected value

$$E[s_4^2] = \sigma^2 + \frac{nt \sum_i^r \eta_i^2}{r-1}. \tag{2.11}$$

Similarly, if we define s_3^2 as

$$s_3^2 = \frac{nr \sum_j^t (\bar{x}_{.j.} - \bar{x}_{...})^2}{t-1}, \tag{2.12}$$

it will have expected value

$$E[s_3^2] = \sigma^2 + \frac{nr \sum_j^t \zeta_j^2}{t-1}. \tag{2.13}$$

We can summarize all of this in a tabular form (Table 13.3).

The tests of significance are obvious from the expected mean squares. If the $\theta_{ij}=0$ for all i, j, then s_2^2 is an estimate of σ^2 independent of s_1^2, which is also an estimate of σ^2. The ratio s_2^2/s_1^2 will be distributed as $F((r-1)(t-1), rt(n-1))$ under the null hypothesis. If the null hypothesis is rejected, then the true cell means are not given by an additive

Table 13.3

Source of variance	Sums of squares	Degrees of freedom	Mean squares	E[M.S.]
Rows	$nt\sum_i^r (\bar{x}_{i\cdot\cdot}-\bar{x}_{\cdot\cdot\cdot})^2$	$(r-1)$	s_4^2	$\sigma^2+\dfrac{nt\sum_i^r \eta_i^2}{r-1}$
Columns	$nr\sum_j^t (\bar{x}_{\cdot j\cdot}-\bar{x}_{\cdot\cdot\cdot})^2$	$(t-1)$	s_3^2	$\sigma^2+\dfrac{nr\sum_j^t \zeta_j^2}{t-1}$
Interaction	$n\sum_i^r\sum_j^t (\bar{x}_{ij\cdot}-\bar{x}_{i\cdot\cdot}-\bar{x}_{\cdot j\cdot}+\bar{x}_{\cdot\cdot\cdot})^2$	$(r-1)(t-1)$	s_2^2	$\sigma^2+\dfrac{n\sum_i^r\sum_j^t \theta_{ij}^2}{(r-1)(t-1)}$
Within cells	$\sum_i^r\sum_j^t\sum_\nu^n (x_{ij\nu}-\bar{x}_{ij\cdot})^2$	$rt(n-1)$	s_1^2	σ^2
Total	$\sum_i^r\sum_j^t\sum_\nu^n (x_{ij\nu}-\bar{x}_{\cdot\cdot\cdot})^2$	$rtn-1$		

model, and we might as well deal with the individual cell means. On the other hand, if the null hypothesis is acceptable, then we may assume that the θ_{ij} are zero, and proceed to test the row and column effects. If the $\eta_i=0$ for all i, then s_4^2 is an estimate of σ^2 independent of s_1^2, and the ratio s_4^2/s_1^2 will be distributed as $F((r-1), rt(n-1))$.

We may wish to construct confidence limits for the difference between two row means, say the ith and i'th. The model (1.13) is

$$x_{ij\nu}=\xi+\eta_i+\zeta_j+\theta_{ij}+z_{ij\nu}\,;$$

so averaging over j and ν gives

$$\bar{x}_{i\cdot\cdot}=\xi+\eta_i+\bar{\zeta}_{\cdot}+\bar{\theta}_{i\cdot}+\bar{z}_{i\cdot\cdot}=\xi+\eta_i+\bar{z}_{i\cdot\cdot}, \tag{2.14}$$

since $\bar{\zeta}. = \frac{1}{t}\sum_j^t \zeta_j = 0$ by (1.5) and $\bar{\theta}_{i\cdot} = \frac{1}{t}\sum_j^t \theta_{ij} = 0$ by (1.11). Hence

$$\bar{x}_{i\cdot\cdot} - \bar{x}_{i'\cdot\cdot} = (\eta_i - \eta_{i'}) + (\bar{z}_{i\cdot\cdot} - \bar{z}_{i'\cdot\cdot}), \tag{2.15}$$

with expectation

$$E[\bar{x}_{i\cdot\cdot} - \bar{x}_{i'\cdot\cdot}] = \eta_i - \eta_{i'}, \tag{2.16}$$

and variance

$$V[\bar{x}_{i\cdot\cdot} - \bar{x}_{i'\cdot\cdot}] = V[\bar{z}_{i\cdot\cdot}] + V[\bar{z}_{i'\cdot\cdot}] = \frac{2\sigma^2}{tn}. \tag{2.17}$$

We can therefore derive confidence limits for $(\eta_i - \eta_{i'})$ from

$$\frac{(\bar{x}_{i\cdot\cdot} - \bar{x}_{i'\cdot\cdot}) - (\eta_i - \eta_{i'})}{\sqrt{2s_1^2/tn}} \sim t(rt(n-1)). \tag{2.18}$$

Since, using (1.3),

$$\eta_i - \eta_{i'} = (\xi_{i\cdot} - \xi) - (\zeta_{i'\cdot} - \xi) = \xi_{i\cdot} - \xi_{i'\cdot},$$

the confidence limits for $(\eta_i - \eta_{i'})$ are identical with confidence limits for $(\xi_{i\cdot} - \xi_{i'\cdot})$, the difference in the true row averages.

Usually, there is little or no point in constructing confidence limits for $(\xi_{i\cdot} - \xi_{i'\cdot})$ unless $(\xi_{ij} - \xi_{i'j})$ is constant over j, i.e., unless the difference between the two rows is the same for all columns. From (1.8),

$$\xi_{ij} - \xi_{i'j} = \eta_i - \eta_{i'} + \theta_{ij} - \theta_{i'j}. \tag{2.19}$$

Thus (2.18) will also give confidence limits for $(\xi_{ij} - \xi_{i'j})$ if we can assume that the interaction constants θ_{ij} are zero. If we cannot make this assumption, we can obtain confidence limits for $(\xi_{ij} - \xi_{i'j})$ as follows. Since

$$\bar{x}_{ij\cdot} - \bar{x}_{i'j\cdot} = \eta_i - \eta_{i'} + \theta_{ij} - \theta_{i'j} + \bar{z}_{ij\cdot} - \bar{z}_{i'j\cdot} \tag{2.20}$$

has expectation

$$E[\bar{x}_{ij\cdot} - \bar{x}_{i'j\cdot}] = \eta_i - \eta_{i'} + \theta_{ij} - \theta_{i'j} = \xi_{ij} - \xi_{i'j}, \tag{2.21}$$

from (2.19), and variance

$$V[\bar{x}_{ij\cdot} - \bar{x}_{i'j\cdot}] = V[\bar{z}_{ij\cdot}] + V[\bar{z}_{i'j\cdot}] = \frac{2\sigma^2}{n}, \tag{2.22}$$

confidence limits for $(\xi_{ij} - \xi_{i'j})$ can be obtained from

$$\frac{(\bar{x}_{ij\cdot} - \bar{x}_{i'j\cdot}) - (\xi_{ij} - \xi_{i'j})}{\sqrt{2s_1^2/n}} \sim t(rt(n-1)). \tag{2.23}$$

Comparison of the denominator of (2.23) with the denominator of (2.18) shows the advantage gained if the assumption of zero interaction is permissible.

13.3. Computing Forms for Two-Way Analysis of Variance

Table 13.4 gives the per cent reduction in blood sugar a certain time after injection of insulin into rabbits. A group of 24 rabbits was divided at random into six groups of four rabbits each, and each rabbit received an injection of insulin. Two factors were involved, the dose at three levels and the preparation of insulin, A and B, at two levels.

Table 13.4

	Dose			
Preparation	2.29	3.63	5.75	$\sum_{j}^{t}\sum_{\nu}^{n} x_{ij\nu}$
A	17	64	62	
	21	49	72	
	49	34	61	
	54	63	91	
$\sum_{\nu}^{n} x_{1j\nu}$	141	209	286	636
B	33	41	56	
	37	64	62	
	40	34	57	
	16	64	72	
$\sum_{\nu}^{n} x_{2j\nu}$	126	203	247	576
$\sum_{i}^{r}\sum_{\nu}^{n} x_{ij\nu}$	267	412	533	1212

The closed forms of sums of squares in Table 13.3 are inconvenient for calculation. We need five sums of squares defined as follows:

$$A = \sum_{i}^{r}\sum_{j}^{t}\sum_{\nu}^{n} x_{ij\nu}^2 = 17^2 + 21^2 + \cdots + 72^2 = 69{,}358,$$

$$B = \frac{1}{n}\sum_{i}^{r}\sum_{j}^{t}\left(\sum_{\nu}^{n} x_{ij\nu}\right)^2 = \frac{141^2 + \cdots + 247^2}{4} = 65{,}863.00,$$

$$C = \frac{1}{nr}\sum_{j}^{t}\left(\sum_{i}^{r}\sum_{\nu}^{n} x_{ij\nu}\right)^2 = \frac{267^2 + \cdots + 533^2}{4 \times 2} = 65{,}640.25,$$

$$D = \frac{1}{nt}\sum_i^r (\sum_j^t \sum_v^n x_{ijv})^2 = \frac{636^2 + 576^2}{4 \times 3} = 61{,}356.00,$$

$$E = \frac{1}{nrt}(\sum_i^r \sum_j^t \sum_v^n x_{ijv})^2 = \frac{(1212)^2}{4 \times 2 \times 3} = 61{,}206.00.$$

The sums of squares in Table 13.3 are then computed as follows. The total sum of squares is

$$\sum_i^r \sum_j^t \sum_v^n (x_{ijv} - \bar{x}_{...})^2 = \sum_i^r \sum_j^t \sum_v^n x_{ijv}^2 - \frac{1}{nrt}\left(\sum_i^r \sum_j^t \sum_v^n x_{ijv}\right)^2 = [A] - [E] \tag{3.1}$$

$$= 69{,}358.00 - 61{,}206.00 = 8152.00.$$

The within-cells sum of squares is

$$\sum_i^r \sum_j^t \sum_v^n (x_{ijv} - \bar{x}_{ij\cdot})^2$$

$$= \sum_i^r \sum_j^t \sum_v^n x_{ijv}^2 + n \sum_i^r \sum_j^t \left(\frac{\sum_v^n x_{ijv}}{n}\right)^2 - 2 \sum_i^r \sum_j^t \frac{\sum_v^n x_{ijv}}{n} \sum_v^n x_{ijv}$$

$$= \sum_i^r \sum_j^t \sum_v^n x_{ijv}^2 - \frac{1}{n}\sum_i^r \sum_j^t \left(\sum_v^n x_{ijv}\right)^2 = [A] - [B] \tag{3.2}$$

$$= 69{,}358.00 - 65{,}863.00 = 3495.00.$$

The rows sums of squares is

$$nt \sum_i^r (\bar{x}_{i..} - \bar{x}_{...})^2$$

$$= nt \sum_i^r \left(\frac{\sum_j^t \sum_v^n x_{ijv}}{tn}\right)^2 + ntr\left(\frac{\sum_i^r \sum_j^t \sum_v^n x_{ijv}}{ntr}\right)^2$$

$$- 2nt\left[\sum_i^r \left(\frac{\sum_j^t \sum_v^n x_{ijv}}{tn}\right)\right]\frac{\sum_i^r \sum_j^t \sum_v^n x_{ijv}}{rtn}$$

$$= \frac{1}{tn}\sum_i^r \left(\sum_j^t \sum_v^n x_{ijv}\right)^2 - \frac{1}{rtn}\left(\sum_i^r \sum_j^t \sum_v^n x_{ijv}\right)^2 = [D] - [E] \tag{3.3}$$

$$= 61{,}356.00 - 61{,}206.00 = 150.00.$$

Similarly, the columns sum of squares is

$$nr \sum_j^t (\bar{x}_{.j.} - \bar{x}_{...})^2$$

$$= \frac{1}{rn} \sum_j^t \Big(\sum_i^r \sum_v^n x_{ijv}\Big)^2 - \frac{1}{rtn} \Big(\sum_i^r \sum_j^t \sum_v^n x_{ijv}\Big)^2 = [C] - [E] \tag{3.4}$$

$$= 65{,}640.25 - 61{,}206.00 = 4434.25.$$

A convenient computing form for the interaction sum of squares is

$$n \sum_i^r \sum_j^t (\bar{x}_{ij.} - \bar{x}_{i..} - \bar{x}_{.j.} + \bar{x}_{...})^2$$

$$= n \sum_i^r \sum_j^t (\bar{x}_{ij.} - \bar{x}_{...})^2 + nt \sum_i^r (\bar{x}_{i..} - \bar{x}_{...})^2 + nr \sum_j^t (\bar{x}_{.j.} - \bar{x}_{...})^2$$

$$+ 2n \sum_i^r \sum_j^t (\bar{x}_{i..} - \bar{x}_{...})(\bar{x}_{.j.} - \bar{x}_{...}) - 2n \sum_i^r (\bar{x}_{i..} - \bar{x}_{...}) \sum_j^t (\bar{x}_{ij.} - \bar{x}_{...})$$

$$- 2n \sum_j^t (\bar{x}_{.j.} - \bar{x}_{...}) \sum_i^r (\bar{x}_{ij.} - \bar{x}_{...})$$

$$= n \sum_i^r \sum_j^t \left(\frac{\sum_v^n x_{ijv}}{n} \right)^2 + ntr \left(\frac{\sum_i^r \sum_j^t \sum_v^n x_{ijv}}{rtn} \right)^2 - 2n \frac{\sum_i^r \sum_j^t \sum_v^n x_{ijv}}{rtn} \frac{\sum_i^r \sum_j^t \sum_v^n x_{ijv}}{n}$$

$$+ nt \sum_i^r (\bar{x}_{i..} - \bar{x}_{...})^2 + nr \sum_j^t (\bar{x}_{.j.} - \bar{x}_{...})^2$$

$$+ 2n \sum_i^r (\bar{x}_{i..} - \bar{x}_{...}) \sum_j^t (\bar{x}_{.j.} - \bar{x}_{...}) - 2n \sum_i^r (\bar{x}_{i..} - \bar{x}_{...}) \cdot t(\bar{x}_{i..} - \bar{x}_{...})$$

$$- 2n \sum_j^t (\bar{x}_{.j.} - \bar{x}_{...}) \cdot r(\bar{x}_{.j.} - \bar{x}_{...})$$

$$= \frac{1}{n} \sum_i^r \sum_j^t \Big(\sum_v^n x_{ijv}\Big)^2 - \frac{1}{rtn} \Big(\sum_i^r \sum_j^t \sum_v^n x_{ijv}\Big)^2$$

$$- nt \sum_i^r (\bar{x}_{i..} - \bar{x}_{...})^2 - nr \sum_j^t (\bar{x}_{.j.} - \bar{x}_{...})^2$$

$$= [B] - [E] - (\text{S.S. for rows}) - (\text{S.S. for columns}) \tag{3.5}$$

$$= 65{,}863.00 - 61{,}206.00 - 150.00 - 4434.25 = 72.75.$$

It will sometimes be worth while to calculate directly the interaction sum of squares, rather than using the identity (3.5). The procedure is to calculate

$$(\bar{x}_{ij.} - \bar{x}_{i..} - \bar{x}_{.j.} + \bar{x}_{...}) = \bar{x}_{ij.} - [\bar{x}_{...} + (\bar{x}_{i..} - \bar{x}_{...}) + (\bar{x}_{.j.} - \bar{x}_{...})],$$

see (1.14), for each cell. The cell means $\bar{x}_{ij\cdot}$ for the data of Table 13.4 are given in Table 13.5. For the cell $i = 1, j = 1$, for example,

$$\bar{x}_{11\cdot} = \sum_{\nu}^{n} \frac{x_{11\nu}}{n} = \frac{141}{4} = 35.25.$$

Table 13.5

	$i = 1$	$i = 2$	$i = 3$
$j = 1$	35.25	52.25	71.50
$j = 2$	31.50	50.75	61.75

Table 13.6

	$i = 1$	$i = 2$	$i = 3$
$j = 1$	-0.625	-1.750	$+2.375$
$j = 2$	$+0.625$	$+1.750$	-2.375

The values predicted for the ijth cell are obtained by calculating

$$\bar{x}_{\cdots} + (\bar{x}_{i\cdot\cdot} - \bar{x}_{\cdots}) + (\bar{x}_{\cdot j\cdot} - \bar{x}_{\cdots})$$

for each cell. For example, $\bar{x}_{\cdots} = 1212/4 \times 2 \times 3 = 50.500$, $\bar{x}_{1\cdot\cdot} = 636/4 \times 3 = 53.000$, $\bar{x}_{\cdot 1\cdot} = 267/4 \times 2 = 33.375$, and so

$$\begin{aligned}\bar{x}_{\cdots} + (\bar{x}_{1\cdot\cdot} - \bar{x}_{\cdots}) + (\bar{x}_{\cdot 1\cdot} - \bar{x}_{\cdots})& \\ &= 50.500 + (53.000 - 50.500) + (33.375 - 50.500) \\ &= 50.500 + 2.500 - 17.125 = 35.875.\end{aligned}$$

Thus $\quad (\bar{x}_{11\cdot} - \bar{x}_{1\cdot\cdot} - \bar{x}_{\cdot 1\cdot} + \bar{x}_{\cdots}) = 35.250 - 35.875 = -0.625.$

The complete set of these quantities is given in Table 13.6. They have the property, like their population analogs in (1.11) and (1.12), of summing to zero in each row and in each column, which gives a useful arithmetical check.

The interaction sum of squares (see Table 13.3) is

$$\begin{aligned} n \sum_{i}^{r} \sum_{j}^{t} (\bar{x}_{ij\cdot} - \bar{x}_{i\cdot\cdot} - \bar{x}_{\cdot j\cdot} + \bar{x}_{\cdots})^2 & \\ &= [(-0.625)^2 + \cdots + (-2.375)^2] = 72.75,\end{aligned}$$

which of course agrees with the value obtained with the identity (3.5).

These results are assembled in Table 13.7. It is apparent that the null hypothesis that the interaction is zero is acceptable, and likewise the null hypothesis that the difference between preparations is zero is acceptable. The variance ratio for the dose effect, 2217.125/194.167 = 11.4 is distributed under the null hypothesis as $F(2, 18)$ and is highly significant.

Table 13.7

Source of variance	Sums of squares	Degrees of freedom	Mean squares	E[M.S.]
Rows = preparations	150.00	1	150.000	$\sigma^2 + 12\sum_i^r \frac{\eta_i^2}{1}$
Columns = doses	4434.25	2	2217.125	$\sigma^2 + 8\sum_j^t \frac{\zeta_j}{2}$
Interaction	72.75	2	36.375	$\sigma^2 + 4\sum_i^r\sum_j^t \frac{\theta_{ij}^2}{2}$
Within cells	3495.00	18	194.167	σ^2
Total	8152.00	23		

13.4. Two-Way Analysis of Variance: Model II

In model II two-way analysis of variance we assume that both rows and columns are random effects, sampled from infinite populations. For example, in a large factory with very many identical machines, machines could correspond to rows, columns to a random sample of batches of raw material, and the replicates in the cells are several items made from each batch on each machine. The model is

$$x_{ij\nu} = \xi + g_i + e_j + y_{ij} + z_{ij\nu} \tag{4.1}$$

where g_i, e_j, y_{ij}, and $z_{ij\nu}$ are independently sampled from normal populations with zero means and variances ψ_1^2, ψ_2^2, ω^2, and σ^2, respectively. The usual objective of the analysis is to estimate and construct confidence limits for the parameters of the model, namely, the grand mean and the four components of variance.

The analysis of variance involves the same equation (2.6) as in the model I analysis. The computing forms, the degrees of freedom, and the mean squares are all the same as in Table 13.3, and the only differences between the two models lie in the expectations and distributions of the mean squares.

The mean square s_1^2 continues to have the same expected value σ^2 and the same distribution as before.

To find the expected value of the interaction mean square s_2^2, we proceed as follows. We form various averages of the model (4.1),

$$\begin{aligned}
\bar{x}_{ij\cdot} &= \xi + g_i + e_j + y_{ij} + \bar{z}_{ij\cdot}\,, \\
\bar{x}_{i\cdot\cdot} &= \xi + g_i + \bar{e}_\cdot + \bar{y}_{i\cdot} + \bar{z}_{i\cdot\cdot}\,, \\
\bar{x}_{\cdot j\cdot} &= \xi + \bar{g}_\cdot + e_j + \bar{y}_{\cdot j} + \bar{z}_{\cdot j\cdot}\,, \\
\bar{x}_{\cdots} &= \xi + \bar{g}_\cdot + \bar{e}_\cdot + \bar{y}_{\cdot\cdot} + \bar{z}_{\cdots}\,;
\end{aligned}$$

so we have the identity

$$\bar{x}_{ij\cdot} - \bar{x}_{i\cdot\cdot} - \bar{x}_{\cdot j\cdot} + \bar{x}_{\cdots} = (y_{ij} - \bar{y}_{i\cdot} - \bar{y}_{\cdot j} + \bar{y}_{\cdot\cdot}) + (\bar{z}_{ij\cdot} - \bar{z}_{i\cdot\cdot} - \bar{z}_{\cdot j\cdot} + \bar{z}_{\cdots}).$$

Now

$$\begin{aligned}
\frac{1}{n} E[(r-1)(t-1)s_2^2] &= E\Big[\sum_i^r \sum_j^t (\bar{x}_{ij\cdot} - \bar{x}_{i\cdot\cdot} - \bar{x}_{\cdot j\cdot} + \bar{x}_{\cdots})^2\Big] \\
&= E\Big[\sum_i^r \sum_j^t (y_{ij} - \bar{y}_{i\cdot} - \bar{y}_{\cdot j} + \bar{y}_{\cdot\cdot})^2\Big] + E\Big[\sum_i^r \sum_j^t (\bar{z}_{ij\cdot} - \bar{z}_{i\cdot\cdot} - \bar{z}_{\cdot j\cdot} + \bar{z}_{\cdots})^2\Big],
\end{aligned} \tag{4.2}$$

the expectation of the cross product being zero since our model assumes independence of the y's and z's. Consider the two parts of (4.2) separately. Since

$$E[\bar{z}_{ij\cdot}] = E[\bar{z}_{i\cdot\cdot}] = E[\bar{z}_{\cdot j\cdot}] = E[\bar{z}_{\cdots}] = 0,$$

we have

$$\begin{aligned}
E[\bar{z}_{ij\cdot}^2] &= V[\bar{z}_{ij\cdot}] = \frac{\sigma^2}{n}, \qquad & E[\bar{z}_{i\cdot\cdot}^2] &= V[\bar{z}_{i\cdot\cdot}] = \frac{\sigma^2}{tn}, \\
E[\bar{z}_{\cdot j\cdot}^2] &= V[\bar{z}_{\cdot j\cdot}] = \frac{\sigma^2}{rn}, \qquad & E[\bar{z}_{\cdots}^2] &= V[\bar{z}_{\cdots}] = \frac{\sigma^2}{rtn}.
\end{aligned} \tag{4.3}$$

Now, evaluating the second term in (4.2),

$$\begin{aligned}
&E\Big[\sum_i^r \sum_j^t (\bar{z}_{ij\cdot} - \bar{z}_{i\cdot\cdot} - \bar{z}_{\cdot j\cdot} + \bar{z}_{\cdots})^2\Big] \\
&\quad = E\Big[\sum_i^r \sum_j^t (\bar{z}_{ij\cdot}^2 + \bar{z}_{i\cdot\cdot}^2 + \bar{z}_{\cdot j\cdot}^2 + \bar{z}_{\cdots}^2)\Big] \\
&\qquad + 2E\Big[\sum_i^r \sum_j^t (-\bar{z}_{ij\cdot}\bar{z}_{\cdot j\cdot} - \bar{z}_{ij\cdot}\bar{z}_{i\cdot\cdot} + \bar{z}_{ij\cdot}\bar{z}_{\cdots} + \bar{z}_{i\cdot\cdot}\bar{z}_{\cdot j\cdot} - \bar{z}_{i\cdot\cdot}\bar{z}_{\cdots} - \bar{z}_{\cdot j\cdot}\bar{z}_{\cdots})\Big]
\end{aligned}$$

$$= E[\sum_i^r \sum_j^t (\bar{z}_{ij\cdot}^2 + \bar{z}_{i\cdot\cdot}^2 + \bar{z}_{\cdot j\cdot}^2 + \bar{z}_{\cdots}^2) - 2\sum_j^t \bar{z}_{\cdot j\cdot} \sum_i^r \bar{z}_{ij\cdot} - 2\sum_i^r \bar{z}_{i\cdot\cdot} \sum_j^t \bar{z}_{ij\cdot}$$

$$+ 2\bar{z}_{\cdots} \sum_i^r \sum_j^t \bar{z}_{ij\cdot} + 2\sum_i^r \bar{z}_{i\cdot\cdot} \sum_j^t \bar{z}_{\cdot j\cdot} - 2\bar{z}_{\cdots} \sum_i^r \sum_j^t \bar{z}_{i\cdot\cdot} - 2\bar{z}_{\cdots} \sum_i^r \sum_j^t \bar{z}_{j\cdot\cdot}]$$

$$= E[\sum_i^r \sum_j^t \bar{z}_{ij\cdot}^2 + t\sum_i^r \bar{z}_{i\cdot\cdot}^2 + r\sum_j^t \bar{z}_{\cdot j\cdot}^2 + rt\bar{z}_{\cdots}^2 - 2r\sum_j^t \bar{z}_{\cdot j\cdot}^2 - 2t\sum_i^r \bar{z}_{i\cdot\cdot}^2$$

$$+ 2rt\bar{z}_{\cdots}^2 + 2rt\bar{z}_{\cdots}^2 - 2rt\bar{z}_{\cdots}^2 - 2rt\bar{z}_{\cdots}^2\ ]$$

$$= E[\sum_i^r \sum_j^t \bar{z}_{ij\cdot}^2 - t\sum_i^r \bar{z}_{i\cdot\cdot}^2 - r\sum_j^t \bar{z}_{\cdot j\cdot}^2 + rt\bar{z}_{\cdots}^2]$$

$$= \sum_i^r \sum_j^t E[\bar{z}_{ij\cdot}^2] - t\sum_i^r E[z_{i\cdot\cdot}^2] - r\sum_j^t E[\bar{z}_{\cdot j\cdot}^2] + rt\, E[\bar{z}_{\cdots}^2]$$

$$= rt\left(\frac{\sigma^2}{n}\right) - tr\left(\frac{\sigma^2}{tn}\right) - rt\left(\frac{\sigma^2}{rn}\right) + rt\left(\frac{\sigma^2}{rtn}\right) = \left(\frac{\sigma^2}{n}\right)(r-1)(t-1). \qquad (4.4)$$

The consideration of $E[\sum_i^r \sum_j^t (y_{ij} - \bar{y}_{i\cdot} - \bar{y}_{\cdot j} + \bar{y}_{\cdot\cdot})^2]$, the other part of (4.2), will follow the analogous course, the only difference being that terms of the type $V[y_{ij}] = \omega^2$, $V[\bar{y}_{\cdot j}] = \omega^2/r$, etc., involve ω^2 and not σ^2, and omit the factor $1/n$. We can thus assert

$$E[\sum_i^r \sum_j^t (y_{ij} - \bar{y}_{i\cdot} - \bar{y}_{\cdot j} + \bar{y}_{\cdot\cdot})^2] = \omega^2(r-1)(t-1). \qquad (4.5)$$

Substituting (4.4) and (4.5) in (4.2), we have

$$\frac{1}{n} E[(r-1)(t-1)s_2^2] = \omega^2(r-1)(t-1) + \frac{\sigma^2}{n}(r-1)(t-1);$$

so

$$E[s_2^2] = \sigma^2 + n\omega^2. \qquad (4.6)$$

Now consider $E[s_4^2]$: We have

$$\frac{r-1}{tn} E[s_4^2] = E[\sum_i^r (\bar{x}_{i\cdot\cdot} - \bar{x}_{\cdots})^2]$$

$$= E[\sum_i^r \{(g_i - \bar{g}_\cdot) + (\bar{y}_{i\cdot} - \bar{y}_{\cdot\cdot}) + (\bar{z}_{i\cdot\cdot} - \bar{z}_{\cdots})\}^2]$$

$$= E[\sum_i^r (g_i - \bar{g}_\cdot)^2] + E[\sum_i^r (\bar{y}_{i\cdot} - \bar{y}_{\cdot\cdot})^2] + E[\sum_i^r (\bar{z}_{i\cdot\cdot} - \bar{z}_{\cdots})^2]. \qquad (4.7)$$

Considering the last term, $\sum_i^r (\bar{z}_{i\cdot\cdot} - \bar{z}_{\cdots})^2/(r-1)$ is the unbiased sample estimator of the variance of $\bar{z}_{i\cdot\cdot}$. The variance of $\bar{z}_{i\cdot\cdot}$ is σ^2/nt; so

$$E[\sum_i^r (\bar{z}_{i\cdot\cdot} - \bar{z}_{\cdots})^2] = \frac{(r-1)\sigma^2}{nt}.$$

The y's and g's can be handled similarly, with ω^2 and ψ_1^2 substituting for σ^2, and the factors $1/n$, $1/nt$ being omitted. Thus

$$\frac{r-1}{nt}\,E[s_4^2] = (r-1)\psi_1^2 + \frac{(r-1)\omega^2}{t} + \frac{(r-1)\sigma^2}{nt};$$

so

$$E[s_4^2] = \sigma^2 + n\omega^2 + tn\psi_1^2. \tag{4.8}$$

Similarly,

$$E[s_3^2] = \sigma^2 + n\omega^2 + rn\psi_2^2. \tag{4.9}$$

These results are assembled in Table 13.8.

Table 13.8

Source of variance	Sums of squares	Degrees of freedom	Mean squares	E[M.S.]
Rows	$nt\sum_i(\bar{x}_{i\cdot\cdot} - \bar{x}_{\cdots})^2$	$(r-1)$	s_4^2	$\sigma^2 + n\omega^2 + tn\psi_1^2$
Columns	$nr\sum_j^t(\bar{x}_{\cdot j\cdot} - \bar{x}_{\cdots})^2$	$(t-1)$	s_3^2	$\sigma^2 + n\omega^2 + rn\psi_2^2$
Interaction	$n\sum_i^r\sum_j^t(\bar{x}_{ij\cdot} - \bar{x}_{i\cdot\cdot} - \bar{x}_{\cdot j\cdot} + \bar{x}_{\cdots})^2$	$(r-1)(t-1)$	s_2^2	$\sigma^2 + n\omega^2$
Within cells	$\sum_i^r\sum_j^t\sum_\nu^n(x_{ij\nu} - \bar{x}_{ij\cdot})^2$	$rt(n-1)$	s_1^2	σ^2
Total	$\sum_i^r\sum_j^t\sum_\nu^n(x_{ij\nu} - \bar{x}_{\cdots})^2$	$rtn-1$		

13.5. The Interpretation of a Model II Analysis

The tests of significance for the null hypotheses $\omega^2 = 0$, $\psi_1^2 = 0$, $\psi_2^2 = 0$ are obvious from the column of expected mean squares in Table 13.8. Whereas, in the model I analysis (Table 13.3), the main effects for rows and columns were tested against the within-cells mean square, here they are tested against the interaction mean square.

The parameters of the model are estimated in the obvious ways:

$$\hat{\xi} = \bar{x}_{\dots}, \qquad \hat{\sigma}^2 = s_1^2, \qquad \hat{\omega}^2 = \frac{s_2^2 - s_1^2}{n}, \qquad \hat{\psi}_1^2 = \frac{s_4^2 - s_2^2}{tn}, \qquad \hat{\psi}_2^2 = \frac{s_3^2 - s_2^2}{rn}. \tag{5.1}$$

Confidence limits for σ^2, for ω^2/σ^2, ω^2, ψ_1^2, and ψ_2^2 can be obtained by the same methods as in the one-way model II analysis (Section 10.5). For confidence limits for ξ, we have seen that

$$\bar{x}_{\dots} = \xi + \bar{g}_{\cdot} + \bar{e}_{\cdot} + \bar{y}_{\cdot\cdot} + \bar{z}_{\dots};$$

so

$$E[\bar{x}_{\dots}] = \xi,$$

$$V[\bar{x}_{\dots}] = \frac{\psi_1^2}{r} + \frac{\psi_2^2}{t} + \frac{\omega^2}{rt} + \frac{\sigma^2}{rtn}$$
$$= \frac{\sigma^2 + n\omega^2 + nt\psi_1^2 + nr\psi_2^2}{rtn}. \tag{5.2}$$

The analysis of variance does not give us a mean square with expected value equal to the quantity in parentheses. However, if we form the linear combination $(s_4^2 + s_3^2 - s_2^2)$, it has expected value

$$E[s_4^2 + s_3^2 - s_2^2] = \sigma^2 + n\omega^2 + nt\psi_1^2 + nr\psi_2^2, \tag{5.3}$$

and can be used in the numerator of (5.2) to estimate $V[\bar{x}_{\dots}]$, and will have approximate degrees of freedom f' given by the application of (9.7.8). Thus

$$\frac{\bar{x}_{\dots} - \xi}{\sqrt{(s_4^2 + s_3^2 - s_2^2)/rtn}} \underset{\text{approx}}{\sim} t(f'). \tag{5.4}$$

13.6. Two-Way Analysis of Variance with Only One Observation per Cell

Sometimes we have data in a two-way classification with only one observation per cell. The analysis is similar to that with n observations per cell, but, with $n = 1$ the model becomes, in the model I case,

$$x_{ij} = \xi + \eta_i + \zeta_j + \theta_{ij} + z_{ij} \tag{6.1}$$

and in the model II case

$$x_{ij} = \xi + g_i + e_j + y_{ij} + z_{ij}. \tag{6.2}$$

Table 13.9

Source of variance	Sums of squares	Degrees of freedom	Mean squares
Rows	$t\sum_i^r (\bar{x}_{i\cdot} - \bar{x}_{\cdot\cdot})^2$ $= \sum_i^r \left(\sum_j^t x_{ij}\right)^2 \Big/ t - \left(\sum_i^r \sum_j^t x_{ij}\right)^2 \Big/ rt$	$(r - 1)$	s_4^2
Columns	$r\sum_j^t (\bar{x}_{\cdot j} - \bar{x}_{\cdot\cdot})^2$ $= \sum_j^t \left(\sum_i^r x_{ij}\right)^2 \Big/ r - \left(\sum_i^r \sum_j^t x_{ij}\right)^2 \Big/ rt$	$(t - 1)$	s_3^2
Remainder	(by difference)	$(r - 1)(t - 1)$	s_2^2
Total	$\sum_i^r \sum_j^t (x_{ij} - \bar{x}_{\cdot\cdot})^2$ $= \sum_i^r \sum_j^t x_{ij}^2 - \left(\sum_i^r \sum_j^t x_{ij}\right)^2 \Big/ rt$	$rt - 1$	

Table 13.10

Source of variance	Mean squares	E[M.S.] Model I	E[M.S.] Model II
Rows	s_4^2	$\sigma^2 + \dfrac{t\sum_i^r \eta_i^2}{r - 1}$	$\sigma^2 + \omega^2 + t\psi_1^2$
Columns	s_3^2	$\sigma^2 + \dfrac{r\sum_j^t \zeta_j^2}{t - 1}$	$\sigma^2 + \omega^2 + r\psi_2^2$
Remainder	s_2^2	$\sigma^2 + \dfrac{\sum_i^r \sum_j^t \theta_{ij}^2}{(r - 1)(t - 1)}$	$\sigma^2 + \omega^2$

In the table of analysis of variance there is no item "within cells," and the analysis is as in Table 13.9.

The expectations of the mean squares for the two models are given in Table 13.10.

In both models there is no test for interaction. In the model II analysis, the tests for the main effects of rows and columns are unchanged. In the model I analysis, the test for the row and column main effects may, if there is appreciable interaction so that $\sum_i^r \sum_j^t \theta_{ij}^2 \neq 0$, be inefficient, since the denominator mean square will be inflated by the extra component. On the other hand, if either variance ratio is significant, then it may be taken that the corresponding effect is real.

13.7. Nested or Hierarchical Analysis of Variance

In our discussion of one-way model II analysis of variance in Section 10.4 we postulated a sampling situation in which sacks of wool were taken from a large consignment, and then samples were taken from each sack at random. If we now suppose that several analyses are performed on each sample, an appropriate model would be

$$x_{ijv} = \xi + v_i + y_{ij} + z_{ijv} \tag{7.1}$$

where ξ is the grand mean, v_i corresponds to the sack effect, y_{ij} to the sample within sack effect, and z_{ijv} to analyses within samples. The random variables v_i, y_{ij}, and z_{ijv} are independently normally distributed with zero means and variances ψ^2, ω^2, and σ^2. Suppose there are r sacks, t samples per sack, and n analyses per sample.

Squaring and summing the identity

$$x_{ijv} - \bar{x}_{...} = (\bar{x}_{i..} - \bar{x}_{...}) + (\bar{x}_{ij.} - \bar{x}_{i..}) + (x_{ijv} - \bar{x}_{ij.}) \tag{7.2}$$

gives

$$\sum_i^r \sum_j^t \sum_v^n (x_{ijv} - \bar{x}_{...})^2 = nt \sum_i^r (\bar{x}_{i..} - \bar{x}_{...})^2 + n \sum_i^r \sum_j^t (\bar{x}_{ij.} - \bar{x}_{i..})^2 + \sum_i^r \sum_j^t \sum_v^n (x_{ijv} - \bar{x}_{ij.})^2. \tag{7.3}$$

These sums of squares are entered in Table 13.11, along with their degrees of freedom. We now determine the expected value of these mean squares, as given in the last column.

Considering s_1^2, averaging the model (7.1) over ν gives

$$\bar{x}_{ij\cdot} = \xi + v_i + y_{ij} + \bar{z}_{ij\cdot}; \tag{7.4}$$

so

$$x_{ij\nu} - \bar{x}_{ij\cdot} = z_{ij\nu} - \bar{z}_{ij\cdot}\,.$$

Squaring and summing over ν gives

$$\sum_{\nu}^{n} (x_{ij\nu} - \bar{x}_{ij\cdot})^2 = \sum_{\nu}^{n} (z_{ij\nu} - \bar{z}_{ij\cdot})^2.$$

Table 13.11

Source of variance	Sums of squares	Degrees of freedom	Mean squares	E[M.S.]
Between sacks	$nt\sum_{i}^{r} (\bar{x}_{i\cdot\cdot} - \bar{x}_{\cdots})^2$	$(r - 1)$	s_3^2	$\sigma^2 + n\omega^2 + nt\psi^2$
Between bags within sacks	$n\sum_{i}^{r}\sum_{j}^{t} (\bar{x}_{ij\cdot} - \bar{x}_{i\cdot\cdot})^2$	$r(t - 1)$	s_2^2	$\sigma^2 + n\omega^2$
Between analyses within samples	$\sum_{i}^{r}\sum_{j}^{t}\sum_{\nu}^{n} (x_{ij\nu} - \bar{x}_{ij\cdot})^2$	$rt(n - 1)$	s_1^2	σ^2
Total	$\sum_{i}^{r}\sum_{j}^{t}\sum_{\nu}^{n} (x_{ij\nu} - \bar{x}_{\cdots})^2$	$rtn - 1$		

Divided by $(n - 1)$, this is a sample estimate of the variance of the $z_{ij\nu}$, namely, σ^2. Pooling the sums of squares and degrees of freedom through summation over i and j leaves this unchanged; so we obtain

$$E[s_1^2] = E\left[\frac{\sum_{i}^{r}\sum_{j}^{t}\sum_{\nu}^{n} (x_{ij\nu} - \bar{x}_{ij\cdot})^2}{rt(n - 1)}\right] = \sigma^2. \tag{7.5}$$

Now consider s_2^2: Averaging (7.4) over j gives

$$\bar{x}_{i\cdot\cdot} = \xi + v_i + \bar{y}_{i\cdot} + \bar{z}_{i\cdot\cdot}; \tag{7.6}$$

so

$$\bar{x}_{ij\cdot} - \bar{x}_{i\cdot\cdot} = (y_{ij} - \bar{y}_{i\cdot}) + (\bar{z}_{ij\cdot} - \bar{z}_{i\cdot\cdot}).$$

Squaring and summing over j and then taking expectations gives

$$E[\sum_{j}^{t} (\bar{x}_{ij\cdot} - \bar{x}_{i\cdot\cdot})^2] = E[\sum_{j}^{t} (y_{ij} - \bar{y}_{i\cdot})^2] + E[\sum_{j}^{t} (\bar{z}_{ij\cdot} - \bar{z}_{i\cdot\cdot})^2], \tag{7.7}$$

the expectation of the cross product vanishing by reason of the independence of the y_{ij} and $z_{ij\nu}$. It is apparent that $\sum_j^t (y_{ij} - \bar{y}_{i\cdot})^2/(t-1)$ is a sample estimate of the variance of the y_{ij}, namely, ω^2. Similarly $\sum_j^t (\bar{z}_{ij\cdot} - \bar{z}_{i\cdot\cdot})^2/(t-1)$ is a sample estimate of the variance of the $\bar{z}_{ij\cdot}$. Since the $z_{ij\nu}$ have variance σ^2, the $\bar{z}_{ij\cdot}$ have variance σ^2/n, and so

$$E\left[\frac{\sum_j^t (\bar{x}_{ij\cdot} - \bar{x}_{i\cdot\cdot})^2}{t-1}\right] = \omega^2 + \frac{\sigma^2}{n}.$$

Therefore

$$E[s_2^2] = E\left[\frac{n\sum_i^r\sum_j^t (\bar{x}_{ij\cdot} - \bar{x}_{\cdot\cdot\cdot})^2}{r(t-1)}\right] = \sigma^2 + n\omega^2. \tag{7.8}$$

Now consider s_3^2: Averaging (7.6) over i gives

$$\bar{x}_{\cdot\cdot\cdot} = \xi + \bar{v}_\cdot + \bar{y}_{\cdot\cdot} + \bar{z}_{\cdot\cdot\cdot}; \tag{7.9}$$

so, subtracting this from (7.6) gives

$$\bar{x}_{i\cdot\cdot} - \bar{x}_{\cdot\cdot\cdot} = (v_i - \bar{v}_\cdot) + (\bar{y}_{i\cdot} - \bar{y}_{\cdot\cdot}) + (\bar{z}_{i\cdot\cdot} - \bar{z}_{\cdot\cdot\cdot}),$$

whence

$$E\left[\frac{\sum_i^r (\bar{x}_{i\cdot\cdot} - \bar{x}_{\cdot\cdot\cdot})^2}{r-1}\right] = E\left[\frac{\sum_i^r (v_i - \bar{v}_\cdot)^2}{r-1}\right] + E\left[\frac{\sum_i^r (\bar{y}_{i\cdot} - \bar{y}_{\cdot\cdot})^2}{r-1}\right] + E\left[\frac{\sum_i^r (\bar{z}_{i\cdot\cdot} - \bar{z}_{\cdot\cdot\cdot})^2}{r-1}\right]$$

$$= \psi^2 + \frac{\omega^2}{t} + \frac{\sigma^2}{tn},$$

since these are the variances of v_i, $\bar{y}_{i\cdot}$, and $\bar{z}_{i\cdot\cdot}$. Therefore

$$E[s_3^2] = E\left[\frac{nt\sum_i^r (\bar{x}_{i\cdot\cdot} - \bar{x}_{\cdot\cdot\cdot})^2}{r-1}\right] = \sigma^2 + n\omega^2 + nt\psi^2. \tag{7.10}$$

Equations (7.5), (7.8), and (7.10) are entered in the last column of Table 13.11.

Table 13.12

		x' = Quantity				$x = 100(\log x' - 1)$			
Batch	Sample	Subsamples		Sample totals	Batch totals	Subsamples		Sample totals	Batch totals
1	1 (1)	76	85	161		88	93	181	
	2 (1)	69	82	151		84	91	175	
	3 (1)	72	78	150		86	89	175	
	4 (1)	75	84	159	621	88	92	180	711
2	1 (2)	110	109	219		104	104	208	
	2 (2)	119	106	225		108	103	211	
	3 (2)	120	121	241		108	108	216	
	4 (2)	111	119	230	915	105	108	213	848
3	1 (3)	130	140	270		111	115	226	
	2 (3)	143	121	264		116	108	224	
	3 (3)	141	147	288		115	117	232	
	4 (3)	129	140	269	1091	111	115	226	908
4	1 (4)	62	67	129		79	83	162	
	2 (4)	50	61	111		70	79	149	
	3 (4)	71	74	145		85	87	172	
	4 (4)	66	67	133	518	82	83	165	648
5	1 (5)	62	64	126		79	81	160	
	2 (5)	48	50	98		68	70	138	
	3 (5)	80	86	166		90	93	183	
	4 (5)	87	91	178	568	94	96	190	671
6	1 (6)	91	97	188		96	99	195	
	2 (6)	87	90	177		94	95	189	
	3 (6)	78	74	152		89	87	176	
	4 (6)	87	83	170	687	94	92	186	746
7	1 (7)	101	97	198		100	99	199	
	2 (7)	89	96	185		95	98	193	
	3 (7)	78	96	174		89	98	187	
	4 (7)	76	87	163	720	88	94	182	761
8	1 (8)	136	123	259		113	109	222	
	2 (8)	108	131	239		103	112	215	
	3 (8)	128	119	247		111	108	219	
	4 (8)	96	82	178	923	98	91	189	845
9	1 (9)	140	136	276		115	113	228	
	2 (9)	92	80	172		96	90	186	
	3 (9)	107	114	221		103	106	209	
	4 (9)	84	113	197	866	92	105	197	820

		x' = Quantity				$x = 100(\log x' - 1)$			
Batch	Sample	Subsamples		Sample totals	Batch totals	Subsamples		Sample totals	Batch totals
10	1(10)	81	99	180		91	100	191	
	2(10)	86	83	169		93	92	185	
	3(10)	103	94	197		101	97	198	
	4(10)	85	87	172	718	93	94	187	761
11	1(11)	108	98	206		103	99	202	
	2(11)	102	102	204		101	101	202	
	3(11)	102	103	205		101	101	202	
	4(11)	109	111	220	835	104	105	209	815
12	1(12)	106	107	213		103	103	206	
	2(12)	100	104	204		100	102	202	
	3(12)	99	98	197		100	99	199	
	4(12)	102	91	193	807	101	96	197	804
13	1(13)	93	89	182		97	95	192	
	2(13)	85	89	174		93	95	188	
	3(13)	78	80	158		89	90	179	
	4(13)	89	87	176	690	95	94	189	748
14	1(14)	116	117	233		106	107	213	
	2(14)	104	116	220		102	106	208	
	3(14)	118	119	237		107	108	215	
	4(14)	112	109	221	911	105	104	209	845

The data of Table 13.12 give the results of taking four samples from each of 14 batches of a slurry. The quantity of matter in suspension in each sample x' was determined in duplicate by dividing each sample into two subsamples. The model for the analysis will be (7.1).

The range w_{ij} between the duplicates $x'_{ij\nu}$ and $x'_{ij\nu'}$ can be used as an estimate of the standard deviation σ, since $\hat{\sigma}_{ij} = w_{ij}/d_2$; see (6.5.2). If we tabulate the ranges according as the batch total is in the intervals (500 − 599), (600 − 699), etc., we get mean ranges of 4.25, 5.50, 7.75, 6.83, 8.25, and 12.25. It appears that the standard deviation σ is increasing approximately linearly with the mean. The model (7.1) makes the assumption that the $z_{ij\nu}$ are distributed normally with a constant variance σ^2. However, we saw in Section 3.4 that, when the variance is proportional to the square of the mean, the logarithm of the variable will have a constant variance. The analysis will therefore be performed on $x = 100\ [(\log x') - 1]$, this transformation producing numbers easy to handle.

Computing forms for the sums of squares in Table 13.11 are easily obtained. Defining

$$A = \sum_i^r \sum_j^t \sum_v^n x_{ijv}^2 = 88^2 + 93^2 + \cdots + 104^2 = 1{,}078{,}281,$$

$$B = \frac{1}{n} \sum_i^r \sum_j^t \left(\sum_v^n x_{ijv} \right)^2 = \frac{181^2 + \cdots + 209^2}{2} = 1{,}077{,}756.5,$$

$$C = \frac{1}{tn} \sum_i^r \left(\sum_j^t \sum_v^n x_{ijv} \right)^2 = \frac{711^2 + \cdots + 845^2}{4 \times 2} = 1{,}075{,}573.375,$$

$$D = \frac{1}{rtn} \left(\sum_i^r \sum_j^t \sum_v^n x_{ijv} \right)^2 = \frac{(10{,}931)^2}{14 \times 4 \times 2} = 1{,}066{,}846.080,$$

straightforward manipulation yields

$$nt \sum_i^r (\bar{x}_{i\cdot\cdot} - \bar{x}_{\cdot\cdot\cdot})^2 = C - D = 8727.295, \tag{7.11}$$

$$n \sum_i^r \sum_j^t (\bar{x}_{ij\cdot} - \bar{x}_{i\cdot\cdot})^2 = B - C = 2183.125, \tag{7.12}$$

$$\sum_i^r \sum_j^t \sum_v^n (x_{ijv} - \bar{x}_{ij\cdot})^2 = A - B = 524.500, \tag{7.13}$$

$$\sum_i^r \sum_j^t \sum_v^n (x_{ijv} - \bar{x}_{\cdot\cdot\cdot})^2 = A - D = 11{,}434.920. \tag{7.14}$$

The analysis of variance is in Table 13.13. The test of the null hypothesis $\omega^2 = 0$ is given by the variance ratio $51.979/9.366 = 5.55$: $F_{0.9995}(30, 50) = 2.86$; so clearly this null hypothesis is rejected. The test of the null hypothesis $\psi^2 = 0$ is given by the variance ratio $671.330/51.979 = 12.9$: $F_{0.9995}(10, 40) = 4.21$, so this null hypothesis is rejected. The point estimates of the components of variance are

$$\hat{\sigma}^2 = 9.366, \quad \hat{\omega}^2 = \frac{51.979 - 9.366}{2} = 21.3, \quad \hat{\psi}^2 = \frac{671.330 - 51.979}{4 \times 2} = 77.4.$$

It is apparent that there is considerable variation between samples within a batch. The largest component of variance, however, is between batches. For estimating the mean of a batch, the estimated variance of one subsample from one sample would be $\hat{\sigma}^2 + \hat{\omega}^2 = 9.4 + 21.3 = 30.7$. The estimated variance of two subsamples from one sample would be $\hat{\sigma}^2/2 + \hat{\omega}^2 = 9.4/2 + 21.3 = 26.0$; so there is very little gain in the precision of the estimation of a batch mean through analyzing two subsamples instead of one. It might, nevertheless, be justifiable to analyze two subsamples as a check against gross errors and mistakes.

Table 13.13

Source of variance	Sums of squares	Degrees of freedom	Mean squares	E[M.S.]
Between batches	8,727.295	13	671.330	$\sigma^2 + 2\omega^2 + 8\psi^2$
Between samples within batches	2,183.125	42	51.979	$\sigma^2 + 2\omega^2$
Between subsamples within samples	524.500	56	9.366	σ^2
Total	11,434.900	111		

Confidence limits for the over-all mean of the process, averaged over batches, can be constructed as follows. The variance of (7.9) is

$$V[\bar{x}_{...}] = V[\bar{v}_{.}] + V[\bar{y}_{..}] + V[\bar{z}_{...}] = \frac{\psi^2}{r} + \frac{\omega^2}{rt} + \frac{\sigma^2}{rtn} = \frac{\sigma^2 + n\omega^2 + nt\psi^2}{rtn}, \tag{7.15}$$

and

$$\hat{V}[\bar{x}_{...}] = \frac{s_3^2}{rtn} = \frac{671.330}{14 \times 4 \times 2} = 5.994.$$

Since

$$\frac{\bar{x}_{...} - \xi}{\sqrt{\hat{V}[\bar{x}_{...}]}} \sim t(r-1), \tag{7.16}$$

we find 95 per cent confidence limits for ξ to be (92.3, 102.9). These are on our transformed scale. Transforming back, the 95 per cent confidence limits for the process average on the original scale are approximately (83.3, 106.9).

13.8. The Two-Way Crossed Finite-Population Model

The model II analysis of Section 13.4 postulated random sampling from infinite populations. Random sampling from finite populations was first considered by Tukey [1], Cornfield and Tukey [2], and Bennett and Franklin [3]. This finite-population model is of interest in itself, for sometimes the assumption that a population, e.g., of machines, is infinite is too gross. This model is also of interest because, if we let the population sizes go to infinity, with the additional assumption of normality, then we get model II, and, if we decrease the population size until it equals the sample size, so that the sample contains the entire population, then we get model I. Our main motivation for considering the finite-population model, however, it is that it will give us a procedure for handling the mixed model, in which one category, say rows, is model I and the other, columns, is model II. Such mixed models occur frequently in practice.

The arguments to follow only involve the ideas of expectation and of combinations but they are somewhat lengthy and involved and some readers may be content to read only through (8.6) and then proceed to Section 13.9.

For a two-way crossed classification with replication in the cells the model is

$$x_{ij\nu} = \xi + \eta_i + \zeta_j + \theta_{ij} + z_{ij\nu}, \tag{8.1}$$

similar to (1.13), with $i = 1, \ldots, r$; $j = 1, \ldots, t$; $\nu = 1, \ldots, n$. However, here the η_i and ζ_j, referring to rows and columns, respectively, are random samples from populations of sizes R and T and satisfy the conditions

$$\sum_i^R \eta_i = 0 = \sum_j^T \zeta_j. \tag{8.2}$$

Selecting a particular i and a particular j determines the row and column and hence the cell that forms their intersection, and with this cell is associated the interaction constant θ_{ij}. The interaction constants satisfy the conditions

$$\sum_i^R \theta_{ij} = 0 \quad \text{for each } j, \qquad \sum_j^T \theta_{ij} = 0 \quad \text{for each } i. \tag{8.3}$$

We make the following definitions:

$$\sigma_\eta^2 = \frac{1}{R-1} \sum_i^R \eta_i^2, \tag{8.4}$$

$$\sigma_\zeta^2 = \frac{1}{T-1} \sum_j^T \zeta_j^2, \tag{8.5}$$

$$\sigma_\theta^2 = \frac{1}{(R-1)(T-1)} \sum_i^R \sum_j^T \theta_{ij}^2. \tag{8.6}$$

These definitions are not consistent with (7.4.2) which would give, for example, $\sigma_\eta^2 = \frac{1}{R}\sum_i^R \eta_i^2$, but they are more convenient in the present instance.

The conventional partitioning of the total sum of squares is identical with that of Table 13.3. We will now evaluate the expectations of the corresponding mean squares under this different model. We will first need the expected values of the squares of certain sums of the z_{ij}, θ_{ij}, ζ_j, and η_i.

The $z_{ij\nu}$ have zero expectation and are independent and hence have zero covariances, and so

$$V[z_{ij\nu}] = \sigma^2 = E[z_{ij\nu}^2].$$

Therefore

$$E[\sum_i^r \sum_j^t \sum_\nu^n z_{ij\nu}^2] = \sum_i^r \sum_j^t \sum_\nu^n E[z_{ij\nu}^2] = rtn\sigma^2. \tag{8.7}$$

Also

$$V[\sum_\nu^n z_{ij\nu}] = E[(\sum_\nu^n z_{ij\nu})^2].$$

But the variance of the sum of n independent observations each with variance σ^2 is $n\sigma^2$, and so

$$E[\sum_i^r \sum_j^t (\sum_\nu^n z_{ij\nu})^2] = \sum_i^r \sum_j^t E[(\sum_\nu^n z_{ij\nu})^2] = \sum_i^r \sum_j^t n\sigma^2 = rtn\sigma^2. \tag{8.8}$$

Similarly,

$$E[\sum_i^r (\sum_j^t \sum_\nu^n z_{ij\nu})^2] = E[\sum_j^t (\sum_i^r \sum_\nu^n z_{ij\nu})^2] = E[(\sum_i^r \sum_j^t \sum_\nu^n z_{ij\nu})^2] = rtn\sigma^2. \tag{8.9}$$

We next find $E[\sum_i^r \eta_i^2]$. The total number of ways a sample of r can be taken from R is $\binom{R}{r}$, and these are all assumed equally likely. Thus

$$E[\sum_i^r \eta_i^2] = \frac{1}{\binom{R}{r}}[(\eta_1^2 + \cdots + \eta_r^2) + \cdots + (\eta_{R-r+1}^2 + \cdots + \eta_R^2)]. \tag{8.10}$$

Any particular η_i will occur in $\binom{R-1}{r-1}$ samples and hence appear in the square brackets this number of times as η_i^2. Therefore, using (8.4),

$$E[\sum_i^r \eta_i^2] = \frac{1}{\binom{R}{r}} \cdot \binom{R-1}{r-1} \sum_i^R \eta_i^2 = r\left(1 - \frac{1}{R}\right)\sigma_\eta^2. \tag{8.11}$$

We next find $E[(\sum_i^r \eta_i)^2]$. By similar arguments,

$$E[(\sum_i^r \eta_i)^2] = \frac{1}{\binom{R}{r}}[(\eta_1 + \cdots + \eta_r)^2 + \cdots + (\eta_{R-r+1} + \cdots + \eta_R)^2]$$

$$= \frac{1}{\binom{R}{r}}\left[\binom{R-1}{r-1}\sum_i^R \eta_i^2 + \binom{R-2}{r-2}\sum_{\substack{i \\ i \neq j}}^R \sum_j^R \eta_i \eta_j\right]. \tag{8.12}$$

Now
$$(\sum_i^R \eta_i)^2 = \sum_i^R \eta_i^2 + \sum_{\substack{i \\ i \neq j}}^R \sum_j^R \eta_i \eta_j \tag{8.13}$$

and by (8.2) the left hand is zero. Hence, substituting in (8.12),

$$E[(\sum_i^r \eta_i)^2] = \frac{1}{\binom{R}{r}}\left[\binom{R-1}{r-1} - \binom{R-2}{r-2}\right]\sum_i^R \eta_i^2 = r\left(1 - \frac{r}{R}\right)\sigma_\eta^2. \tag{8.14}$$

Expressions for ζ_j similar to (8.11) and (8.14) are obtained by the same arguments.

We now find $E[(\sum_i^r \sum_j^t \theta_{ij})^2]$. Specifying a particular row, say the pth, and a particular column, say the qth, determines a particular cell, and associated with this cell is the constant θ_{pq}. The total number of ways we can choose r rows out of a possible R, and t columns out of a possible T, is $\binom{R}{r}\binom{T}{t}$. However, if we specify that the sample of r rows is to include the pth row, and the sample of t columns is to include the qth column, the number of ways in which we can select the remaining $(r - 1)$ rows and $(t - 1)$ columns is $\binom{R-1}{r-1}\binom{T-1}{t-1}$. Thus, in the summation of all possible $(\sum_i^r \sum_j^t \theta_{ij})^2$, the coefficient of the direct square of each element θ_{ij} is $\binom{R-1}{r-1}\binom{T-1}{t-1}$.

The cross products in $(\sum_i^r \sum_j^t \theta_{ij})^2$ are of three types:

1. Those with both θ's in the same row but different columns, $2\,\theta_{pq}\,\theta_{pu}$, $q \neq u$.

2. Those with both θ's in the same column but different rows, $2\,\theta_{pq}\,\theta_{sq}$, $p \neq s$.

3. Those with the two θ's differing both in row and in column number, $2\,\theta_{pq}\,\theta_{su}$, $p \neq s$, $q \neq u$.

In how many of the possible $(\sum_i^r \sum_j^t \theta_{ij})^2$ does a particular cross product of the first type, $2\,\theta_{pq}\,\theta_{pu}$, occur? A sample of the θ_{ij} will arise from a choice of r rows and t columns. Suppose that it contains a specified row, say the pth, and two specified columns, say the qth and the uth. Then the remaining $(r-1)$ rows can be selected from the $(R-1)$ available in $\binom{R-1}{r-1}$ ways, and the remaining $(t-2)$ columns from the $(T-2)$ available in $\binom{T-2}{t-2}$ ways. Thus a specified $2\,\theta_{pq}\,\theta_{pu}$ occurs $\binom{R-1}{r-1}\binom{T-2}{t-2}$ times when we consider all possible $(\sum_i^r \sum_j^t \theta_{ij})^2$.

From (8.3) we can write

$$0 = \sum_j^T \theta_{pj} = \theta_{pq} + \sum_{j \neq q}^T \theta_{pj}\,; \tag{8.15}$$

so

$$-\,\theta_{pq}^2 = \theta_{pq} \sum_{j \neq q}^T \theta_{pj} = \theta_{pq}(\theta_{p1} + \cdots + \theta_{p(q-1)} + \theta_{p(q+1)} + \cdots + \theta_{pT}). \tag{8.16}$$

We now write down the $2\,\theta_{pq}\,\theta_{pu}$, $q \neq u$, for a fixed p:

$$\begin{aligned}\theta_{p1}(\theta_{p2} + \cdots + \theta_{pT}) &+ \theta_{p2}(\theta_{p1} + \theta_{p3} + \cdots + \theta_{pT}) + \cdots \\ &+ \theta_{pq}(\theta_{p1} + \cdots + \theta_{p(q-1)} + \theta_{p(q+1)} + \cdots + \theta_{pT}) + \cdots \\ &+ \theta_{pT}(\theta_{p1} + \cdots + \theta_{p(T-1)}).\end{aligned} \tag{8.17}$$

From (8.16) each term in (8.17) is equal to $-\theta_{pj}^2$, $j = 1, \ldots, T$, and so the sum of all terms in (8.17) is $-\sum_j^T \theta_{pj}^2$. Therefore the sum of all possible $2\,\theta_{pq}\,\theta_{pu}$, $q \neq u$, summed over all p, is $-\sum_i^R \sum_j^T \theta_{ij}^2$. But we saw above that each $2\,\theta_{pq}\,\theta_{pu}$ occurs $\binom{R-1}{r-1}\binom{T-2}{t-2}$ times in all possible $(\sum_i^r \sum_j^t \theta_{ij})^2$, and so the sum of the $2\,\theta_{pq}\,\theta_{pu}$ over all possible $(\sum_i^r \sum_j^t \theta_{ij})^2$ is

$$-\binom{R-1}{r-1}\binom{T-2}{t-2}\sum_i^R \sum_j^T \theta_{ij}^2. \tag{8.18}$$

For cross products of the second type, formed by θ's in the same column, the corresponding sum is

$$-\binom{R-2}{r-2}\binom{T-1}{t-1}\sum_{i}^{R}\sum_{j}^{T}\theta_{ij}^{2}. \tag{8.19}$$

With cross products of the third type, with θ's differing in both row and column number, a specified $2\,\theta_{pq}\,\theta_{su}$ will occur in $\binom{R-2}{r-2}\binom{T-2}{t-2}$ possible samples, since with two rows fixed the remaining $(r-2)$ can be selected from the $(R-2)$ available in $\binom{R-2}{r-2}$ ways, analogously for columns.

The sum of all possible cross products of the third type containing θ_{pq} is

$$\begin{aligned}
\theta_{pq}\sum_{s\neq p}^{R}\sum_{u\neq q}^{T}\theta_{su}
&= \theta_{pq}(\theta_{11}+\cdots+\theta_{1(q-1)}) + \theta_{1(q+1)}+\cdots+\theta_{1T}\\
&\qquad + \theta_{21}+\cdots+\theta_{2(q-1)}+\theta_{2(q+1)}+\cdots+\theta_{2T}\\
&\qquad \vdots\\
&\qquad + \theta_{(p-1)1}+\cdots+\theta_{(p-1)(q-1)}+\theta_{(p-1)(q+1)}+\cdots+\theta_{(p-1)T}\\
&\qquad + \theta_{(p+1)1}+\cdots+\theta_{(p+1)(q-1)}+\theta_{(p+1)(q+1)}+\cdots+\theta_{(p+1)T}\\
&\qquad \vdots\\
&\qquad + \theta_{R1}+\cdots+\theta_{R(q-1)}+\theta_{R(q+1)}+\cdots+\theta_{RT})\\
&= \theta_{pq}(\sum_{j\neq q}^{T}\theta_{1j}+\cdots+\sum_{j\neq q}^{T}\theta_{(p-1)j}+\sum_{j\neq q}^{T}\theta_{(p+1)j}+\cdots+\sum_{j\neq q}^{T}\theta_{Rj})\\
&= \theta_{pq}(-\theta_{1q}-\cdots-\theta_{(p-1)q}-\theta_{(p+1)q}-\cdots-\theta_{Rq})\\
&= \theta_{pq}(-\sum_{i\neq p}^{R}\theta_{iq}) = \theta_{pq}^{2}.
\end{aligned} \tag{8.20}$$

This was for a specified pq. Therefore the sum of all possible cross products of the third type is

$$\sum_{i}^{R}\sum_{j}^{T}\theta_{ij}^{2}, \tag{8.21}$$

and the sum of all possible cross products of the third type in all possible $(\sum_{i}^{r}\sum_{j}^{t}\theta_{ij})^2$ is

$$\binom{R-2}{r-2}\binom{T-2}{t-2}\sum_{i}^{R}\sum_{j}^{T}\theta_{ij}^{2}. \tag{8.22}$$

Hence the sum of all possible $(\sum_i^r \sum_j^t \theta_{ij})^2$ is given by summing the pure squared terms and the three types of cross products:

$$\left[\binom{R-1}{r-1}\binom{T-1}{t-1} - \binom{R-1}{r-1}\binom{T-2}{t-2} - \binom{R-2}{r-2}\binom{T-1}{t-1} + \binom{R-2}{r-2}\binom{T-2}{t-2}\right] \sum_i^R \sum_j^T \theta_{ij}^2$$

$$= \binom{R-1}{r-1}\binom{T-1}{t-1} \frac{(R-r)(T-t)}{(R-1)(T-1)} \sum_i^R \sum_j^T \theta_{ij}^2 . \quad (8.23)$$

Dividing by the number of possible samples $\binom{R}{r}\binom{T}{t}$, and substituting σ_θ^2 from (8.6), we get

$$E[(\sum_i^r \sum_j^t \theta_{ij})^2] = rt\left(1 - \frac{r}{R}\right)\left(1 - \frac{t}{T}\right) \sigma_\theta^2 . \quad (8.24)$$

When we put $t = 1$ and $r = 1$ separately and then jointly, we get

$$E[(\sum_i^r \theta_{ij})^2] = r\left(1 - \frac{r}{R}\right)\left(1 - \frac{1}{T}\right) \sigma_\theta^2 , \quad (8.25)$$

$$E[(\sum_j^t \theta_{ij})^2] = t\left(1 - \frac{1}{R}\right)\left(1 - \frac{t}{T}\right) \sigma_\theta^2 . \quad (8.26)$$

$$E[\theta_{ij}^2] = \left(1 - \frac{1}{R}\right)\left(1 - \frac{1}{T}\right) \sigma_\theta^2 . \quad (8.27)$$

We can now evaluate the expectations of the various mean squares. From the model (8.1),

$$\bar{x}_{i..} = \xi + \eta_i + \frac{1}{t}\sum_j^t \zeta_j + \frac{1}{t}\sum_j^t \theta_{ij} + \frac{1}{tn}\sum_j^t \sum_\nu^n z_{ij\nu} , \quad (8.28)$$

$$\bar{x}_{...} = \xi + \frac{1}{r}\sum_i^r \eta_i + \frac{1}{t}\sum_j^t \zeta_j + \frac{1}{rt}\sum_i^r \sum_j^t \theta_{ij} + \frac{1}{rtn}\sum_i^r \sum_j^t \sum_\nu^n z_{ij\nu} ; \quad (8.29)$$

so $$\bar{x}_{i..} - \bar{x}_{...} = \left(\eta_i - \frac{1}{r}\sum_i^r \eta_i\right) + \left(\frac{1}{t}\sum_j^t \theta_{ij} - \frac{1}{rt}\sum_i^r \sum_j^t \theta_{ij}\right) + \left(\frac{1}{tn}\sum_j^t \sum_\nu^n z_{ij\nu} - \frac{1}{rtn}\sum_i^r \sum_j^t \sum_\nu^n z_{ij\nu}\right). \quad (8.30)$$

When we square (8.30) and sum over i, the expectations of the sums of cross products are zero. For example,

$$
\begin{aligned}
E\Big[\frac{1}{t}\sum_i^r\Big(\eta_i-\frac{1}{r}\sum_i^r\eta_i\Big)\Big(\sum_j^t\theta_{ij}-\frac{1}{r}\sum_i^r\sum_j^t\theta_{ij}\Big)\Big]& \\
=E\Big[\frac{1}{t}\sum_i^r\Big\{\eta_i\sum_j^t\theta_{ij}-\frac{1}{r}\eta_i\sum_i^r\sum_j^t\theta_{ij}-\frac{1}{r}\Big(\sum_i^r\eta_i\Big)\Big(\sum_j^t\theta_{ji}\Big)& \\
+\frac{1}{r^2}\Big(\sum_i^r\eta_i\Big)\Big(\sum_i^r\sum_j^t\theta_{ij}\Big)\Big\}\Big]& \\
=\frac{1}{t}E\Big[\sum_i^r\eta_i\sum_j^t\theta_{ij}-\frac{1}{r}\Big(\sum_i^r\eta_i\Big)\Big(\sum_i^r\sum_j^t\theta_{ij}\Big)-\frac{1}{r}\Big(\sum_i^r\eta_i\Big)\Big(\sum_i^r\sum_j^t\theta_{ij}\Big)& \\
+\frac{1}{r}\Big(\sum_i^r\eta_i\Big)\Big(\sum_i^r\sum_j^t\theta_{ij}\Big)\Big]& \\
=\frac{1}{t}E\Big[\sum_i^r\eta_i\sum_j^t\theta_{ij}\Big]-\frac{1}{rt}E\Big[\Big(\sum_i^r\eta_i\Big)\Big(\sum_i^r\sum_j^t\theta_{ij}\Big)\Big].& \qquad (8.31)
\end{aligned}
$$

For the first term, the products $\sum_i^r \eta_i \sum_j^t \theta_{ij}$ can be formed by picking r rows out of R, and t columns out of T; this can be done in $\binom{R}{r}\binom{T}{t}$ ways.

Thus

$$
\begin{aligned}
&E[\sum_i^r \eta_i \sum_j^t \theta_{ij}] \\
&=\frac{1}{\binom{R}{r}\binom{T}{t}}[\eta_1(\theta_{11}+\cdots+\theta_{1t})+\cdots+\eta_1(\theta_{1(T-t+1)}+\cdots+\theta_{1T} \\
&\qquad +\eta_2(\theta_{21}+\cdots+\theta_{2t})+\cdots+\eta_2(\theta_{2(T-t+1)}+\cdots+\theta_{2T}) \\
&\qquad +\cdots \\
&\qquad +\eta_R(\theta_{R1}+\cdots+\theta_{RT})+\cdots+\eta_R(\theta_{R(T-t+1)}+\cdots+\theta_{RT})]. \qquad (8.32)
\end{aligned}
$$

In any row in the square brackets, the θ_{ij} have a fixed i, say p, and in this row any particular value of j, say q, occurs $\binom{T-1}{t-1}$ times. Thus

$$
\begin{aligned}
E\Big[\sum_i^r\eta_i\sum_j^t\theta_{ij}\Big]&=\frac{1}{\binom{R}{r}\binom{T}{t}}\Big[\eta_1\binom{T-1}{t-1}\sum_j^T\theta_{1j}+\cdots+\eta_R\binom{T-1}{t-1}\sum_j^T\theta_{Rj}\Big] \\
&=\frac{\binom{T-1}{t-1}}{\binom{R}{r}\binom{T}{t}}\sum_i^R\eta_i\sum_j^T\theta_{ij}=0, \qquad (8.33)
\end{aligned}
$$

using (8.3). For the second term in (8.31) we have

$$E[(\sum_i^r \eta_i)(\sum_i^r \sum_j^t \theta_{ij})]$$

$$= \frac{1}{\binom{R}{r}\binom{T}{t}}[(\eta_1 + \cdots + \eta_r)\{(\theta_{11} + \cdots + \theta_{1t}) + \cdots + (\theta_{r1} + \cdots + \theta_{rt}) + \cdots$$
$$+ (\theta_{1(T-t+1)} + \cdots + \theta_{1T}) + \cdots + (\theta_{r(T-t+1)} + \cdots + \theta_{rT})\} + \cdots$$
$$+ (\eta_{R-r+1} + \cdots + \eta_R)\{(\theta_{(R-r+1)1} + \cdots + \theta_{(R-r+1)t}) + \cdots$$
$$+(\theta_{R1} + \cdots + \theta_{Rt}) + \cdots + (\theta_{(R-r+1)(T-t+1)} + \cdots + \theta_{(R-r+1)T}) + \cdots$$
$$+ (\theta_{R(T-t+1)} + \cdots + \theta_{RT})\}]$$

$$= (\text{constant}) \times \sum_i^R \eta_i (\sum_j^T \theta_{ij}) = 0, \tag{8.34}$$

using (8.3). Hence (8.31) is zero, and so from (8.30) we have

$$E[nt \sum_i^r (\bar{x}_{i..} - \bar{x}_{...})^2]$$
$$= nt\, E\left[\sum_i^r \left(\eta_i - \frac{1}{r}\sum_i^r \eta_i\right)^2\right] + \frac{n}{t} E\left[\sum_i^r \left(\sum_j^t \theta_{ij} - \frac{1}{r}\sum_i^r \sum_j^t \theta_{ij}\right)^2\right]$$
$$+ \frac{1}{nt} E\left[\sum_i^r \left(\sum_j^t \sum_v^n z_{ijv} - \frac{1}{r}\sum_i^r \sum_j^t \sum_v^n z_{ijv}\right)^2\right]. \tag{8.35}$$

The first term is

$$nt\, E\left[\sum_i^r \left(\eta_i - \frac{1}{r}\sum_i^r \eta_i\right)^2\right] = nt\, E\left[\sum_i^r \left\{\eta_i^2 - 2\frac{\eta_i}{r}\sum_i^r \eta_i + \frac{1}{r^2}\left(\sum_i^r \eta_i\right)^2\right\}\right]$$
$$= nt\, E\left[\sum_i^r \eta_i^2\right] - \frac{nt}{r} E\left[\left(\sum_i^r \eta_i\right)^2\right]$$
$$= nt \cdot r\left(1 - \frac{1}{R}\right)\sigma_\eta^2 - \frac{nt}{r} \cdot r\left(1 - \frac{r}{R}\right)\sigma_\eta^2 = nt(r-1)\sigma_\eta^2, \tag{8.36}$$

using (8.11) and (8.14). The second term is

$$\frac{n}{t} E\left[\sum_i^r \left(\sum_j^t \theta_{ij} - \frac{1}{r}\sum_i^r \sum_j^t \theta_{ij}\right)^2\right]$$
$$= \frac{n}{t}\sum_i^r E\left[\left(\sum_j^t \theta_{ij}\right)^2\right] - \frac{n}{rt} E\left[\left(\sum_i^r \sum_j^t \theta_{ij}\right)^2\right]$$
$$= \frac{n}{t} \cdot r \cdot t\left(1 - \frac{1}{R}\right)\left(1 - \frac{t}{T}\right)\sigma_\theta^2 - \frac{n}{rt} \cdot rt\left(1 - \frac{r}{R}\right)\left(1 - \frac{t}{T}\right)\sigma_\theta^2$$
$$= n(r-1)\left(1 - \frac{t}{T}\right)\sigma_\theta^2, \tag{8.37}$$

using (8.24) and (8.26). The third term is

$$\frac{1}{nt}E\left[\sum_i^r\left(\sum_j^t\sum_\nu^n z_{ij\nu}-\frac{1}{r}\sum_i^r\sum_j^t\sum_\nu^n z_{ij\nu}\right)^2\right]$$
$$=\frac{1}{nt}E\left[\sum_i^r\left(\sum_j^t\sum_\nu^n z_{ij\nu}\right)^2\right]-\frac{1}{rtn}E\left[\left(\sum_i^r\sum_j^t\sum_\nu^n z_{ij\nu}\right)^2\right]=(r-1)\sigma^2, \tag{8.38}$$

using (8.9).

Inserting (8.36), (8.37), and (8.38) in (8.35) and dividing by $(r-1)$, we obtain for the expectation of the row mean square

$$E\left[\frac{nt}{r-1}\sum_i^r(\bar{x}_{i..}-\bar{x}_{...})^2\right]=nt\sigma_\eta^2+n\left(1-\frac{t}{T}\right)\sigma_\theta^2+\sigma^2 \tag{8.39}$$

The expectation of the column mean square is similarly

$$E\left[\frac{nr}{t-1}\sum_j^t(\bar{x}_{.j.}-\bar{x}_{...})^2\right]=nr\sigma_\zeta^2+n\left(1-\frac{r}{R}\right)\sigma_\theta^2+\sigma^2. \tag{8.40}$$

For the interaction sum of squares, after averaging the model (8.1) over the appropriate indices we get

$$\bar{x}_{ij.}-\bar{x}_{i..}-\bar{x}_{.j.}+\bar{x}_{...}$$
$$=\theta_{ij}-\frac{1}{r}\sum_i^r\theta_{ij}-\frac{1}{t}\sum_j^t\theta_{ij}+\frac{1}{rt}\sum_i^r\sum_j^t\theta_{ij}+\frac{1}{n}\sum_\nu^n z_{ij\nu}-\frac{1}{rn}\sum_i^r\sum_\nu^n z_{ij\nu}$$
$$-\frac{1}{tn}\sum_j^t\sum_\nu^n z_{ij\nu}+\frac{1}{rtn}\sum_i^r\sum_j^t\sum_\nu^n z_{ij\nu}. \tag{8.41}$$

When we square and sum and take expectations, the result is a set of terms involving θ and a set of terms involving z. The former reduces to

$$n\,E\left[\sum_i^r\sum_j^t\theta_{ij}^2-\frac{1}{t}\sum_i^r\left(\sum_j^t\theta_{ij}\right)^2-\frac{1}{r}\sum_j^t\left(\sum_i^r\theta_{ij}\right)^2+\frac{1}{rt}\left(\sum_i^r\sum_j^t\theta_{ij}\right)^2\right]$$
$$=n\left[rt\left(1-\frac{1}{R}\right)\left(1-\frac{1}{T}\right)-\frac{r}{t}\cdot t\left(1-\frac{1}{R}\right)\left(1-\frac{t}{T}\right)-\frac{t}{r}\cdot r\left(1-\frac{r}{R}\right)\left(1-\frac{1}{T}\right)\right.$$
$$\left.+\frac{1}{rt}\cdot rt\left(1-\frac{r}{R}\right)\left(1-\frac{t}{T}\right)\right]\sigma_\theta^2$$
$$=n(r-1)(t-1)\sigma_\theta^2. \tag{8.42}$$

Similarly the expectation of the term involving the z's reduces to $(r-1)(t-1)\sigma^2$. Hence the expected value of the interaction mean square is

$$E\left[\frac{n\sum_i^r\sum_j^t(\bar{x}_{ij\cdot}-\bar{x}_{i\cdot\cdot}-\bar{x}_{\cdot j\cdot}+\bar{x}_{\cdots})^2}{(r-1)(t-1)}\right]=\sigma^2+n\sigma_\theta^2. \tag{8.43}$$

These results, (8.39), (8.40), and (8.43) are assembled in Table 13.14.

Table 13.14

Source of variance	Sums of squares	Mean squares	E[M.S.]
Rows	$nt\sum_i^r(\bar{x}_{i\cdot\cdot}-\bar{x}_{\cdots})^2$	s_4^2	$\sigma^2+n\left(1-\frac{t}{T}\right)\sigma_\theta^2+nt\sigma_\eta^2$
Columns	$nr\sum_j^t(\bar{x}_{\cdot j\cdot}-\bar{x}_{\cdots})^2$	s_3^2	$\sigma^2+n\left(1-\frac{r}{R}\right)\sigma_\theta^2+nr\sigma_\zeta^2$
Inter-action	$n\sum_i^r\sum_j^t(\bar{x}_{ij\cdot}-\bar{x}_{i\cdot\cdot}-\bar{x}_{\cdot j\cdot}+\bar{x}_{\cdots})^2$	s_2^2	$\sigma^2+n\sigma_\theta^2$
Within cells	$\sum_i^r\sum_j^t\sum_\nu^n(x_{ij\nu}-\bar{x}_{ij\cdot})^2$	s_1^2	σ^2
Total	$\sum_i^r\sum_j^t\sum_\nu^n(x_{ij\nu}-\bar{x}_{\cdots})^2$		

13.9. Discussion of the Two-Way Crossed Finite-Population Model

In Table 13.14, if both the populations are infinite in extent, so that $(1-t/T)$ and $(1-r/R)$ both tend to 1, then we have exactly the expectations of the mean squares given in Table 13.8 for the model II case. If we further assume that the η_i, ζ_j, and θ_{ij} are normally distributed with variances σ_η^2, σ_ζ^2, and σ_θ^2, then we have exactly model II.

On the other hand, if the samples constitute the entire population, so that $t=T$ and $r=R$, then $(1-t/T)=(1-r/R)=0$ and the expectations of the mean squares become those given in Table 13.3 for model I, and the finite model becomes exactly model I.

If the rows are a sample from an infinite population and the sample of columns is the entire population, then we have the mixed model with the expectations of the mean squares as given in Table 13.15 on page 406.

The appropriate denominator for the F test, the *error term*, for the random-row effect is the within-cell mean square, whereas the error term for the fixed-column effect is the interaction mean square. While σ_ζ^2 continues to be a sum of squares of a set of fixed constants, with an appropriate divisor, σ^2, σ_θ^2, and σ_η^2 are true components of variance and can be estimated in the

Table 13.15

Source of variance	Type of effect	Squares	E[M.S.]
Rows	II	s_4^2	$\sigma^2 + nt\sigma_\eta^2$
Columns	I	s_3^2	$\sigma^2 + n\sigma_\theta^2 + nr\sigma_\zeta^2$
Interactions	Mixed	s_2^2	$\sigma^2 + n\sigma_\theta^2$
Within cells	II	s_1^2	σ^2
Total			

usual way. The fixed-column effects can be estimated from the column averages $\bar{x}_{\cdot j\cdot}$. We obtain confidence limits for the difference between two column means as follows. Averaging the model (8.1) over i and ν, given

$$\bar{x}_{\cdot j\cdot} = \xi + \bar{\eta}_\cdot + \zeta_j + \bar{\theta}_{\cdot j} + \bar{z}_{\cdot j\cdot} \tag{9.1}$$

where $\bar{\eta}_\cdot = \frac{1}{r}\sum_i^r \eta_i$, $\quad \bar{\theta}_{\cdot j} = \frac{1}{r}\sum_i^r \theta_{ij}$, $\quad \bar{z}_{\cdot j\cdot} = \frac{1}{rn}\sum_i^r\sum_\nu^n z_{ij\nu}$.

Then

$$\bar{x}_{\cdot j\cdot} - \bar{x}_{\cdot j'\cdot} = (\zeta_j - \zeta_{j'}) + (\bar{\theta}_{\cdot j} - \bar{\theta}_{\cdot j'}) + (\bar{z}_{\cdot j\cdot} - \bar{z}_{\cdot j'\cdot}). \tag{9.2}$$

If we now assume that θ_{ij} is distributed normally with zero mean and variance σ_θ^2 for each value of j, then $\bar{\theta}_{\cdot j}$ is distributed normally with zero mean and variance σ_θ^2/r for each value of j. Thus $E[\bar{\theta}_{\cdot j}] = 0$, and

$$E[\bar{x}_{\cdot j\cdot} - \bar{x}_{\cdot j'\cdot}] = \zeta_j - \zeta_{j'}, \tag{9.3}$$

$$V[\bar{x}_{\cdot j\cdot} - \bar{x}_{\cdot j'\cdot}] = \frac{2\sigma_\theta^2}{r} + \frac{2\sigma^2}{rn} = \frac{2(\sigma^2 + n\sigma_\theta^2)}{rn}. \tag{9.4}$$

Confidence limits can be obtained from the relation

$$\frac{(\bar{x}_{\cdot j\cdot} - \bar{x}_{\cdot j'\cdot}) - (\zeta_j - \zeta_{j'})}{\sqrt{2s_2^2/rn}} \sim t((r-1)(t-1)). \tag{9.5}$$

With only one observation per cell, there is no within-cell mean square. Reference to Table 13.15, with $n = 1$, shows that the validity of the test for the model I effect, columns, is not affected by the change, the interaction being a satisfactory error term, but the test for the model II effect, rows, will only be satisfactory if the interaction component σ_θ^2 is small compared with σ^2.

13.10. Nested Classifications in the Finite Model

Similar to (7.1), we have the model

$$x_{ijv} = \xi + \eta_i + \lambda_{j(i)} + z_{ijv} \tag{10.1}$$

where $i = 1, \ldots, r$; $j = 1, \ldots, t$; $v = 1, \ldots, n$. The η_i are random samples drawn from a population of size R, and $\sum_i^R \eta_i = 0$. Associated with each i is a population of $\lambda_{j(i)}$: For each of these populations, of size T, we have the condition that $\sum_j^T \lambda_{j(i)} = 0$. The z_{ijv} are distributed independently $N(0, \sigma^2)$. We define

$$\sigma_\eta^2 = \frac{1}{R-1} \sum_i^R \eta_i^2 \tag{10.2}$$

$$\sigma_\lambda^2 = \frac{1}{R(T-1)} \sum_i^R \sum_j^T \lambda_{j(i)}^2 \,. \tag{10.3}$$

The analysis of variance is based on the partitioning of the sum of squares in (7.3). The derivation of the expectations of the mean squares follows the same general lines of the crossed situation in Section 13.8, and leads to the following results for the mean squares listed in Table 13.11:

$$E[s_3^2] = \sigma^2 + n\left(1 - \frac{t}{T}\right)\sigma_\lambda^2 + nt\sigma_\lambda^2\,, \tag{10.4}$$

$$E[s_2^2] = \sigma^2 + n\sigma_\lambda^2, \tag{10.5}$$

$$E[s_1^2] = \sigma^2. \tag{10.6}$$

If the population size of bags within sacks can be regarded as infinite, using the terminology of Table 13.11, $T = \infty$ and these expectations become identical with those of Table 13.11.

REFERENCES

1. Tukey, John W., "Interaction in a row-by-column design," Memorandum Report 18, Statistical Research Group, Princeton University.
2. Cornfield, Jerome, and John W. Tukey, "Average values of mean squares in factorials," *Annals of Mathematical Statistics*, 27(1956), 907–949.
3. Bennett, Carl A., and Norman L. Franklin, *Statistical Analysis in Chemistry and the Chemical Industry*. New York: John Wiley & Sons, 1954.

EXERCISES

13.1. The table below gives the total acidities of samples of three types of brown coal determined in duplicate, using ethanolic NaOH of three concentrations.

(*a*) Make a conventional analysis of variance of these data. Regard both factors as model I effects.

(*b*) Can the null hypothesis that there is no interaction between the three methods of analysis and the three types of coal be accepted?

(*c*) Can the null hypothesis that there is no difference between the three methods of analysis be accepted?

(*d*) Construct a simple 95 per cent confidence interval for the difference between $0.404N$ and $0.786N$ ethanolic NaOH, assuming that the factor type of coal is (i) model I, (ii) model II.

Ethanolic NaOH	Morwell	Yallourn	Maddingley
$0.404N$	8.27, 8.17	8.66, 8.61	8.14, 7.96
$0.626N$	8.03, 8.21	8.42, 8.58	8.02, 7.89
$0.786N$	8.60, 8.20	8.61, 8.76	8.13, 8.07

Data taken from B. Sternhall, "Chemistry of brown coals, VI," *Australian Journal of Applied Science*, 9(1958), 375–379.

CHAPTER 14

Three-Way and Four-Way Analysis of Variance

14.1. The Model

The methods of analysis of two-way classification of data in the previous chapter generalize to the three-way case, in which observations can be classified according to three independent criteria. Imagine a three-dimensional lattice in which the index i refers to rows which might correspond to varieties of corn, j to columns which might correspond to quantity of fertilizer, and k to arrays, say date of harvesting. Suppose that in general in the population there are R rows, T columns, and U arrays, so that there will be RTU cells in the lattice. Suppose that in the sample there are rtu cells formed by the intersection of r rows, t columns, and u arrays. Let ν be the index of the observation in each cell, going to n in the sample. Let ξ_{ijk} be the true mean for the ijkth cell. Then the model is

$$x_{ijk\nu} = \xi_{ijk} + z_{ijk\nu} , \tag{1.1}$$

where the $z_{ijk\nu}$ are normally distributed with zero mean and variance σ^2.

To represent averaging of the ξ_{ijk} over any suffix, we will use a bar over the ξ and replace the suffix averaged over by an x. The over-all average of the ξ_{ijk}, i.e., $\bar{\xi}_{xxx}$, we will however represent simply by ξ. The deviation of the ith row mean from the over-all mean we represent by $\eta_{i\cdot\cdot}$:

$$\eta_{i\cdot\cdot} = \bar{\xi}_{ixx} - \xi. \tag{1.2}$$

Similarly the column and array effects are

$$\eta_{\cdot j \cdot} = \bar{\xi}_{xjx} - \xi, \tag{1.3}$$

$$\eta_{\cdot\cdot k} = \bar{\xi}_{xxk} - \xi. \tag{1.4}$$

The deviations of the cell means in the row and column table, formed by averaging over arrays, from the values expected on the assumption that they would be the grand mean ξ plus the row effect plus the column effect are denoted by $\zeta_{ij\cdot}$:

$$\zeta_{ij\cdot} = \bar{\xi}_{ijx} - (\xi + \eta_{i\cdot\cdot} + \eta_{\cdot j \cdot}). \tag{1.5}$$

The $\zeta_{ij\cdot}$ are the constants for the row $\times$ column interaction. The row $\times$ array interaction will be represented by $\zeta_{i\cdot k}$ and the column $\times$ array interaction by $\zeta_{\cdot jk}$. The deviations of the cell means ξ_{ijk} from the values expected on the assumption that they would be the grand mean plus the row, column, and array effects plus the three two-way interactions are represented by θ_{ijk}:

$$\theta_{ijk} = \xi_{ijk} - (\xi + \eta_{i\cdot\cdot} + \eta_{\cdot j\cdot} + \eta_{\cdot\cdot k} + \zeta_{ij\cdot} + \zeta_{i\cdot k} + \zeta_{\cdot jk}). \tag{1.6}$$

The θ_{ijk} are the constants for the three-way interaction among rows, columns, and arrays.

We can now rewrite the model (1.1) in the form

$$x_{ijkv} = \xi + \eta_{i\cdot\cdot} + \eta_{\cdot j\cdot} + \eta_{\cdot\cdot k} + \zeta_{ij\cdot} + \zeta_{i\cdot k} + \zeta_{\cdot jk} + \theta_{ijk} + z_{ijkv}\,. \tag{1.7}$$

To represent averaging any of the constants we will use the same convention as for the ξ_{ijk}. Thus $\bar{\zeta}_{\cdot jx}$ is the average over arrays for the jth column of the column $\times$ array interaction constants.

We will consider the finite-population model which will give the other models as special cases. The algebra of the partitioning of the sums of squares and the arithmetic of the calculation of the sums of squares are identical for all models. In the finite-population model we suppose that the $\eta_{i\cdot\cdot}$ are a sample of size r from a population of size R, and the $\eta_{\cdot j\cdot}$ and the $\eta_{\cdot\cdot k}$ are samples of t and u from populations of size T and U, respectively. In the population, the various parameters sum to zero over each index:

$$\begin{aligned}
&\sum_i^R \eta_{i\cdot\cdot} = \sum_j^T \eta_{\cdot j\cdot} = \sum_k^U \eta_{\cdot\cdot k} = 0,\\
&\sum_i^R \zeta_{ij\cdot} = \sum_j^T \zeta_{ij\cdot} = \sum_i^R \zeta_{i\cdot k} = \sum_k^U \zeta_{i\cdot k} = \sum_j^T \zeta_{\cdot jk} = \sum_k^U \zeta_{\cdot jk} = 0,\\
&\sum_i^R \theta_{ijk} = \sum_j^T \theta_{ijk} = \sum_k^U \theta_{ijk} = 0.
\end{aligned} \tag{1.8}$$

We will use A, B, C to refer to rows, columns, and arrays. We make the definitions

$$\sigma_A^2 = \sum_i^R \frac{\eta_{i\cdot\cdot}^2}{R-1}, \qquad \text{etc.,}$$

$$\sigma_{AB}^2 = \sum_i^R \sum_j^T \frac{\zeta_{ij\cdot}^2}{(R-1)(T-1)}, \qquad \text{etc.,} \tag{1.9}$$

$$\sigma_{ABC}^2 = \sum_i^R \sum_j^T \sum_k^U \frac{\theta_{ijk}^2}{(R-1)(T-1)(U-1)}.$$

We can write the deviation of $x_{ijk\nu}$ from the grand mean $\bar{x}_{....}$ as an identity in which the successive terms are sample estimates of the parameters:

$$\begin{aligned} x_{ijk\nu} - \bar{x}_{....} = {} & (\bar{x}_{i...} - \bar{x}_{....}) + (\bar{x}_{.j..} - \bar{x}_{....}) + (\bar{x}_{..k.} - \bar{x}_{....}) \\ & + (\bar{x}_{ij..} - \bar{x}_{i...} - \bar{x}_{.j..} + \bar{x}_{....}) + (\bar{x}_{i\cdot k\cdot} - \bar{x}_{i...} - \bar{x}_{..k\cdot} + \bar{x}_{....}) \\ & + (\bar{x}_{.jk\cdot} - \bar{x}_{.j..} - \bar{x}_{..k\cdot} + \bar{x}_{....}) \\ & + (\bar{x}_{ijk\cdot} - \bar{x}_{ij..} - \bar{x}_{i\cdot k\cdot} - \bar{x}_{.jk\cdot} + \bar{x}_{i...} + \bar{x}_{.j..} + \bar{x}_{..k\cdot} - \bar{x}_{....}) \\ & + (x_{ijk\nu} - \bar{x}_{ijk\cdot}). \end{aligned} \tag{1.10}$$

If we write $(\bar{x}_{ij..} - \bar{x}_{i...} - \bar{x}_{.j..} + \bar{x}_{....})$ in the form

$$\bar{x}_{ij..} - [\bar{x}_{....} + (\bar{x}_{i...} - \bar{x}_{....}) + (\bar{x}_{.j..} - \bar{x}_{....})] \tag{1.11}$$

it is more obviously as sample estimate of ζ_{ij}; see (1.5). Similarly, the penultimate term in (1.10) is more obviously a sample estimate of θ_{ijk}, see (1.6), if written as

$$\begin{aligned} \bar{x}_{ijk\cdot} - [\bar{x}_{....} & + (\bar{x}_{i...} - \bar{x}_{....}) + (\bar{x}_{.j..} - \bar{x}_{....}) + (\bar{x}_{..k\cdot} - \bar{x}_{....}) \\ & + (\bar{x}_{ij..} - \bar{x}_{i...} - \bar{x}_{.j..} + \bar{x}_{....}) + (\bar{x}_{i\cdot k\cdot} - \bar{x}_{i...} - \bar{x}_{..k\cdot} + \bar{x}_{....}) \\ & + (\bar{x}_{.jk\cdot} - \bar{x}_{.j..} - \bar{x}_{..k\cdot} + \bar{x}_{....})]. \end{aligned} \tag{1.12}$$

Squaring and summing (1.10) over all indices gives an equation which is entered in column 2 of Table 14.1: the sums of all the cross products are zero. The last column gives the expectations of the mean squares, which can be derived by an extension of the methods of Section 13.10 [1].

The closed forms of sums of squares in Table 14.1 are inconvenient for calculation, and open forms involving totals instead of means analogous to those of Section 13.3 can be obtained. For example the sum of squares for the main effect for A is

$$tun\sum_i^r\left(\bar{x}_{i...} - \bar{x}_{....}\right)^2 = \frac{1}{tun}\sum_i^r\left(\sum_j^t\sum_\nu^u\sum_k^n x_{ijk\nu}\right)^2 - \frac{1}{rtun}\left(\sum_i^r\sum_j^t\sum_k^u\sum_\nu^n x_{ijk\nu}\right)^2. \tag{1.13}$$

Table 14.1

Source of variance	Sums of squares	Degrees of freedom	E[M.S.]
A	$ntu\sum_i^r(\bar{x}_{i\cdots}-\bar{x}_{\cdots\cdot})^2$	$(r-1)$	$\sigma^2+n\left(1-\frac{t}{T}\right)\left(1-\frac{u}{U}\right)\sigma^2_{ABC}+nu\left(1-\frac{t}{T}\right)\sigma^2_{AB}+nt\left(1-\frac{u}{U}\right)\sigma^2_{AC}+ntu\sigma^2_A$
B	$nru\sum_j^t(\bar{x}_{\cdot j\cdot\cdot}-\bar{x}_{\cdots\cdot})^2$	$(t-1)$	$\sigma^2+n\left(1-\frac{r}{R}\right)\left(1-\frac{u}{U}\right)\sigma^2_{ABC}+nu\left(1-\frac{r}{R}\right)\sigma^2_{AB}+nr\left(1-\frac{u}{U}\right)\sigma^2_{BC}+nru\sigma^2_B$
C	$nrt\sum_k^u(\bar{x}_{\cdot\cdot j\cdot}-\bar{x}_{\cdots\cdot})^2$	$(u-1)$	$\sigma^2+n\left(1-\frac{t}{T}\right)\left(1-\frac{r}{R}\right)\sigma^2_{ABC}+nt\left(1-\frac{r}{R}\right)\sigma^2_{AC}+nr\left(1-\frac{t}{T}\right)\sigma^2_{BC}+nrt\sigma^2_C$
AB	$nu\sum_i^r\sum_j^t(\bar{x}_{ij\cdot\cdot}-\bar{x}_{i\cdots}-\bar{x}_{\cdot j\cdot\cdot}+\bar{x}_{\cdots\cdot})^2$	$(r-1)(t-1)$	$\sigma^2+n\left(1-\frac{u}{U}\right)\sigma^2_{ABC}+nu\sigma^2_{AB}$
AC	$nt\sum_i^r\sum_k^u(\bar{x}_{i\cdot k\cdot}-\bar{x}_{i\cdots}-\bar{x}_{\cdot\cdot k\cdot}+\bar{x}_{\cdots\cdot})^2$	$(r-1)(u-1)$	$\sigma^2+n\left(1-\frac{t}{T}\right)\sigma^2_{ABC}+nt\sigma^2_{AC}$
BC	$nr\sum_j^t\sum_k^u(\bar{x}_{\cdot jk\cdot}-\bar{x}_{\cdot j\cdot\cdot}-\bar{x}_{\cdot\cdot k\cdot}+\bar{x}_{\cdots\cdot})^2$	$(t-1)(u-1)$	$\sigma^2+n\left(1-\frac{r}{R}\right)\sigma^2_{ABC}+nr\sigma^2_{BC}$
ABC	$n\sum_i^r\sum_j^t\sum_k^u(\bar{x}_{ijk\cdot}-\bar{x}_{ij\cdot\cdot}-\bar{x}_{i\cdot k\cdot}-\bar{x}_{\cdot jk\cdot}+\bar{x}_{i\cdots}+\bar{x}_{\cdot j\cdot\cdot}+\bar{x}_{\cdot\cdot k\cdot}-\bar{x}_{\cdots\cdot})^2$	$(r-1)(t-1)(u-1)$	$\sigma^2+n\sigma^2_{ABC}$
Within cells	$\sum_i^r\sum_j^t\sum_k^u\sum_\nu^n(x_{ijk\nu}-\bar{x}_{ijk\cdot})^2$	$rtu(n-1)$	σ^2
Total	$\sum_i^r\sum_j^t\sum_k^u\sum_\nu^n(x_{ijk\nu}-\bar{x}_{\cdots\cdot})^2$	$rtun-1$	

For the AB interaction

$$nu \sum_{i}^{r} \sum_{j}^{t} (\bar{x}_{ij..} - \bar{x}_{i...} - \bar{x}_{.j..} + \bar{x}_{....})^2$$
$$= \frac{1}{un} \sum_{i}^{r} \sum_{j}^{t} \left(\sum_{k}^{u} \sum_{v}^{n} x_{ijkv} \right)^2 - \frac{1}{rtun} \left(\sum_{i}^{r} \sum_{j}^{t} \sum_{k}^{u} \sum_{v}^{n} x_{ijkv} \right)^2$$
$$- ntu \sum_{i}^{r} (\bar{x}_{i...} - \bar{x}_{....})^2 - nru \sum_{j}^{t} (\bar{x}_{.j..} - \bar{x}_{....})^2 \qquad (1.14)$$

where the last two terms are the sums of squares for the A and B main effects. The total sum of squares is

$$\sum_{i}^{r} \sum_{j}^{t} \sum_{k}^{u} \sum_{v}^{n} x_{ijkv}^2 - \frac{1}{rtun} \left(\sum_{i}^{r} \sum_{j}^{t} \sum_{k}^{u} \sum_{v}^{n} x_{ijkv} \right)^2, \qquad (1.15)$$

and the within-cells sum of squares is

$$\sum_{i}^{r} \sum_{j}^{t} \sum_{k}^{u} \sum_{v}^{n} x_{ijkv}^2 - \frac{1}{n} \sum_{i}^{r} \sum_{j}^{t} \sum_{k}^{u} \left(\sum_{v}^{n} x_{ijkv} \right)^2. \qquad (1.16)$$

The sum of squares for the ABC interaction is obtained by difference.

14.2. Models I and II

We will get the expected mean squares for a model I three-way analysis of variance by putting $r = R$, $t = T$, and $u = U$ in the coefficients of the components of variance in the last column in Table 14.1. All the factors in parentheses will be zero, giving the second column of Table 14.2, in which all the components of variance are really sums of squares of constants, e.g., $\sigma_A^2 = \sum_{i}^{R} \eta_{i..}^2/(R-1)$, and are not true variances. All the effects are clearly to be tested against the within-cell mean square.

If there is only one observation per cell, the analysis will be unsatisfactory unless σ_{ABC}^2 is small compared with σ^2.

We will get the expected mean squares for a model II analysis by putting $R = T = U = \infty$ in the coefficients of the components of variance in the last column of Table 14.1. All the factors in parentheses will be equal to 1, giving the last column of Table 14.2. Here the components of variance are true variances, and we will adopt the convention of using lower-case letters in the subscript to denote this fact.

The usual testing procedure is to test the three-way interaction against the within-cells mean square. The next step depends on our point of view. A strict "nonpooler" proceeds to test the two-way interactions against the three-way interaction, irrespective of the outcome of this first test. Then he would test the main effects against appropriate linear combinations. For example, to test the A main effect he would use the mean squares for $(AB + AC - ABC)$, since the expected value for this combination is

$$\sigma^2 + n\sigma_{abc}^2 + nu\sigma_{ab}^2 + nt\sigma_{ac}^2.$$

This linear combination of three mean squares would have its approximate degrees of freedom estimated by (9.7.8).

Table 14.2

Source of variance	E[M.S.] Model I	E[M.S.] Model II
A	$\sigma^2 + ntu\sigma_A^2$	$\sigma^2 + n\sigma_{abc}^2 + nu\sigma_{ab}^2 + nt\sigma_{ac}^2 + ntu\sigma_a^2$
B	$\sigma^2 + nru\sigma_B^2$	$\sigma^2 + n\sigma_{abc}^2 + nu\sigma_{ab}^2 + nr\sigma_{bc}^2 + nru\sigma_b^2$
C	$\sigma^2 + nrt\sigma_C^2$	$\sigma^2 + n\sigma_{abc}^2 + nt\sigma_{ac}^2 + nr\sigma_{bc}^2 + nrt\sigma_c^2$
AB	$\sigma^2 + nu\sigma_{AB}^2$	$\sigma^2 + n\sigma_{abc}^2 + nu\sigma_{ab}^2$
AC	$\sigma^2 + nt\sigma_{AC}^2$	$\sigma^2 + n\sigma_{abc}^2 + nt\sigma_{ac}^2$
BC	$\sigma^2 + nr\sigma_{BC}^2$	$\sigma^2 + n\sigma_{abc}^2 + nr\sigma_{bc}^2$
ABC	$\sigma^2 + n\sigma_{ABC}^2$	$\sigma^2 + n\sigma_{abc}^2$
Within cells	σ^2	σ^2

Alternatively, some people would indulge in some judicious pooling. If at the first test, the mean square for ABC was neither statistically significant at the chosen level of significance nor had a variance ratio exceeding 2, the "sometimes-pooler" would pool the sums of squares and degrees of freedom of the ABC and within-cells term, and use this as an estimate of σ^2. The assumption is being made that $\sigma_{abc}^2 = 0$, and so σ_{abc}^2 is stricken out of all the expected mean squares. Similarly, if one of the interactions, say AB, was statistically significant at the chosen level of significance, or if the variance ratio exceeded 2, the sometimes-pooler would leave this mean square untouched, but otherwise he would assume that σ_{ab}^2 was zero, pool its sum of squares and degrees of freedom with those for (ABC + within cells) to get a better estimate of σ^2, and also strike σ_{ab}^2 out of the expectations of the mean squares wherever it occurred. With this procedure, if none of the two-way interactions was significant nor had variance ratios exceeding 2, they would all end up by being pooled with the within-cells mean square, and the three main effects would be tested against this pooled error term.

The "never-pooler" can be confident that his errors of the first kind have the stated probability. The sometimes-pooler may be somewhat uncomfortable about this, but he will claim that his errors of the second kind have smaller probability than those of the never-pooler. If the sample sizes are large, so that degrees of freedom are plentiful, the motivation, or temptation, to be a sometimes-pooler are less. The rule about the factor 2 comes from Paull [2].

If, in a model II analysis, there is only one observation per cell, of course there is no within-cell mean square, but putting $n = 1$ in the expectations of mean squares in Table 14.2 does not affect the testing procedure.

A further complication in the testing of complicated analyses of variance is the multiplicity of tests being performed. For example, in a five-factor analysis there will be 5 main effects, 10 two-way interactions, and 10 three-way interactions. Thus, ignoring the four-way and the five-way interactions, we may be testing $5 + 10 + 10 = 25$ effects.

Suppose that $x_1, \ldots, x_n$ are identically distributed independent observations. Then one of the sample of n will be the largest: Call this $x_{\max}$. The condition that the largest is less than some value, say x, is the same as the condition that they are all less than x, i.e.,

$$\Pr\{x_1 < x, x_2 < x, \ldots\} = \Pr\{x_{\max} < x\}.$$

Also, since the observations are independent,

$$\Pr\{x_1 < x, x_2 < x, \ldots .\} = \Pr\{x_1 < x\} \cdot \Pr\{x_2 < x\} \cdots = (\Pr\{x_i < x\})^n;$$

so

$$\Pr\{x_{\max} < x\} = (\Pr\{x_i < x\})^n. \tag{2.1}$$

Now there will be a P point of the cumulative distribution of $x_{\max}$ such that

$$\Pr\{x_{\max} < x_{\max,P}\} = P. \tag{2.2}$$

Also, substituting $x_{\max,P}$ for x in (2.1),

$$\Pr\{x_{\max} < x_{\max,P}\} = (\Pr\{x_i < x_{\max,P}\})^n. \tag{2.3}$$

Comparing (2.2) and (2.3), we see that

$$\Pr\{x_i < x_{\max,P}\} = P^{1/n}, \tag{2.4}$$

or

$$\Pr\{x_i < x_{\max,P^n}\} = P. \tag{2.5}$$

In other words, the P^n point of the distribution of $x_{\max}$ is equal to the P point of the distribution of x. Thus, if we are testing 10 independent F ratios, all with the same degrees of freedom, so that they have the same distribution under the various null hypotheses, the 0.99 point of the distribution for the largest of the 10 is actually the $\sqrt[10]{0.99} \simeq 0.999$ point of the ordinary F distribution. Of course, in the usual analysis-of-variance situation the F ratios are not independent since they use a common denominator mean square. Finney [3] showed that for moderately large, say greater than 10 or preferably 20, denominator degrees of freedom the F ratios could be assumed to be independent without serious error. For the special case where the numerator degrees of freedom are 1, Nair [4] tabulated the 0.95 and 0.99 points of the largest variance ratio for denominator degrees of freedom starting at 10, reproduced as Table IX of the appendix. Unfortunately his table only goes to the largest of 10 variance ratios.

Daniel [5] and Birnbaum [6] have developed a scheme for the significance testing of a large number of mean squares with single degrees of freedom which has promise. However, a completely satisfactory procedure must give weight to the relevant a priori probabilities. It is found by experience that main effects are more frequently significant than two-way interactions, and two-way interactions are more frequently significant than three-way interactions, and so on. Thus, if we find two effects, one a main effect and the other a four-way interaction, both significant at the 0.025 level, we would have little hesitation in accepting the former as real and dismissing the latter as an instance of random fluctuation. Also, the pattern of significance conveys relative information. If we find the main effects A, B, and C and their interactions AB, AC, and BC significant, we would not be surprised to find ABC significant, whereas, if ABC was significant without any of the other effects mentioned being significant, we would be tempted to regard this as an accident of random fluctuation.

It seems clear that an efficient analysis of a multi-factor experiment is at present somewhat subjective. One could certainly lay down certain rules, but they would lead to a higher proportion of errors, of the first and second kinds, than an intelligent and experienced practitioner would commit.

14.3. Mixed Models

In three-way analysis of variance there are two mixed models, one in which one factor is random and two factors are fixed, and vice versa. In the first case, if a is random and B and C are fixed, we put $R = \infty$, $t = T$, and $u = U$ in the expectations of mean squares in Table 14.1, and obtain the left-hand side of Table 14.3. On a nonpooling basis, the tests of significance are clear. For example, aB and aC are tested against within cells whereas BC is tested against aBC, and a is tested against within cells whereas B and C are tested against the aB and aC interactions. If there is only one observation per cell, then satisfactory tests for a, aB, and aC exist only if σ^2_{aBC} is small, but the tests for B, C, and BC remain valid.

The case of a and b random and C fixed is given by putting $R = T = \infty$, $u = U$ in Table 14.1, and this gives the right-hand side of Table 14.3. The tests are straightforward except that a linear combination of mean squares $(aC + bC - abC)$ is necessary to provide a satisfactory error term for C. If there is only one observation per cell, so that there is no within-cell mean square, the tests are unchanged except for ab, which requires σ^2_{abC} to be small for a satisfactory test.

Table 14.3

a random, *B* and *C* fixed		*a* and *b* random, *C* fixed	
Effect	E[M.S.]	Effect	E[M.S.]
a	$\sigma^2 + ntu\sigma^2_a$	a	$\sigma^2 + nu\sigma^2_{ab} + ntu\sigma^2_a$
B	$\sigma^2 + nu\sigma^2_{aB} + nru\sigma^2_B$	b	$\sigma^2 + nu\sigma^2_{ab} + nru\sigma^2_b$
C	$\sigma^2 + nt\sigma^2_{aC} + nrt\sigma^2_C$	C	$\sigma^2 + n\sigma^2_{abC} + nt\sigma^2_{aC} + nr\sigma^2_{bC} + nrt\sigma^2_C$
aB	$\sigma^2 + nu\sigma^2_{aB}$	ab	$\sigma^2 + nu\sigma^2_{ab}$
aC	$\sigma^2 + nt\sigma^2_{aC}$	aC	$\sigma^2 + n\sigma^2_{abC} + nt\sigma^2_{aC}$
BC	$\sigma^2 + n\sigma^2_{aBC} + nr\sigma^2_{BC}$	bC	$\sigma^2 + n\sigma^2_{abC} + nr\sigma^2_{bC}$
aBC	$\sigma^2 + n\sigma^2_{aBC}$	abC	$\sigma^2 + n\sigma^2_{abC}$
Within cells	σ^2	Within cells	σ^2

14.4. Confidence Limits in Three-Way Analysis

We will discuss the situation in which there is only one observation per cell and it is assumed that the three-way interaction is zero.

In the model I case, the model is

$$x_{ijk} = \xi + \eta_{i..} + \eta_{.j.} + \eta_{..k} + \zeta_{ij.} + \zeta_{i.k} + \zeta_{.jk} + z_{ijk}. \tag{4.1}$$

If we are going to construct confidence limits for the difference between two row means $(\eta_{i..} - \eta_{i'..})$, we will be making the assumption that the interactions involving rows, namely, the $\zeta_{ij.}$ and $\zeta_{i.k}$, are zero; so the model becomes

$$x_{ijk} = \xi + \eta_{i..} + \eta_{.j.} + \eta_{..k} + \zeta_{.jk} + z_{ijk} . \tag{4.2}$$

Averaging over j and k, we get

$$\bar{x}_{i..} = \xi + \eta_{i..} + \bar{\eta}_{.x.} + \bar{\eta}_{..x} + \bar{\zeta}_{.xx} + \bar{z}_{i..} = \xi + \eta_{i..} + \bar{z}_{i..} ,$$

since

$$\bar{\eta}_{.x.} = \frac{1}{t}\sum_{i}^{t} \eta_{.j.} = \frac{1}{t}\sum_{j}^{T} \eta_{.j.} = 0,$$

since $t = T$, and similarly $\bar{\eta}_{\cdot\cdot x} = \bar{\zeta}_{\cdot xx} = 0$. Thus

$$\bar{x}_{i\cdot\cdot} - \bar{x}_{i'\cdot\cdot} = (\eta_{i\cdot\cdot} - \eta_{i'\cdot\cdot}) + (\bar{z}_{i\cdot\cdot} - \bar{z}_{i'\cdot\cdot}),$$

with expectation and variance

$$E[\bar{x}_{i\cdot\cdot} - \bar{x}_{i'\cdot\cdot}] = \eta_{i\cdot\cdot} - \eta_{i'\cdot\cdot}\,, \tag{4.3}$$

$$V[\bar{x}_{i\cdot\cdot} - \bar{x}_{i'\cdot\cdot}] = V[\bar{z}_{i\cdot\cdot}] + V[\bar{z}_{i'\cdot\cdot}] = \frac{2\sigma^2}{tu}. \tag{4.4}$$

Confidence limits for $\eta_{i\cdot\cdot} - \eta_{i'\cdot\cdot}$ can be obtained by inserting in place of σ^2 the mean square for ABC, which is assumed to estimate σ^2. Since, using (1.2),

$$\eta_{i\cdot\cdot} - \eta_{i'\cdot\cdot} = (\bar{\xi}_{ixx} - \xi) - (\bar{\xi}_{i'xx} - \xi) = \bar{\xi}_{ixx} - \bar{\xi}_{i'xx}\,,$$

the confidence limits for $\eta_{i\cdot\cdot} - \eta_{i'\cdot\cdot}$ are identical with confidence limits for $\bar{\xi}_{ixx} - \bar{\xi}_{i'xx}$.

In the mixed model of the type (a, B, C), if we are going to construct confidence limits for the difference between two column means, $(\eta_{\cdot j\cdot} - \eta_{\cdot j'\cdot})$, we will be making the assumption that the BC interaction $\zeta_{\cdot jk} = 0$, and so the model (4.1) becomes

$$x_{ijk} = \xi + \eta_{i\cdot\cdot} + \eta_{\cdot j\cdot} + \eta_{\cdot\cdot k} + \zeta_{ij\cdot} + \zeta_{i\cdot k} + z_{ijk}\,. \tag{4.5}$$

Averaging over i and k, we get

$$\bar{x}_{\cdot j\cdot} = \xi + \bar{\eta}_{x\cdot\cdot} + \eta_{\cdot j\cdot} + \bar{\eta}_{\cdot\cdot x} + \bar{\zeta}_{xj\cdot} + \bar{\zeta}_{x\cdot x} + \bar{z}_{\cdot j\cdot}\,,$$

whence

$$\bar{x}_{\cdot j\cdot} - \bar{x}_{\cdot j'\cdot} = (\eta_{\cdot j\cdot} - \eta_{\cdot j'\cdot}) + (\bar{\zeta}_{xj\cdot} - \bar{\zeta}_{xj'\cdot}) + (\bar{z}_{\cdot j\cdot} - \bar{z}_{\cdot j'\cdot}). \tag{4.6}$$

The $\zeta_{ij\cdot}$ is a mixed interaction subject to the conditions $\sum_i^R \zeta_{ij\cdot} = \sum_j^T \zeta_{ij\cdot} = 0$, but, since $R = \infty$ and $T = t$, these conditions become $\sum_i^\infty \zeta_{ij\cdot} = \sum_j^t \zeta_{ij\cdot} = 0$. Thus $\zeta_{ij\cdot}$ is distributed normally with zero mean and variance σ_{aB}^2 for each level of j, and hence $\bar{\eta}_{xj\cdot}$ is distributed normally with zero mean and variance σ_{aB}^2/r for each level of j. Hence

$$E[\bar{x}_{\cdot j\cdot} - \bar{x}_{\cdot j'\cdot}] = (\eta_{\cdot j\cdot} - \eta_{\cdot j'\cdot}), \tag{4.7}$$

$$V[\bar{x}_{\cdot j\cdot} - \bar{x}_{\cdot j'\cdot}] = \frac{2\sigma_{aB}^2}{r} + \frac{2\sigma^2}{ru} = \frac{2}{ru}(\sigma^2 + u\sigma_{aB}^2), \tag{4.8}$$

$$\hat{V}[\bar{x}_{\cdot j\cdot} - \bar{x}_{\cdot j'\cdot}] = \frac{2}{ru}(\text{M.S. for } aB), \tag{4.9}$$

and confidence limits follow in the usual way.

In the mixed model of the type (a, b, C), we have

$$\bar{x}_{\cdot\cdot k} = \xi + \bar{\eta}_{x\cdot\cdot} + \bar{\eta}_{\cdot x\cdot} + \eta_{\cdot\cdot k} + \bar{\zeta}_{xx\cdot} + \bar{\zeta}_{x\cdot k} + \bar{\zeta}_{\cdot xk} + \bar{z}_{\cdot\cdot k},$$

$$\bar{x}_{\cdot\cdot k} - \bar{x}_{\cdot\cdot k'} = (\eta_{\cdot\cdot k} - \eta_{\cdot\cdot k'}) + (\bar{\zeta}_{x\cdot k} - \bar{\zeta}_{x\cdot k'}) + (\bar{\zeta}_{\cdot xk} - \bar{\zeta}_{\cdot xk'}) + (\bar{z}_{\cdot\cdot k} - \bar{z}_{\cdot\cdot k'}). \tag{4.10}$$

The $\zeta_{i\cdot k}$ and $\zeta_{\cdot jk}$ are mixed interactions distributed normally with zero means and variances σ_{aC}^2, σ_{bC}^2 for each level of k. Hence

$$E[\bar{x}_{\cdot\cdot k} - \bar{x}_{\cdot\cdot k'}] = \eta_{\cdot\cdot k} - \eta_{\cdot\cdot k'},$$

$$V[\bar{x}_{\cdot\cdot k} - \bar{x}_{\cdot\cdot k'}] = \frac{2\sigma_{aC}^2}{r} + \frac{2\sigma_{bC}^2}{t} + \frac{2\sigma^2}{rt} = \frac{2}{rt}(\sigma^2 + t\sigma_{aC}^2 + r\sigma_{bC}^2), \tag{4.11}$$

$$\hat{V}[\bar{x}_{\cdot\cdot k} - \bar{x}_{\cdot\cdot k'}] = \frac{2}{rt}[\text{M.S. for } aC + bC - abC], \tag{4.12}$$

and the linear combination of mean squares will have its approximate degrees of freedom given by (9.7.8).

It will be noticed from the foregoing results that it is unnecessary in practice to go through these calculations to obtain the estimated variance of the difference between two means, since the answer always comes out to be twice the appropriate error mean square for testing the corresponding effect divided by the number of original observations in each mean being compared.

14.5. An Example of Three-Way Analysis of Variance

The date of Table 14.4 (taken from [7]) were obtained in a research program aimed at developing procedures for the bacteriological testing of milk. Milk samples were tested in an apparatus which involved two major components, a bottle and a tube. The result of a single test is simply recorded as growth or failure to grow. All six combinations of two types of bottle and three types of tube were tested on each sample, and 10 tests were run with each sample $\times$ bottle $\times$ tube combination. Table 14.4 gives the number of positive tubes in each set of 10. As discussed in Section 3.4, this variable should be binomially distributed, and, to obtain a variable with a stable variance, we should use the inverse sine transformation. However, our main purpose in presenting this example is as an illustration of the calculations for a three-way analysis of variance, and this will be achieved better by using the simple integers of Table 14.4. It is, however, instructive to also carry out the analysis of variance on the transformed variable and see how little the conclusions are affected. Let i refer to samples, j to tubes, and k to bottles.

Regarding Table 14.4 as a three-way classification with one observation per cell, the operations of summing over cells and calculating a within-cells sum of squares do not arise. As will be apparent from the computing

Table 14.4

Milk sample	Tube					
	Bottle I			Bottle II		
	A	*B*	*C*	*A*	*B*	*C*
1	1	1	1	1	3	2
2	3	4	2	2	1	3
3	3	2	4	3	3	6
4	2	4	1	1	0	0
5	2	1	3	2	4	6
6	1	1	2	0	2	1
7	5	5	5	3	5	5
8	1	1	1	0	2	0
9	0	1	2	2	2	2
10	3	4	5	1	1	3
11	0	0	4	0	2	1
12	0	1	2	0	3	1

formulas given in (1.13) and (1.14), the first step in the analysis is to form sums over every index and every combination of indices; i.e., we

1. Sum over rows i to obtain a column $\times$ array table containing $\sum_{i}^{r} x_{ijk}$ (Table 14.5).

2. Sum over columns j to obtain a row $\times$ array table containing $\sum_{j}^{t} x_{ijk}$ (Table 14.6).

3. Sum over arrays k to obtain a row $\times$ column table containing $\sum_{k}^{u} x_{ijk}$ (Table 14.7).

4. Form the marginal totals of each of these three tables.

5. Form the sums of the marginal totals, which of course must be identically equal, being the grand sum of all observations.

Table 14.5. Summing over Samples (i)

	Tube			
Bottle	A	B	C	Total
I	21	25	32	78
II	15	28	30	73
Total	36	53	62	151

Table 14.6. Summing over Tubes (j)

	Bottle		
Sample	I	II	Total
1	3	6	9
2	9	6	15
3	9	12	21
4	7	1	8
5	6	12	18
6	4	3	7
7	15	13	28
8	3	2	5
9	3	6	9
10	12	5	17
11	4	3	7
12	3	4	7
Total	78	73	151

Table 14.7. Summing over Bottles (k)

	Tube			
Sample	A	B	C	Total
1	2	4	3	9
2	5	5	5	15
3	6	5	10	21
4	3	4	1	8
5	4	5	9	18
6	1	3	3	7
7	8	10	10	28
8	1	3	1	5
9	2	3	4	9
10	4	5	8	17
11	0	2	5	7
12	0	4	3	7
Total	36	53	62	151

With these preliminary summations the subsequent calculations are straightforward. The sum of squares for samples is given by (1.13) with the modification that $n = 1$ and summation over v is not involved.

$$\text{S.S. for samples} = \frac{9^2 + 15^2 + \cdots + 7^2}{2 \times 3} - \frac{(151)^2}{2 \times 3 \times 12} = 93.486,$$

$$\text{S.S. for tubes} = \frac{36^2 + 53^2 + 62^2}{12 \times 2} - \frac{(151)^2}{2 \times 3 \times 12} = 14.527,$$

$$\text{S.S. for bottles} = \frac{78^2 + 73^2}{12 \times 3} - \frac{(151)^2}{2 \times 3 \times 12} = 0.347.$$

For the sample × tube interaction, the sums of squares is given by (1.14):

$$\frac{2^2 + 5^2 + 6^2 + \cdots + 3^2}{2} - \frac{(151)^2}{2 \times 3 \times 12} - 93.486 - 14.527 = 22.806.$$

The other two interactions are calculated similarly. The total sum of squares is given by (1.15):

$$(1^2 + 3^2 + \cdots + 1^2) - \frac{(151)^2}{2 \times 3 \times 12} = 184.319.$$

All these items are entered in Table 14.8 and the three-way interaction is calculated by difference.

Table 14.8

Source of variance	Sums of squares	Degrees of freedom	Mean squares	E[M.S.]
Samples	93.486	11	8.499	$\sigma^2 + 3 \times 2\sigma_s^2$
Tubes	14.527	2	7.263	$\sigma^2 + 2\sigma_{sT}^2 + 2 \times 12\sigma_T^2$
Bottles	0.347	1	0.347	$\sigma^2 + 3\sigma_{sB}^2 + 3 \times 12\sigma_B^2$
Samples × tubes	22.806	22	1.037	$\sigma^2 + 2\sigma_{sT}^2$
Samples × bottles	27.153	11	2.468	$\sigma^2 + 3\sigma_{sB}^2$
Tubes × bottles	1.695	2	0.847	$\sigma^2 + 12\sigma_{TB}^2$
Samples × tubes × bottles	24.305	22	1.105	σ^2
Total	184.319	71		

The tube and bottle are fixed effects and the sample is a random effect. If s, T, and B refer to samples, tubes, and bottles, application of the left half of Table 14.3, with $n = 1$ and $\sigma_{sTB}^2 = 0$, gives the expectations of mean squares in the last column of Table 14.8.

Interpreting this table as a nonpooler, it is apparent that bottles, samples × bottles, and tubes × bottles are nonsignificant. Samples × bottles has a variance ratio 2.23, and $F_{0.95}(11, 22) = 2.26$; so it does not quite reach the 0.05 level of significance. The tube main effect, tested against the sample × tube interaction, has a variance ratio of 7.00, and $F_{0.995}(2, 22) = 6.81$; so there is no doubt as to the significance of the tube effect. The sample effect is also highly significant, and the component of variance σ_s^2 is estimated as $(8.499 - 1.105)/6 = 1.232$.

Confidence limits can be constructed with (4.9). For example, for 95 per cent confidence limits between the two bottles, we want $t_{0.975}(11) = 2.201$, and $(\bar{x}_{\cdot\cdot\mathrm{I}} - \bar{x}_{\cdot\cdot\mathrm{II}}) = (78 - 73)/12 \times 3 = 0.139$: Also

$$\hat{V}[\bar{x}_{\cdot\cdot\mathrm{I}} - \bar{x}_{\cdot\cdot\mathrm{II}}] = \frac{2}{12 \times 3}\,[\text{M.S. for samples} \times \text{bottles}] = 0.1371.$$

The confidence limits are $0.139 \pm 2.201\sqrt{0.1371}$, or $(-0.676, 0.954)$. Confidence limits for the difference between any two tube averages can be constructed similarly, although if we are interested in more than one comparison it would be advisable to use Tukey's multiple-comparison technique (cf. Section 10.3).

14.6. Orthogonal Contrasts

It is possible to split the $(r - 1)$ degrees of freedom of a model I factor up into $(r - 1)$ separate single degrees of freedom, each corresponding to a specific contrast, in such a way that the $(r - 1)$ contrasts are independent and the sum of the sums of squares corresponding to each contrast adds up to the original unpartitioned sum of squares.

Suppose that we have r means $\bar{x}_i$ distributed normally with means ξ_i and variances (σ^2/n_i). We define a contrast as in (10.3.1) as $\theta = \sum_i^r c_i\xi_i$, where $\sum_i^r c_i = 0$. As in (10.3.2) the contrast is estimated as $H = \sum_i^r c_i\bar{x}_i$, and H has expectation θ and variance $V[H] = \sigma^2 \sum_i^r \frac{c_i^2}{n_i}$. Since H is distributed normally, then under the null hypothesis $\theta = 0$ we have that $H/\sqrt{V[H]}$ is a unit normal deviate, and so

$$\frac{\left(\sum_i^r c_i\bar{x}_i\right)^2}{\sum_i^r \frac{c_i^2}{n_i}} \sim \sigma^2\chi^2(1). \tag{6.1}$$

Under this null hypothesis, (6.1) will have an expected value σ^2, and, if we have an independent estimate s^2 with f degrees of freedom of σ^2, then (6.1) divided by s^2 will be distributed as $F(1, f)$. If the $\bar{x}_i$ are based on totals T_i, so that $\bar{x}_i = T_i/n_i$, then (6.1) can be written as

$$\frac{\left(\sum_i^r \frac{c_iT_i}{n_i}\right)^2}{\sum_i^r \frac{c_i^2}{n_i}}$$

and, when the n_i all equal n, this becomes

$$\frac{\left(\sum_i^r c_i T_i\right)^2}{n \sum_i^r c_i^2}. \tag{6.2}$$

Suppose now that we have two contrasts,

$$H_1 = \sum_i^r c_{1i}\bar{x}_i , \qquad H_2 = \sum_i^r c_{2i}\bar{x}_i ,$$

and we require these to be independent. We saw in Section 12.3 that for independence it is sufficient, when H_1, H_2 are jointly normal, to show that they have zero covariance. Now

$$V[H_1 + H_2] = V[H_1] + V[H_2] + 2\,\text{Cov}[H_1, H_2];$$

so $$2\,\text{Cov}[H_1, H_2] = V[H_1 + H_2] - V[H_1] - V[H_2].$$

But
$$\begin{aligned} V[H_1 + H_2] &= V\left[\sum_i^r c_{1i}\bar{x}_i + \sum_i^r c_{2i}\bar{x}_i\right] \\ &= V\left[\sum_i^r (c_{1i} + c_{2i})\bar{x}_i\right] = \sum_i^r (c_{1i} + c_{2i})^2\, V[\bar{x}_i] \\ &= \sigma^2\left[\sum_i^r \frac{c_{1i}^2}{n_i} + \sum_i^r \frac{c_{2i}^2}{n_i} + 2\sum_i^r \frac{c_{1i}c_{2i}}{n_i}\right]; \end{aligned}$$

so $$2\,\text{Cov}[H_1, H_2] = 2\sigma^2 \sum_i^r \frac{c_{1i}c_{2i}}{n_i}.$$

Thus independence between H_1 and H_2 implies

$$\sum_i^r \frac{c_{1i}c_{2i}}{n_i} = 0, \tag{6.3}$$

or, when the n_i are all equal to n,

$$\sum_i^r c_{1i}c_{2i} = 0. \tag{6.4}$$

For $(r - 1)$ degrees of freedom, it is possible to construct infinitely many sets of $(r - 1)$ orthogonal contrasts, but we are only interested in contrasts that are reasonable.

In the milk testing example in Section 14.5, the three tubes were such that tubes B and C were quite similar in size but A was much smaller. It is therefore reasonable to define contrasts with coefficients

$$c_{1j} = 0, -1, 1, \qquad c_{2j} = -2, 1, 1.$$

These coefficients do define contrasts since $\sum_j^t c_{mj} = 0$ for $m = 1$ and 2. Also they are orthogonal as they satisfy (6.4):

$$\sum_j^t c_{1j}c_{2j} = 0 \times (-2) + (-1) \times 1 + 1 \times 1 = 0.$$

The first contrast will measure the difference between B and C, and the second will measure twice the difference between A and the mean of B and C. By (6.2) the sum of squares for the contrast H_m will be

$$\frac{\left(\sum_j^t c_{mj} \sum_i^r \sum_k^u x_{ijk}\right)^2}{ru \sum_j^t c_{mj}^2}. \tag{6.5}$$

For $m = 1$, this is

$$\frac{(0 \times 36 + (-1) \times 53 + 1 \times 62)^2}{12 \times 2[(0)^2 + (-1)^2 + (1)^2]} = 1.687,$$

and, for $m = 2$, it is

$$\frac{[(-2) \times 36 + 1 \times 53 + 1 \times 62]^2}{12 \times 2[(-2)^2 + (1)^2 + (1)^2]} = 12.840.$$

Each of these sums of squares has one degree of freedom, and the sum $1.687 + 12.840 = 14.527$ is the unpartitioned sum of squares for tubes with two degrees of freedom. The appropriate error term for the partitioned mean square is the same as for the unpartitioned mean square, the sample × tube interaction in this case. For the two components the F's are $1.687/1.037 = 1.63$ and $12.840/1.037 = 12.4$. The first contrast, between the similar tubes, is completely nonsignificant, but the second contrast, between the small tube and the mean of the larger tubes, is highly significant.

The set of orthogonal contrasts in Table 14.9 is applicable to the case where the factor is a numerically valued variable for which the gaps between successive levels are equal. The coefficients ξ_1', ξ_2', etc., will give the sums of squares for linear, quadratic, cubic, etc., terms in a polynomial of the dependent variable y on the factor x. Obviously, for k levels only $(k - 1)$ terms can be fitted. To construct the polynomial regression equation is not difficult, but we will not deal with it here: See [8], Chapter 16. Coefficients up to the fifth degree for numbers of levels k up to 52 are given in [9].

Table 14.9

$k = 3$		$k = 4$			$k = 5$			
ξ_1'	ξ_2'	ξ_1'	ξ_2'	ξ_3'	ξ_1'	ξ_2'	ξ_3'	ξ_4'
−1	1	−3	1	−1	−2	2	−1	1
0	−2	−1	−1	3	−1	−1	2	−4
1	1	1	−1	−3	0	−2	0	+6
		3	1	1	1	−1	−2	−4
					2	2	1	1

14.7. The Partitioning of Interactions into Orthogonal Contrasts

A $t \times u$ two-way table will have $(t - 1)(u - 1)$ degrees of freedom for interaction, and, if both the classifications are fixed effects which have been partitioned into orthogonal contrasts, it is possible to compute sums of squares with single degrees of freedom corresponding to the pairwise interaction of single degrees of freedom of the two sets of orthogonal contrasts. An example will make this much clearer.

Table 14.10a

	c_{11}	c_{12}	c_{13}
	0	−1	1
$d_1 = -1$	0	1	−1
$d_2 = 1$	0	−1	1

Table 14.10b

	c_{21}	c_{22}	c_{23}
	−2	1	1
$d_1 = -1$	2	−1	−1
$d_1 = 1$	−2	1	1

For the milk testing example in Section 14.5, we partitioned the main effect of tubes into two contrasts in Section 14.6. The other fixed effect, bottles, has only two levels, and so only one degree of freedom, but we can regard this as a single contrast defined by coefficients d_k: $d_1 = -1$, $d_2 = 1$. We then set up Table 14.10. We form the products $(d_k c_{mj})$ in the body of the table. The coefficients so formed are contrasts, since within each table they sum to zero, and they are orthogonal, since the sum of products of corresponding coefficients is zero. (If the factor bottles had four levels, and we had partitioned it into three contrasts, there would have been three sets of d's, namely, d_{1k}, d_{2k}, and d_{3k}, and we would have gotten 6 two-way tables of coefficients corresponding to the 6 individual degrees of freedom of the interaction.)

To get the sums of squares corresponding to these two degrees of freedom, we use (6.2) again, and get the sum of the products of the coefficients in Tables 14.10*a* and *b* with the totals in Table 14.5. From Table 14.10*a*,

$$\frac{[0 \times 21 + 1 \times 25 + (-1) \times 32 + 0 \times 15 + (-1) \times 28 + 1 \times 30]^2}{12[(0)^2 + (1)^2 + (-1)^2 + (0)^2 + (-1)^2 + (1)^2]} = \frac{(-5)^2}{12 \times 4} = 0.521.$$

Table 14.10*b* gives a sum of squares 1.173, and the sum of these two components is 1.694 with 2 degrees of freedom, which is equal to the unpartitioned sum of squares for the bottle $\times$ tube interaction.

In the example of Section 14.5, two of the two-way interactions are mixed model interactions. For example, the tube $\times$ sample interaction has tube as a fixed effect, which is partitionable into orthogonal contrasts, and samples as a random effect, which cannot be partitioned into individual degrees of freedom. However, the $(r - 1)(t - 1)$ degrees of freedom can be partitioned into $(t - 1)$ components, each consisting of $(r - 1)$ degrees of freedom, representing the interaction of each component of the tube effect with samples. We calculate the value of the contrast for each sample, and then find the variance of these.

For example, consider the contrast defined by the coefficients $c_{1j} = 0$, -1, 1. Let H_{1i} be the value of this contrast for the ith sample.

$$H_{1i} = \sum_j^t c_{1j}\bar{x}_{ij\cdot} = \sum_j^t c_{1j} \sum_k^u x_{ijk}/u$$

The sum of squares due to the interaction of the contrast H_1 with the other (random) factor is equal to the sum of squares of deviations of the H_{1i} from their mean, with the appropriate numerical factors, namely a numerator u and a denominator $\sum_j^t c_{1j}^2$:

$$\frac{u}{\sum_j^t c_{ij}^2} \sum_i^r (H_{1i} - \bar{H}_1)^2 = \frac{u}{\sum_j^t c_{ij}^2} \left[\sum_i^r H_{1i}^2 - \left(\sum_i^r H_{1i}\right)^2 \Big/ r \right]$$
$$= \frac{\sum_i^r \left(\sum_j^t c_{1j} \sum_k^u x_{ijk}\right)^2}{u \sum_j^t c_{1j}^2} - \frac{\left(\sum_j^t c_{1j} \sum_i^r \sum_k^u x_{ijk}\right)^2}{ru \sum_j^t c_{1j}^2}. \tag{7.1}$$

The second term is identical with the sum of squares for the main effect for this contrast; see (6.5) which was calculated in this example to be 1.687. To obtain the first term we proceed as follows.

The sums $\sum_k^u x_{ijk}$ are obtained by summing over bottles and were given in Table 14.7. The sums $\sum_k^u x_{11k}$, $\sum_k^u x_{12k}$, and $\sum_k^u x_{13k}$ are given by the entries in the first row, $i = 1$, in that table: 2, 4, and 3, respectively. Then for $i = 1, 2, 3, \ldots, r$, we have uH_{1i} taking the values

$$uH_{11} = \sum_j^t c_{1j} \sum_k^u x_{1jk} = [0 \times 2 + (-1) \times 4 + 1 \times 3] = -1,$$

$$uH_{12} = \sum_j^t c_{1j} \sum_k^u x_{2jk} = [0 \times 5 + (-1) \times 5 + 1 \times 5] = 0,$$

$$uH_{13} = \sum_j^t c_{1j} \sum_k^u x_{3jk} = [0 \times 6 + (-1) \times 5 + 1 \times 10] = 5,$$

$$\vdots$$

$$uH_{1r} = \sum_j^t c_{1j} \sum_k^u x_{rjk} = [0 \times 0 + (-1) \times 4 + 1 \times 3] = -1.$$

Then, since $u = 2$, the first term in (7.1) is

$$\frac{\sum_i^r \left(\sum_i^t c_{1j} \sum_k^u x_{ijk}\right)^2}{u \sum_j^t c_{1j}^2} = \frac{(-1)^2 + 0^2 + 5^2 + \cdots + (-1)^2}{2 \times [0^2 + (-1)^2 + 1^2]} = \frac{75}{2 \times 2} = 18.750,$$

whence the sum of squares for the interaction of this contrast with samples is $18.750 - 1.687 = 17.063$.

A similar calculation for the second contrast gives for the interaction sum of squares

$$\frac{3^2 + 0^2 + 3^2 + \cdots + 7^2}{2[(-2)^2 + 1^2 + 1^2]} - 12.840 = 18.583 - 12.840 = 5.743.$$

The sum of these two components, $18.750 + 5.743 = 22.806$, equals the unpartitioned sum of squares for the sample $\times$ tube interaction.

14.8. Four-Way Analysis of Variance

The analysis of a four-way classification is the obvious extension of three-way analysis, and we will review it only briefly. The model is

$$x_{ijkm\nu} = \xi_{ijkm} + z_{ijkm\nu} \tag{8.1}$$

where the ξ_{ijkm} have the structure

$$\begin{aligned}\xi_{ijkm} &= \xi + \eta_{i\cdots} + \eta_{\cdot j\cdot\cdot} + \eta_{\cdot\cdot k\cdot} + \eta_{\cdots m} \\ &\quad + \zeta_{ij\cdot\cdot} + \zeta_{i\cdot k\cdot} + \zeta_{i\cdot\cdot m} + \zeta_{\cdot jk\cdot} + \zeta_{\cdot j\cdot m} + \zeta_{\cdot\cdot km} \\ &\quad + \theta_{ijk\cdot} + \theta_{ij\cdot m} + \theta_{i\cdot km} + \theta_{\cdot jkm} + \omega_{ijkm}\end{aligned} \tag{8.2}$$

and the $z_{ijkm\nu}$, $\nu = 1, \ldots, n$, are normally distributed with zero mean and variance σ^2. The sample sizes for i, j, k, m are r, t, u, v, and the population sizes are R, T, U, V. The $\eta_{i\cdots}$ are a sample of size r from a population of size R and sum to zero in the population

$$\sum_i^R \eta_{i\cdots} = 0; \tag{8.3}$$

similarly for the other main effects. The two-way terms sum to zero in the population over each index, e.g.,

$$\sum_i^R \zeta_{ij\cdot\cdot} = \sum_j^T \zeta_{ij\cdot\cdot} = 0. \tag{8.4}$$

The three-way terms and the four-way terms also sum to zero in the population over each index, e.g.,

$$\sum_i^R \theta_{ijk\cdot} = \sum_j^T \theta_{ijk\cdot} = \sum_k^U \theta_{ijk\cdot} = 0 \tag{8.5}$$

and

$$\sum_i^R \omega_{ijkm} = \sum_j^T \omega_{ijkm} = \sum_k^U \omega_{ijkm} = \sum_m^V \omega_{ijkm} = 0. \tag{8.6}$$

If A refers to i, B to j, C to k, and D to m, we define

$$\begin{aligned}\sigma_A^2 &= \sum_i^R \frac{\eta_{i\cdots}^2}{R-1}, \qquad \text{etc.,} \\ \sigma_{AB}^2 &= \sum_i^R \sum_j^T \frac{\zeta_{ij\cdot\cdot}^2}{(R-1)(T-1)}, \qquad \text{etc.,} \\ \sigma_{ABC}^2 &= \sum_i^R \sum_j^T \sum_k^U \frac{\theta_{ijk\cdot}^2}{(R-1)(T-1)(U-1)}, \qquad \text{etc.,} \\ \sigma_{ABCD}^2 &= \sum_i^R \sum_j^T \sum_k^U \sum_m^V \frac{\omega_{ijkm}^2}{(R-1)(T-1)(U-1)(V-1)}.\end{aligned} \tag{8.7}$$

The usual identity $(x_{ijkm\nu} - \bar{x}_{\cdots\cdot\cdot}) =$ etc. has on its right-hand side the following groups of terms:

1. Four sample estimates of the four main effects, e.g., $(\bar{x}_{i\cdots\cdot} - \bar{x}_{\cdots\cdot\cdot})$, which is an estimate of $\eta_{i\cdots}$.

2. Six sample estimates of the two-way interactions, e.g., $(\bar{x}_{ij\cdots} - \bar{x}_{i\cdots\cdot} - \bar{x}_{\cdot j\cdots} + \bar{x}_{\cdots\cdot\cdot})$, which is an estimate of $\zeta_{ij\cdot\cdot}$.

3. Four sample estimates of the three-way interactions, e.g., $(\bar{x}_{ijk\cdot\cdot} - \bar{x}_{ij\cdots} - \bar{x}_{i\cdot k\cdot\cdot} - \bar{x}_{\cdot jk\cdot\cdot} + \bar{x}_{i\cdots\cdot} + \bar{x}_{\cdot j\cdots} + \bar{x}_{\cdot\cdot k\cdot\cdot} - \bar{x}_{\cdots\cdot\cdot})$, which is an estimate of $\theta_{ijk\cdot}$.

4. The sample estimate of the single four-way interaction, which will have the form $\bar{x}_{ijkm\cdot} - [\bar{x}_{\cdot\cdot\cdot\cdot\cdot}$ + main effects + two-way interactions + three-way interactions].

5. The deviations of the individual observations from the cell means, e.g.,

$$(x_{ijkmv} - \bar{x}_{ijkm\cdot}).$$

Squaring and summing over all indices gives the partitioning of the total sum of squares. Typical sums of squares and computing identities are

$$A = nvut \sum_i^r (\bar{x}_{i\cdot\cdot\cdot\cdot} - \bar{x}_{\cdot\cdot\cdot\cdot\cdot})^2 = \frac{\sum_i^r (\sum_j^t \sum_k^u \sum_m^v \sum_v^n x_{ijkmv})^2}{tuvn} - \frac{(\sum_i^r \sum_j^t \sum_k^u \sum_m^v \sum_v^n x_{ijkmv})^2}{rtuvn}, \tag{8.8}$$

$$AB = nvu \sum_i^r \sum_j^t (\bar{x}_{ij\cdot\cdot\cdot} - \bar{x}_{i\cdot\cdot\cdot\cdot} - \bar{x}_{\cdot j\cdot\cdot\cdot} + \bar{x}_{\cdot\cdot\cdot\cdot\cdot})^2 = \frac{\sum_i^r \sum_j^t (\sum_k^u \sum_m^v \sum_v^n x_{ijkmv})^2}{uvn} - \frac{(\sum_i^r \sum_j^t \sum_k^u \sum_m^v \sum_v^n x_{ijkmv})^2}{rtuvn} - \text{sum of squares for } A - \text{sum of squares for } B, \tag{8.9}$$

$$ABC = nv \sum_i^r \sum_j^t \sum_k^u (\bar{x}_{ijk\cdot\cdot} - \bar{x}_{ij\cdot\cdot\cdot} - \bar{x}_{i\cdot k\cdot\cdot} - \bar{x}_{\cdot jk\cdot\cdot} + \bar{x}_{i\cdot\cdot\cdot\cdot} + \bar{x}_{\cdot j\cdot\cdot\cdot} + \bar{x}_{\cdot\cdot k\cdot\cdot} - \bar{x}_{\cdot\cdot\cdot\cdot\cdot})^2 = \frac{\sum_i^r \sum_j^t \sum_k^u (\sum_m^v \sum_v^n x_{ijkmv})^2}{vn} - \frac{(\sum_i^r \sum_j^t \sum_k^u \sum_m^v \sum_v^n x_{ijkmv})^2}{rtuvn} - (\text{sums of squares for } A, B, C, AB, AC, BC), \tag{8.10}$$

$$ABCD = \frac{1}{n} \sum_i^r \sum_j^t \sum_k^u \sum_m^v \left(\sum_v^n x_{ijkmv}\right)^2 - \frac{(\sum_i^r \sum_j^t \sum_k^u \sum_m^v \sum_v^n x_{ijkmv})^2}{rtuvn} - \begin{pmatrix}\text{sums of squares for all main effects} \\ \text{two-way and three-way interactions}\end{pmatrix}, \tag{8.11}$$

$$\text{Within cells} = \sum_i^r \sum_j^t \sum_k^u \sum_m^v \sum_v^n x_{ijkmv}^2 - \frac{1}{n} \sum_i^r \sum_j^t \sum_k^u \sum_m^v \left(\sum_v^n x_{ijkmv}\right)^2. \tag{8.12}$$

The degrees of freedom for the foregoing are $(r-1)$, $(r-1)(t-1)$, $(r-1)(t-1)(u-1)$, $(r-1)(t-1)(u-1)(v-1)$, and $rtuv(n-1)$, respectively.

The expectations of the mean squares are as follows:

$$E[\text{M.S. for } A] = \sigma^2 + n\left(1 - \frac{v}{V}\right)\left(1 - \frac{u}{U}\right)\left(1 - \frac{t}{T}\right)\sigma^2_{ABCD}$$
$$+ nv\left(1 - \frac{u}{U}\right)\left(1 - \frac{t}{T}\right)\sigma^2_{ABC} + nu\left(1 - \frac{v}{V}\right)\left(1 - \frac{t}{T}\right)\sigma^2_{ABD}$$
$$+ nt\left(1 - \frac{v}{V}\right)\left(1 - \frac{u}{U}\right)\sigma^2_{ACD} + nuv\left(1 - \frac{t}{T}\right)\sigma^2_{AB}$$
$$+ ntv\left(1 - \frac{u}{U}\right)\sigma^2_{AC} + ntu\left(1 - \frac{v}{V}\right)\sigma^2_{AD} + ntuv\sigma^2_A , \quad (8.13)$$

$$E[\text{M.S. for } AB] = \sigma^2 + n\left(1 - \frac{u}{U}\right)\left(1 - \frac{v}{V}\right)\sigma^2_{ABCD} + nv\left(1 - \frac{u}{U}\right)\sigma^2_{ABC}$$
$$+ nu\left(1 - \frac{v}{V}\right)\sigma^2_{ABD} + nuv\sigma^2_{AB} , \quad (8.14)$$

$$E[\text{M.S. for } ABC] = \sigma^2 + n\left(1 - \frac{v}{V}\right)\sigma^2_{ABCD} + nv\sigma^2_{ABC} , \quad (8.15)$$

$$E[\text{M.S. for } ABCD] = \sigma^2 + n\sigma^2_{ABCD} . \quad (8.16)$$

The various models can be obtained from this finite-population model. For all factors model I, the samples in every case include the entire population; so $r = R$, etc., and all the terms in parentheses are zero. Hence the expected mean squares become

$$A: \sigma^2 + ntuv\sigma^2_A$$
$$AB: \sigma^2 + nuv\sigma^2_{AB}$$
$$ABC: \sigma^2 + nv\sigma^2_{ABC}$$
$$ABCD: \sigma^2 + n\sigma^2_{ABCD} .$$

For all factors model II, the population sizes R, etc., are all infinite, and so all the terms in parentheses become 1. Hence the expected value of the A mean square, for example, includes σ^2 and all components of variance with A as part of the suffix, namely σ^2_{ABCD}, σ^2_{ABC}, σ^2_{ABD}, σ^2_{ACD}, σ^2_{AB}, σ^2_{AC}, σ^2_{AD}, and σ^2_A, each with appropriate coefficients.

The various possible types of mixed models, namely, (*aBCD*), (*abCD*), and (*abcD*), to use our previous convention, can be derived from the foregoing equations.

REFERENCES

1. Cornfield, Jerome, and John W. Tukey, "Average values of mean squares in factorials," *Annals of Mathematical Statistics*, 27(1956), 907–949.
2. Paull, A. E., "On a preliminary test for pooling mean squares in the analysis of variance," *Annals of Mathematical Statistics*, 21(1950), 539–556.

3. Finney, D. J., "The joint distribution of variance ratios based on a common error mean square," *Annals of Eugenics*, 11(1941), 136–140.
4. Nair, K. R., "The studentized form of the extreme mean square test in the analysis of variance," *Biometrika*, 35(1948), 16–31.
5. Daniel, C., "Fractional replication in industrial research," *Third Berkeley Symposium on Mathematical Statistics and Probability*, vol. V, 87–98. J. Neyman (ed.). Berkeley: University of California Press, 1956.
6. Birnbaum, A., "On the analysis of factorial experiments without replication." Contributed paper at Annual Meeting of the Institute of Mathematical Statistics, Cambridge, Massachusetts, August 25–28, 1958.
7. Barkworth, H., and J. O. Irwin, "Comparative detection of coliform organisms in milk and water by the presumptive coliform test," *Journal of Hygiene*, 43(1943), 129–135.
8. Anderson, R. L., and T. A. Bancroft, *Statistical Theory in Research*. New York: McGraw-Hill Book Co., 1952.
9. Fisher, R. A., and F. Yates, *Statistical Tables for Biological, Agricultural, and Medical Research*. 3d ed.; Edinburgh: Oliver & Boyd, 1948.
10. Wagner, R., F. M. Strong, and C. A. Elvehyem, "Effects of blenching on the retention of ascorbic acid, thiamine, and niacin in vegetables," *Industrial and Engineering Chemistry*, 39(1947), 990–993.

EXERCISES

14.1. Four strains of a microorganism producing an antibiotic in a fermentation process were to be compared. The comparison was made on four batches of the main ingredient of the broth. A further factor was introduced into the experiment, namely, concentration of the broth, at three levels, equally spaced. The yields were as follows:

		Concentration		
Batch	Strain	1	2	3
1	*A*	40	69	70
	B	52	71	91
	C	78	100	110
	D	59	76	108
2	*A*	47	76	91
	B	64	72	99
	C	73	122	143
	D	77	106	127
3	*A*	55	79	102
	B	61	83	94
	C	71	106	106
	D	78	103	127
4	*A*	44	77	85
	B	69	75	116
	C	87	106	131
	D	76	107	125

The strains are a model I effect, and in fact the main objective of the experiment is to select the best strain. The batches are a model II effect, and the concentration is a model I effect, partitionable into linear and quadratic components.

(*a*) Give the conventional analysis of variance with the expectations of the mean squares. Make tests of significance of the various effects. State succinctly your interpretation of the effects of the various factors.

(*b*) Give 95 per cent confidence limits for the difference between strain C and strain D, averaged over batches and concentrations.

14.2. The table below gives the results of an experiment on the amounts of niacin found in peas after various treatments [10]. The factors were:

(*a*) A comparison between blanched peas P_0 and processed peas P_1.

(*b*) Two temperatures of cooking: $C_0 = 175°\text{F}$, $C_1 = 200°\text{F}$.

(*c*) Two times of cooking: $T_0 = 2\frac{1}{2}$ min, $T_1 = 8$ min.

(*d*) Three different sieve sizes of peas: S_1, S_2, S_3.

		P_0		P_1	
C	S	T_0	T_1	T_0	T_1
0	1	91	72	86	68
	2	92	68	85	72
	3	112	73	101	73
1	1	84	78	83	76
	2	94	78	90	71
	3	98	73	94	76

Make an analysis of variance of these data. Suppose that the levels of the factor sieve size are spaced equally, and partition the main effect of sieve size into components corresponding to linear and quadratic terms: likewise for the first-order interactions. Include in the analysis the second-order interactions, but do not bother with any partitioning of these. The highest-order interaction mean square will have too few degrees of freedom to be a satisfactory estimate of error (since there is no replication, there is no explicit estimate available). Therefore, for an estimate of error pool the second-order interactions with the highest-order interaction (i.e., assume that the second- and third-order interactions are all zero and hence the corresponding mean squares are all estimates of σ^2).

What effects do you consider to be statistically significant at the 0.05 level? For uniformity,

(*a*) Be a never-pooler (apart from that recommended in the previous paragraph).

(*b*) In testing the first-order interactions, make due allowance for the fact that there are quite a large number of them.

(*c*) On the other hand, be more generous to the main effects, and test them individually.

Summarize in appropriate tables the effects you find statistically significant, and list the effects you consider nonsignificant.

CHAPTER 15

Partially Hierarchical Situations

15.1. A Partially Hierarchical Situation and Its Model

In an investigation of the can-making properties of tin plate, two methods of annealing were studied. Three coils were selected at random out of a supposedly infinite population of coils made by each of these two methods. From each coil, samples were taken from two particular and reproducible locations, namely, the head and tail of each coil. From each sample, two sets of cans were made up independently, and from each set an estimate of the can life was obtained: These are the data in Table 15.1, taken from [1]. For a definitive study, one would require a substantially larger sample of coils, but the data of Table 15.1 will suffice to demonstrate the principles involved in the analysis.

The structure of this experiment is rather different from what we have previously encountered. If the coils were crossed across annealing method, so that the first coil with annealing method 1 corresponded in some way with the first coil with annealing method 2, and the second coils likewise, etc., then we would have a three-way analysis with replication in the cells. However, this is not the case: The coils are not so crossed, but instead are nested within the annealing methods. Alternatively, if the locations were random samples from each coil, so that they were nested within the coils, with no crossing of location 1 across coils or annealing methods, then we would have a purely nested or hierarchical situation, with four classifications, namely, annealing methods, coils within annealing methods, locations within coils, and replications within locations. However, this is not the case: The locations are a model I effect crossed across coils and annealing methods.

What we have is a *partially hierarchical* or *crossed nested* situation, which can be represented by the model

$$x_{ijkv} = \xi + \alpha_i + \{c(\alpha)\}_{j(i)} + \lambda_k + (\lambda\alpha)_{ik} + \{\lambda c(\alpha)\}_{kj(i)} + z_{ijkv}, \qquad (1.1)$$

in which ξ is the grand mean, α_i is the annealing method effect, $\{c(\alpha)\}_{j(i)}$ represents the random coil effect within annealing method, λ_k represents the location effect, $(\lambda\alpha)_{ik}$ represents the interaction of locations with annealing methods, $\{\lambda c(\alpha)\}_{kj(i)}$ represents the interaction of locations with coils within anneals, and z_{ijkv} is a random error distributed normally with zero mean and variance σ^2.

Table 15.1

		Annealing method i					
		1			2		
		Coils within anneals $j(i)$					
Location k	Duplicates v	1(1)	2(1)	3(1)	1(2)	2(2)	3(2)
1	1	288	355	329	310	303	299
	2	295	369	343	282	321	328
2	1	278	336	320	288	302	289
	2	272	342	315	287	297	284

In (1.1), single symbols could be used in place of $\{c(\alpha)\}$, $(\lambda\alpha)$, $\{\lambda c(\alpha)\}$, but the use of these multiple symbols is helpful in identifying immediately the meaning of each. It is also helpful to use Greek letters to denote fixed, model I, effects, e.g., α and λ, and Roman letters for random, model II, effects, e.g., c and z, and this has been done in (1.1), somewhat prematurely, as we will first consider the finite-population model and then move to this particular case. Thus for the finite-population model, i goes to r in the sample and R in the population, j to t in the sample and T in the population, k to u in the sample and U in the population, and v, which is from an infinite population, to n in the sample.

Side restrictions on the model are

$$\sum_i^R \alpha_i = 0, \qquad \sum_k^U \lambda_k = 0, \qquad \sum_i^R (\lambda\alpha)_{ik} = \sum_k^U (\lambda\alpha)_{ik} = 0. \qquad (1.2)$$

The coils-within-annealing-methods term is a standard nested term as described at the beginning of Section 13.10 and subject to the condition

$$\sum_{j}^{T} \{c(\alpha)\}_{j(i)} = 0 \qquad \text{for each } i, \tag{1.3}$$

and similarly
$$\sum_{k}^{U} \{\lambda c(\alpha)\}_{kj(i)} = 0 \qquad \text{for all } j(i), \tag{1.4}$$

$$\sum_{j}^{T} \{\lambda c(\alpha)\}_{kj(i)} = 0 \qquad \text{for all } k,\, i. \tag{1.5}$$

15.2. Calculation of Sums of Squares, Etc.

The identity corresponding to the model (1.1) is

$$\begin{aligned} x_{ijkv} - \bar{x}_{....} = {} & (\bar{x}_{i...} - \bar{x}_{....}) + (\bar{x}_{ij..} - \bar{x}_{i...}) + (\bar{x}_{..k.} - \bar{x}_{....}) \\ & + (\bar{x}_{i\cdot k\cdot} - \bar{x}_{i...} - \bar{x}_{..k.} + \bar{x}_{....}) + (\bar{x}_{ijk\cdot} - \bar{x}_{ij..} - \bar{x}_{i\cdot k\cdot} + \bar{x}_{i...}) \\ & + (x_{ijkv} - \bar{x}_{ijk\cdot}). \end{aligned} \tag{2.1}$$

The terms on the right-hand side are the sample estimates of the terms on the right-hand side of the model (1.1), excluding the grand mean. The first and third terms need no comment. The second term is similar to an ordinary nested term such as the second term in (13.7.2). The fourth term is an ordinary two-way interaction resembling (14.1.11). The fifth term can be obtained by regarding it as the difference between $\bar{x}_{ijk\cdot}$ and what would be predicted as the grand sum $\bar{x}_{....}$ plus the annealing-method effect $(\bar{x}_{i...} - \bar{x}_{....})$ plus the coils-within-annealing-method effect $(\bar{x}_{ij..} - \bar{x}_{....})$ plus the location effect $(\bar{x}_{..k\cdot} - \bar{x}_{....})$ plus the location $\times$ anneal two-way interaction $(\bar{x}_{i\cdot k\cdot} - \bar{x}_{i...} - \bar{x}_{..k\cdot} + \bar{x}_{....})$, i.e.,

$$\begin{aligned} \bar{x}_{ijk\cdot} - [\bar{x}_{....} + (\bar{x}_{i...} - \bar{x}_{....}) + (\bar{x}_{ij..} - \bar{x}_{i...}) + (\bar{x}_{..k.} - \bar{x}_{....}) \\ + (\bar{x}_{i\cdot k\cdot} - \bar{x}_{i...} - \bar{x}_{..k\cdot} + \bar{x}_{....})] \\ = \bar{x}_{ijk\cdot} - \bar{x}_{ij..} - \bar{x}_{i\cdot k\cdot} + \bar{x}_{i...}\,. \end{aligned} \tag{2.2}$$

An alternative way of constructing partially hierarchical models is to consider them as degenerate cases of fully crossed models. For example, we suppose momentarily that the coil effect is fully crossed, so that there will be a coil main effect $(\bar{x}_{\cdot j..} - \bar{x}_{....})$ and an anneal $\times$ coil interaction $(\bar{x}_{ij..} - \bar{x}_{i...} - \bar{x}_{\cdot j..} + \bar{x}_{....})$. Now we admit that the coil effect is not a main effect and pool it with its interaction with anneals:

$$(\bar{x}_{.j..} - \bar{x}_{....}) + (\bar{x}_{ij..} - \bar{x}_{i...} - \bar{x}_{.j..} + \bar{x}_{....}) = \bar{x}_{ij..} - \bar{x}_{i...} \tag{2.3}$$

Table 15.2

Source of variance	Sums of squares	Degrees of freedom	E[M.S.]
Annealing methods	$nut\sum_i^r (\bar{x}_{i\cdots} - \bar{x}_{\cdots\cdot})^2$	$(r-1)$	$\sigma^2 + \left(1-\frac{t}{T}\right)\left(1-\frac{u}{U}\right)n\sigma^2_{\lambda c(\alpha)} + t\left(1-\frac{u}{U}\right)n\sigma^2_{\lambda\alpha} + \left(1-\frac{t}{T}\right)un\sigma^2_{c(\alpha)} + tun\sigma^2_{\alpha}$
Coils within annealing methods	$nu\sum_i^r\sum_j^t (\bar{x}_{ij\cdot\cdot} - \bar{x}_{i\cdots})^2$	$r(t-1)$	$\sigma^2 + \left(1-\frac{u}{U}\right)n\sigma^2_{\lambda c(\alpha)} + un\sigma^2_{c(\alpha)}$
Locations	$nrt\sum_k^u (\bar{x}_{\cdot\cdot k\cdot} - \bar{x}_{\cdots\cdot})^2$	$(u-1)$	$\sigma^2 + \left(1-\frac{t}{T}\right)n\sigma^2_{\lambda c(\alpha)} + \left(1-\frac{r}{R}\right)tn\sigma^2_{\lambda\alpha} + rtn\sigma^2_{\lambda}$
Locations $\times$ annealing methods	$nt\sum_i^r\sum_k^u (\bar{x}_{i\cdot k\cdot} - \bar{x}_{i\cdots} - \bar{x}_{\cdot\cdot k\cdot} + \bar{x}_{\cdots\cdot})^2$	$(r-1)(u-1)$	$\sigma^2 + n\left(1-\frac{t}{T}\right)\sigma^2_{\lambda c(\alpha)} + tn\sigma^2_{\lambda\alpha}$
Locations $\times$ coils within annealing methods	$n\sum_i^r\sum_j^t\sum_k^u (\bar{x}_{ijk\cdot} - \bar{x}_{ij\cdot\cdot} - \bar{x}_{i\cdot k\cdot} + \bar{x}_{i\cdots})^2$	$r(t-1)(u-1)$	$\sigma^2 + n\sigma^2_{\lambda c(\alpha)}$
Within cells	$\sum_i^r\sum_j^t\sum_k^u\sum_\nu^n (x_{ijk\nu} - \bar{x}_{ijk\cdot})^2$	$rtu(n-1)$	σ^2
Total	$\sum_i^r\sum_j^t\sum_k^u\sum_\nu^n (x_{ijk\nu} - \bar{x}_{\cdots\cdot})^2$	$rtun-1$	

which is the second term on the right-hand side of (2.1). Similarly, if coils was a crossed effect, then it would have an interaction with locations, and its interaction with anneals would also have an interaction with locations. But, since coils is not a crossed effect, these two interactions are pooled together:

$$(\bar{x}_{\cdot jk\cdot} - \bar{x}_{\cdot j\cdot\cdot} - \bar{x}_{\cdot\cdot k\cdot} + \bar{x}_{\cdot\cdot\cdot\cdot}) + (\bar{x}_{ijk\cdot} - \bar{x}_{ij\cdot\cdot} - \bar{x}_{i\cdot k\cdot} - \bar{x}_{\cdot jk\cdot} + \bar{x}_{i\cdot\cdot\cdot} + \bar{x}_{\cdot j\cdot\cdot} + \bar{x}_{\cdot\cdot k\cdot} - \bar{x}_{\cdot\cdot\cdot\cdot}) = \bar{x}_{ijk\cdot} - \bar{x}_{ij\cdot\cdot} - \bar{x}_{i\cdot k\cdot} + \bar{x}_{i\cdot\cdot\cdot}, \tag{2.4}$$

which is identical with (2.2).

This viewpoint also applies to the degrees of freedom. For coils within anneals, each anneal contributes $(t - 1)$ degrees of freedom and there are r anneals; so the degrees of freedom are $r(t - 1)$. But, taking the viewpoint of (2.3), the degrees of freedom should be

$$(t - 1) + (r - 1)(t - 1) = r(t - 1)$$

which is the same result.

For the interaction of locations × coils within anneals, since locations have $(u - 1)$ degrees of freedom and coils within anneals have $r(t - 1)$ degrees of freedom, their interaction will have $r(t - 1)(u - 1)$ degrees of freedom. From the viewpoint of (2.4), the degrees of freedom will be

$$(t - 1)(u - 1) + (r - 1)(u - 1)(t - 1) = r(t - 1)(u - 1),$$

which is the same result.

Squaring and summing over all indices (2.1) gives an equation entered in tabular form in Table 15.2. The closed forms of the sums of squares are unsuitable for calculation, and we need satisfactory identities. The first and third with permutations of the indices are identical with (14.1.13). The fourth is identical in principle with (14.1.14), differing only in the indices. The second is identical with (14.9.4), and the last is identical with (14.9.6). This leaves us with only the fifth, which from (2.2) can be written as

$$n\sum_i^r\sum_j^t\sum_k^u(\bar{x}_{ijk\cdot} - \bar{x}_{ij\cdot\cdot} - \bar{x}_{i\cdot k\cdot} + \bar{x}_{i\cdot\cdot\cdot})^2 = n\sum_i^r\sum_j^t\sum_k^u(\bar{x}_{ijk\cdot} - \bar{x}_{\cdot\cdot\cdot\cdot})^2 - nut\sum_i^r(\bar{x}_{i\cdot\cdot\cdot} - \bar{x}_{\cdot\cdot\cdot\cdot})^2 - nu\sum_i^r\sum_j^t(\bar{x}_{ij\cdot\cdot} - \bar{x}_{i\cdot\cdot\cdot})^2 - nrt\sum_k^u(\bar{x}_{\cdot\cdot k\cdot} - \bar{x}_{\cdot\cdot\cdot\cdot})^2 - nt\sum_i^r\sum_k^u(\bar{x}_{i\cdot k\cdot} - \bar{x}_{i\cdot\cdot\cdot} - \bar{x}_{\cdot\cdot k\cdot} + \bar{x}_{\cdot\cdot\cdot\cdot})^2 \tag{2.5}$$

where

$$n\sum_i^r\sum_j^t\sum_k^u(\bar{x}_{ijk\cdot}-\bar{x}_{....})^2=\frac{\sum_i^r\sum_j^t\sum_k^u(\sum_v^n x_{ijkv})^2}{n}-\frac{(\sum_i^r\sum_j^t\sum_k^u\sum_v^n x_{ijkv})^2}{rtun}. \quad (2.6)$$

The remaining sums of squares, with minus signs, are the sums of squares for annealing methods, coils within annealing methods, locations, and the location $\times$ annealing-method interaction.

We first need a table formed by summing over v (Table 15.3). We next sum over k to get the coils-within-annealing-method table. We also sum over j to get the locations $\times$ annealing-method table. Summing this over i gives the location totals and over k gives the annealing-method totals.

We now compute the sums of squares listed in Table 15.2, and enter them in Table 15.4, as we get them.

The sums of squares for annealing methods, by (14.1.13), is

$$nut\sum_i^r(\bar{x}_{i...}-\bar{x}_{....})^2$$

$$=\frac{1}{ntu}\sum_i^r\left(\sum_j^t\sum_k^u\sum_v^n x_{ijkv}\right)^2-\frac{1}{rtun}\left(\sum_i^r\sum_j^t\sum_k^u\sum_v^n x_{ijkv}\right)^2$$

$$=\frac{3842^2+3590^2}{2\times 3\times 2}-\frac{(7432)^2}{2\times 3\times 2\times 2}=2646.000.$$

The sum of squares for coils within anneals is

$$nu\sum_i^r\sum_j^t(\bar{x}_{ij..}-\bar{x}_{i...})^2$$

$$=\frac{1}{un}\sum_i^r\sum_j^t\left(\sum_k^u\sum_v^n x_{ijkv}\right)^2-\frac{1}{tun}\sum_i^r\left(\sum_j^t\sum_k^u\sum_v^n x_{ijkv}\right)^2$$

$$=\frac{1133^2+1402^2+\cdots+1200^2}{2\times 2}-\frac{3842^2+3590^2}{3\times 2\times 2}$$

$$=9701.333.$$

The sum of squares for locations, permuting the indices of (14.1.13), is

$$nrt\sum_k^u(\bar{x}_{..k\cdot}-\bar{x}_{....})^2$$

$$=\frac{1}{rtn}\sum_k^u\left(\sum_i^r\sum_j^t\sum_v^n x_{ijkv}\right)^2-\frac{1}{rtun}\left(\sum_i^r\sum_j^t\sum_k^u\sum_v^n x_{ijkv}\right)^2$$

$$=\frac{3822^2+3610^2}{2\times 3\times 2}-\frac{(7432)^2}{2\times 3\times 2\times 2}=1872.667.$$

Table 15.3. The x_{ijkv} of Table 15.1 Summed over v, $\sum_{v}^{n} x_{ijkv}$

Annealing method i	$i = 1$				$i = 2$				Sum
Coils within annealing method $j(i)$	1(1)	2(1)	3(1)	$\sum_{j}^{t}\sum_{v}^{n} x_{1jkv}$	1(2)	2(2)	3(2)	$\sum_{j}^{t}\sum_{v}^{n} x_{2jkv}$	$\sum_{i}^{r}\sum_{j}^{t}\sum_{v}^{n} x_{ijkv}$
Location, $k = 1$	583	724	672	1979	592	624	627	1843	3822
$k = 2$	550	678	635	1863	575	599	573	1747	3610
$\sum_{k}^{u}\sum_{v}^{n} x_{ijkv}$	1133	1402	1307		1167	1223	1200		$\sum_{i}^{r}\sum_{j}^{t}\sum_{k}^{u}\sum_{v}^{n} x_{ijkv}$
	$\sum_{k}^{u}\sum_{j}^{t}\sum_{v}^{n} x_{1jkv} = 3842$				$\sum_{k}^{u}\sum_{j}^{t}\sum_{v}^{n} x_{2jkv} = 3590$				$= 7432$

The sum of squares for locations × annealing methods is, by (14.1.14),

$$nt \sum_i^r \sum_k^u (\bar{x}_{i \cdot k \cdot} - \bar{x}_{i \dots} - \bar{x}_{\cdot \cdot k \cdot} + \bar{x}_{\dots \cdot})^2$$

$$= \frac{1}{nt} \sum_i^r \sum_k^u \left(\sum_j^t \sum_v^n x_{ijkv} \right)^2 - \frac{1}{rtun} \left(\sum_i^r \sum_j^t \sum_k^u \sum_v^n x_{ijkv} \right)^2 - nut \sum_i^r (\bar{x}_{i \dots} - \bar{x}_{\dots \cdot})^2 - nrt \sum_k^u (\bar{x}_{\cdot \cdot k \cdot} - \bar{x}_{\dots \cdot})^2$$

$$= \frac{1979^2 + \cdots + 1747^2}{2 \times 3} - \frac{(7432)^2}{2 \times 3 \times 2 \times 2} - 2646.000 - 1872.667$$

$$= 16.667.$$

Table 15.4

Source of variance	Sums of squares	Degrees of freedom	Mean squares	E[M.S.]
Annealing methods	2,646.000	1	2646.000	$\sigma^2 + un\sigma^2_{c(\alpha)} + tun\sigma^2_{\alpha}$
Coils within annealing methods	9,701.333	4	2425.333	$\sigma^2 + un\sigma^2_{c(\alpha)}$
Locations	1,872.667	1	1872.667	$\sigma^2 + n\sigma^2_{\Lambda c(\alpha)} + rtn\sigma^2_{\Lambda}$
Locations × annealing methods	16.667	1	16. 667	$\sigma^2 + n\sigma^2_{\Lambda c(\alpha)} + tn\sigma^2_{\Lambda\alpha}$
Locations × coils within annealing methods	211.667	4	52.917	$\sigma^2 + n\sigma^2_{\Lambda c(\alpha)}$
Within cells	1,269.000	12	105.750	σ^2
Total	15,717.333	23		

The sum of squares for location × coils within anneals is given by (2.5) as

$$\frac{(583^2 + \cdots + 573^2)}{2} - \frac{7432^2}{2 \times 3 \times 2 \times 2} - 2646.000 - 9701.333 - 1872.667 - 16.667 = 211.667.$$

The sum of squares within cells is

$$(288^2 + \cdots + 284^2) - \frac{583^2 + \cdots + 573^2}{2} = 1269.000.$$

These sums of squares, and the corresponding degrees of freedom, are entered in Table 15.4. In the next section we shall discuss obtaining the expected values of the mean squares.

15.3. The Expectations of Mean Squares in Partially Hierarchical Models

Bennett and Franklin [2] have given a procedure for obtaining the expected values of mean squares in partially hierarchical situations. Of course, wholly hierarchical and wholly crossed models are special cases.

The procedure is to construct a two-way table, columns corresponding to the indices used in the model, i, j, k, ν in the present case, rows corresponding to the terms in the model. This has been done for the model (1.1) in Table 15.5. The numbers of elements in the sample and in the population are entered in parentheses. The orders of the rows and the columns are not important other than that a systematic order of some kind helps to avoid mistakes.

We now consider any row. For those columns whose indices are *not* in the suffix for the term defining that row, enter the number of elements in the sample.

Table 15.5

	i (r, R)	j (t, T)	k (u, U)	ν n
$z_{ijk\nu}$	1	1	1	1
$\{\lambda c(\alpha)\}_{kj(i)}$	1	$1 - t/T$	$1 - u/U$	n
$(\lambda\alpha)_{ik}$	$1 - r/R$	t	$1 - u/U$	n
λ_k	r	t	$1 - u/U$	n
$\{c(\alpha)\}_{j(i)}$	1	$1 - t/T$	u	n
α_i	$1 - r/R$	t	u	n

For example, the j, k, and ν indices do *not* appear in the suffix to α_i; hence we enter t, u, and n in the corresponding columns opposite α_i.

Next, if any term is an unrestricted random variable, enter 1 in the cells left vacant after the previous stage. Here $z_{ijk\nu}$ is the only unrestricted random variable, and 1's are entered in all columns.

Next, if any term contains a suffix inside parentheses, enter 1 in the column corresponding to the index inside the parentheses. Here $\{c(\alpha)\}_{j(i)}$ and $\{\lambda c(\alpha)\}_{kj(i)}$ each have i inside parentheses; so 1 goes in the i column opposite these terms.

Finally, wherever a cell is still empty after the preceding operations, enter $(1 - c/C)$ where c and C are the number of elements in the sample and in the population. This last step will fill up all the cells in the table. For any mean square, the expectation will include all terms that include in their suffix the indices that are in the suffix of that mean square. For example, for the sum of squares corresponding to λ_k, the following terms will be included: $(\lambda\alpha)_{ik}$, $\{\lambda c(\alpha)\}_{kj(i)}$, and z_{ijkv}, since they all include k in their suffixes. The numerical coefficient for each component of variance making up the expectation of the mean square is made up of the product of the entries in all columns whose indices are *not* in the suffix of the variance component. For example, for the expected value of the mean square for locations, σ_λ^2 will have the coefficient rtn; $\sigma_{\lambda\alpha}^2$ the coefficient $(1 - r/R)tn$; $\sigma_{\lambda c(\alpha)}^2$ the coefficient $(1 - t/T)n$; and σ^2 the coefficient 1. The expected value for the location mean square is thus

$$\sigma^2 + \left(1 - \frac{t}{T}\right)n\sigma_{\lambda c(\alpha)}^2 + \left(1 - \frac{r}{R}\right)tn\sigma_{\lambda\alpha}^2 + rtn\sigma_\lambda^2 .$$

This is entered in the last column of Table 15.2, and the other entries in that column are obtained similarly.

In the specific example we have been considering, the annealing methods and the locations were fixed effects; so the sample contained the entire population, and hence $(1 - r/R) = (1 - u/U) = 0$. On the other hand, the coils were samples from infinite populations; so $(1 - t/T) = 1$. Inserting these values in the expectations of the mean squares in Table 15.2, we get the particular results in Table 15.4. The appropriate error term for testing each mean square is now obvious.

15.4. Confidence Limits in Partially Hierarchical Models

Calculation of confidence limits in a partially hierarchical model requires some care. They are derived from the model (1.1).

$$x_{ijkv} = \xi + \alpha_i + \{c(\alpha)\}_{j(i)} + \lambda_k + (\lambda\alpha)_{ik} + \{\lambda c(\alpha)\}_{kj(i)} + z_{ijkv} . \tag{4.1}$$

Two of the terms need particular attention. The term $\{c(\alpha)\}_{j(i)}$ is a standard nested term and by (1.3) sums to zero in the population T. However, $T = \infty$, so

$$\{c(\alpha)\}_{j(i)} \sim N(0, \sigma_{c(\alpha)}^2), \tag{4.2}$$

and

$$\overline{\{c(\alpha)\}}_{\cdot(i)} = \frac{1}{t}\sum_j^t \{c(\alpha)\}_{j(i)} \sim N(0, \sigma_{c(\alpha)}^2/t). \tag{4.3}$$

The term $\{\lambda c(\alpha)\}_{kj(i)}$ is more troublesome. As stated in (1.4) and (1.5),

$$\sum_k^U \{\lambda c(\alpha)\}_{kj(i)} = \sum_j^T \{\lambda c(\alpha)\}_{kj(i)} = 0; \tag{4.4}$$

i.e., it sums to zero in the population over j and k. However, the sample of locations u includes the entire population U; i.e., $u = U$; so

$$\overline{\{\lambda c(\alpha)\}}_{\cdot j(i)} = \frac{1}{u}\sum_k^u \{\lambda c(\alpha)\}_{kj(i)} = \frac{1}{u}\sum_k^U \{\lambda c(\alpha)\}_{kj(i)} = 0. \tag{4.5}$$

Since this is zero, averaging over another suffix will leave it zero:

$$\overline{\{\lambda c(\alpha)\}}_{\cdot\cdot(i)} = 0. \tag{4.6}$$

However, the sample of coils t is from an infinite population, $T = \infty$; so

$$\overline{\{\lambda c(\alpha)\}}_{k\cdot(i)} \sim N\left(0, \frac{\sigma^2_{\lambda c(\alpha)}}{t}\right), \tag{4.7}$$

and, if we further average over i,

$$\overline{\{\lambda c(\alpha)\}}_{k\cdot(\cdot)} \sim N\left(0, \frac{\sigma^2_{\lambda c(\alpha)}}{rt}\right). \tag{4.8}$$

We will now compute the variance of the difference between two annealing methods averaged over locations and of course over coils. We would only be looking at the annealing main effect if we assume that its interaction with the other fixed effect, locations, $(\lambda\alpha)_{ik}$, is zero. From the model (4.1)

$$\bar{x}_{i\cdots} = \xi + \alpha_i + \overline{\{c(\alpha)\}}_{\cdot(i)} + \bar{\lambda}. + \overline{\{\lambda c(\alpha)\}}_{\cdot\cdot(i)} + \bar{z}_{i\cdots}\,.$$

However, by (4.6), $\overline{\{\lambda c(\alpha)\}}_{\cdot\cdot(i)} = 0$; so

$$\bar{x}_{i\cdots} - \bar{x}_{i'\cdots} = (\alpha_i - \alpha_{i'}) + \overline{\{c(\alpha)\}}_{\cdot(i)} - \overline{\{c(\alpha)\}}_{\cdot(i')} + \bar{z}_{i\cdots} - \bar{z}_{i'\cdots}\,. \tag{4.9}$$

$$E[\bar{x}_{i\cdots} - \bar{x}_{i'\cdots}] = (\alpha_i - \alpha_{i'}),$$

$$V[\bar{x}_{i\cdots} - \bar{x}_{i'\cdots}] = 2\left[\frac{\sigma^2_{c(\alpha)}}{t} + \frac{\sigma^2}{tun}\right] = \frac{2}{tun}[\sigma^2 + un\sigma^2_{c(\alpha)}], \tag{4.10}$$

$$\hat{V}[\bar{x}_{i\cdots} - \bar{x}_{i'\cdots}] = \frac{2}{tun}\left[\begin{matrix}\text{M.S. for coils within} \\ \text{annealing methods}\end{matrix}\right]. \tag{4.11}$$

We next compute the variance of the difference between two locations, averaged over annealing methods and coils, and again assuming $(\lambda\alpha)_{ik} = 0$:

$$\bar{x}_{\cdot\cdot k\cdot} = \xi + \bar{\alpha}. + \overline{\{c(\alpha)\}}_{\cdot(\cdot)} + \lambda_k + \overline{\{\lambda c(\alpha)\}}_{k\cdot(\cdot)} + \bar{z}_{\cdot\cdot k\cdot}\,,$$

$$\bar{x}_{\cdot\cdot k\cdot} - \bar{x}_{\cdot\cdot k'\cdot} = (\lambda_k - \lambda_{k'}) + \overline{\{\lambda c(\alpha)\}}_{k\cdot(\cdot)} - \overline{\{\lambda c(\alpha)\}}_{k'\cdot(\cdot)} + \bar{z}_{\cdot\cdot k\cdot} - \bar{z}_{\cdot\cdot k'\cdot}\,, \tag{4.12}$$

$$E[\bar{x}_{\cdot\cdot k\cdot} - \bar{x}_{\cdot\cdot k'\cdot}] = \lambda_k - \lambda_{k'} , \tag{4.13}$$

$$V[\bar{x}_{\cdot\cdot k\cdot} - \bar{x}_{\cdot\cdot k'\cdot}] = 2\left[\frac{\sigma^2_{\lambda c(\alpha)}}{rt} + \frac{\sigma^2}{rtn}\right] = \frac{2}{rtn}\left[\sigma^2 + n\sigma^2_{\lambda c(\alpha)}\right], \tag{4.14}$$

$$\hat{V}[\bar{x}_{\cdot\cdot k\cdot} - \bar{x}_{\cdot\cdot k'\cdot}] = \frac{2}{rtn}\begin{bmatrix}\text{M.S. for locations} \times \text{coils} \\ \text{within annealing methods}\end{bmatrix}. \tag{4.15}$$

If we are unwilling to assume that the location $\times$ annealing-method interaction is zero, i.e., we admit the possibility that $(\lambda\alpha)_{ik} \neq 0$ in general, then it makes little sense to compare annealing methods averaged over locations or to compare locations averaged over annealing methods. We would rather compare annealing methods for a particular location and locations for a particular annealing method. To compute the variance of the difference between two locations for the same annealing method we start with

$$\bar{x}_{i\cdot k\cdot} = \xi + \alpha_i + \overline{\{c(\alpha)\}}_{\cdot(i)} + \lambda_k + (\lambda\alpha)_{ik} + \overline{\{\lambda c(\alpha)\}}_{k\cdot(i)} + \bar{z}_{i\cdot k\cdot};$$

so

$$\bar{x}_{i\cdot k\cdot} - \bar{x}_{i\cdot k'\cdot} = \lambda_k - \lambda_{k'} + (\lambda\alpha)_{ik} - (\lambda\alpha)_{ik'} + \overline{\{\lambda c(\alpha)\}}_{k\cdot(i)} - \overline{\{\lambda c(\alpha)\}}_{k'\cdot(i)} + \bar{z}_{i\cdot k\cdot} - \bar{z}_{i\cdot k'\cdot} . \tag{4.16}$$

Thus

$$V[\bar{x}_{i\cdot k\cdot} - \bar{x}_{i\cdot k'\cdot}] = 2\left[\frac{\sigma^2_{\lambda c(\alpha)}}{t} + \frac{\sigma^2}{tn}\right] = \frac{2}{nt}\left[\sigma^2 + n\sigma^2_{\lambda c(\alpha)}\right], \tag{4.17}$$

$$\hat{V}[\bar{x}_{i\cdot k\cdot} - \bar{x}_{i\cdot k'\cdot}] = \frac{2}{nt}\begin{bmatrix}\text{M.S. for locations} \times \text{coils} \\ \text{within annealing methods}\end{bmatrix}. \tag{4.18}$$

Now we compute the variance of the difference between two annealing methods for the same location:

$$\bar{x}_{i\cdot k\cdot} - \bar{x}_{i'\cdot k\cdot} = (\alpha_i - \alpha_{i'}) + \overline{\{c(\alpha)\}}_{\cdot(i)} - \overline{\{c(\alpha)\}}_{\cdot(i')} + (\lambda\alpha)_{ik} - (\lambda\alpha)_{i'k} + \overline{\{\lambda c(\alpha)\}}_{k\cdot(i)} - \overline{\{\lambda c(\alpha)\}}_{k\cdot(i')} + \bar{z}_{i\cdot k\cdot} - \bar{z}_{i'\cdot k\cdot} , \tag{4.19}$$

$$V[\bar{x}_{i\cdot k\cdot} - \bar{x}_{i'\cdot k\cdot}] = 2\left[\frac{\sigma^2_{c(\alpha)}}{t} + \frac{\sigma^2_{\lambda c(\alpha)}}{t} + \frac{\sigma^2}{tn}\right] = \frac{2}{nt}\left[\sigma^2 + n\sigma^2_{\lambda c(\alpha)} + n\sigma^2_{c(\alpha)}\right]. \tag{4.20}$$

The analysis-of-variance tables does not provide any mean square with the appropriate expected value. If, as is often the case, the term $\{\lambda c(\alpha)\}$

is omitted from the model, we have to construct a linear combination of mean squares with expected value $(\sigma^2 + n\sigma^2_{c(\alpha)})$. This is given by

$$\frac{1}{u}[(u-1)(\text{M.S. for remainder}) + \text{M.S. for coils within annealing methods}], \tag{4.21}$$

which has the expected value

$$= \frac{1}{u}[(u-1)\sigma^2 + \sigma^2 + un\sigma^2_{c(\alpha)}] = \sigma^2 + n\sigma^2_{c(\alpha)}.$$

The omission of $\{\lambda c(\alpha)\}$ from the model has the end result of pooling the sums of squares and degrees of freedom of this term with those for within cells to form the "remainder" sum of squares. If we are unwilling to make the foregoing simplifying assumption, we can obtain a linear combination with the desired expected value included in the brackets [ ] in (4.20) by using

$$\frac{1}{u}[-(\text{M.S. for within cells}) + u(\text{M.S. for locations} \times \text{coils within annealing methods}) + (\text{M.S. for coils within anneals})], \tag{4.22}$$

which has the expected value

$$\frac{1}{u}[-\sigma^2 + u\sigma^2 + un\sigma^2_{\lambda c(\alpha)} + \sigma^2 + un\sigma^2_{c(\alpha)}] = \sigma^2 + n\sigma^2_{\lambda c(\alpha)} + n\sigma^2_{c(\alpha)}.$$

Finally, the variance of the difference between the combination of the ith annealing method with the kth location and the combination of the i'th annealing method with the k'th location is the same as that just discussed, the difference between two annealing methods for the same location.

15.5. A More Complicated Partially Hierarchical Experiment

The data of Table 15.6, taken from [3], give the quality of a cellulose product. The final product was subject to excessive variation, and it was desired to find out at which stages of the process the larger part of the variation was occurring. The cellulose derivative enters the process in large homogenous blends in aqueous suspension, and from them a number of batches are mixed. Usually the whole of a mix is put into a single truck, which it fills, for the next stage of the process, drying. This makes it impossible to separate the variation due to mixing from the variation due to drying. Therefore, for this experiment each mix was split into two halves which were placed in two trucks. The remaining halves of these two trucks were filled with the two halves of the next mix. A second pair of mixes was taken from that blend and similarly treated. The whole procedure was repeated on a number of blends. From each truck $\times$ mix combination two samples were taken for quality determination. A reasonable model for this experiment is

$$x_{ijkm\nu} = \xi + b_i + \{p(b)\}_{j(i)} + \{t(p(b))\}_{k(j(i))} + \mu_m + (b\mu)_{im} + \{\mu p(b)\}_{mj(i)} + \{\mu t(p(b))\}_{mk(j(i))} + z_{ijkm\nu}. \quad (5.1)$$

Table 15.6

Blend number	Pair number	Truck number	First mix in a pair		Second mix in a pair	
			$m = 1$		$m = 2$	
i	$j(i)$	$k(j(i))$	$\nu = 1$	$\nu = 2$	$\nu = 1$	$\nu = 2$
1	1(1)	1(1(1))	11	16	0	0
		2(1(1))	17	16	14	13
	2(1)	1(2(1))	12	12	6	6
		2(2(1))	10	8	1	3
2	1(2)	1(1(2))	9	9	3	1
		2(1(2))	19	18	6	6
	2(2)	1(2(2))	8	9	6	8
		2(2(2))	14	13	6	7
3	1(3)	1(1(3))	15	17	21	20
		2(1(3))	22	21	13	13
	2(3)	1(2(3))	18	18	6	6
		2(2(3))	19	21	6	4
4	1(4)	1(1(4))	11	10	5	6
		2(1(4))	3	2	1	0
	2(4)	1(2(4))	8	8	4	4
		2(2(4))	6	6	7	8

The notation is clumsy but explicit and intelligible. ξ is the grand mean, b_i the blend effect, $p(b)_{j(i)}$ pairs within blends, $t(p(b))_{k(j(i))}$ trucks within pairs within blends, μ_m the mix effect, $(b\mu)_{im}$ the blend $\times$ mix interaction, $\{\mu p(b)\}_{mj(i)}$ the mix $\times$ pairs-within-blends interaction, $\{\mu t(p(b))\}_{mk(j(i))}$ the mix $\times$ trucks-within-pairs-within-blends interaction, and $z_{ijkm\nu}$ a random variable $\sim N(0, \sigma^2)$.

At first sight it might seem that mixes and trucks should be on a similar basis, but there is a difference; there is a distinct order effect for mixes,

Table 15.7. Table 15.6 Summed over ν

Blend number	Pair number	Truck number	First mix $m = 1$			Second mix $m = 2$			Truck totals	Pair totals	Blend totals
i	$j(i)$	$k(j(i))$	$\sum_{\nu}^{n}$	$\sum_{k}^{u}\sum_{\nu}^{n}$	$\sum_{j}^{t}\sum_{k}^{u}\sum_{\nu}^{n}$	$\sum_{\nu}^{n}$	$\sum_{k}^{u}\sum_{\nu}^{n}$	$\sum_{j}^{t}\sum_{k}^{u}\sum_{\nu}^{n}$	$\sum_{m}^{v}\sum_{\nu}^{n}$	$\sum_{k}^{u}\sum_{m}^{r}\sum_{\nu}^{n}$	$\sum_{j}^{t}\sum_{k}^{u}\sum_{m}^{v}\sum_{\nu}^{n}$
1	1(1)	1(1(1))	27			0			27		
		2(1(1))	33	60		27	27		60	87	
	2(1)	1(2(1))	24			12			36		
		2(2(1))	18	42	102	4	16	43	22	58	145
2	1(2)	1(1(2))	18			4			22		
		2(1(2))	38	55		12	16		49	71	
	2(2)	1(2(2))	17			14			31		
		2(2(2))	27	44	99	13	27	43	40	71	142
3	1(3)	1(1(3))	32			41			73		
		2(1(3))	43	75		26	67		69	142	
	2(3)	1(2(3))	36			12			48		
		2(2(3))	40	76	151	10	22	89	50	98	240
4	1(4)	1(1(4))	21			11			32		
		2(1(4))	5	26		1	12		6	38	
	2(4)	1(2(4))	16			8			24		
		2(2(4))	12	28	54	15	23	35	27	51	89
	$\sum_{i}^{r}\sum_{j}^{t}\sum_{k}^{u}\sum_{\nu}^{n}$				406			210			$\sum_{i}^{r}\sum_{j}^{t}\sum_{k}^{u}\sum_{m}^{v}\sum_{\nu}^{n} = 616$

but not for trucks. The first mix has to wait for the second mix for the trucks to be filled and moved off to the drying station. The two trucks are moved simultaneously; so there is no order effect for trucks, and they are nested within pairs. Mixes are a crossed effect.

We first sum the entries in Table 15.6 over v to obtain Table 15.7. Table 15.7 also contains the various sums which we need for the analysis of variance.

We now calculate sums of squares for each term in the model. Blends are a simple main effect, with sum of squares

$$\frac{(145^2 + 142^2 + 240^2 + 89^2)}{16} - \frac{(616)^2}{64} = 740.375$$

and degrees of freedom $(4 - 1) = 3$.

Pairs are nested within blends, with sum of squares

$$\frac{87^2 + 58^2 + \cdots + 51^2}{8} - \frac{145^2 + \cdots + 89^2}{16} = 184.125$$

and degrees of freedom $4(2 - 1) = 4$.

Trucks are nested within pairs, with sum of squares

$$\frac{27^2 + 60^2 + 36^2 + \cdots + 27^2}{4} - \frac{87^2 + \cdots + 51^2}{8} = 350.000$$

and degrees of freedom $4 \times 2(2 - 1) = 8$.

Mixes are a simple main effect. The sum of squares, with 1 degree of freedom, is

$$\frac{406^2 + 210^2}{32} - \frac{616^2}{64} = 600.250.$$

The sum of squares for the blend $\times$ mix interaction is

$$\frac{102^2 + 43^2 + \cdots + 35^2}{8} - \frac{616^2}{64} - 600.250 - 740.375 = 76.125$$

with degrees of freedom $(4 - 1)(2 - 1) = 3$.

The interaction mixes $\times$ pairs within blends is similar in nature to the locations $\times$ coils-within-annealing-methods interaction discussed in the previous section; a suitable form was given in (2.5):

$$\frac{60^2 + 27^2 + \cdots + 23^2}{4} - \frac{616^2}{64} - 740.375 - 184.125 - 600.250 - 76.125$$
$$= 170.625.$$

The interaction mixes × trucks within pairs within blends is obtained from the sum of squares of deviations of the table formed by summing over the remaining suffix v, and subtracting all the foregoing sums of squares:

$$\frac{27^2 + 0^2 + 24^2 + \cdots + 15^2}{2} - \frac{616^2}{64} - 740.375 - 184.125 - 350.000 - 600.250 - 76.125 - 170.625 = 194.500.$$

This will have degrees of freedom $1 \times 8 = 8$.

The within-cells sum of squares is

$$(11^2 + 16^2 + 0^2 + \cdots + 8^2) - \frac{27^2 + 0^2 + \cdots + 15^2}{2} = 33.000.$$

These sums of squares are assembled in Table 15.8.

Table 15 8

Source of variance	Sums of squares	Degrees of freedom	Mean squares	E[M.S.]
Blends	740.375	3	246.792	$\sigma^2 + nv\sigma^2_{t(p(b))} + nvu\sigma^2_{p(b)} + nvut\sigma^2_b$
Pairs within blends	184.125	4	46.031	$\sigma^2 + nv^2_{t(p(b))} + nvu\sigma^2_{p(b)}$
Trucks within pairs	350.000	8	43.750	$\sigma^2 + nv\sigma^2_{t(p(b))}$
Mixes	600.250	1	600.250	$\sigma^2 + n\sigma^2_{\mu t(p(b))} + nu\sigma^2_{\mu p(b)} + nut\sigma^2_{\mu b} + nutr\sigma^2_\mu$
Mixes × blends	76.125	3	25.375	$\sigma^2 + n\sigma^2_{\mu t(p(b))} + nu\sigma^2_{\mu p(b)} + nut\sigma^2_{\mu b}$
Mixes × pairs within blends	170.625	4	42.656	$\sigma^2 + n\sigma^2_{\mu t(p(b))} + nu\sigma^2_{\mu p(b)}$
Mixes × trucks within pairs	194.500	8	24.312	$\sigma^2 + n\sigma^2_{\mu t(p(b))}$
Within cells	33.000	32	1.031	σ^2
Total	2349.00	63		

The calculation of the expected values of the mean squares follows the procedure given in Section 15.3. From Table 15.9 we can write down the last column of Table 15.8. Table 15.9 has been constructed for the finite-population model, and in writing down the expectations of the mean squares in Table 15.8 we put the terms in parentheses equal to the values given at the bottom.

Table 15.9

	i	j	k	m	ν
$z_{ijkm\nu}$	1	1	1	1	1
$\{\mu t(p(b))\}_{mk(j(i))}$	1	1	$(1 - u/U)$	$(1 - v/V)$	n
$\{\mu p(b)\}_{mj(i)}$	1	$(1 - t/T)$	u	$(1 - v/V)$	n
$(\mu b)_{im}$	$(1 - r/R)$	t	u	$(1 - v/V)$	n
μ_m	r	t	u	$(1 - v/V)$	n
$\{t(p(b))\}_{k(j(i))}$	1	1	$(1 - u/U)$	v	n
$\{p(b)\}_{j(i)}$	1	$(1 - t/T)$	u	v	n
b_i	$(1 - r/R)$	t	u	v	n
	$R = \infty$	$T = \infty$	$U = \infty$	$v = V$	
	$(1 - r/R) = 1$	$(1 - t/T) = 1$	$(1 - u/U) = 1$	$(1 - v/V) = 0$	

Considering Table 15.8, $\sigma^2_{\mu b}$ can be regarded as zero. Pooling its sum of squares with that for $\sigma^2_{\mu p(b)}$, we get a mean square of 35.750 with 7 degrees of freedom. This has $F = 35.250/24.312 = 1.45$, which can be compared with $F_{0.90}(7, 8) = 2.62$. It seems reasonable to assume that it also is zero, and pool it with $\sigma^2_{\mu t(p(b))}$. Also $\sigma^2_{p(b)}$ can be regarded as zero. These assumptions give us Table 15.10.

It is clear that the mix effect is highly significant. To construct confidence limits for it, from the model (5.1) we form

$$\bar{x}_{\cdots m\cdot} = \xi + \bar{b}_{\cdot} + \overline{\{p(b)\}}_{\cdot(\cdot)} + \overline{\{t(p(b))\}}_{\cdots} + \mu_m + \overline{(b\mu)}_{\cdot m} + \overline{\{\mu p(b)\}}_{m\cdot\cdot} + \overline{\{\mu t(p(b))\}}_{m\cdots} + \bar{z}_{\cdots m\cdot}\,,$$

$$\bar{x}_{\cdots m\cdot} - \bar{x}_{\cdots m'\cdot} = \mu_m - \mu_{m'} + \overline{(b\mu)}_{\cdot m} - \overline{(b\mu)}_{\cdot m'} + \overline{\{\mu p(b)\}}_{m\cdot\cdot} - \overline{\{\mu p(b)\}}_{m'\cdot\cdot} + \overline{\{\mu t(p(b))\}}_{m\cdots} - \overline{\{\mu t(p(b))\}}_{m'\cdots} + \bar{z}_{\cdots m\cdot} - \bar{z}_{\cdots m'\cdot}\,,$$

$$V[\bar{x}_{\cdots m\cdot} - \bar{x}_{\cdots m'\cdot}] = 2\left[\frac{\sigma^2_{\mu b}}{r} + \frac{\sigma^2_{\mu p(b)}}{rt} + \frac{\sigma^2_{\mu t(p(b))}}{rtu} + \frac{\sigma^2}{rtun}\right]$$

$$= \frac{2}{rtun}[\sigma^2 + n\sigma^2_{\mu t(p(b))} + un\sigma^2_{\mu p(b)} + tun\sigma^2_{\mu b}], \quad (5.2)$$

$$\hat{V}[\bar{x}_{\cdots m\cdot} - \bar{x}_{\cdots m'\cdot}] = \frac{2}{rtun}[\text{M.S. for mixes} \times \text{blends}]. \quad (5.3)$$

Table 15.10

Source of variance	Sums of squares	Degrees of freedom	Mean squares	E[M.S.]
Blends	740.375	3	246.792	$\sigma^2 + nv\sigma^2_{t(p(b))} + nvut\sigma^2_b$
Trucks within blends (pooled)	534.125	12	44.510	$\sigma^2 + nv\sigma^2_{t(p(b))}$
Mixes	600.250	1	600.250	$\sigma^2 + n\sigma^2_{\mu t(p(b))} + nutr\sigma^2_\mu$
Mixes × trucks within pairs (pooled)	441.250	15	29.417	$\sigma^2 + n\sigma^2_{\mu t(p(b))}$
Within cells	33.000	32	1.031	σ^2
Total	2349.00	63		

However, in this particular instance we have decided to assume $\sigma^2_{\mu b} = \sigma^2_{\mu p(b)} = 0$, which implies that

$$\hat{V}[\bar{x}_{\cdots m\cdot} - \bar{x}_{\cdots m'\cdot}] = \frac{2}{rtun}[\text{M.S. for mixes} \times \text{trucks}]$$

$$= \frac{2}{4 \times 2 \times 2 \times 2} \times 29.417 = 1.8386,$$

with 15 degrees of freedom: $t_{0.975}(15) = 2.131$, $t\sqrt{\hat{V}[\ ]} = 2.980$, and $(\bar{x}_{\cdots 1\cdot} - \bar{x}_{\cdots 2\cdot}) = (406 - 210)/32 = 6.125$, whence the 95 per cent confidence interval for $\mu_1 - \mu_2$ is (3.235, 9.015).

The estimates of the other parameters are

$$\hat{\sigma}^2 = 1.03,$$
$$\hat{\sigma}^2_{\mu t(p(b))} = (29.417 - 1.031)/2 = 14.19,$$
$$\hat{\sigma}^2_{t(p(b))} = (44.510 - 1.301)/4 = 3.77,$$
$$\hat{\sigma}^2_b = (246.792 - 44.510)/16 = 12.64.$$

We have already concluded that $\sigma^2_{\mu b}$ and $\sigma^2_{\mu p(b)}$ can be regarded as zero.

REFERENCES

1. Vaurio, V. W., and C. Daniel, "Evaluation of several sets of constants and several sources of variability," *Chemical Engineering Progress*, 50(1954), 81–86.
2. Bennett, Carl A., and Norman L. Franklin, *Statistical Analysis in Chemistry and the Chemical Industry*. New York, John Wiley & Sons, 1954.
3. Brownlee, K. A., *Industrial Experimentation*. 3d American ed.; Brooklyn: Chemical Publishing Company, 1949.
4. Hyde, Edward P., "A comparison of the unit of luminous intensity of the United States with those of Germany, England, and France," *Bulletin of the Bureau of Standards*, 3(1907), 68–80.

EXERCISES

15.1. Five laboratories cooperated in measuring the brightness of six lamps of each of two types. The lamps were sent from laboratory to laboratory for measurement.

(*a*) Make an appropriate analysis of variance of these data, including giving the E[M.S.]. We are particularly interested in testing the main effect of laboratories and the laboratory $\times$ type-of-lamp interaction.

(*b*) Construct 95 per cent confidence limits for the difference between types (for purposes of this question assume that laboratory $\times$ type-of-lamp interaction is zero).

(*c*) Construct 95 per cent confidence limits for the difference between laboratory A and laboratory E (again assuming laboratory $\times$ type-of-lamp interaction to be zero).

(*d*) Construct 95 per cent confidence limits for the difference between type 1 in laboratory A and type 2 in laboratory B.

(*e*) Estimate the component of variance for lamps within types.

Actually the lamps initially were measured in laboratory A (the Bureau of Standards), were then sent to laboratory B (National Physical Laboratory) who sent them on to laboratory C (Laboratoire Centrale), who returned them to the National Physical Laboratory (denoted this time by D), who returned them to the Bureau of Standards (denoted this time by E). Let the Bureau of Standards and the National Physical Laboratory on the second time around, E and D, be denoted by A' and B'. Then the following comparisons seem to be of particular interest:

(i) Early measurements versus late measurements: i.e., $(A + B) - (A' + B')$

(ii) Change with time in difference between A and B, i.e. $(A - B) - (A' - B')$

(iii) Difference between $(B + B')$ and C: i.e., $(B + B') - 2C$

(iv) Difference between (mean of $B + B'$ and C) and (mean of A and A'), i.e., $2(B + B' + C) - 3(A + A')$

(*f*) Construct contrasts to provide the above comparisons.

(*g*) Are these contrasts orthogonal?

(*h*) Partition the sums of squares for main effect for laboratories and for the interaction laboratory $\times$ type into components corresponding to these contrasts.

Values of Candlepower Obtained at Different Laboratories

All figures have been multiplied by 100 and then 1000 subtracted from them.*

		Laboratory					
Type	Lamp	*A*	*B*	*C*	*D*	*E*	Totals
I	1	741	768	770	772	738	3,789
	2	731	763	755	742	724	3,715
	3	731	763	757	760	728	3,739
	4	759	779	775	774	752	3,839
	5	738	758	750	750	730	3,726
	6	770	795	800	800	768	3,933
	Totals	4470	4626	4607	4598	4440	22,741
II	1	625	650	655	651	615	3,196
	2	590	611	605	625	588	3,019
	3	602	630	640	630	605	3,107
	4	578	607	640	608	581	3,014
	5	578	604	605	608	573	2,968
	6	625	673	670	664	631	3,263
	Totals	3598	3775	3815	3786	3593	18,567
	Totals	8068	8401	8422	8384	8033	41,308

*Data taken from [4].

15.2. A machine pressing tablets has a hopper mechanism with three separate compartments which first fills the three holes arranged as a row. The hopper then moves over to the second row and fills a further three holes. Finally the hopper moves over to the fifth row and fills a further three holes. Thus 15 holes arranged in five rows and three columns are filled with powder. The hopper moves out of the way and the powder in the holes is pressed into tablets.

The machine was set producing tablets and on four random occasions the 15 tablets from a single pressing were weighed. The whole process was repeated with two further batches of powder.

Regard the batches tested as a random sample from an infinite population of batches, the pressings obtained with each batch of powder as random samples from infinite populations of pressings from that batch, and the rows and columns as fixed effects made up partly of the fixed sizes of holes and partly of the systematic movement of the three compartments of the hopper over the five rows (e.g., the hopper always starts with row 1 and ends with row 5, the first compartment in the hopper always fills the first hole in a row, i.e. the first column is filled from the first compartment).

For notational consistency, let

$i = 1, \ldots, r\ (= 3)$ refer to batches b,
$j = 1, \ldots, t\ (= 4)$ refer to pressings p,
$k = 1, \ldots, u\ (= 5)$ refer to rows ρ,
$m = 1, \ldots, v\ (= 3)$ refer to colums γ.

The weights of the tablets, minus a constant, are given below.

Pressing j		1			2			3			4		
Column m		1	2	3	1	2	3	1	2	3	1	2	3
Batch i	Row k												
1	1	86	88	89	77	88	82	76	99	76	78	95	88
	2	101	80	107	83	93	91	84	100	93	81	89	93
	3	79	98	78	91	97	89	91	101	89	87	97	90
	4	54	83	91	92	99	87	96	96	99	95	101	97
	5	73	89	85	83	84	79	87	89	91	90	88	96
2	1	92	90	74	80	89	73	100	94	82	102	87	81
	2	96	85	88	92	86	85	110	91	94	99	97	98
	3	99	94	76	103	96	98	105	96	92	105	108	90
	4	89	96	86	103	99	96	100	101	96	101	101	101
	5	87	88	85	97	87	95	89	86	88	100	93	90
3	1	84	88	79	82	93	81	86	88	78	82	93	112
	2	87	80	90	87	94	87	87	86	85	79	100	83
	3	91	93	94	86	96	85	83	97	86	91	94	90
	4	90	105	91	83	93	87	80	91	84	84	87	93
	5	86	92	92	79	98	78	77	88	77	68	77	86

Certain sums of squares derived from this table, some of which *may* be of help in making the analysis are as follows:

$$\sum_i \sum_j \sum_k \sum_m x_{ijkm}^2 = 1{,}461{,}942.$$

$$\sum_i \sum_j \sum_k \Big(\sum_m x_{ijkm}\Big)^2 = 4{,}366{,}248. \qquad \sum_i \sum_j \Big(\sum_k \sum_m x_{ijkm}\Big)^2 = 21{,}773{,}086.$$

$$\sum_i \sum_j \sum_m \Big(\sum_k x_{ijkm}\Big)^2 = 7{,}272{,}442. \qquad \sum_i \sum_k \Big(\sum_j \sum_m x_{ijkm}\Big)^2 = 17{,}425{,}106.$$

$$\sum_i \sum_k \sum_m \Big(\sum_j x_{ijkm}\Big)^2 = 5{,}821{,}110. \qquad \sum_i \sum_m \Big(\sum_j \sum_k x_{ijkm}\Big)^2 = 29{,}052{,}310.$$

$$\sum_j \sum_k \sum_m \Big(\sum_i x_{ijkm}\Big)^2 = 4{,}362{,}528. \qquad \sum_j \sum_k \Big(\sum_i \sum_m x_{ijkm}\Big)^2 = 13{,}064{,}392.$$

$$\sum_i \Big(\sum_j \sum_k \sum_m x_{ijkm}\Big)^2 = 87{,}024{,}194. \qquad \sum_j \sum_m \Big(\sum_i \sum_k x_{ijkm}\Big)^2 = 21{,}760{,}766.$$

$$\sum_j \Big(\sum_i \sum_k \sum_m x_{ijkm}\Big)^2 = 65{,}241{,}578. \qquad \sum_k \sum_m \Big(\sum_i \sum_j x_{ijkm}\Big)^2 = 17{,}424{,}124.$$

$$\sum_k \Big(\sum_i \sum_j \sum_m x_{ijkm}\Big)^2 = 52{,}225{,}508. \qquad \Big(\sum_i \sum_j \sum_k \sum_m x_{ijkm}\Big)^2 = (16{,}152)^2.$$

$$\sum_m \Big(\sum_i \sum_j \sum_k x_{ijkm}\Big)^2 = 87{,}004{,}242.$$

(*a*) Write down an appropriate linear model, and make an analysis of variance of these data, including the expected values of the various mean squares.

(*b*) Give simple 95 per cent confidence limits for the difference between the averages for rows 1 and 3. (The row totals are 3112, 3261, 3335, 3327, and 3117.)

(*c*) Estimate the various components of variance, and give their sum.

(*d*) Suppose that by more careful attention to the sizes of the holes and to the hopper mechanism the row and column effects and their various interactions could be eliminated, what is the sum of the remaining components of variance?

(*e*) As in (*d*), but further suppose that all pressings are made with the same batch of powder.

15.3. Five laboratories cooperated in a comparison of their testing procedures for impact strength of a type of fiberboard. Panels from two batches of board were sent to the five laboratories. Each laboratory tested each batch in duplicate on three days. There is no correspondence between the three days in one laboratory and the three days in any other laboratory.

For notational consistency let

$i = 1, \ldots, r\ (= 5)$ refer to laboratories λ (model 1),
$j = 1, \ldots, t\ (= 2)$ refer to batches B (model I),
$k = 1, \ldots, u\ (= 3)$ refer to days d (model II),
$m = 1, \ldots, v\ (= 2)$ refer to duplications of a lot within a day (model II).

The impact strengths reported were as given in the table.

		Laboratory				
Day	Batch	*A*	*B*	*C*	*D*	*E*
1	1	1483	1449	1499	1428	1509
		1496	1400	1472	1401	1439
	2	1504	1465	1506	1407	1480
		1505	1423	1537	1416	1429
2	1	1441	1477	1483	1404	1416
		1416	1471	1509	1419	1441
	2	1477	1418	1578	1455	1364
		1457	1445	1486	1435	1441
3	1	1450	1446	1489	1414	1419
		1478	1398	1435	1446	1444
	2	1435	1424	1499	1423	1437
		1478	1426	1491	1442	1438

(*a*) Write down an appropriate linear model, and make an analysis of variance of these data, including the expected values of the mean squares. Make the appropriate tests of significance.

(*b*) Give simple 95 per cent confidence limits for the difference between laboratories *B* and *C*.

(*c*) Estimate the within-day component of variance averaged over laboratories.

(*d*) Estimate the between-day component of variance averaged over laboratories.

(*e*) A batch measured repeatedly by laboratory *A* had an average impact strength of 1420. If a single test is made on this batch in laboratory *D*, estimate the probability of this batch being rejected by this laboratory, if the specification is to reject if the observed impact strength is less than 1400.

If we subtract 1000 from every figure in the table, two sums of squares which may be useful are:

$$\sum_i^r \sum_j^t \sum_k^u \sum_m^v x_{ijkm}^2 = 12{,}414{,}257,$$

$$\sum_i^r \sum_j^t \sum_k^u \left(\sum_m^v x_{ijkm}\right)^2 = 24{,}786{,}137.$$

CHAPTER 16

Some Simple Experimental Designs

16.1. Completely Randomized Designs

We have in previous chapters developed techniques suitable for analyzing the simpler experimental designs. The simplest experiment perhaps is to compare r levels of a single experimental factor: We may be comparing three brands of gasoline, or four thicknesses of shoe leather, or five quantities of supplement to a hog ration. If we make n_i independent observations on each level of the factor, in a completely random order, the model for the experiment will be

$$x_{ij} = \xi + \eta_i + z_{ij} ,$$

and the appropriate analysis will be model I one-way analysis of variance as discussed in Section 10.2. Usually it will be preferable to have the n_i all equal, since then the variances of the differences between any pair will be the same, and also since Tukey's method of multiple comparisons, which requires equal n_i and is more efficient than Scheffé's method for simple comparisons, can then be applied. However, if our objective is to compare all the other levels of the factor with one particular level, the "control," as can be done effectively with Dunnett's technique, it is advantageous to have the n_i for the control equal to $\sqrt{k}$ times the n_i for the other levels, where k is the number of other levels.

The next simplest experiment is to investigate two factors simultaneously in all combinations with n independent replicates per combination. For example, one factor could be brand of gasoline at r levels, and the other mean speed of automobile at t levels. Or one factor could be quantity of supplement to the hog ration and the other factor the breed of hog. The total number of observations required is (rtn), and these should be obtained in a completely random order. The appropriate analysis will be two-way analysis of variance as discussed in Chapter 13. The model may be model I, or II, or mixed, depending on the nature of the factors. For example, in the hog example just given, the first factor, the quantity of supplement, is a fixed or model I factor, and the second factor, breed of hog, would be a model I factor if we were interested only in these particular breeds, but a model II factor if we were interested in generalizing to a larger population of breeds.

In discussing the principles of experimental design, it is convenient to have a general word for the basic experimental unit that gives rise to the measurement which we analyze. In the preceding paragraph, a given trip with a particular automobile using a particular gasoline will give rise to a single determination of gasoline consumption and is the basic experimental unit. In the hog feeding example, the individual hog is the experimental unit. The great bulk of the theory of experimental design was developed in agronomy, in which the basic experimental unit is a plot of ground on which is grown a crop and to which is applied fertilizers, etc. It is convenient to use the word *plot* for basic experimental unit in general.

Randomization of treatments on to plots is best performed with a table of random numbers (Table X). Suppose that we have an experiment involving three replicates of five treatments. We can denote the jth replicate of the ith treatment as (ij). We write out in any order, systematic if convenient, these $3 \times 5 = 15$ treatments (Table 16.1, first row). Under each treatment we enter a two-digit random number from Table X. We then order in increasing magnitude these random numbers. The particular set we chose happens to have a tie, two 69's. This tie is resolved by picking two further random digits and attaching one to each of the ties. The next two-digit random number is 28, and so the first 69 is regarded as 69.2 and the second as 69.8. The third row gives the ordering of the random numbers. Then plot 1 receives treatment (33), plot 2 receives treatment (13), etc.

Table 16.1

Treatments	11	12	13	14	15	21	22	23	24	25	31	32	33	34	35
Random numbers	15	77	01	64	69(2)	69(8)	58	40	81	16	60	20	00	84	22
Ordering	3	13	2	10	11	12	8	7	14	4	9	5	1	15	6

16.2. Randomized-Block Designs

If we are studying a single factor at t levels, with r replicates on each level, it may be possible to arrange the observations in r blocks of t observations. In agricultural experimentation each observation of, say, yield, comes from a plot of ground, and we may group t adjacent plots to form a block. In executing the experiment, we randomly allocate the t levels to the t plots in the first block, repeat the randomization for the second block, and so on. This is quite different from the completely randomized experiment where there was a single randomization of rn treatments, actually r treatments repeated n times, on to rn plots.

Usually the blocks will be regarded as a random or model II factor, and the factor under study will be a model I factor. The appropriate analysis will be a mixed model with one observation per cell. A suitable modification of the model (13.11.1) to this circumstance would be

$$x_{ij} = \xi + b_i + \zeta_j + \theta_{ij} + z_{ij} \tag{2.1}$$

and Table 13.15 with no within-cell term and $n = 1$ becomes Table 16.2. The remainder mean square is an appropriate error term for testing the effect of the factor and for constructing confidence limits for differences. The test of the block effect is only satisfactory if it can be assumed that σ_θ^2 is small compared to σ^2. This limitation is usually of small import as our main objective is to study the factor.

Table 16.2

Source of variance	Type of effect	Mean square	E[M.S.]
Blocks	II	s_4^2	$\sigma^2 + t\sigma_b^2$
Factor	I	s_3^2	$\sigma^2 + \sigma_\theta^2 + r\sigma_\zeta^2$
Remainder		s_2^2	$\sigma^2 + \sigma_\theta^2$

16.3. The Efficiency of Randomized Blocks

The objective of using a randomized-blocks design instead of a completely randomized arrangement is to reduce experimental error. Adjacent plots clustered together in a block should be more alike in their response to the same treatment than plots at opposite ends of the field.

We will now compute the magnitude of the gain achieved by running an experiment in randomized blocks instead of completely randomized. Let σ_{0b}^2 and σ_{0r}^2 be the error terms in the two forms. We define the more efficient design, the randomized blocks, as the standard, and the efficiency of the other is defined as

$$I = \frac{\sigma_{0b}^2}{\sigma_{0r}^2}. \tag{3.1}$$

This is a reasonable definition of efficiency, for to get the same accuracy on the comparison of treatment means we would have to use $1/I$ as many times replicates with the less efficient design; e.g., if the efficiency is 0.50, we need $1/0.5 = 2$ times as many observations with the inefficient design compared with the efficient design to get the same accuracy.

Suppose that we have t treatments and r blocks, or replicates. Suppose that we had run the experiment in blocks, but that the treatments were "dummy," i.e., imaginary. The analysis of variance would have been as in Table 16.3. The sums of squares would be (the degrees of freedom) $\times$ (the mean squares) as given in the last column, and the total sum of squares is given in the last row.

Table 16.3

Source of variance	Degrees of freedom	Mean squares	E[M.S.]	Sums of squares
Blocks	$r - 1$	B		$(r - 1)B$
Within blocks	$r(t - 1)$	E	σ_{0b}^2	$r(t - 1)E$
	$rt - 1$			$(r - 1)B + r(t - 1)E$

Table 16.4

Source of variance	Degrees of freedom	Mean squares	Sums of squares	E[M.S.]
Treatments	$t - 1$	T	$(t - 1)T$	$\sigma_{0r}^2 + r\sigma_T^2$
Within treatments	$t(r - 1)$	E'	$t(r - 1)E'$	σ_{0r}^2
Total	$rt - 1$		$(t - 1)T + t(r - 1)E'$	σ_{0r}^2

We now imagine that the experiment had been run completely randomized, again with dummy treatments. The analysis would have been as in Table 16.4. Since the treatments are dummy, $\sigma_T^2 = 0$, and the treatment mean-square estimates σ_{0r}^2. We can thus estimate σ_{0r}^2 from the mean square formed by pooling the treatment sum of squares with the within-treatment sum of squares, i.e., $\hat{\sigma}_{0r}^2 = [(t - 1)T + t(r - 1)E']/(rt - 1)$.

Now since the field is the same in the two hypothetical situations, the total sum of squares must be the same; so

$$(r - 1)B + r(t - 1)E = (t - 1)T + t(r - 1)E',$$

and we can estimate σ_{0r}^2 as

$$\hat{\sigma}_{0r}^2 = \frac{(r-1)B + r(t-1)E}{rt-1} .$$

We estimate σ_{0b}^2 by E. Hence the estimated efficiency of the completely randomized design relative to the randomized-block design is

$$\hat{I} = \frac{\hat{\sigma}_{0b}^2}{\hat{\sigma}_{0r}^2} = \frac{E}{[(r-1)B + r(t-1)E]/(rt-1)} = \frac{rt-1}{F(r-1) + r(t-1)}, \quad (3.2)$$

where $F = B/E$ is the ratio of the block mean square to the within-block mean square. As we would expect, the larger the F, the lower is the relative efficiency of the completely randomized design.

16.4. Two Factors in Randomized Blocks

If we have two factors, say B and C, at t and u levels, and r blocks containing tu plots, we can randomly allocate the tu treatment combinations to the plots in the first block, repeat the process for the second block, etc. If the blocks are regarded as a random effect and the two factors are fixed effects, the appropriate analysis is similar to that discussed in Section 14.3, and the expected values of the mean squares are like those given in the left-hand side of Table 14.3, where σ_a^2 corresponds to blocks, with the modification that $n = 1$ and there is no within-cells sum of squares. The appropriate error term for the factor B is its interaction with blocks, and analogously for C, and the two-way interaction $B \times C$ is to be tested against the remainder mean square.

Actually, many practitioners of the art pool the sums of squares and degrees of freedom for all the interactions with blocks, namely aB, aC, and aBC, and use this pooled mean square as an error term. This procedure has implicit in it the assumption that $\sigma_{aB}^2 = \sigma_{aC}^2 = \sigma_{aBC}^2 = 0$. It is not clear in what fields of experimentation such a set of assumptions is or is not valid.

16.5. The Split-Plot Situation

Suppose that we have two factors, for specificity say B corresponding to varieties of potato and C to quantity of fertilizer. We might plan the experiment as in the previous section, in r randomized blocks, each block containing tu plots.

Alternatively, suppose we group these tu plots into t groups of u plots, and now change the terminology so that the ultimate unit is a *subplot* and the groups of u subplots are *whole plots*, the block containing t such whole plots.

We now design the experiment as follows. We randomly allocate the t levels of factor B (variety of potato) to the t whole plots in the first block, repeat this procedure for the second block, etc. We now randomly allocate the u levels of factor C (quantity of fertilizer) to the u subplots contained in the first whole plot in the first block, repeat this procedure for the second whole plot, etc. If there are three varieties and four fertilizers, the first two blocks might have the arrangement shown in Table 16.5.

Table 16.5

Block I	v_3f_4	v_3f_2	v_1f_1	v_1f_3	v_2f_2	v_2f_1
	v_3f_1	v_3f_3	v_1f_2	v_1f_4	v_2f_4	v_2f_3
Block II	v_1f_1	v_1f_3	v_3f_1	v_3f_4	v_2f_2	v_2f_1
	v_1f_4	v_1f_2	v_3f_2	v_3f_3	v_2f_3	v_2f_4

This randomization procedure is different from that used in the simple randomized-block design of the previous section. The motivation for using a split-plot design can arise from the nature of the experimental material. For example, if factor A is temperature and factor B is quantity of fertilizer in the growing of tomatoes, it would be difficult in practice to have a separate greenhouse for each plant, whereas it is easy to have quite a large number of pots in each greenhouse. Or, in an experiment involving various alloy mixtures melted at various temperatures, probably several crucibles containing different compositions could be put in the furnace at one time.

An appropriate model for such an experiment is

$$x_{ijk} = \xi + b_i + \psi_j + e_{j(i)} + \phi_k + (\phi\psi)_{jk} + (b\phi)_{ik} + z_{ijk} \,. \qquad (5.1)$$

In this model, b_i is the random-block effect, ψ_j is the fixed-variety effect, ϕ_k is the fixed-fertilizer effect, $(\phi\psi)_{jk}$ is their interaction, and $(b\phi)_{ik}$ is the interaction of blocks with fertilizer. The motivation for writing $e_{j(i)}$ in this form is that, if there were no treatments, i.e., the experiment was run with dummy treatments, then we would have a simple nested situation. The random variation of whole plots within the block is represented by the unrestricted error term $e_{j(i)}$, and the random variation of the subplots within the whole plots is represented by the unrestricted error term z_{ijk}. Let e and z have variances ω^2 and σ^2, respectively.

To obtain the expected values of the mean squares in the analysis of variance we follow the procedure of Section 15.3 and set up Table 16.6.

Table 16.6

	i (r, R)	j (t, T)	k (u, U)
z_{ijk}	1	1	1
$(b\phi)_{ik}$	$1 - r/R$	t	$1 - u/U$
$(\phi\psi)_{jk}$	r	$1 - t/T$	$1 - u/U$
ϕ_k	r	t	$1 - u/U$
$e_{j(i)}$	1	1	u
ψ_j	r	$1 - t/T$	u
b_i	$1 - r/R$	t	u

Table 16.7

Source of variance	Degrees of freedom	E[M.S.]
Blocks	$(r - 1)$	$\phi^2 + u\omega^2 + tu\sigma_b^2$
Varieties	$(t - 1)$	$\phi^2 + u\omega^2 + ru\sigma_\psi^2$
Whole-plot error	$(r - 1)(t - 1)$	$\phi^2 + u\omega^2$
Fertilizers	$(u - 1)$	$\phi^2 + t\sigma_{b\phi}^2 + rt\sigma_\phi^2$
Varieties × fertilizers	$(t - 1)(u - 1)$	$\phi^2 + r\sigma_{\phi\psi}^2$
Blocks × fertilizers	$(r - 1)(u - 1)$	$\phi^2 + t\sigma_{b\phi}^2$
Subplot error	$(r - 1)(t - 1)(u - 1)$	ϕ^2
Total	$rtu - 1$	

In the specific case which we are considering, $R = \infty$, and so $1 - r/R = 1$; and $t = T$ and $u = U$, and so $1 - t/T = 1 - u/U = 0$. We can now write down the expectations of the mean squares in Table 16.7. It is a matter of opinion in any particular instance whether the term $(b\phi)_{ik}$ should or should not be included in the model. It is perhaps more usual to exclude it. In that case its sum of squares and degrees of freedom get pooled with subplot error to form a new estimate of σ^2 based on $t(r-1)(k-1)$ degrees of freedom, and of course $t\sigma^2_{b\phi}$ gets stricken out of the expectation of the fertilizer mean square.

16.6. Relationship of Split Plot to Partially Hierarchical Situations

In our discussion of the split-plot experiment of the preceding section, there was nothing essential to the split-plot concept that the experiment be run in randomized blocks. As far as the whole-plot part of the experiment is concerned, it might just as well be run as r completely randomized replicates of the t whole-plot treatments. If we omit the block effects from the model (5.1), we get

$$x_{ijk} = \xi + \psi_j + e_{ij} + \phi_k + (\phi\psi)_{jk} + z_{ijk} . \tag{6.1}$$

If we now refer back to the model (15.1.1) for the partially hierarchical situation discussed in Section 15.1, and modify it to conform to the situation where there is only one replicate per cell by omitting the suffix ν and the final error term $z_{ijk\nu}$ and by substituting z_{ijk} for $\{\lambda c(\alpha)\}_{kj(i)}$, we get

$$x_{ijk} = \xi + \alpha_i + \{c(\alpha)\}_{j(i)} + \lambda_k + (\lambda\alpha)_{ik} + z_{ijk} , \tag{6.2}$$

which is essentially identical with (6.1).

We therefore see that the split-plot situation is an agricultural example of a partially hierarchical classification, and the two can be considered together. We can use the results of Section 15.4 on variances of various types of differences, with the afore-mentioned differences. Thus the analog of (15.4.11) becomes

$$\hat{V}[\bar{x}_{\cdot j\cdot} - \bar{x}_{\cdot j'\cdot}] = \frac{2}{ru}\,[\text{M.S. for whole-plot error}]. \tag{6.3}$$

Since, with $\nu = 1$, the $\{\lambda c(\alpha)\}_{kj(i)}$ has been replaced by z_{ijk}, (15.4.15) becomes

$$\hat{V}[\bar{x}_{\cdot\cdot k} - \bar{x}_{\cdot\cdot k'}] = \frac{2}{rt}\,[\text{M.S. for subplot error}], \tag{6.4}$$

and (15.4.18) becomes

$$\hat{V}[\bar{x}_{\cdot jk} - \bar{x}_{\cdot jk'}] = \frac{2}{r}\,[\text{M.S. for subplot error}]. \tag{6.5}$$

From (15.4.20) and (15.4.21),

$$\hat{V}[\bar{x}_{\cdot jk} - \bar{x}_{\cdot j'k}] = \frac{1}{ru}[(u-1)(\text{M.S. for subplot error}) + (\text{M.S. for whole-plot error})]. \tag{6.6}$$

EXERCISES

16.1. An experiment was run to compare three similar magnesium salts, *A*, *B*, *C*, in the production of an antibiotic by fermentation. In the first replication, three fermentations were started, one containing salt *A*, another salt *B*, and the third salt *C*. After five days, samples for analysis were withdrawn from each fermentation, and likewise after six days. The whole operation was repeated a total of four times. The replications should be regarded as blocks.

(*a*) Make an appropriate analysis of variance for these data, and report the *F* values, with the corresponding degrees of freedom, for the main effects of salt, age (five days versus six), and their interaction.

(*b*) Give 95 per cent confidence limits for the following differences:

(i) Salt *A* − salt *B*.
(ii) Six days − five days.
(iii) Salt *A* − salt *B*, both at six days.

	Magnesium salt					
	A		*B*		*C*	
Replication	5 days	6 days	5 days	6 days	5 days	6 days
1	69	84	91	98	81	86
2	82	78	75	82	72	77
3	67	74	78	92	66	79
4	69	77	85	92	73	81

16.2. An experiment is run at one place to compare c treatments τ_k, $k = 1, \ldots, c$, in b randomized blocks r_j, $j = 1, \ldots, b$. The whole experiment is replicated at a different places p_i, $i = 1, \ldots, a$. The treatments are a model I effect; places and blocks are model II effects.

(*a*) Write down a suitable linear model for this experiment.

(*b*) Prepare a table listing the names of the mean squares you would compute, with the corresponding numbers of degrees of freedom and the expectations of the mean squares.

(*c*) Indicate how you would test the main effect for treatments.

16.3. The experiment described in Exercise 16.2 is repeated at the same places in d different years y_l, $l = 1, \ldots, d$. Each year, a fresh sample of blocks is selected at each place. Assume the particular d years to be a random sample of all years.

Answer questions (*a*), (*b*), and (*c*) as in 16.2.

16.4. As in 16.3, but each year a fresh sample of places is taken.

16.5. An experiment is planned to compare three types of anti-g suit at four different values of g, there thus being 12 suit $\times$ g combinations to be tested. The experiment may be run in the following ways:

(*a*) Six observations on each suit $\times$ g combination, the entire set of 72 observations being obtained with one subject.

(*b*) One observation on each suit $\times$ g combination from a single subject (each subject thus giving 12 observations), and the whole being repeated on a further five subjects.

(*c*) One observation on each level of g with a given suit with a given subject (a subject thus gives four observations, namely, the four levels of g, all with a particular suit); these observations repeated with a further five subjects; then the foregoing repeated with the other two suits, using new subjects.

(*d*) Six observations on each suit $\times$ g combination, each observation coming from a different subject, and no subject being used for more than one observation.

For each of these experiments, write down an appropriate linear model, list the sums of squares by name with their degrees of freedom, and give the expected values of all mean squares. What are the various relative advantages and disadvantages of these four experiments?

Use the following symbolism:

$$\sigma_i \text{ for suits, } i = 1, \ldots, k,$$
$$\gamma_j \text{ for } g \text{ values, } j = 1, \ldots, m.$$

Where a symbol for subjects is required, use p, and also assume that we have q replicates per suit $\times$ g combination, instead of six as specified above. Regard subjects as selected at random from an infinite population, but the four levels of g and the three suits are both fixed (model I) effects. In all cases assume that appropriate randomization was employed.

CHAPTER 17

Regression on Several Independent Variables

17.1. Introduction

Chapter 11 dealt with the regression of a dependent variable y on a single independent variable x. This chapter will deal with the regression of y on r independent variables x_i. Although it is merely a special case, we will deal with $r = 2$ before the general case of any r, but before that we will establish an essential result.

17.2. Linear Transformation of the Variables in a Bivariate Normal Distribution to Give Independent Variables

We suppose that x_1, x_2 are distributed in a bivariate normal distribution such as (12.3.16). Now introduce new variables y_1, y_2 defined as

$$
\begin{aligned}
y_1 &= f_1(x_1, x_2) = (x_1 - \xi_1) \cos \alpha + (x_2 - \xi_2) \sin \alpha \\
y_2 &= f_2(x_1, x_2) = -(x_1 - \xi_1) \sin \alpha + (x_2 - \xi_2) \cos \alpha.
\end{aligned}
\tag{2.1}
$$

The y's correspond to a new set of coordinates centered at $x_1 = \xi_1$, $x_2 = \xi_2$, and rotated with respect to the original coordinates through an angle α. The inverse functions are

$$
\begin{aligned}
x_1 &= g_1(y_1, y_2) = \xi_1 + y_1 \cos \alpha - y_2 \sin \alpha \\
x_2 &= g_2(y_1, y_2) = \xi_2 + y_1 \sin \alpha + y_2 \cos \alpha.
\end{aligned}
\tag{2.2}
$$

We now use (12.2.6) for the probability density function of a transformation:

$$p(y_1, y_2) = p_x\{g_1(y_1, y_2), g_2(y_1, y_2)\} \begin{vmatrix} \dfrac{\partial g_1}{\partial y_1} & \dfrac{\partial g_2}{\partial y_1} \\ \dfrac{\partial g_1}{\partial y_2} & \dfrac{\partial g_2}{\partial y_2} \end{vmatrix}.$$

Here p_x is the usual bivariate normal distribution (12.3.16) for variables x_1, x_2. Differentiating (2.2) gives

$$\frac{\partial g_1}{\partial y_1} = \cos\alpha, \qquad \frac{\partial g_1}{\partial y_2} = -\sin\alpha, \qquad \frac{\partial g_2}{\partial y_1} = \sin\alpha, \qquad \frac{\partial g_2}{\partial y_2} = \cos\alpha; \tag{2.3}$$

so the determinant is

$$\cos\alpha \cdot \cos\alpha - (-\sin\alpha)(\sin\alpha) = 1. \tag{2.4}$$

Hence

$$p(y_1, y_2) = \frac{1}{2\pi\sigma_1\sigma_2\sqrt{1-\rho^2}} \exp\left\{-\frac{1}{2(1-\rho^2)}\left[\left(\frac{y_1\cos\alpha - y_2\sin\alpha}{\sigma_1}\right)^2 + \left(\frac{y_1\sin\alpha + y_2\cos\alpha}{\sigma_2}\right)^2 - 2\rho\,\frac{(y_1\cos\alpha - y_2\sin\alpha)(y_1\sin\alpha + y_2\cos\alpha)}{\sigma_1\sigma_2}\right]\right\}. \tag{2.5}$$

Denote the exponent of this function by G. Recalling that $2\sin\alpha\cos\alpha = \sin 2\alpha$, $\cos^2\alpha - \sin^2\alpha = \cos 2\alpha$, G can be written as

$$G = -\frac{1}{2(1-\rho^2)}\left[y_1^2\left(\frac{\cos^2\alpha}{\sigma_1^2} + \frac{\sin^2\alpha}{\sigma_2^2} - \rho\,\frac{\sin 2\alpha}{\sigma_1\sigma_2}\right) + y_2^2\left(\frac{\sin^2\alpha}{\sigma_1^2} + \frac{\cos^2\alpha}{\sigma_2^2} + \rho\frac{\sin 2\alpha}{\sigma_1\sigma_2}\right) - y_1y_2\left(\frac{\sin 2\alpha}{\sigma_1^2} - \frac{\sin 2\alpha}{\sigma_2^2} + 2\rho\,\frac{\cos 2\alpha}{\sigma_1\sigma_2}\right)\right]. \tag{2.6}$$

Thus $p(y_1, y_2)$ has the form of a bivariate normal distribution with mean (0, 0) and variances and correlation coefficient which are some functions of σ_1^2, σ_2^2, ρ, and α. If we make the coefficient of (y_1y_2) in (2.6) zero, we will have y_1, y_2 with zero correlation. Putting this coefficient equal to zero requires

$$\frac{\sin 2\alpha}{\sigma_1^2} - \frac{\sin 2\alpha}{\sigma_2^2} + 2\rho\,\frac{\cos 2\alpha}{\sigma_1\sigma_2} = 0, \tag{2.7}$$

or
$$\tan 2\alpha = \frac{2\rho\sigma_1\sigma_2}{\sigma_1^2 - \sigma_2^2}. \tag{2.8}$$

If we use the value of α determined by this equation, we will have $\rho_{y_1 y_2} = 0$. Now the probability density function of y_1, y_2 with zero correlation is

$$p(y_1, y_2) = \frac{1}{2\pi\sigma_{y_1}\sigma_{y_2}} \exp\left\{-\frac{1}{2}\left[\left(\frac{y_1}{\sigma_{y_1}}\right)^2 + \left(\frac{y_2}{\sigma_{y_2}}\right)^2\right]\right\}. \tag{2.9}$$

But we already have an equation for $p(y_1, y_2)$, namely, (2.5). These must be identical for all values of y_1, y_2. Since this includes $y_1 = 0$, $y_2 = 0$, we can insert these values in the two equations and equate the results:

$$\frac{1}{2\pi\sigma_{y_1}\sigma_{y_2}} = \frac{1}{2\pi\sigma_1\sigma_2\sqrt{1-\rho^2}},$$

or
$$\sigma_{y_1}\sigma_{y_2} = \sigma_1\sigma_2\sqrt{1-\rho^2}. \tag{2.10}$$

Also (2.5) and (2.9) must be identical for $y_1 = 1$, $y_2 = 1$: This implies

$$\begin{aligned}
&\frac{1}{\sigma_{y_1}^2} + \frac{1}{\sigma_{y_2}^2} \\
&= \frac{1}{1-\rho^2}\left[\left(\frac{\cos^2\alpha}{\sigma_1^2} + \frac{\sin^2\alpha}{\sigma_2^2} - \rho\frac{\sin 2\alpha}{\sigma_1\sigma_2}\right) + \left(\frac{\sin^2\alpha}{\sigma_1^2} + \frac{\cos^2\alpha}{\sigma_2^2} + \rho\frac{\sin 2\alpha}{\sigma_1\sigma_2}\right)\right] \\
&= \frac{1}{1-\rho^2}\left(\frac{1}{\sigma_1^2} + \frac{1}{\sigma_2^2}\right);
\end{aligned}$$

so, if we multiply each side by the square of the corresponding side of (2.10), we get

$$\sigma_{y_1}^2 + \sigma_{y_2}^2 = \sigma_1^2 + \sigma_2^2.$$

Adding and subtracting (2.10) gives

$$\begin{aligned}
(\sigma_{y_1} + \sigma_{y_2})^2 &= \sigma_1^2 + \sigma_2^2 + 2\sigma_1\sigma_2\sqrt{1-\rho^2}, \\
(\sigma_{y_1} - \sigma_{y_2})^2 &= \sigma_1^2 + \sigma_2^2 - 2\sigma_1\sigma_2\sqrt{1-\rho^2}.
\end{aligned} \tag{2.11}$$

Thus, if we know σ_1, σ_2, and ρ for the original distribution of (x_1, x_2), we can determine σ_{y_1} and σ_{y_2} to use in the equation for the probability density of (y_1, y_2), (2.9).

If we substitute back for x_1, x_2 in (2.5), we get

$$\begin{aligned}
p(y_1, y_2) &= \frac{1}{2\pi\sigma_1\sigma_2\sqrt{1-\rho^2}} \\
&\exp\left\{-\frac{1}{2(1-\rho)^2}\left[\left(\frac{x_1-\xi_1}{\sigma_1}\right)^2 - 2\rho\left(\frac{x_1-\xi_1}{\sigma_1}\right)\left(\frac{x_2-\xi_2}{\sigma_2}\right) + \left(\frac{x_2-\xi_2}{\sigma_2}\right)^2\right]\right\}.
\end{aligned}$$

But $p(y_1, y_2)$ is also given by (2.9). Equating these two, and using (2.10), we get

$$\frac{1}{(1-\rho^2)}\left[\left(\frac{x_1-\xi_1}{\sigma_1}\right)^2 - 2\rho\left(\frac{x_1-\xi_1}{\sigma_1}\right)\left(\frac{x_2-\xi_2}{\sigma_2}\right) + \left(\frac{x_2-\xi_2}{\sigma_2}\right)^2\right] = \left(\frac{y_1}{\sigma_{y_1}}\right)^2 + \left(\frac{y_2}{\sigma_{y_2}}\right)^2. \quad (2.12)$$

The y's have zero means and zero covariance; so the right-hand side is the sum of squares of two independent unit normal deviates, which must have the χ^2 distribution with 2 degrees of freedom. Hence the left-hand side of (2.12) has the same distribution:

$$\frac{1}{1-\rho^2}\left[\left(\frac{x_1-\xi_1}{\sigma_1}\right)^2 - 2\rho\left(\frac{x_1-\xi_1}{\sigma_1}\right)\left(\frac{x_2-\xi_2}{\sigma_2}\right) + \left(\frac{x_2-\xi_2}{\sigma_2}\right)^2\right] \sim \chi^2(2). \quad (2.13)$$

We will need this result in the following section.

17.3. Regression on Two Independent Variables: Estimation of the Parameters

We assume that y is distributed normally about an expected value η with variance σ^2, and that the observations are independent. We assume that η is a simple linear function of two *independent variables* x_1 and x_2:

$$\eta = \alpha + \beta_1(x_1 - \bar{x}_1) + \beta_2(x_2 - \bar{x}_2). \quad (3.1)$$

Although this is the standard terminology for x_1 and x_2, it is misleading in that there is no requirement that x_1, x_2 be independent in the statistical sense. All that is required is that they be variables whose values $x_{1\nu}$, $x_{2\nu}$ be known for each value of ν.

We assume that we have n triplets of observations (y_ν, $x_{1\nu}$, $x_{2\nu}$). We wish to obtain sample estimates a, b_1, b_2, and s^2 of the parameters α, β_1, β_2, and σ^2.

The estimated equation is

$$Y = a + b_1(x_1 - \bar{x}_1) + b_2(x_2 - \bar{x}_2), \quad (3.2)$$

and the sum of squares of deviations between the observed values y_ν and the values predicted by the estimated equation is

$$R = \sum_{\nu}^{n} (y_\nu - Y_\nu)^2 = \sum_{\nu}^{n} [y_\nu - \{a + b_1(x_{1\nu} - \bar{x}_1) + b_2(x_{2\nu} - \bar{x}_2)\}]^2. \quad (3.3)$$

To minimize this we differentiate with respect to a, b_1, b_2 and equate to zero:

$$\frac{\partial R}{\partial a} = -2\sum_{\nu}^{n}[y_\nu - a - b_1(x_{1\nu} - \bar{x}_1) - b_2(x_{2\nu} - \bar{x}_2)] = 0, \tag{3.4}$$

$$\frac{\partial R}{\partial b_1} = -2\sum_{\nu}^{n}[y_\nu - a - b_1(x_{1\nu} - \bar{x}_1) - b_2(x_{2\nu} - \bar{x}_2)](x_{1\nu} - \bar{x}_1) = 0, \tag{3.5}$$

$$\frac{\partial R}{\partial b_2} = -2\sum_{\nu}^{n}[y_\nu - a - b_1(x_{1\nu} - \bar{x}_1) - b_2(x_{2\nu} - \bar{x}_2)](x_{2\nu} - \bar{x}_2) = 0. \tag{3.6}$$

Since $\sum_{\nu}^{n}(x_{1\nu} - \bar{x}_1) = 0 = \sum_{\nu}^{n}(x_{2\nu} - \bar{x}_2)$, (3.4) gives us

$$\sum_{\nu}^{n} y_\nu - na - b_1\sum_{\nu}^{n}(x_{1\nu} - \bar{x}_1) - b_2\sum_{\nu}^{n}(x_{2\nu} - \bar{x}_2) = \sum_{\nu}^{n} y_\nu - na = 0,$$

whence

$$a = \frac{1}{n}\sum_{\nu}^{n} y_\nu \tag{3.7}$$

Equation (3.4) also implies

$$\sum_{\nu}^{n}(y_\nu - Y_\nu) = 0. \tag{3.8}$$

Equations (3.5) and (3.6) imply

$$\sum_{\nu}^{n}(y_\nu - Y_\nu)(x_{1\nu} - \bar{x}_1) = 0 = \sum_{\nu}^{n}(y_\nu - Y_\nu)(x_{2\nu} - \bar{x}_2), \tag{3.9}$$

and

$$\begin{aligned} b_1\sum_{\nu}^{n}(x_{1\nu} - \bar{x}_1)^2 + b_2\sum_{\nu}^{n}(x_{1\nu} - \bar{x}_1)(x_{2\nu} - \bar{x}_2) &= \sum_{\nu}^{n} y_\nu(x_{1\nu} - \bar{x}_1), \\ b_1\sum_{\nu}^{n}(x_{1\nu} - \bar{x}_1)(x_{2\nu} - \bar{x}_2) + b_2\sum_{\nu}^{n}(x_{2\nu} - \bar{x}_2)^2 &= \sum_{\nu}^{n} y_\nu(x_{2\nu} - \bar{x}_2). \end{aligned} \tag{3.10}$$

The pair of simultaneous equations (3.10), known as the *normal equations*, involve sums of squares and sums of products which can be evaluated from the data, and hence solutions for b_1 and b_2 can be obtained.

In principle, the sum of squares for s^2 could be obtained from (3.3) by substituting the solutions for a, b_1, and b_2. A more convenient identity is obtained as follows. We note that

$$y_\nu - \bar{y} = (y_\nu - Y_\nu) + (Y_\nu - \bar{y}),$$

and

$$\sum_{\nu}^{n}(y_\nu - \bar{y})^2 = \sum_{\nu}^{n}(y_\nu - Y_\nu)^2 + \sum_{\nu}^{n}(Y_\nu - \bar{y})^2, \tag{3.11}$$

since the cross product

$$2\sum_{\nu}^{n}(y_\nu - Y_\nu)(Y_\nu - \bar{y})$$
$$= 2\sum_{\nu}^{n}(y_\nu - Y_\nu)[\bar{y} + b_1(x_{1\nu} - \bar{x}_1) + b_2(x_{2\nu} - \bar{x}_2) - \bar{y}]$$
$$= 2b_1\sum_{\nu}^{n}(y_\nu - Y_\nu)(x_{1\nu} - \bar{x}_1) + 2b_2\sum_{\nu}^{n}(y_\nu - Y_\nu)(x_{2\nu} - \bar{x}_2)$$
$$= 0,$$

by (3.9). Rearranged, (3.11) becomes

$$\sum_{\nu}^{n}(y_\nu - Y_\nu)^2 = \sum_{\nu}^{n}(y_\nu - \bar{y})^2 - \sum_{\nu}^{n}(Y_\nu - \bar{y})^2. \tag{3.12}$$

The first term on the right-hand side is simply the sum of squares of deviations about the grand mean, and so we are left with finding a convenient form for $\sum_{\nu}^{n}(Y_\nu - \bar{y})^2$. Multiply the normal equations (3.10) by b_1 and b_2, respectively,

$$b_1^2\sum_{\nu}^{n}(x_{1\nu} - \bar{x}_1)^2 + b_1b_2\sum_{\nu}^{n}(x_{1\nu} - \bar{x}_1)(x_{2\nu} - \bar{x}_2) = b_1\sum_{\nu}^{n}y_\nu(x_{1\nu} - \bar{x}_1),$$
$$b_1b_2\sum_{\nu}^{n}(x_{1\nu} - \bar{x}_1)(x_{2\nu} - \bar{x}_2) + b_2^2\sum_{\nu}^{n}(x_{2\nu} - \bar{x}_2)^2 = b_2\sum_{\nu}^{n}y_\nu(x_{2\nu} - \bar{x}_2),$$

and add, interchanging left- and right-hand sides:

$$b_1\sum_{\nu}^{n}y_\nu(x_{1\nu} - \bar{x}_1) + b_2\sum_{\nu}^{n}y_\nu(x_{2\nu} - \bar{x}_2)$$
$$= \sum_{\nu}^{n}[b_1^2(x_{1\nu} - \bar{x}_1)^2 + 2b_1b_2(x_{1\nu} - \bar{x}_1)(x_{2\nu} - \bar{x}_2) + b_2^2(x_{2\nu} - \bar{x}_2)^2] \tag{3.13}$$
$$= \sum_{\nu}^{n}[b_1(x_{1\nu} - \bar{x}_1) + b_2(x_{2\nu} - \bar{x}_2)]^2 = \sum_{\nu}^{n}(Y_\nu - \bar{y})^2. \tag{3.14}$$

This is the form usually used for computing $\sum_{\nu}^{n}(Y_\nu - \bar{y})^2$, and with it (3.12) gives the sum of squares for s^2. Since three parameters, a, b_1, and b_2, have been fitted to the data, the degrees of freedom for s^2 are $(n - 3)$.

We have now completed the operation of estimating the parameters α, β_1, and β_2.

17.4. Distributional Considerations

We will now compute directly the variances of the sample estimates of the regression coefficients. We first solve the normal equations (3.10) for b_1 by multiplying the first by $\sum_{\nu}^{n}(x_{2\nu}-\bar{x}_2)^2$, the second by $\sum_{\nu}^{n}(x_{1\nu}-\bar{x}_1)(x_{2\nu}-\bar{x}_2)$, and subtracting. Space can be saved by using the definitions

$$\begin{aligned}\sum{}'x_1^2 &= \sum_{\nu}^{n}(x_{1\nu}-\bar{x}_1)^2, \qquad \sum{}'x_2^2 = \sum_{\nu}^{n}(x_{2\nu}-\bar{x}_2)^2,\\ \sum{}'x_1x_2 &= \sum_{\nu}^{n}(x_{1\nu}-\bar{x}_1)(x_{2\nu}-\bar{x}_2),\\ \sum{}'yx_1 &= \sum_{\nu}^{n}y_\nu(x_{1\nu}-\bar{x}_1), \qquad \sum{}'yx_2 = \sum_{\nu}^{n}y_\nu(x_{2\nu}-\bar{x}_2).\end{aligned} \tag{4.1}$$

We get

$$\begin{aligned}b_1\sum{}'x_1^2\sum{}'x_2^2 + b_2\sum{}'x_1x_2\sum{}'x_2^2 &= \sum{}'yx_1\sum{}'x_2^2,\\ b_1\left(\sum{}'x_1x_2\right)^2 + b_2\sum{}'x_1x_2\sum{}'x_2^2 &= \sum{}'yx_2\sum{}'x_1x_2.\end{aligned}$$

Solving for b_1 gives

$$b_1 = \frac{\sum{}'yx_1\sum{}'x_2^2 - \sum{}'yx_2\sum{}'x_1x_2}{\sum{}'x_1^2\sum{}'x_2^2 - \left(\sum{}'x_1x_2\right)^2}. \tag{4.2}$$

This can be written in the form

$$\begin{aligned}b_1 &= \frac{1}{\sum{}'x_1^2\sum{}'x_2^2-\left(\sum{}'x_1x_2\right)^2}\left[\sum{}'x_2^2\sum_{\nu}^{n}(x_{1\nu}-\bar{x}_1)y_\nu-\sum{}'x_1x_2\sum_{\nu}^{n}(x_{2\nu}-\bar{x}_2)y_\nu\right]\\ &= \frac{1}{\sum{}'x_1^2\sum{}'x_2^2-\left(\sum{}'x_1x_2\right)^2}\left\{\sum_{\nu}^{n}\left[\left(\sum{}'x_2^2\right)(x_{1\nu}-\bar{x}_1)-\left(\sum{}'x_1x_2\right)(x_{2\nu}-\bar{x}_2)\right]y_\nu\right\},\end{aligned} \tag{4.3}$$

which shows that b_1 is a linear function of the y's, and, since the y's are normally distributed, b_1 will be normally distributed, with variance

$$\begin{aligned}V[b_1] &= \frac{\sum_{\nu}^{n}\left[\left(\sum{}'x_2^2\right)(x_{1\nu}-\bar{x}_1)-\left(\sum{}'x_1x_2\right)(x_{2\nu}-\bar{x}_2)\right]^2 V[y_\nu]}{\left[\sum{}'x_1^2\sum{}'x_2^2-\left(\sum{}'x_1x_2\right)^2\right]^2}\\ &= \sigma^2\frac{\left(\sum{}'x_2^2\right)^2\left(\sum{}'x_1^2\right)-2\left(\sum{}'x_2^2\right)\left(\sum{}'x_1x_2\right)\left(\sum{}'x_1x_2\right)+\left(\sum{}'x_1x_2\right)^2\left(\sum{}'x_2^2\right)}{\left[\sum{}'x_1^2\sum{}'x_2^2-\left(\sum{}'x_1x_2\right)^2\right]^2}\\ &= \sigma^2\frac{\sum{}'x_2^2}{\sum{}'x_1^2\sum{}'x_2^2-\left(\sum{}'x_1x_2\right)^2}.\end{aligned} \tag{4.4}$$

Similarly

$$V[b_2] = \sigma^2\frac{\sum{}'x_1^2}{\sum{}'x_1^2\sum{}'x_2^2-\left(\sum{}'x_1x_2\right)^2}. \tag{4.5}$$

The same type of manipulation leads to

$$\text{Cov}[b_1, b_2] = -\sigma^2\frac{\sum{}'x_1x_2}{\sum{}'x_1^2\sum{}'x_2^2-\left(\sum{}'x_1x_2\right)^2} \tag{4.6}$$

whence
$$\rho_{b_1b_2} = -\frac{\sum' x_1 x_2}{\sqrt{\sum' x_1^2 \sum' x_2^2}}. \tag{4.7}$$

By substituting s^2 for σ^2, (4.4) and (4.5) can be used to test the separate null hypotheses $\beta_1 = 0$ and $\beta_2 = 0$, and to construct separate confidence limits for β_1 and for β_2. Also, if we substitute b_1 for x_1, b_2 for x_2, etc., in (2.13), we get

$$\frac{1}{1-\rho_{b_1b_2}^2}\left[\left(\frac{b_1-\beta_1}{\sqrt{V[b_1]}}\right)^2 - 2\rho_{b_1b_2}\left(\frac{b_1-\beta_1}{\sqrt{V[b_1]}}\right)\left(\frac{b_2-\beta_2}{\sqrt{V[b_2]}}\right) + \left(\frac{b_2-\beta_2}{\sqrt{V[b_2]}}\right)^2\right], \tag{4.8}$$

which is distributed as $\chi^2(2)$. From (4.7),

$$1 - \rho_{b_1b_2}^2 = 1 - \frac{(\sum' x_1x_2)^2}{\sum' x_1^2 \sum' x_2^2} = \frac{\sum' x_1^2 \sum' x_2^2 - (\sum' x_1 x_2)^2}{\sum' x_1^2 \sum' x_2^2}.$$

Making the appropriate substitutions in (4.8), we get, on multiplying by σ^2,

$$[(b_1-\beta_1)^2 \textstyle\sum' x_1^2 + 2(b_1-\beta_1)(b_2-\beta_2)\sum' x_1x_2 + (b_2-\beta_2)^2\sum' x_2^2] \sim \sigma^2\chi^2(2). \tag{4.9}$$

We will assume without proof the obvious generalization of this to r independent variables $x_1, \ldots, x_r$:

$$\sum_i^r (b_i-\beta_i)^2 \textstyle\sum' x_i^2 + 2\displaystyle\sum_{i=1}^{r-1}\sum_{j=i+1}^{r}(b_i-\beta_i)(b_j-\beta_j)\textstyle\sum' x_ix_j \sim \sigma^2\,\chi^2(r). \tag{4.10}$$

17.5. Analysis-of-Variance Viewpoint for Two Independent Variables

We can write the deviation between the observation y_ν and the true value η_ν as

$$\begin{aligned} y_\nu - \eta_\nu &= (y_\nu - Y_\nu) + (Y_\nu - \eta_\nu) \\ &= (y_\nu - Y_\nu) + (a-\alpha) + (b_1-\beta_1)(x_{1\nu}-\bar{x}_1) + (b_2-\beta_2)(x_{2\nu}-\bar{x}_2). \end{aligned} \tag{5.1}$$

Squaring and summing, and using (3.8) and (3.9) to dispose of cross products,

$$\begin{aligned} \sum_\nu^n (y_\nu-\eta_\nu)^2 &= \sum_\nu^n (y_\nu - Y_\nu)^2 + n(a-\alpha)^2 + (b_1-\beta_1)^2\sum_\nu^n (x_{1\nu}-\bar{x}_1)^2 \\ &\quad + 2(b_1-\beta_1)(b_2-\beta_2)\sum_\nu^n (x_{1\nu}-\bar{x}_1)(x_{2\nu}-\bar{x}_2) \\ &\quad + (b_2-\beta_2)^2\sum_\nu^n (x_{2\nu}-\bar{x}_2)^2. \end{aligned} \tag{5.2}$$

The left-hand side of this equation is distributed as $\sigma^2 \chi^2(n)$. On the right-hand side $\sum_{\nu}^{n} (y_\nu - Y_\nu)^2$ has $(n - 3)$ degrees of freedom since the $(y_\nu - Y_\nu)$ have to satisfy the three linear restrictions (3.8) and (3.9). The second term, involving a, has one degree of freedom. Since $a = \sum_{\nu}^{n} y_\nu/n$, $V[a] = \sigma^2/n$ and

$$\frac{a - \alpha}{\sigma/\sqrt{n}} \sim u;$$

so

$$n(a - \alpha)^2 \sim \sigma^2 \chi^2(1) .$$

Third, we showed in (4.9) that the last three terms jointly are distributed as $\sigma^2\chi^2(2)$. Thus the conditions for Cochran's theorem are satisfied, and the three component sums of squares, namely, $\sum_{\nu}^{n} (y_\nu - Y_\nu)^2$, $n(a - \alpha)^2$, and (4.9) are independently distributed as $\sigma^2\chi^2$. Since

$$s^2 = \frac{1}{n-3} \sum_{\nu}^{n} (y_\nu - Y_\nu)^2 \tag{5.3}$$

it will have expected value

$$E[s^2] = \frac{1}{n-3} E[\sigma^2 \chi^2(n - 3)] = \sigma^2. \tag{5.4}$$

As indicated above, we can make separate tests of the null hypotheses $\beta_1 = 0$ and $\beta_2 = 0$, but in general these tests are not independent since usually $\text{Cov}[b_1, b_2] \neq 0$. We can make a joint test of the null hypothesis $\beta_1 = \beta_2 = 0$ as follows. Since (4.9) is distributed as $\sigma^2\chi^2(2)$,

$$E\{\tfrac{1}{2}[(b_1 - \beta_1)^2\textstyle\sum' x_1^2 + 2(b_1 - \beta_1)(b_2 - \beta_2)\sum' x_1x_2 + (b_2 - \beta_2)^2\sum' x_2^2]\} = \sigma^2. \tag{5.5}$$

Thus (4.9), divided by 2, is an estimate of σ^2 independent of s^2, which is also an estimate of σ^2. Their ratio will therefore be distributed as $F(2, n - 3)$. Hence, under the null hypothesis $\beta_1 = \beta_2 = 0$,

$$\frac{1}{2s^2} (b_1^2\textstyle\sum' x_1^2 + 2b_1b_2\sum' x_1x_2 + b_2^2\sum' x_2^2) \sim F(2, n - 3). \tag{5.6}$$

This is satisfactory as it stands, but usually the quantity in ( ) will be computed from (3.13) as

$$b_1 \sum_{\nu}^{n} y_\nu(x_{1\nu} - \bar{x}_1) + b_2 \sum_{\nu}^{n} y_\nu(x_{2\nu} - \bar{x}_2) . \tag{5.7}$$

Finally, the predicted value Y,

$$Y = a + b_1(x_1 - \bar{x}_1) + b_2(x_2 - \bar{x}_2)$$

has expected value

$$\eta = \alpha + \beta_1(x_1 - \bar{x}_1) + \beta_2(x_2 - \bar{x}_2).$$

Since a is independent of b_1 and b_2,

$$\begin{aligned} V[Y] &= V[a] + (x_1 - \bar{x}_1)^2\, V[b_1] + (x_2 - \bar{x}_2)^2\, V[b_2] \\ &\qquad + 2(x_1 - \bar{x}_1)(x_2 - \bar{x}_2)\,\mathrm{Cov}[b_1, b_2] \\ &= \sigma^2\left[\frac{1}{n} + \frac{(x_1-\bar{x}_1)^2\sum' x_2^2 - 2(x_1-\bar{x}_1)(x_2-\bar{x}_2)\sum' x_1x_2 + (x_2-\bar{x}_2)^2\sum' x_1^2}{\sum' x_1^2 \sum' x_2^2 - (\sum' x_1x_2)^2}\right], \end{aligned} \tag{5.8}$$

using (4.4), (4.5), and (4.6). The test implicit in (5.6) can be put into a table of analysis of variance. The equation (3.11) is the basis of the table, and from (3.13) the sum of squares due to regression is

$$\sum_{\nu}^{n} (Y_\nu - \bar{y})^2 = b_1 \sum_{\nu}^{n} y_\nu(x_{1\nu} - \bar{x}_1) + b_2 \sum_{\nu}^{n} y_\nu(x_{2\nu} - \bar{x}_2). \tag{5.9}$$

This gives Table 17.1. This table can be modified to give an additional test.

Table 17.1

Source of variance	Sums of squares	Degrees of freedom	Mean squares
Due to regression	$b_1\Sigma' yx_1 + b_2\Sigma' yx_2$	2	s_2^2
Remainder (about regression plane)	$\sum_{\nu}^{n} (y_\nu - Y_\nu)^2$ (By difference)	$n - 3$	s^2
Total	$\sum_{\nu}^{n} (y_\nu - \bar{y})^2$	$n - 1$	

The sum of squares due to regression on a single independent variable, say, x_1, is, by (11.4.1),

$$\frac{(\sum' yx_1)^2}{\sum' x_1^2} = b_1' \sum' yx_1,$$

where the b_1 is the simple regression coefficient of y on x_1 alone, $(\sum' yx_1)/\sum' x_1^2$. We can thus construct Table 17.2.

Table 17.2

Source of variance	Sums of squares	Degrees of freedom	Mean squares
Due to regression jointly on x_1, x_2	$b_1\Sigma' yx_1 + b_2\Sigma' yx_2 = A$	2	$A/2$
Due to regression on x_1 alone	$b_1'\Sigma' yx_1 = B$	1	B
Difference due to adding x_2 to x_1	$A - B$	1	$(A - B)$
Remainder (about regression plane on x_1, x_2)	$C - A$	$n - 3$	s^2
Total	$\sum_{\nu}^{n} (y_\nu - \bar{y})^2 = C$	$n - 1$	

The test of whether x_2 adds significantly to the regression on x_1 is given by the variance ratio $(A - B)/s^2$, which, under the null hypothesis that it does not, will be distributed as $F(1, n - 3)$.

17.6. Polynomial Regression

The conventional designation of x_1, x_2 as "independent" variables is unfortunate, for, in general, except in suitably designed experiments, they are not independent, since usually their covariance is not zero. Nothing in the foregoing development is assumed about the x_i except that they are known variables measured without error. We are therefore quite at liberty to use as x_2 the square of x_1, i.e., to fit the equation

$$\eta = \alpha + \beta_1(x_1 - \bar{x}_1) + \beta_2[(x_1^2) - \overline{(x_1^2)}]$$
$$= \text{constant} + \beta_1 x_1 + \beta_2 x_1^2. \tag{6.1}$$

The foregoing techniques can therefore be used to fit a second-degree curve if we think it necessary. The test of Table 17.2 enables us to test whether a second-degree curve gives a significantly better fit than a straight line.

17.7. The Partial-Correlation Coefficient

In the preceding discussion of this chapter the so-called independent variables x_1, x_2 were regarded as fixed variables. They may, however, be random variables, in which case they may be distributed along with y in the trivariate normal distribution, a generalization of the bivariate normal. Just as a bivariate normal distribution in x_1, x_2, when integrated over x_2 gives a marginal distribution in x_1 which is univariate normal, so a trivariate normal distribution in x_1, x_2, x_3, when integrated over say x_2, gives a bivariate normal distribution in x_1 and x_3. This bivariate normal distribution in x_1 and x_3 will have the usual properties of a bivariate normal, including a regression line of x_1 on x_3:

$$E[x_1 \mid x_3] = \xi_1 + \beta_{13}(x_3 - \xi_3). \tag{7.1}$$

Similarly, if the trivariate normal distribution is integrated over x_1, it will give a bivariate normal distribution in x_2, x_3, which will have a regression line of x_2 on x_3:

$$E[x_2 \mid x_3] = \xi_2 + \beta_{23}(x_3 - \xi_3). \tag{7.2}$$

We now define

$$x_{1\cdot3} = x_1 - E[x_1 \mid x_3] = x_1 - \xi_1 - \beta_{13}(x_3 - \xi_3), \tag{7.3}$$

$$x_{2\cdot3} = x_2 - E[x_2 \mid x_3] = x_2 - \xi_2 - \beta_{23}(x_3 - \xi_3). \tag{7.4}$$

The *partial-correlation coefficient* between x_1 and x_2, "eliminating" x_3, is defined as the correlation coefficient of $x_{1.3}$ and $x_{2.3}$:

$$\rho_{12\cdot3} = \frac{\operatorname{Cov}[x_{1.3}, x_{2.3}]}{\sqrt{V[x_{1.3}]\,V[x_{2.3}]}}. \tag{7.5}$$

We will now express $\rho_{12.3}$ in terms of ρ_{12}, ρ_{13}, and ρ_{23}, i.e., in terms of the simple correlation coefficient of x_1 with x_2, ignoring x_3, etc. From (7.3), using from (12.4.12) the relationship $\beta_{13} = \rho_{13}(\sigma_1/\sigma_3)$,

$$\begin{aligned} V[x_{1.3}] &= V[x_1] + \beta_{13}^2\, V[x_3] + 2(-\beta_{13}) \operatorname{Cov}[x_1, x_3] \\ &= \sigma_1^2 + \left(\rho_{13}\frac{\sigma_1}{\sigma_3}\right)^2 \sigma_3^2 - 2\left(\rho_{13}\frac{\sigma_1}{\sigma_3}\right)\rho_{13}\sigma_1\sigma_3 \\ &= \sigma_1^2(1 - \rho_{13}^2). \end{aligned} \tag{7.6}$$

Similarly,

$$V[x_{2.3}] = \sigma_2^2(1 - \rho_{23}^2). \tag{7.7}$$

Also,

$$\begin{aligned} \operatorname{Cov}[x_{1.3}, x_{2.3}] &= E[x_{1.3}x_{2.3}] - E[x_{1.3}]\, E[x_{2.3}] \\ &= \sigma_1\sigma_2(\rho_{12} - \rho_{13}\rho_{23}), \end{aligned} \tag{7.8}$$

by straightforward substitution. Substituting these results in (7.5) gives

$$\rho_{12.3} = \frac{\rho_{12} - \rho_{13}\rho_{23}}{\sqrt{(1 - \rho_{13}^2)(1 - \rho_{23}^2)}}. \tag{7.9}$$

The sample partial-correlation coefficient $r_{12.3}$ is the analogous expression with r's in place of ρ's:

$$r_{12.3} = \frac{r_{12} - r_{13}r_{23}}{\sqrt{(1 - r_{13}^2)(1 - r_{23}^2)}}. \tag{7.10}$$

Thus we can calculate $r_{12.3}$ from the simple correlation coefficients r_{12}, etc. The null hypothesis that $\rho_{12.3} = 0$ can be tested by the analog of (12.6.1):

$$\frac{r_{12.3}\sqrt{n-3}}{\sqrt{1 - r_{12.3}^2}} \tag{7.11}$$

will be distributed under the null hypothesis as $t(n - 3)$.

We recall that there is a relationship between the simple correlation coefficient between x_1 and x_2, say ρ_{12}, and the simple regression coefficient of x_1 on x_2, say β_{12}. By (12.4.12), $\beta_{12} = \rho_{12}(\sigma_1/\sigma_2)$, where σ_1^2, σ_2^2 are the simple variances of x_1 and x_2. Let us use the notation $\beta_{12.3}$ for the regression coefficient of x_1 on x_2 in the multiple-regression equation of x_1 on x_2 and x_3, and $\sigma_{1.3}^2$ and $\sigma_{2.3}^2$ for the variances of $x_{1.3}$ and $x_{1.3}$ as defined in (7.3) and (7.4). It can be shown that, analogous to (12.4.12),

$$\beta_{12.3} = \rho_{12.3}\frac{\sigma_{1.3}}{\sigma_{2.3}}. \tag{7.12}$$

Thus the partial-correlation coefficient of x_1 on x_2, "eliminating x_3," is directly related to the multiple-regression coefficient of x_1 on x_3 in the multiple-regression equation of x_1 on x_2 and x_3.

17.8. Regression on Several Independent Variables

The extension of regression analysis to r independent variables is straightforward. We have $(r + 1)$-tuples of observations, $(y_\nu, x_{1\nu}, \ldots, x_{r\nu})$, $\nu = 1, \ldots, n$. We assume that y is normally distributed with variance σ^2 about η, where η is a simple linear function:

$$\eta = \alpha + \beta_1(x_1 - \bar{x}_1) + \cdots + \beta_r(x_r - \bar{x}_r). \tag{8.1}$$

The estimated equation is

$$Y = a + b_1(x_1 - \bar{x}_1) + \cdots + b_r(x_r - \bar{x}_r) \tag{8.2}$$

and the sample estimates, $a, b_1, \ldots, b_r$ are obtained by minimizing the sum of squares of deviations between the observed and predicted values,

$$R = \sum_{\nu}^{n} (y_\nu - Y_\nu)^2 = \sum_{\nu}^{n} \{y_\nu - [a + b_1(x_{1\nu} - \bar{x}_1) + \cdots + b_r(x_{r\nu} - \bar{x}_r)]\}^2, \tag{8.3}$$

by differentiating with respect to $a, b_1, \ldots, b_r$ and equating to zero. This procedure gives

$$a = \frac{1}{n} \sum_{\nu}^{n} y_\nu = \bar{y} \tag{8.4}$$

and a set of r simultaneous linear equations, the so-called *normal equations*:

$$\begin{aligned} b_1\sum' x_1^2 + b_2\sum' x_1x_2 + \cdots + b_r\sum' x_1x_r &= \sum' yx_1\,, \\ b_1\sum' x_1x_2 + b_2\sum' x_2^2 + \cdots + b_r\sum' x_2x_r &= \sum' yx_2\,, \\ &\vdots \\ b_1\sum' x_1x_r + b_2\sum' x_2x_r + \cdots + b_r\sum' x_r^2 &= \sum' yx_r\,. \end{aligned} \tag{8.5}$$

These equations can be solved for the b's. However, an alternative procedure which will also give us $V[b_i]$ and $\text{Cov}[b_i, b_j]$ is to be preferred.

Suppose that there exist constants $c_{11}, c_{12}, \ldots, c_{1r}$ with properties to be defined later. Multiply the first of the normal equations by c_{11}, the second by c_{12}, etc., sum the resulting equations, and rearrange so as to collect all the coefficients of b_1 together, all the coefficients of b_2 together, etc.:

$$\begin{aligned} &b_1(c_{11}\sum' x_1^2 + c_{12}\sum' x_1x_2 + \cdots + c_{1r}\sum' x_1x_r) \\ &\quad + b_2(c_{11}\sum' x_1x_2 + c_{12}\sum' x_2^2 + \cdots + c_{1r}\sum' x_2x_r) \\ &\quad\vdots \\ &\quad + b_r(c_{11}\sum' x_1x_r + c_{12}\sum' x_2x_r + \cdots + c_{1r}\sum' x_r^2) \\ &\qquad = c_{11}\sum' yx_1 + c_{12}\sum' yx_2 + \cdots + c_{1r}\sum' yx_r. \end{aligned} \tag{8.6}$$

Let us require that the coefficient of b_1 in this equation is 1 and the coefficients of all the other b's are zero, i.e., that

$$\begin{aligned} c_{11}\sum' x_1^2 + c_{12}\sum' x_1x_2 + \cdots + c_{1r}\sum' x_1x_r &= 1, \\ c_{11}\sum' x_1x_2 + c_{12}\sum' x_2^2 + \cdots + c_{1r}\sum' x_2x_r &= 0, \\ &\vdots \\ c_{11}\sum' x_1x_r + c_{12}\sum' x_2x_r + \cdots + c_{1r}\sum' x_r^2 &= 0. \end{aligned} \tag{8.7}$$

This is a set of r simultaneous linear equations for r unknowns, namely, the constants c_{1j}, $j = 1, \ldots, r$, and they can be solved to give solutions for the c_{1j} in terms of the observed $x_{i\nu}$, since the various sums of squares and products $\sum' x_i^2$, $\sum' x_i x_j$ are readily calculated. Substituting the equations (8.7) in (8.6) gives

$$b_1 = c_{11}\sum' yx_1 + c_{12}\sum' yx_2 + \cdots + c_{1r}\sum' yx_r; \tag{8.8}$$

so once the c_{1j} have been found b_1 can be calculated simply, since the $\sum' yx_j$ are known numbers.

For each b_i, we can find a similar set of c_{ij} ($i = 1, \ldots, r$) which will do the same trick for b_i as (8.8) does for b_1. For b_i we have the set of simultaneous equations

$$\begin{aligned} c_{i1}\sum' x_1^2 + c_{i2}\sum' x_1x_2 + \cdots + c_{ir}\sum' x_1x_r &= 0, \\ &\vdots \\ c_{i1}\sum' x_1x_i + c_{i2}\sum' x_2x_i + \cdots + c_{ir}\sum' x_ix_r &= 1, \\ &\vdots \\ c_{i1}\sum' x_1x_r + c_{i2}\sum' x_2x_r + \cdots + c_{ir}\sum' x_r^2 &= 0, \end{aligned} \tag{8.9}$$

where the right-hand sides are 1 for the ith equation and zero for all the others. The ith equation has $\sum' x_i^2$ as the coefficient of c_{ii}. Analogous to (8.8), using (8.9) in (8.6),

$$b_i = c_{i1}\sum' yx_1 + c_{i2}\sum' yx_2 + \cdots + c_{ir}\sum' yx_r\,. \tag{8.10}$$

Recalling that $\sum' yx_i = \sum_{\nu}^{n} y_\nu(x_{i\nu} - \bar{x}_i)$, we can write this as

$$b_i = \sum_{\nu}^{n} y_\nu[c_{i1}(x_{1\nu} - \bar{x}_1) + c_{i2}(x_{2\nu} - \bar{x}_2) + \cdots + c_{ir}(x_{r\nu} - \bar{x}_r)], \tag{8.11}$$

which shows that b_i is a linear function of the y_ν. Since the y_ν are normally distributed, b_i will be also. The quantity in square brackets [ ] in (8.11) is solely a function of the x's. It will be convenient to have a symbol for it, say

$$k_{i\nu} = c_{i1}(x_{1\nu} - \bar{x}_1) + c_{i2}(x_{2\nu} - \bar{x}_2) + \cdots + c_{ir}(x_{r\nu} - \bar{x}_r). \tag{8.12}$$

Then
$$b_i = \sum_{\nu}^{n} y_\nu k_{i\nu}\,, \tag{8.13}$$

and
$$V[b_i] = \sum_{\nu}^{n} k_{i\nu}^2\, V[y_\nu] = \sigma^2 \sum_{\nu}^{n} k_{i\nu}^2\,. \tag{8.14}$$

Thus when we have found $\sum_{\nu}^{n} k_{i\nu}^2$, we will have $V[b_i]$. Now

$$\begin{aligned} \sum_{\nu}^{n} k_{i\nu}^2 &= \sum_{\nu}^{n} k_{i\nu}k_{i\nu} = \sum_{\nu}^{n} k_{i\nu}[c_{i1}(x_{1\nu} - \bar{x}_1) + \cdots + c_{ir}(x_{r\nu} - \bar{x}_r)] \\ &= c_{i1}\sum_{\nu}^{n} k_{i\nu}(x_{1\nu} - \bar{x}_1) + \cdots + c_{ir}\sum_{\nu}^{n} k_{i\nu}(x_{r\nu} - \bar{x}_r). \end{aligned} \tag{8.15}$$

In the sequence of terms with the index ij on the c's, i fixed and $j = 1, \ldots, r$, examine a particular one, say that for $j = h$:

$$\begin{aligned}
c_{ih} \sum_{\nu}^{n} k_{i\nu}(x_{h\nu} - \bar{x}_h) &= c_{ih}\sum_{\nu}^{n}[c_{i1}(x_{1\nu} - \bar{x}_1) + \cdots + c_{ih}(x_{h\nu} - \bar{x}_h) \\
&\qquad + \cdots + c_{ir}(x_{r\nu} - \bar{x}_r)](x_{h\nu} - \bar{x}_h) \\
&= c_{ih}[c_{i1} \sum_{\nu}^{n} (x_{1\nu} - \bar{x}_1)(x_{h\nu} - \bar{x}_h) + \cdots + c_{ih} \sum_{\nu}^{n} (x_{h\nu} - \bar{x}_h)^2 + \cdots \\
&\qquad + c_{ir} \sum_{\nu}^{n} (x_{h\nu} - \bar{x}_h)(x_{r\nu} - \bar{x}_r)] \\
&= c_{ih}(c_{i1}\textstyle\sum' x_1 x_h + c_{i2}\sum' x_2 x_h + \cdots + c_{ih}\sum' x_h^2 + \cdots + c_{ir}\sum' x_h x_r).
\end{aligned} \tag{8.16}$$

We have two cases to consider; $h = i$ and $h \neq i$. If $h = i$, (8.16) is

$$c_{ii}[c_{i1}\textstyle\sum' x_1 x_i + c_{i2}\sum' x_2 x_i + \cdots + c_{ii}\sum' x_i^2 + \cdots + c_{ir}\sum' x_i x_r]$$

and the part in [ ] is identically equal to the left-hand side of the ith equation in the set (8.9), for which the right-hand side is 1. Thus, when $h = i$, (8.16) equals c_{ii}. For all values of h other than i, the part in [ ] of (8.16) is one of the equations (8.9) which equals zero. Thus in (8.15) all the terms for which $i \neq j$ are zero, and the one term for which $i = j$ is equal to c_{ii}:

$$\sum_{\nu}^{n} k_{i\nu}^2 = c_{ii}, \tag{8.17}$$

so, from (8.14),

$$V[b_i] = \sigma^2 c_{ii}. \tag{8.18}$$

To obtain the covariance of b_i, b_j, we proceed as follows:

$$2\,\mathrm{Cov}[b_i, b_j] = V[b_i + b_j] - V[b_i] - V[b_j]. \tag{8.19}$$

From (8.13),

$$b_i + b_j = \sum_{\nu}^{n} y_\nu k_{i\nu} + \sum_{\nu}^{n} y_\nu k_{j\nu} = \sum_{\nu}^{n} y_\nu(k_{i\nu} + k_{j\nu}), \tag{8.20}$$

with variance

$$\begin{aligned}
V[b_i + b_j] &= \sum_{\nu}^{n} (k_{i\nu} + k_{j\nu})^2\, V[y_\nu] = \sigma^2 \sum_{\nu}^{n} (k_{i\nu} + k_{j\nu})^2 \\
&= \sigma^2 \sum_{\nu}^{n} k_{i\nu}^2 + \sigma^2 \sum_{\nu}^{n} k_{j\nu}^2 + 2\sigma^2 \sum_{\nu}^{n} k_{i\nu} k_{j\nu} \\
&= V[b_i] + V[b_j] + 2\sigma^2 \sum_{\nu}^{n} k_{i\nu} k_{j\nu}.
\end{aligned}$$

Substituting in (8.19) gives

$$\mathrm{Cov}[b_i, b_j] = \sigma^2 \sum_{\nu}^{n} k_{i\nu} k_{j\nu} . \tag{8.21}$$

From the definition of $k_{i\nu}$ (8.12),

$$\sum_{\nu}^{n} k_{i\nu} k_{j\nu} = c_{i1} \sum_{\nu}^{n} k_{j\nu}(x_{1\nu} - \bar{x}_1) + \cdots + c_{ir} \sum_{\nu}^{n} k_{j\nu}(x_{r\nu} - \bar{x}_r). \tag{8.22}$$

In the sequence of these terms with the index il on the c's, i fixed and $l = 1, \ldots, r$, examine a particular one, say that for $l = h$:

$$\begin{aligned} & c_{ih} \sum_{\nu}^{n} k_{j\nu}(x_{h\nu} - \bar{x}_h) \\ &= c_{ih} \sum_{\nu}^{n} [c_{j1}(x_{1\nu} - \bar{x}_1) + \cdots + c_{jh}(x_{h\nu} - \bar{x}_h) + \cdots + c_{jr}(x_{r\nu} - \bar{x}_r)](x_{h\nu} - \bar{x}_h) \\ &= c_{ih}[c_{j1}{\textstyle\sum}' x_1 x_h + \cdots + c_{jh}{\textstyle\sum}' x_h^2 + \cdots + c_{jr}{\textstyle\sum}' x_h x_r]. \end{aligned} \tag{8.23}$$

We have two cases to consider: $h = j$ and $h \neq j$. If $h = j$, (8.23) is

$$c_{ij}[c_{j1}{\textstyle\sum}' x_1 x_j + \cdots + c_{jj}{\textstyle\sum}' x_j^2 + \cdots + c_{jr}{\textstyle\sum}' x_j x_r],$$

and, except that j appears in place of i, the part in [ ] is identical with the ith equation in the set (8.9), for which the right-hand side is 1. For all values of h other than j, the part in [ ] of (8.23) is one of the equations (8.9) for which the right-hand side is zero. Thus, in (8.22), all the terms are zero except one, which is c_{ij}. Therefore

$$\sum_{\nu}^{n} k_{i\nu} k_{j\nu} = c_{ij} ,$$

and so, from (8.21),

$$\mathrm{Cov}[b_i, b_j] = \sigma^2 c_{ij} . \tag{8.24}$$

The square assembly of the c_{ij},

$$\begin{matrix} c_{11} & c_{12} & \cdots & c_{1r} , \\ c_{21} & c_{22} & \cdots & c_{2r} , \\ \vdots & & & \\ c_{r1} & c_{r2} & & c_{rr} , \end{matrix} \tag{8.25}$$

is known as the c matrix. It is actually the inverse of the matrix of the coefficients of the normal equations (8.9)

$$\begin{matrix} \sum' x_1^2 & \sum' x_1 x_2 & \cdots & \sum' x_1 x_r , \\ \sum' x_1 x_2 & \sum' x_2^2 & & \sum' x_2 x_r , \\ \vdots & & & \\ \sum' x_r x_1 & \sum' x_r x_2 & & \sum' x_r^2 . \end{matrix} \tag{8.26}$$

Incidentally, the c matrix is symmetric about the principal diagonal, so that $c_{ij} = c_{ji}$. Also the terms on the principal diagonal, c_{ii}, cannot be negative. These rules are sometimes useful in pointing out arithmetical errors.

17.9. Analysis-of-Variance Viewpoint for Several Independent Variables

We can write the deviation between the observation y_ν and the true value η_ν as

$$y_\nu - \eta_\nu = (y_\nu - Y_\nu) + (a - \alpha) + (b_1 - \beta_1)(x_{1\nu} - \bar{x}_1) + \cdots + (b_r - \beta_r)(x_{r\nu} - \bar{x}_r). \tag{9.1}$$

Squaring and summing gives

$$\sum_\nu^n (y_\nu - \eta_\nu)^2 = \sum_\nu^n (y_\nu - Y_\nu)^2 + n(a - \alpha)^2 + \sum_i^r (b_i - \beta_i)^2 \sum' x_i^2 + 2\sum_{i=1}^{r-1} \sum_{j=i+1}^{r} (b_i - \beta_i)(b_j - \beta_j)\sum' x_i x_j \,. \tag{9.2}$$

The left-hand side is distributed as $\sigma^2\chi^2(n)$. On the right-hand side $\sum_\nu^n (y_\nu - Y_\nu)^2$ is distributed as $\sigma^2\chi^2(n - 1 - r)$, $n(a - \alpha)^2$ as $\sigma^2\chi^2(1)$, and the remaining part, as surmised in (4.10), is distributed as $\sigma^2\chi^2(r)$. Each of these components is independent of the other. If we define

$$s^2 = \frac{1}{n - 1 - r} \sum_\nu^n (y_\nu - Y_\nu)^2 \tag{9.3}$$

it has expected value σ^2. The sample estimate a is normally distributed about α with variance σ^2/n. The variance of the predicted value Y given by the estimated equation (8.2) for a set of specified values of $x_1, \ldots, x_r$, about the true value η is

$$V[Y] = V[a] + \sum_{i=1}^r (x_i - \bar{x}_i)^2 \, V[b_i] + 2\sum_{i=1}^{r-1} \sum_{j=i+1}^{r} (x_i - \bar{x}_i)(x_j - \bar{x}_j) \operatorname{Cov}[b_i, b_j]$$

$$= \sigma^2 \left[\frac{1}{n} + \sum_{i=1}^r (x_i - \bar{x}_i)^2 c_{ii} + 2\sum_{i=1}^{r-1} \sum_{j=i+1}^{r} (x_i - \bar{x}_i)(x_j - \bar{x}_j) c_{ij} \right]. \tag{9.4}$$

Separate tests of the individual hypotheses $\beta_i = 0$ can be made using (8.18) with s^2 substituted for σ^2, but these are not in general independent since usually $\text{Cov}[b_i, b_j] \neq 0$. We can make a joint test of the null hypothesis $\beta_i = 0$ for all i as follows. Since (4.10) is distributed as $\sigma^2 \chi^2(r)$,

$$E\left[\frac{1}{r}\left\{\sum_i^r (b_i - \beta_i)^2 \sum' x_i^2 + 2\sum_{i=1}^{r-1} \sum_{j=i+1}^{r} (b_i - \beta_i)(b_j - \beta_j)\sum' x_i x_j\right\}\right] = \sigma^2, \tag{9.5}$$

and is independent of s^2 defined in (9.3). Hence, under the null hypothesis $\beta_i = 0$ for all i,

$$\frac{1}{rs^2}\left\{\sum_i^r b_i^2 \sum' x_i^2 + 2\sum_{i=1}^{r-1} \sum_{j=i+1}^{r} b_i b_j \sum' x_i x_j\right\} \sim F(r, n-1-r). \tag{9.6}$$

Usually the quantity in { }, known as the sum of squares due to regression, is obtained from the following identity. We multiply the normal equations (8.5) by b_1, b_2, etc., and sum:

$$\begin{aligned} b_1^2\sum' x_1^2 + b_2^2 \sum' x_2^2 + \cdots + b_r^2 \sum' x_r^2 + 2b_1 b_2 \sum' x_1 x_2 + \cdots + 2b_{r-1} b_r \sum' x_{r-1} x_r \\ = \sum_i^r b_i^2 \sum' x_i^2 + 2\sum_{i=1}^{r-1} \sum_{j=i+1}^{r} b_i b_j \sum' x_i x_j \\ = b_1 \sum' y x_1 + \cdots + b_r \sum' y x_r, \end{aligned} \tag{9.7}$$

which is the usual form for computing the sum of squares due to regression. Another identity for the left-hand side of (9.7) is useful: Writing the equation the other way round,

$$\begin{aligned} & b_1 \sum' y x_1 + \cdots + b_r \sum' y x_r \\ &= \sum_v^n [b_1^2 (x_{1v} - \bar{x}_1)^2 + \cdots + b_r^2 (x_{rv} - \bar{x}_r)^2 + 2b_1 b_2 (x_{1v} - \bar{x}_1)(x_{2v} - \bar{x}_2) \\ &\qquad + \cdots + 2b_{r-1} b_r (x_{r-1,v} - \bar{x}_{r-1})(x_{rv} - \bar{x}_r)] \\ &= \sum_v^n [b_1 (x_{1v} - \bar{x}_1) + \cdots + b_r (x_{rv} - \bar{x}_r)]^2 = \sum_v^n (Y_v - a)^2 = \sum_v^n (Y_v - \bar{y})^2. \end{aligned} \tag{9.8}$$

Since $$y_v - \bar{y} = (y_v - Y_v) + (Y_v - \bar{y}),$$

and $$\sum_v^n (y_v - \bar{y})^2 = \sum_v^n (y_v - Y_v)^2 + \sum_v^n (Y_v - \bar{y})^2, \tag{9.9}$$

the sum of squares of deviations about the regression plane, the numerator of s^2, is the total sum of squares about the mean minus the sum of squares due to regression:

$$\sum_v^n (y_v - Y_v)^2 = \sum_v^n (y_v - \bar{y})^2 - \sum_v^n (Y_v - \bar{y})^2, \tag{9.10}$$

where $\sum_{\nu}^{n} (Y_\nu - \bar{y})^2$ can be calculated from (9.8). This is the easiest way of obtaining $\sum_{\nu}^{n} (y_\nu - Y_\nu)^2$.

Analogs of Table 17.2 can be used for testing whether x_r adds significantly to the regression on $x_1, \ldots, x_{r-1}$.

17.10. Further Uses for the c Matrix

A further advantage of the c-matrix method of handling multiple regression is that it gives us directly the regression equation of each x on the other x's.

Write out the equations (8.9) with $i = \mu$, omitting that with 1 on the right-hand side; at the same time move over to the right-hand side the terms involving $c_{\mu\mu}$:

$$\begin{aligned}
c_{\mu1}\textstyle\sum' x_1^2 + c_{\mu2}\sum' x_1x_2 + \cdots + c_{\mu r}\sum' x_1x_r &= -c_{\mu\mu}\textstyle\sum' x_\mu x_1 \\
c_{\mu1}\textstyle\sum' x_1x_2 + c_{\mu2}\sum' x_2^2 + \cdots + c_{\mu r}\sum' x_2x_r &= -c_{\mu\mu}\textstyle\sum' x_\mu x_2 \\
&\vdots \\
c_{\mu1}\textstyle\sum' x_1x_r + c_{\mu2}\sum' x_2x_r + \cdots + c_{\mu r}\sum' x_r^2 &= -c_{\mu\mu}\textstyle\sum' x_\mu x_r.
\end{aligned} \tag{10.1}$$

Now divide throughout by $(-c_{\mu\mu})$:

$$\begin{aligned}
\left(-\frac{c_{\mu1}}{c_{\mu\mu}}\right)\textstyle\sum' x_1^2 + \left(-\frac{c_{\mu2}}{c_{\mu\mu}}\right)\sum' x_1x_2 + \cdots + \left(-\frac{c_{\mu r}}{c_{\mu\mu}}\right)\sum' x_1x_r &= \textstyle\sum' x_\mu x_1 \\
\left(-\frac{c_{\mu1}}{c_{\mu\mu}}\right)\textstyle\sum' x_1x_2 + \left(-\frac{c_{\mu2}}{c_{\mu\mu}}\right)\sum' x_2^2 + \cdots + \left(-\frac{c_{\mu r}}{c_{\mu\mu}}\right)\sum' x_2x_r &= \textstyle\sum' x_\mu x_2 \\
&\vdots \\
\left(-\frac{c_{\mu1}}{c_{\mu\mu}}\right)\textstyle\sum' x_1x_r + \left(-\frac{c_{\mu2}}{c_{\mu\mu}}\right)\sum' x_2x_r + \cdots + \left(-\frac{c_{\mu r}}{c_{\mu\mu}}\right)\sum' x_r^2 &= \textstyle\sum' x_\mu x_r.
\end{aligned} \tag{10.2}$$

Comparing this set of equations with a typical set of normal equations (8.5), it is apparent that these are the normal equations for the regression of x_μ on $x_1, \ldots, x_r$ (omitting x_μ), and the regression coefficient of x_μ on x_1 is $(-c_{\mu1}/c_{\mu\mu})$, etc. Thus, having found the c matrix (8.25), we can immediately write down the regression equation of x_μ on the other x's:

$$x_\mu = \bar{x}_\mu + \left(-\frac{c_{\mu1}}{c_{\mu\mu}}\right)(x_1 - \bar{x}_1) + \cdots + \left(-\frac{c_{\mu r}}{c_{\mu\mu}}\right)(x_r - \bar{x}_r). \tag{10.3}$$

Obviously in the sequence $i = 1, \ldots, r$ on the right-hand side, $i = \mu$ is omitted. Each row in the c matrix gives us the regression equation of a different x on the remaining x's.

A more explicit notation for regression coefficients is sometimes desirable. Let x_j stand for the sequence $x_1, x_2, \ldots, x_r$ in which x_μ and x_k are omitted. Then by $b_{x_\mu x_k \cdot x_j}$ we mean the regression coefficient of x_μ on x_k in the regression equation of x_μ on all the x's, x_1 to x_r (but naturally excluding x_μ). Thus in (10.3)

$$-\frac{c_{\mu 1}}{c_{\mu\mu}} = b_{x_\mu x_1 \cdot x_j}, \qquad j = 1, \ldots, r\,(\text{but } j \neq 1, \mu).$$

So far in this chapter we have required that the x_i, $i = 1, \ldots, r$, be known fixed variables. In general, however, they may be obtained in any of three different ways;

1. They may be chosen deliberately in some specified pattern. In particular, suppose that there are three variables on numerical scales, x_1 taking only r values, x_2 only t values, and x_3 only u values, and we obtain an observation on y for every combination of x_1 with x_2 and with x_3. The total number of observations will be rtu. In this case the simple and multiple-regression coefficients of each x on each of the other x's will be zero, and by (12.4.12) and (7.13) the corresponding correlation coefficients will be zero also.

2. Certain ranges for the variables x_i may be selected, and combinations of values of x_1, x_2, and x_3 chosen by some randomization procedure. So far the only difference from case 1 is that the x's are chosen at random instead of by some deliberate pattern or design. However, now the regression coefficients of the x's among themselves will be distributed about expected values of zero with some variance. Furthermore, if the original choices of the x_i were made from normal distributions, then we will have a multivariate normal distribution.

3. We may observe a system from the outside, without exercising any control over it. If the x_i have normal distributions, then we may have a multivariate normal distribution. Unlike case 2, in general the expected values of the regression coefficients of the x's among themselves will not now be zero.

In cases 2 and 3 we may be prepared to assume the multivariate normality. As implied in Section 17.7, just as we can carry out a simple regression analysis on a bivariate normal population, so we can carry out a multiple-regression analysis on a multivariate normal population. We may wish to make tests of significance and set confidence limits on the regression coefficients of x_μ on the other x's in the regression equation (10.3). For this we calculate the variance of these regression coefficients as follows.

Denote the estimated residual variance of x_μ about the regression plane on the remaining x's as s_μ^2.

In the set of equations (10.1) we omitted the equation in (8.9) whose right-hand side was 1:

$$c_{\mu 1}\sum' x_1 x_\mu + c_{\mu 2}\sum' x_2 x_\mu + \cdots + c_{\mu r}\sum' x_\mu x_r = 1 - c_{\mu\mu}\sum' x_\mu^2 .$$

Dividing by $(-c_{\mu\mu})$:

$$\left(-\frac{c_{\mu 1}}{c_{\mu\mu}}\right)\sum' x_1 x_\mu + \left(-\frac{c_{\mu 2}}{c_{\mu\mu}}\right)\sum' x_2 x_\mu + \cdots + \left(-\frac{c_{\mu r}}{c_{\mu\mu}}\right)\sum' x_\mu x_r = \sum' x_\mu^2 - \frac{1}{c_{\mu\mu}}. \tag{10.4}$$

Since $-c_{\mu 1}/c_{\mu\mu}$ is the regression coefficient of x_μ on x_1, etc., the left-hand side of this is exactly (9.7), the sum of squares due to regression. But we do not need to calculate it in that form, for (10.4) gives it as $(\sum' x_\mu^2 - 1/c_{\mu\mu})$. And, comparing (9.10), it is obvious that the residual sum of squares of x_μ about the regression plane on the other x's is $1/c_{\mu\mu}$. This residual sum of squares will have $(n - r)$ degrees of freedom; so $s_\mu^2 = (1/c_{\mu\mu})/(n - r)$.

So far we have the regression coefficients of x_μ on the other x's, and also the residual variance, but to get the variance and covariance of these regression coefficients we need the c matrix corresponding to the equations (10.2). This can be obtained from the original c matrix by the formula

$$c'_{ij} = c_{ij} - \frac{c_{i\mu}c_{j\mu}}{c_{\mu\mu}}. \tag{10.5}$$

Thus, to get the estimated variance of the regression coefficient of x_μ on x_k, $s_\mu^2 c'_{kk}$, we need

$$c'_{kk} = c_{kk} - \frac{c_{k\mu}c_{k\mu}}{c_{\mu\mu}} = \frac{c_{kk}c_{\mu\mu} - c_{k\mu}^2}{c_{\mu\mu}}, \tag{10.6}$$

and then
$$\hat{V}[b_{x_\mu x_k \cdot x_j}] = \frac{1/c_{\mu\mu}}{n - r}\left(\frac{c_{kk}c_{\mu\mu} - c_{k\mu}^2}{c_{\mu\mu}}\right) = \frac{1}{n - r}\left(\frac{c_{kk}c_{\mu\mu} - c_{k\mu}^2}{c_{\mu\mu}^2}\right). \tag{10.7}$$

The formula (10.5) can be used also to drop from a regression equation a variable, say x_μ, that appears, after construction of the regression equation, to be nonsignificant. We could, of course, start again from the beginning, but, if we have four or more independent variables, it is more expeditious to remove the μth row and column from the c matrix and compute the new b's from (8.10). Alternatively, it can be shown that, if b_i is the regression coefficient of y on x_i in the multiple-regression equation of y on all the x's, and if b'_i is the regression coefficient of y on x_i in the multiple-regression equation of y on all the x's excluding x_μ, then

$$b'_i = b_i - \frac{c_{i\mu}}{c_{\mu\mu}} b_\mu . \tag{10.8}$$

17.11. Biases in Multiple Regression

In (10.8), b'_i represents the regression coefficient of y on x_i, the regression equation containing $x_1, x_2, \ldots, x_m$ but excluding x_μ. We can write this as $b_{yx_i \cdot x_j}$, where x_j is understood to stand for the sequence of x's from x_1 to x_m but excluding x_i and x_μ. Also, b_i represents the regression coefficient of y on x_i, the regression equation containing all the x's. We can write this as $b_{yx_i \cdot x'_j}$, where x'_j is understood to stand for the sequence of x's from x_1 to x_m, excluding x_i, but including x_μ. Also, b_μ is the regression coefficient of y on x_μ, the regression equation containing all the x's. We can write this as $b_{yx_\mu \cdot x''_j}$, where x''_j is understood to stand for the sequence of x's from x_1 to x_m but excluding x_μ.

The remaining item in (10.8) is $-c_{i\mu}/c_{\mu\mu}$. Since $c_{i\mu} = c_{\mu i}$, this item is equal to $-c_{\mu i}/c_{\mu\mu}$. Reference to (10.3) shows that this is the regression coefficient of x_μ on x_i, the regression equation containing as independent variables all the x's except x_μ. We can write this as $b_{x_\mu x_i \cdot x_j}$, where x_j is the same as in the preceding paragraph.

We thus write (10.8) as

$$b_{yx_i \cdot x_j} = b_{yx_i \cdot x'_j} + b_{x_\mu x_i \cdot x_j} b_{yx_\mu \cdot x''_j} \tag{11.1}$$

where

$$x_j = x_1, \ldots, x_m \text{ but excluding } x_i, x_\mu \,.$$

$$x'_j = x_1, \ldots, x_m \text{ but excluding } x_i \,.$$

$$x''_j = x_1, \ldots, x_m \text{ but excluding } x_\mu \,.$$

The implication of this equation may be clearer if we consider a simple specific instance, say $m = 3$, $i = 1$, $\mu = 3$. Then $x_j = x_2$, $x'_j = x_2x_3$, $x''_j = x_1x_2$, and (11.1) reads

$$b_{yx_1 \cdot x_2} = b_{yx_1 \cdot x_2x_3} + b_{x_3x_1 \cdot x_2} b_{yx_3 \cdot x_1x_2} \,. \tag{11.2}$$

This equation shows that the regression coefficient of y on x_1, ignoring x_3, is a biased estimator of the regression coefficient of y on x_1, not ignoring x_3, by an amount a function of the product of the regression coefficient of y on x_3 and the regression coefficient of x_3 on x_1.

Equation (11.2) illustrates why the application of multiple-regression techniques to observational data can be so treacherous and misleading. The apparent regression of y on x_1 may really be due to the fact that y is dependent on x_3, and x_3 is correlated with x_1. We may fail to observe x_3, and attribute the regression of y on x_1 to a functional dependence which may be wholly false.

In most circumstances, therefore, any indications produced by a multiple-regression analysis of observational data are merely a good hint to try for confirmation by a proper experiment. In a true experiment the independent variables will be properly randomized with a table of random numbers and will have low correlations differing from zero by only random fluctuation, or else in a completely balanced experiment the correlations will be exactly zero.

The justification sometimes advanced that a multiple-regression analysis on observational data can be relied upon if there is an adequate theoretical background is utterly specious and disregards the unlimited capability of the human intellect for producing plausible explanations by the carload lot. For attempts to investigate these difficulties, see Tukey [1] and Simon [2].

A further reason for being suspicious of inferences from a multiple-regression analysis on observational data is that there is no guarantee that the residuals are independent.

17.12. An Example of Multiple Regression

The data of Table 17.3 will be used to illustrate the foregoing procedures. It was obtained from 21 days of operation of a plant for the oxidation of ammonia to nitric acid. The first column represents the rate of operation of the plant. The nitric oxides produced are absorbed in a countercurrent absorption tower. The third variable is the concentration of acid circulating, minus 50, times 10: i.e., 89 corresponds to 58.9 per cent acid. The second column is the temperature of cooling water circulated through coils in the absorption tower. The dependent variable y is 10 times the percentage of the ingoing ammonia to the plant that escapes from the absorption column unabsorbed, i.e., an (inverse) measure of the over-all efficiency of the plant.

We will fit a linear regression equation similar to (8.2). We need all the sums, sums of squares, and sums of products (Table 17.4), and these are expressed as sums of squares and products of deviations from the means in Table 17.5. We now set up the equations (8.9). To give more convenient numbers we will temporarily multiply the right-hand sides by 10,000. Also, although we can obtain the b_i from the c matrix from (8.10), we might as well add an additional set of right-hand sides $\sum' yx_i$. We are thus solving four separate sets of three simultaneous linear equations, in which the numerical coefficients on the left-hand sides, $\sum' x_1^2$, $\sum' x_1x_2$, etc., are identical for the four sets, but those on the right-hand sides do differ.

The equations (8.5) and (8.7) are repeated in rows 1 through 3 of Table 17.6, and the numerical values for the coefficients entered from Table 17.5 in rows 4 through 6. The problem of solving simultaneous linear equations, though simple in theory, is arduous in practice, and has a long history. For conventional desk calculation a method known as the

Doolittle, though probably due to Gauss, is one of the most satisfactory. Various modifications have been proposed, but the effort in learning their details seems to outweigh the slight savings they achieve. For r greater

Table 17.3

x_1	x_2	x_3	y
80	27	89	42
80	27	88	37
75	25	90	37
62	24	87	28
62	22	87	18
62	23	87	18
62	24	93	19
62	24	93	20
58	23	87	15
58	18	80	14
58	18	89	14
58	17	88	13
58	18	82	11
58	19	93	12
50	18	89	8
50	18	86	7
50	19	72	8
50	19	79	8
50	20	80	9
56	20	82	15
70	20	91	15

x_1 = air flow
x_2 = cooling water inlet temperature
x_3 = acid concentration
y = stack loss

than 5, the work becomes excessive, and recourse should be made to an electronic digital computer. Programs are available for the standard machines.

The procedure for solving the equations is as follows.

1. In line 7 divide line 4 by minus the coefficient of c_{i1} in line 4, i.e., by -1681.143.

2. In line 8 write out line 5 again. In line 9 multiply line 4 by the coefficient of c_{i2} in line 7, i.e., by -0.269544590. Add lines 8 and 9 together; the coefficient of c_{i1} vanishes, and we get line 10.

3. In line 11 divide line 10 by minus the coefficient of c_{i2} in line 10, i.e., by -77.667756.

4. In line 12 write out line 6 again. In line 13 multiply line 4 by the coefficient of c_{i3} in line 7, i.e., by -0.292318381. In line 14 multiply line 10 by the coefficient of c_{i3} in line 11, i.e., by 0.000425247. Add lines 12, 13, and 14 together; the coefficients of c_{i1} and c_{i2} vanish, and we get line 15.

Table 17.4

	y	x_1	x_2	x_3
y	8518	23,953	8,326	32,189
x_1		78,365	27,223	109,988
x_2			9,545	38,357
x_3				156,924
Totals	368	1,269	443	1,812

Table 17.5

	y	x_1	x_2	x_3
y	2069.238	1715.286	562.952	435.857
x_1		1681.143	453.143	491.429
x_2			199.810	132.429
x_3				574.286

5. In line 16 divide line 15 by the coefficient of c_{i3} in line 15, i.e., by 430.632256. This gives successively, on the right-hand side, $b_3 = -0.152125$, $c_{13} = -6.790783$, $c_{23} = 0.009875$, and $c_{33} = 23.221669$. Of course, the three c_{i3} need multiplying by 10^{-4} to give the correct values.

6. Now go back to line 11. This line represents the following four equations:

$$-1.0b_2 + 0.000425247b_3 = -1.295337256,$$

$$-1.0c_{12} + 0.000425247c_{13} = 34.704825,$$

$$-1.0c_{22} + 0.000425247c_{23} = -128.753559,$$

$$-1.0c_{32} + 0.000425247c_{33} = 0.$$

Table 17.6

	Coefficients of			Right-hand sides			
	c_{i1}	c_{i2}	c_{i3}		$i = 1$	$i = 2$	$i = 3$
1	$\Sigma' x_1^2$	$\Sigma' x_1 x_2$	$\Sigma' x_1 x_3$	$\Sigma' y x_1$	10,000	0	0
2	$\Sigma' x_1 x_2$	$\Sigma' x_2^2$	$\Sigma' x_2 x_3$	$\Sigma' y x_2$	0	10,000	0
3	$\Sigma' x_1 x_3$	$\Sigma' x_2 x_3$	$\Sigma' x_3^2$	$\Sigma' y x_3$	0	0	10,000
4	1681.143	453.143	491.429	1715.286	10,000	0	0
5	453.143	199.810	132.429	562.952	0	10,000	0
6	491.429	132.429	574.286	435.857	0	0	10,000
7	−1.0	−0.269544590	−0.292318381	−1.020309396	−5.94833896	0	0
8	453.143	199.810	132.429	562.952	0	10,000	0
9	−453.143	−122.142244	−132.462028	−462.346062	−2,695.44590	0	0
10		77.667756	−0.033028	100.605938	−2,695.44590	10,000	0
11		−1.0	0.000425247	−1.295337256	34.704825	−128.753559	0

12	491.429	132.429	574.286	435.857	0	0	10,000
13	−491.429	−132.462028	−143.653730	−501.409626	−2,923.18381	0	0
14		0.033027	−0.000014	0.042782	−1.14623	4.25247	0
15		−0.000001	430.632256	−65.509844	−2,924.33004	4.25247	10,000
16			1	−0.152124796	−6.7907826	0.0098749	23.221669
17		−1.0	−0.000064691	−1.295337256			
18			−0.002887760		34.704825		
19			+0.000004199			−128.753559	
20			+0.009874945				0
21		1.0		1.295272565	−34.707713	128.753563	0.009874945
22	−1.0	−0.349133712	0.044468874	−1.020309396			
23		9.355276	1.985070		−5.948339		
24		−34.704837	−0.002887			0	
25		−0.002662	−6.788121				0
26	1.0			0.715644558	17.288615	−34.707724	−6.790783

Substituting the solution for b_3 from line 16, i.e., -0.152124796, gives

$$-1.0b_2 - 0.000064691 = -1.259337256,$$

and this is schematically given in line 17. Solving for b_2 gives $b_2 = 1.295272$, as is schematically given in line 21. Similarly, line 18 corresponds to substituting $c_{13} = -6.7907826$ in the second of the four equations above,

$$-1.0c_{12} - 0.002887760 = 34.704825,$$

whence $c_{12} = -34.707713$, as is given in line 21. The solutions for c_{22} and c_{32} are obtained similarly.

7. Now go back to line 7, which represents the following four equations:

$$-1.0b_1 - 0.269544590b_2 - 0.292318381b_3 = -1.020309396,$$

$$-1.0c_{11} - 0.269544590c_{12} - 0.292318381c_{13} = -5.94833896,$$

$$-1.0c_{21} - 0.269544590c_{22} - 0.292318381c_{23} = 0,$$

$$-1.0c_{31} - 0.269544590c_{32} - 0.292318381c_{33} = 0.$$

Substituting $b_2 = 1.295272$ and $b_3 = -0.152124796$ in the first of these gives

$$-1.0b_1 - 0.349133712 + 0.044468874 = -1.020309396,$$

which is represented schematically in line 22. The solution for b_1 is $b_1 = 0.715644558$, as is given in line 26. The three remaining equations above for c_{11}, c_{21}, and c_{31} give lines 23, 24, and 25, respectively, and the final solutions are in the last three columns of line 26.

8. Assemble these solutions in Table 17.7.

Table 17.7

$10^4 c_{ij}$

$c_{11} =$	17.288615	$c_{12} =$	−34.707713	$c_{13} =$	−6.790783
$c_{21} =$	−34.707724	$c_{22} =$	128.753563	$c_{23} =$	0.009875
$c_{31} =$	−6.790783	$c_{32} =$	0.009875	$c_{33} =$	23.221669
$b_1 =$	0.715645	$b_2 =$	1.295272	$b_3 =$	−0.152125

9. Check the accuracy of these solutions by inserting them in the left-hand side of line 6 and seeing how the right-hand sides coincide with the required values. Here we get as left-hand sides 435.8569994, −0.034, −0.005, 10,000.000, which compare very well with the values in line 6.

However, the need for carrying a large number of significant figures is pointed up by the discrepancy in the fifth decimal place between c_{21} and c_{12}.

In the above calculations we obtained the b_i directly by carrying the column $\sum' yx_i$ as an additional right-hand side. This was not strictly necessary, for we can use (8.10) to obtain, e.g.,

$$b_1 = [1715.286 \times 17.288615 + 562.952 \times (-34.707713) \\ + 435.857 \times (-6.790783)] \times 10^{-4} = 0.715633$$

which differs from the direct solution in the fifth decimal place on account of rounding errors.

To make a joint test of the null hypothesis $\beta_i = 0$ for all i, we compute the sum of squares due to regression from (9.7):

$$0.715644 \times 1715.286 + 1.295273 \times 562.952 + (-0.152125) \times 435.857 \\ = 1890.406.$$

The residual sum of squares about the regression plane is given by (9.10) as $2069.238 - 1890.406 = 178.832$, and with $21 - 1 - 3 = 17$ degrees of freedom this gives $s^2 = 10.520$. These results are assembled in Table 17.8. The variance ratio, $630.135/10.520 = 60$, being distributed as $F(3, 17)$ under the null hypothesis, is overwhelmingly significant.

Table 17.8

Source of variance	Sums of squares	Degrees of freedom	Mean squares
Due to regression	1890.406	3	630.135
About the regression plane	178.832	17	10.520
Total	2069.238		

Separate t tests on the individual b_i are made, using (8.18). In Table 17.9, tests of the individual null hypotheses $\beta_i = 0$ are performed. Under the null hypothesis, the ratios in the last column are distributed as $t(17)$. The first two are obviously very significant, and the last nonsignificant. The individual confidence intervals for the separate b_i can be constructed if desired.

The regression equation of Y on x_1, x_2, x_3 is

$$Y = 17.524 + 0.715633(x_1 - 60.429) + 1.295273(x_2 - 21.095) + (-0.152125)(x_3 - 86.286)$$
$$= -39.919 + 0.7156x_1 + 1.2953x_2 - 0.1521x_3.$$

To test whether x_3 adds significantly to the regression on x_1 and x_2, we need the latter regression. When we have only three independent variables, to drop one it is about as quick to start from scratch with the two we want.

Table 17.9

i	$\hat{V}[b_i] = s^2c_{ii}$	$\sqrt{\hat{V}[b_i]}$	b_i	$t = b_i/\sqrt{\hat{V}[b_i]}$
1	$10.520 \times 17.288 \times 10^{-4}$	0.1349	0.7156	5.305
2	$10.520 \times 128.754 \times 10^{-4}$	0.3680	1.2953	3.520
3	$10.520 \times 23.222 \times 10^{-4}$	0.1563	−0.1521	−0.973

However, we will illustrate the procedure of Section 17.10. Since we are omitting x_3, in (10.6) $\mu = 3$, and

$$c'_{11} = \left[17.288615 - \frac{(-6.790783)^2}{23.221670}\right] \times 10^{-4} = 15.302766 \times 10^{-4}$$

$$c'_{22} = \left[128.753603 - \frac{(0.009875)^2}{23.221670}\right] \times 10^{-4} = 128.753599 \times 10^{-4}$$

and, from (10.5),

$$c'_{12} = \left[-34.707713 - \frac{(-6.790783)(0.009875)}{23.221670}\right] \times 10^{-4}$$
$$= -34.704825 \times 10^{-4} = c'_{21}.$$

We can calculate b_1 from (8.10) as

$$b'_1 = [1715.286 \times 15.302766 + 562.952 \times (-34.704825)] \times 10^{-4}$$
$$= 0.671159$$

and similarly $b'_2 = 1.295338$. Alternatively, we can use (10.8)

$$b'_1 = 0.715645 - \frac{(-6.790783)(-0.152125)}{23.221669} = 0.671159$$

which comes to the same thing. The sum of squares due to regression on x_1 and x_2 only is, again using (9.8),

$$(0.671159 \times 1715.286 + 1.295338 \times 562.952) \times 10^{-4} = 1880.443.$$

We now construct Table 17.10 analogous to Table 17.2. The test of the null hypothesis that adding x_3 to x_1, x_2 does not improve the fit is given by the variance ratio 9.963/10.520, which is clearly nonsignificant. The test of the joint hypothesis $\beta'_1 = \beta'_2 = 0$ is given by the variance ratio 940.221/[(2069.238–1880.443)/(20–2)] which is clearly overwhelmingly significant.

Table 17.10

Source of variance	Sums of squares	Degrees of freedom	Mean squares
Due to regression jointly on x_1, x_2, x_3	1890.406	3	
Due to regression jointly on x_1, x_2	1880.443	2	940.221
Due to adding x_3 to x_1, x_2	9.963	1	9.963
Deviations about regression plane on x_1, x_2, x_3	178.832	17	10.520
Total	2069.238	20	

The regression equation for x_1 and x_2 only is

$$\begin{aligned} Y &= 17.524 + 0.671159(x_1 - 60.429) + 1.295338(x_2 - 21.095) \\ &= -50.359 + 0.671159x_1 + 1.295338x_2\ . \end{aligned}$$

We might ask for 95 per cent confidence limits for η at $x_1 = 50$, $x_2 = 18$. For these values,

$$Y = -50.359 + 0.671159 \times 50 + 1.295338 \times 18 = 6.516.$$

The estimated variance of Y can be calculated from (5.8), which is applicable to the special case of two independent variables, or from (9.4), which is applicable to the general case of r independent variables. We will use the latter form here. Since we are using only two variables, s^2 is given by pooling the last two lines in the body of Table 17.10: $s^2 = (9.963 + 178.832)/(1 + 17) = 10.489$. Also $x_1 - \bar{x}_1 = 50 - 60.4286 = -10.4286$, $x_2 - \bar{x}_2 = 18 - 21.0952 = -3.0952$. Then

$$\begin{aligned} \hat{V}[Y] = 10.489[(1/21) + \{&15.302766 \times (-10.4286)^2 + 128.753603 \\ &\times (-3.0952)^2 + 2(-34.704825)(-10.4286)(-3.0952)\} \times 10^{-4}] \\ = 1.18893.& \end{aligned}$$

The square root of this is 1.0904, and $t_{0.975}(18) = 2.101$; so confidence limits for η are at $6.516 \pm 2.101 \times 1.0904 = (4.23, 8.81)$.

Finally, we will illustrate the use of the c matrix to give the regression equation of x_3 on x_1, x_2. Reading off the third line of Table 17.7, we have, for (10.3),

$$x_3 = \bar{x}_3 + \left(-\frac{-6.790783}{23.221669}\right)(x_1 - \bar{x}_1) + \left(-\frac{0.009875}{23.221669}\right)(x_2 - \bar{x}_2)$$
$$= 86.286 + 0.292433(x_1 - 60.429) - 0.000425(x_2 - 21.095).$$

To test the significance, say, of the regression coefficient of x_3 on x_1, in this equation, we would use (10.7):

$$\hat{V}[b_{31.2}] = \frac{1}{21-3}\left[\frac{17.288615 \times 23.221669 - (-6.790783)^2}{(23.221669)^2}\right] = 0.03651.$$

A test of the null hypothesis $\beta_{31.2} = 0$ is given by $0.292433/\sqrt{0.03651} = 1.53$, which is distributed as $t(18)$.

REFERENCES

1. Tukey, John W., "Causation, regression, and path analysis," Chapter 3, pp. 35–66, in *Statistics and Mathematics in Biology*, Oscar Kempthorne et al. (eds.). Ames, Iowa: Iowa State College Press, 1954.
2. Simon, Herbert A., "Spurious correlation: a causal interpretation," *Journal of the American Statistical Association*, 49(1954), 467–479.
3. Yerushalmy, J., and Herman E. Hilleboe, "Fat in the diet and mortality from heart disease: a methodological note," *New York State Journal of Medicine*, 57(1957), 2343–2354.
4. *World Almanac and Book of Facts*. New York: New York World Telegram, 1951.

EXERCISES

17.1. The table below gives data on death rate due to heart disease in males in the 55 to 59 age group, along with the proportionate number of telephones, and of fat and protein in the diet.

(*a*) Test the significance of the regression of y on x_1.
(*b*) Construct the multiple-regression equation of y on x_1, x_2.
(*c*) Make a joint test of the null hypothesis $\beta_1 = \beta_2 = 0$.
(*d*) Test whether adding x_2 to the regression equation (on x_1) has significantly improved the fit.
(*e*) Construct the multiple-regression equation of y on x_1, x_2, and x_3.
(*f*) Give 95 per cent confidence limits for β_3 in this equation.
(*g*) Give 95 per cent confidence limits for η at $x_1 = 221$, $x_2 = 39$, $x_3 = 7$.
(*h*) Test whether x_2 and x_3 together add anything to the regression of y on x_1.
(*i*) Construct the multiple-regression equation of x_1 on x_2 and x_3.
(*j*) Give 95 per cent confidence limits for the regression coefficient of x_1 on x_3.

	x_1	x_2	x_3	y
Australia	124	33	8	81
Austria	49	31	6	55
Canada	181	38	8	80
Ceylon	4	17	2	24
Chile	22	20	4	78
Denmark	152	39	6	52
Finland	75	30	7	88
France	54	29	7	45
Germany	43	35	6	50
Ireland	41	31	5	69
Israel	17	23	4	66
Italy	22	21	3	45
Japan	16	8	3	24
Mexico	10	23	3	43
Netherlands	63	37	6	38
New Zealand	170	40	8	72
Norway	125	38	6	41
Portugal	15	25	4	38
Sweden	221	39	7	52
Switzerland	171	33	7	52
United Kingdom	97	38	6	66
United States	254	39	8	89

x_1 = 1000 (telephones per head)
x_2 = fat calories as per cent of total calories
x_3 = animal protein calories as per cent of total calories
y = 100 [log (number deaths from heart disease per 100,000 for males in 55 to 59 age group) − 2]

Sources: x_2, x_3, and y from [3].
x_1 from [4], except the figures for Ireland and Ceylon, which were obtained by private communication from the countries concerned.

Sums of Squares and Products

	y	x_1	x_2	x_3
y	78,624	123,591	39,409	7,504
x_1		288,068	68,838	13,226
x_2			21,807	4,042
x_3				772
Sums	1,248	1,926	667	124

Sums of Squares and Products of Deviations

	y	x_1	x_2	x_3
y	7828.364	14,334.273	1,571.909	469.818182
x_1		119,455.455	10,445.182	2370.363636
x_2			1,584.773	282.545455
x_3				73.090909

CHAPTER 18

The Multiple-Regression Approach to Analysis of Variance

18.1. Introduction

In this chapter we will show how model I analysis of variance can be interpreted from the point of view of multiple regression [1]. Our treatment of analysis of variance assumed throughout, except in the simplest one-way case, that we had complete balance throughout, i.e., equal numbers of observations in all cells. The multiple-regression approach will indicate the principles for handling the unbalanced case.

18.2. The Completely Randomized One-Factor Design

Suppose we have observations, y_ν, $\nu = 1, \ldots, n$ from an experiment on n plots, on each of which one and only one of r treatments is applied. Let variables $X_{i\nu}$ be used to represent the level of these treatments. These treatments have only two levels, present or absent, and so can be represented numerically by 1 corresponding to present and 0 to absent.

From a multiple-regression point of view we can regard y_ν as normally distributed with variance σ^2 about η_ν,

$$\eta_\nu = \alpha + \tau_1 X_{1\nu} + \cdots + \tau_r X_{r\nu} . \tag{2.1}$$

This equation is estimated as

$$Y_\nu = a + t_1 X_{1\nu} + \cdots + t_r X_{r\nu} . \tag{2.2}$$

To these equations we add the restrictions

$$\sum_i^r \tau_i = 0 = \sum_i^r t_i. \tag{2.3}$$

We first assume that we have equal numbers t of replicates of each treatment. Now, instead of numbering the observation v, $v = 1, \ldots, n$, let us number them ij, $i = 1, \ldots, r$; $j = 1, \ldots, t$: i.e., the index i refers to treatments, and j refers to the replicate number for each treatment. From the multiple-regression point of view we have $(r + 1)$-tuples $(y_{ij}, X_{1ij}, \ldots, X_{rij})$. In detail some of these are as follows:

1. The t replicates of the first treatment:

$$\begin{aligned}
&(y_{11}, X_{111} = 1, X_{211} = 0, \ldots, X_{r11} = 0),\\
&(y_{12}, X_{112} = 1, X_{212} = 0, \ldots, X_{r12} = 0),\\
&\vdots\\
&(y_{1t}, X_{11t} = 1, X_{21t} = 0, \ldots, X_{r1t} = 0).
\end{aligned} \tag{2.4}$$

2. The t replicates of the second treatment:

$$\begin{aligned}
&(y_{21}, X_{121} = 0, X_{221} = 1, \ldots, X_{r21} = 0),\\
&(y_{22}, X_{122} = 0, X_{222} = 1, \ldots, X_{r22} = 0),\\
&\vdots\\
&(y_{2t}, X_{12t} = 0, X_{22t} = 1, \ldots, X_{r2t} = 0).
\end{aligned} \tag{2.5}$$

3. And so on up to the t replicates of the rth treatment:

$$\begin{aligned}
&(y_{r1}, X_{1r1} = 0, X_{2r1} = 0, \ldots, X_{rr1} = 1),\\
&(y_{r2}, X_{1r2} = 0, X_{2r2} = 0, \ldots, X_{rr2} = 1),\\
&\vdots\\
&(y_{rt}, X_{1rt} = 0, X_{2rt} = 0, \ldots, X_{rrt} = 1).
\end{aligned} \tag{2.6}$$

It is apparent that

$$\begin{aligned}
X_{i'ij} &= 1 \qquad \text{if } i' = i,\\
&= 0 \qquad \text{otherwise.}
\end{aligned} \tag{2.7}$$

Using ij in place of v, (2.1) and (2.2) become

$$\eta_{ij} = \alpha + \tau_1 X_{1ij} + \cdots + \tau_r X_{rij} = \alpha + \sum_{i'=1}^{r} \tau_{i'} X_{i'ij}, \tag{2.8}$$

$$Y_{ij} = a + t_1 X_{1ij} + \cdots + t_r X_{rij} = a + \sum_{i'=1}^{r} t_{i'} X_{i'ij}. \tag{2.9}$$

To construct the normal equations we need the usual sums of squares and sums of products: The sum of squares of deviations of $X_{i'}$ is

$$\sum_{i,j}(X_{i'ij}-\overline{X}_{i'})^2=\sum_{i,j}X_{i'ij}^2-(\sum_{i,j}X_{i'ij})^2/rt. \tag{2.10}$$

Now $\sum_{i,j} X_{i'ij}$ is equal to the number of times $X_{i'ij}$ is equal to 1, since the occasions on which it is equal to zero contribute nothing to the sum. Reference to (2.4) shows that $X_{i'ij}=1$ just t times; so

$$\sum_{i,j}{}' X_{i'ij}^2=t\times 1^2-\frac{(t\times 1)^2}{rt}=\frac{r}{t}(r-1). \tag{2.11}$$

This holds for all i'. For the cross products,

$$\sum_{i,j}(X_{i'ij}-\overline{X}_{i'})(X_{i''ij}-\overline{X}_{i''})=\sum_{i,j}X_{i'ij}X_{i''ij}-(\sum_{i,j}X_{i'ij})(\sum_{i,j}X_{i''ij})/rt.$$

Study of (2.4), (2.5), and (2.6) shows that, for example, X_{1ij} and X_{2ij} are never both 1 simultaneously. This reflects, of course, the fact that each plot receives only one treatment. Hence

$$\sum_{i,j}X_{i'ij}X_{i''ij}=0 \qquad \text{for } i'\neq i''; \tag{2.12}$$

so, for $i'\neq i''$,

$$\sum_{i,j}{}' X_{i'ij}X_{i''ij}=0-\frac{t\cdot t}{rt}=-\frac{t}{r}. \tag{2.13}$$

Finally, we need

$$\sum_{i,j}{}' y_{ij}X_{i'ij}=\sum_{i,j}y_{ij}X_{i'ij}-(\sum_{i,j}y_{ij})(\sum_{i,j}X_{i'ij})/rt.$$

Inspecting (2.4), etc., it is apparent that those ij for which $X_{i'ij}=0$ will contribute nothing to $\sum_{i,j} y_{ij}X_{i'ij}$. In fact, only those ij for which $i=i'$, and hence for which $X_{i'ij}=1$, will contribute, and the contribution will be the sum of the y's corresponding to plots receiving that, the i'th treatment. So

$$\sum_{i,j}y_{ij}X_{i'ij}=\sum_{j}^{t}y_{i'j}, \tag{2.14}$$

and

$$\sum_{i,j}{}' y_{ij}X_{i'ij}=\sum_{j}^{t}y_{i'j}-(\sum_{i,j}y_{ij})\cdot t/rt$$

$$=\sum_{j}^{t}y_{i'j}-(\sum_{i,j}y_{ij})/r=T_{i'}, \quad \text{say.} \tag{2.15}$$

We can now write out the normal equations:

$$
\begin{aligned}
t_1 \cdot \frac{t}{r}(r-1) + t_2\left(-\frac{t}{r}\right) + \cdots + t_r\left(-\frac{t}{r}\right) &= T_1, \\
t_1 \cdot \left(-\frac{t}{r}\right) + t_2 \cdot \frac{t}{r}(r-1) + \cdots + t_r\left(-\frac{t}{r}\right) &= T_2, \\
&\;\;\vdots \\
t_1\left(-\frac{t}{r}\right) + t_2\left(-\frac{t}{r}\right) + \cdots + t_r \cdot \frac{t}{r}(t-1) &= T_r.
\end{aligned}
\tag{2.16}
$$

In (2.3) we assumed $\sum_i^r t_i = 0$, which implies

$$t_1 \cdot \frac{t}{r} + t_2 \cdot \frac{t}{r} + \cdots + t_r \cdot \frac{t}{r} = 0. \tag{2.17}$$

Adding this to both sides of the first normal equation (2.16) gives

$$t_1\left[\frac{t}{r}(r-1) + \frac{t}{r}\right] = T_1;$$

so

$$t_1 = \frac{T_1}{t}, \tag{2.18}$$

and similarly for all the t_i. Referring back to (2.15), we see that t_{i}' is the natural estimate for $\tau_{i'}$,

$$t_{i'} = \frac{\sum_j^t y_{i'j}}{t} - \frac{\sum_i^r \sum_j^t y_{ij}}{rt} = \bar{y}_{i'.} - \bar{y}_{..}, \tag{2.19}$$

namely, the difference between the mean of the $y_{i'j}$ and the mean of all the y_{ij}.

The standard formula for the sum of squares due to regression (17.9.7) here becomes

$$
\begin{aligned}
t_1 T_1 + \cdots + t_r T_r &= \sum_{i'}^r t_{i'} T_{i'} \\
&= \sum_{i'}^r \left(\frac{\sum_j^t y_{i'j}}{t} - \frac{\sum_i^r \sum_j^t y_{ij}}{rt}\right)\left(\sum_j^t y_{i'j} - \frac{\sum_i^r \sum_j^t y_{ij}}{r}\right) \\
&= \frac{1}{t}\sum_{i'}^r \left(\sum_j^t y_{i'j}\right)^2 - \frac{1}{rt}\left(\sum_i^r \sum_j^t y_{ij}\right)^2,
\end{aligned}
\tag{2.20}
$$

which is the usual computing form in the analysis of variance for the sum of squares between groups [see (10.2.17) with the n_i put all equal]. In ordinary regression theory the sum of squares (2.20) would have r degrees of freedom, but since we imposed the restriction $\sum_i^r t_i = 0$ it has only $(r - 1)$ degrees of freedom.

Let us now consider the case in which instead of t replicates on each treatment we have t_i replicates on the ith treatment. Thus the $(r + 1)$-tuples (2.4) will run from 11 to $1t_1$, the $(r + 1)$-tuples (2.5) will run from 21 to $2t_2$, etc. For the sums of squares and products we have

$$\sum_{i,j}{}' X_{i'ij}^2 = t_{i'} - t_{i'}^2 / \sum_i^r t_i , \tag{2.21}$$

$$\sum_{i,j}{}' X_{i'ij} X_{i''ij} = 0 - t_{i'} t_{i''} / \sum_i^r t_i , \tag{2.22}$$

$$\sum_{i,j}{}' y_{ij} X_{i'ij} = \sum_j^{t_{i'}} y_{i'j} - t_{i'} \sum_{i,j} y_{ij} / \sum_i^r t_i . \tag{2.23}$$

The first normal equation is, using f_i in place of the t_i which were used in (2.16),

$$f_1\left(t_1 - \frac{t_1^2}{\sum_i^r t_i} \right) + f_2\left(- \frac{t_1 t_2}{\sum_i^r t_i} \right) + \cdots = \sum_j^{t_1} y_{1j} - \frac{t_1 \sum_{i,j} y_{ij}}{\sum_i^r t_i} . \tag{2.24}$$

Rearranging, this gives

$$f_1 = \frac{\sum_i^r f_i t_i}{\sum_i^r t_i} + \frac{\sum_j^{t_1} y_{1j}}{t_1} - \frac{\sum_{i,j} y_{ij}}{\sum_i^r t_i} . \tag{2.25}$$

The solution for the ith f will be similar:

$$f_i = \frac{\sum_i^r f_i t_i}{\sum_i^r t_i} + \frac{\sum_j^{t_i} y_{ij}}{t_i} - \frac{\sum_{i,j} y_{ij}}{\sum_i^r t_i} . \tag{2.26}$$

Summing over i gives

$$\sum_i^r f_i = r \frac{\sum_i^r f_i t_i}{\sum_i^r t_i} + \sum_i^r \left(\frac{\sum_j^{t_i} y_{ij}}{t_i} \right) - r \frac{\sum_{i,j} y_{ij}}{\sum_i^r t_i} . \tag{2.27}$$

But we have the side condition that $\sum_i^r f_i = 0$, analogous to (2.3), and so

$$\frac{\sum_i^r f_i t_i}{\sum_i^r t_i} = -\frac{1}{r}\sum_i^r\left(\frac{\sum_j^{t_i} y_{ij}}{t_i}\right) + \frac{\sum_{i,j} y_{ij}}{\sum_i^r t_i}. \tag{2.28}$$

Substituting this in (2.26), we get as the solution for f_i:

$$f_i = \frac{\sum_j^{t_i} y_{ij}}{t_i} - \frac{1}{r}\sum_i^r\left(\frac{\sum_j^{t_i} y_{ij}}{t_i}\right). \tag{2.29}$$

This is a reasonable solution: The first term on the right-hand side is the observed mean for the ith treatment, and the second term is the mean of the treatment means (note that it is not the over-all mean $\sum_i^r \sum_j^{t_i} y_{ij} / \sum_i^r t_i$).

The sum of squares due to regression on the X_i, using (17.9.7), analogous to (2.20), is

$$\sum_i^r\left[\frac{\sum_j^{t_i} y_{ij}}{t_i} - \frac{1}{r}\sum_i^r\left(\frac{\sum_j^{t_i} y_{ij}}{t_i}\right)\right]\left[\sum_j^{t_i} y_{ij} - \frac{t_i \sum_{i,j} y_{ij}}{\sum_i^r t_i}\right]$$

which reduces to

$$\sum_i^r \frac{(\sum_j^{t_i} y_{ij})^2}{t_i} - \frac{(\sum_{i,j} y_{ij})^2}{\sum_i^r t_i}, \tag{2.30}$$

the usual computing form in one-way analysis of variance for the sum of squares between groups, (10.2.18).

18.3. Two-Way Classifications

We now extend the treatment of the previous section by supposing that each plot is classified both by the treatment it receives and by the block to which it belongs. We assume a balanced arrangement, so that the number of treatments r equals the number of plots per block. Let variables $Z_{j'ij}$ be associated with the blocks. These variables have only two levels, 1 if a plot is in a particular block and 0 otherwise.

From a multiple-regression point of view we regard y_{ij} as normally distributed with variance σ^2 about

$$\eta_{ij} = \alpha + \tau_1 X_{1ij} + \cdots + \tau_r X_{rij} + \beta_1 Z_{1ij} + \cdots + \beta_t Z_{tij} . \qquad (3.1)$$

This true equation is estimated by

$$Y_{ij} = a + t_1 X_{1ij} + \cdots + t_r X_{rij} + b_1 Z_{1ij} + \cdots + b_t Z_{tij} . \qquad (3.2)$$

We assume, in addition to (2.3), the similar relations

$$\sum_j^t \beta_j = 0 = \sum_j^t b_j . \qquad (3.3)$$

The observations in detail are as follows:

1. The t observations on the first treatment, one in each block:

$$\begin{aligned}
&(y_{11}, X_{111} = 1, X_{211} = 0, \ldots, X_{r11} = 0, Z_{111} = 1, Z_{211} = 0, \ldots, Z_{t11} = 0)\\
&(y_{12}, X_{112} = 1, X_{212} = 0, \ldots, X_{r12} = 0, Z_{112} = 0, Z_{212} = 1, \ldots, Z_{t12} = 0)\\
&\vdots\\
&(y_{1t}, X_{11t} = 1, X_{21t} = 0, \ldots, X_{r1t} = 0, Z_{11t} = 0, Z_{21t} = 0, \ldots, Z_{t1t} = 1).
\end{aligned} \qquad (3.4)$$

2. The t observations on the second treatment, one in each block:

$$\begin{aligned}
&(y_{21}, X_{121} = 0, X_{221} = 1, \ldots, X_{r21} = 0, Z_{121} = 1, Z_{221} = 0, \ldots, Z_{t21} = 0)\\
&(y_{22}, X_{122} = 0, X_{222} = 1, \ldots, X_{r22} = 0, Z_{122} = 0, Z_{222} = 1, \ldots, Z_{t22} = 0)\\
&\vdots\\
&(y_{2t}, X_{12t} = 0, X_{22t} = 1, \ldots, X_{r2t} = 0, Z_{12t} = 0, Z_{22t} = 0, \ldots, Z_{t2t} = 1).
\end{aligned} \qquad (3.5)$$

3. And so on down to the t observations on the rth treatment.

It is apparent that the previous relation (2.7) still holds, and also

$$\begin{aligned} Z_{j'ij} &= 1 \qquad \text{if } j' = j,\\ &= 0 \qquad \text{otherwise.} \end{aligned} \qquad (3.6)$$

The sums of squares and products of the $X_{i'ij}$ are the same as before, and by symmetry

$$\sum_{i,j}{}' Z_{j'ij}^2 = \frac{r}{t}(t-1), \qquad (3.7)$$

$$\sum_{i,j}{}' Z_{j'ij} Z_{j''ij} = -\frac{r}{t}, \qquad (3.8)$$

$$\sum_{i,j}{}' y_{ij} Z_{j'ij} = \sum_i^r y_{ij'} - \sum_{i,j} y_{ij}/t = B_{j'}, \qquad \text{say.} \qquad (3.9)$$

For the normal equations we will also need the sums of products of the X's with the Z's. Inspecting (3.4) and (3.6), it is apparent that $X_{i'ij}$ and $Z_{j'ij}$ both occur together as 1 only once. This, of course, is a reflection of the fact that each treatment occurs only once in each block; so $\sum_{i,j} X_{i'ij}Z_{j'ij} = 1$, and

$$\sum_{i,j}{}' X_{i'ij}Z_{j'ij} = 1 - \frac{tr}{rt} = 0. \tag{3.10}$$

We can now write down the normal equations: The first is

$$t_1 \frac{t}{r}(r-1) + t_2\left(-\frac{t}{r}\right) + \cdots + t_r\left(-\frac{t}{r}\right) + b_1 \cdot 0 + b_2 \cdot 0 + \cdots + b_t \cdot 0 = T_1. \tag{3.11}$$

Since the coefficients of all the b's are zero, this equation is the same as the first equation in (2.16), and it has the same solution (2.18). The $(r+1)$th normal equation is

$$t_1 \cdot 0 + t_2 \cdot 0 + \cdots + t_r \cdot 0 + b_1 \frac{r}{t}(t-1) + b_2\left(-\frac{r}{t}\right) + \cdots + b_t\left(-\frac{r}{t}\right) = B_1. \tag{3.12}$$

If we add

$$b_1 \frac{r}{t} + b_2 \frac{r}{t} + \cdots + b_t \frac{r}{t} = \frac{r}{t}\sum_j^t b_j = 0$$

to this we get

$$b_1\left[\frac{r}{t}(t-1) + \frac{r}{t}\right] = B_1;$$

so

$$b_1 = \frac{B_1}{r} = \frac{\sum_i^r y_{i1}}{r} - \frac{\sum_i^r \sum_j^t y_{ij}}{rt}. \tag{3.13}$$

Thus we will have a sum of squares due to regression on the $X_{i'}$ and $Z_{j'}$ with degrees of freedom $(r-1)+(t-1)$, the two degrees of freedom being lost on account of the relations (2.3) and (3.3). However, this sum of squares can be split into two parts, in the balanced case we are discussing, one for treatments and one for blocks, since we can show that t_i is independent of b_j.

It will suffice to show $\text{Cov}[t_i, b_j] = 0$. Since y is distributed about η with variance σ^2, we can write

$$y_{ij} = \alpha + \tau_1 X_{1ij} + \cdots + \tau_r X_{rij} + \beta_1 Z_{1ij} + \cdots + \beta_t Z_{tij} + z_{ij}$$

where $z_{ij} \sim N(0, \sigma^2)$. In view of (2.7) and (3.6), this reduces to

$$y_{ij} = \alpha + \tau_i + \beta_j + z_{ij}; \tag{3.14}$$

so

$$\sum_j^t y_{ij} = t\alpha + t\tau_i + \sum_j^t \beta_j + \sum_j^t z_{ij} = t(\alpha + \tau_i) + \sum_j^t z_{ij}, \tag{3.15}$$

$$\sum_i^r \sum_j^t y_{ij} = rt\alpha + t\sum_i^r \tau_i + \sum_i^r \sum_j^t z_{ij} = rt\alpha + \sum_i^r \sum_j^t z_{ij}, \tag{3.16}$$

and, substituting in (2.19),

$$t_i = \alpha + \tau_i + \frac{\sum_j^t z_{ij}}{t} - \alpha - \frac{\sum_i^r \sum_j^t z_{ij}}{rt} = \tau_i + \frac{\sum_j^t z_{ij}}{t} - \frac{\sum_i^r \sum_j^t z_{ij}}{rt}. \tag{3.17}$$

Hence $E[t_i] = \tau_i$. Also, similarly

$$b_j = \beta_j + \frac{\sum_i^r z_{ij}}{r} - \frac{\sum_i^r \sum_j^t z_{ij}}{rt}. \tag{3.18}$$

Therefore

$$\begin{aligned}
\text{Cov}[t_i, b_j] &= E[(t_i - E[t_i])(b_j - E[b_j])] \\
&= E\left[\left(\frac{\sum_j^t z_{ij}}{t} - \frac{\sum_i^r \sum_j^t z_{ij}}{rt}\right)\left(\frac{\sum_i^r z_{ij}}{r} - \frac{\sum_i^r \sum_j^t z_{ij}}{rt}\right)\right] \\
&= \frac{1}{rt} E[\sum_j^t z_{ij} \sum_i^r z_{ij}] - \frac{1}{rt^2} E[\sum_j^t z_{ij} \sum_i^r \sum_j^t z_{ij}] \\
&\quad - \frac{1}{r^2 t} [\sum_i^r z_{ij} \sum_i^r \sum_j^t z_{ij}] + \frac{1}{r^2 t^2} E[(\sum_i^r \sum_j^t z_{ij})^2].
\end{aligned} \tag{3.19}$$

Consider these four terms; the first is

$$\begin{aligned}
&\frac{1}{rt} E[(z_{i1} + z_{i2} + \cdots + z_{it})(z_{1j} + z_{2j} + \cdots + z_{rj})] \\
&\quad = \frac{1}{rt} \{E[z_{ij}^2] + E[\text{cross products of dissimilar } z\text{'s}]\} = \frac{\sigma^2}{rt}.
\end{aligned} \tag{3.20}$$

The second is

$$\begin{aligned}
&\frac{1}{rt^2} E[(z_{i1} + \cdots + z_{it}) \sum_i^r \sum_j^t z_{ij}] \\
&= \frac{1}{rt^2} \{E[z_{i1}^2 + \cdots + z_{it}^2] + E[\text{cross products of dissimilar } z\text{'s}]\} \\
&= \frac{t\sigma^2}{rt^2} = \frac{\sigma^2}{rt}.
\end{aligned} \tag{3.21}$$

By a similar argument the third is

$$\frac{1}{r^2 t} E[\sum_i^r z_{ij} \sum_i^r \sum_j^t z_{ij}] = \frac{\sigma^2}{rt}.$$

Finally,

$$\frac{1}{r^2 t^2} E[(\sum_i^r \sum_j^t z_{ij})^2]$$

$$= \frac{1}{r^2 t^2} \{E[\sum_i^r \sum_j^t z_{ij}^2] + E[\text{cross products of dissimilar } z\text{'s}]\}$$

$$= \frac{rt\sigma^2}{r^2 t^2} = \frac{\sigma^2}{rt}. \tag{3.22}$$

Substituting these results in (3.19), we obtain

$$\text{Cov}[t_i, b_j] = 0, \tag{3.23}$$

and hence the t_i are independent of the b_j. The sum of squares due to regression on the $X_{i'}$ and $Z_{j'}$ can be split into two orthogonal components as in Table 18.1.

Table 18.1

Source of variance	Sums of squares	Degrees of freedom
Regression on the $X_{i'}$ ≡ treatments	$\frac{1}{t}\sum_i^r \left(\sum_j y_{ij}\right)^2 - \frac{1}{rt}\left(\sum_i^r \sum_j^t y_{ij}\right)^2$	$(r-1)$
Regression on the $Z_{j'}$ ≡ blocks	$\frac{1}{r}\sum_j^t \left(\sum_i^r y_{ij}\right)^2 - \frac{1}{rt}\left(\sum_i^r \sum_j^t y_{ij}\right)^2$	$(t-1)$
Remainder		$(r-1)(t-1)$
Total	$\sum_i^r \sum_j^t (y_{ij} - \bar{y}_{..})^2$	$rt-1$

This is the conventional two-way model I analysis of variance.

18.4. The Latin Square

In the preceding section we had two sets of variables X_i and Z_j, such that for a particular plot only one X_i and only one Z_j had the values 1. Suppose that we have a square array, so that i and j both go from 1 to r, say, and let the Z_j correspond to rows and the X_i correspond to columns. Now introduce a third set of r variables W with the property that for a particular plot only one of the W's has the value 1 and all the other W's the value 0, and further that each W takes the value 1 only once in each row and only once in each column. For example, one solution for $r = 4$ can be represented as in Table 18.2. Such an arrangement is known as a Latin square.

Table 18.2

	X_1	X_2	X_3	X_4
Z_1	W_1	W_2	W_3	W_4
Z_2	W_4	W_1	W_2	W_3
Z_3	W_3	W_4	W_1	W_2
Z_4	W_2	W_3	W_4	W_1

The regression equation is

$$\eta_{ij} = \alpha + \tau_1 X_{1ij} + \cdots + \tau_r X_{rij} + \beta_1 Z_{1ij} + \cdots + \beta_r Z_{rij} + \gamma_1 W_{1ij} + \cdots + \gamma_r W_{rij}\,.$$

If the ijth plot contains a particular treatment, then the corresponding $W = 1$; otherwise 0.

Essentially, the design is symmetric in all three sets of variables, and the analysis is identical with that of the previous section, the difference being that there is a sum of squares due to treatments

$$\frac{1}{r}\sum^{r}(\text{treatment sums})^2 - \Big(\sum_i \sum_j y_{ij}\Big)^2/r^2$$

with degrees of freedom $(r - 1)$, independent of the other sum of squares, and the remainder sum of squares now has degrees of freedom

$$(r-1)(r-1) - (r-1) = (r-1)(r-2).$$

An illustration of a nonagricultural Latin square is the data of Table 18.3, taken from [2]. In a study of gasoline consumption by city buses, four vehicles were tested. In the first run of the day over a specified course, a particular assignment of four drivers to the four vehicles was used. The lower-case letters represent the four drivers. In the next run the drivers changed vehicles as indicated, and so on for the third and fourth runs. The variable measured was the miles per gallon. It is apparent that each driver takes part in each run, and drives each vehicle, once and only once.

In calculating the analysis of variance (Table 18.4), the sum of squares for drivers, for example, is

$$\frac{36.73^2 + 39.05^2 + 35.51^2 + 37.19^2}{4} - \frac{148.48^2}{16} = 1.61835.$$

Table 18.3

Run	Vehicle A	Vehicle B	Vehicle C	Vehicle D	Run sums
1	9.44(a)	9.83(b)	9.02(c)	9.68(d)	37.97
2	9.61(b)	9.22(d)	9.39(a)	8.76(c)	36.98
3	9.06(d)	9.02(c)	9.88(b)	8.88(a)	36.84
4	8.71(c)	9.02(a)	9.23(d)	9.73(b)	36.69
Vehicle sums	36.82	37.09	37.52	37.05	148.48
Driver sums	36.73(a)	39.05(b)	35.51(c)	37.19(d)	

Table 18.4

Source of variance	Sums of squares	Degrees of freedom	Mean squares
Runs	0.25135	3	0.083783
Vehicles	0.06385	3	0.021283
Drivers	1.61835	3	0.539450
Remainder	0.25065	6	0.041775
Total	2.18420	15	

The only effect which is significant is drivers, significant at the 0.01 level. The effect of runs is not significant as it stands, but, if we partition the 3 degrees of freedom, using the coefficients of Table 14.9, assuming that the runs are an ordered sequence with equal intervals between them, the linear, quadratic, and cubic components, each with one degree of freedom are 0.198005, 0.044100, and 0.009245 respectively. The linear term is significant at the one-sided 0.05 level. A one-sided test is justified since we would anticipate that the gasoline consumption would decline as the engines warmed up.

18.5. Two-Way Analysis with Equal Numbers of Replicates

Suppose that in our two-way analysis we had n replicates of every observation. The analysis would be fundamentally unchanged as far as the sums of squares for the total and for rows and columns (there called treatments and blocks); the only difference is that there would be a further summation over $\nu = 1, \ldots, n$, and additional divisors n would appear in the expressions for sums of squares due to rows and to columns. However, the remainder sum of squares, now with degrees of freedom

$$(rtn - 1) - (r - 1) - (t - 1) = (r - 1)(t - 1) + rt(n - 1)$$

can be partitioned into two components, one with degrees of freedom $rt(n - 1)$ from within cells

$$\frac{1}{n}\sum_{i}^{r}\sum_{j}^{t}(y_{ij\nu} - \bar{y}_{ij})^2$$

and the other with degrees of freedom $(r - 1)(t - 1)$ due to departures from regression. A moment's thought will show that these departures from regression are departures from the additive model of a row effect plus a column effect, and hence this term is identical with what we previously called interaction.

18.6. Two-Way Analysis with Unequal Numbers of Replicates

If in a two-way analysis the numbers of replicates per cell are unequal, two undesirable consequences result.

First, the set of normal equations ceases to have the highly symmetrical and balanced coefficients that it has in the balanced case, and no longer do we get the simple and direct solutions (2.19) and (3.13). Instead, the normal equations are a mess, and tedious computing is necessary to obtain the solutions.

Second, when the solutions b_i, t_j are obtained, they are no longer independent, and so the sum of squares due to regression cannot be split up into two independent components. Instead, we have to follow the procedure analogous to Tables 17.2 and 17.9. The test for the null hypothesis that treatments are without effect is given by the variance ratio of the mean squares corresponding to the sums of squares C and D in Table 18.5.

As an example of this procedure we will consider the data of Table 18.6. These are actually the data from which Table 13.4, used to illustrate balanced two-way analysis of variance, was abstracted. Table 13.4 was made balanced by the simple device of reducing the number of replicate observations in each cell to the largest common number, here 4. As stated in Section 13.3, the data are the per cent reduction in blood sugar a certain time after injection of insulin into rabbits. Two preparations of insulin were used, each at three concentrations, but the numbers of rabbits treated with each preparation concentration combination varied from 4 to 8.

Table 18.5

Source of variance	Degrees of freedom	Sums of squares
Regression on X_i, Z_j	$(r-1)+(t-1)$	A
Regression on Z_j	$(t-1)$	B
Difference due to adding X_i to Z_j	$(r-1)$	$C = A - B$
Remainder	$N-1-[(r-1)+(t-1)]$	$D = T - A$
Total	$N-1$	T

From the multiple-regression point of view the data can be represented as in Table 18.7, where the X_i variables refer to the preparations, the Z_j variables refer to the concentrations, and v is an index giving the number of each rabbit used with a particular preparation concentration combination.

We need the sums of squares and products of the X's, Z's, and y. For example, in computing $\sum' X_{1ijv}^2$, we note that $X_{1ijv} = 1$ on 12 occasions and 0 on 21 occasions; so

$$\sum' X_{1ijv}^2 = \sum X_{1ijv}^2 - \frac{(\sum X_{1ijv})^2}{n}$$

$$= 12 \times (1)^2 + 21 \times (0)^2 - \frac{(12 \times 1 + 21 \times 0)^2}{33}$$

$$= \frac{12 \times 33 - (12)^2}{33} = \frac{252}{33}.$$

As a second example, in computing $\sum' X_{1ijv}Z_{1ijv}$, we note that X_{1ijv} and Z_{1ijv} are simultaneously equal to 1 on only four occasions: Thus

$$\sum' X_{1ijv}Z_{1ijv} = \sum X_{1ijv}Z_{1ijv} - \frac{\sum X_{1ijv} \sum Z_{1ijv}}{n} = 4 - \frac{12 \times 11}{33} = 0.$$

Table 18.6

	Dose			
Preparation	2.29	3.63	5.75	
A	17	64	62	
	21	48	72	
	49	34	61	
	54	63	91	
$\sum_{\nu}^{n} y_{1j\nu}$	141	209	286	$\sum_{j}^{t}\sum_{\nu}^{n} y_{1j\nu} = 636$
n_{1j}	4	4	4	$\sum_{j}^{t} n_{1j} = 12$
B	33	41	56	
	37	64	62	
	40	34	57	
	16	64	72	
	21	48	73	
	18	34	72	
	25		81	
			60	
$\sum_{\nu}^{n} y_{2j\nu}$	190	285	533	$\sum_{j}^{t}\sum_{\nu}^{n} y_{2j\nu} = 1008$
n_{2j}	7	6	8	$\sum_{j}^{t} n_{2j} = 21$
$\sum_{i}^{r}\sum_{\nu}^{n} y_{ij\nu}$	331	494	819	$\sum_{i}^{r}\sum_{j}^{t}\sum_{\nu}^{n} y_{ij\nu} = 1644$
$\sum_{i}^{n} n_{ij}$	11	10	12	$\sum_{i}^{r}\sum_{j}^{t} n_{ij} = 33$

Table 18.7

i	j	v	y_{ijv}	X_{1ij}	X_{2ij}	Z_{1ij}	Z_{2ij}	Z_{3ij}
1	1	1	17	1	0	1	0	0
		2	21	1	0	1	0	0
		3	49	1	0	1	0	0
		4	54	1	0	1	0	0
2	1	1	33	0	1	1	0	0
		2	37	0	1	1	0	0
		3	40	0	1	1	0	0
		4	16	0	1	1	0	0
		5	21	0	1	1	0	0
		6	18	0	1	1	0	0
		7	25	0	1	1	0	0
1	2	1	64	1	0	0	1	0
		2	48	1	0	0	1	0
		3	34	1	0	0	1	0
		4	63	1	0	0	1	0
2	2	1	41	0	1	0	1	0
		2	64	0	1	0	1	0
		3	34	0	1	0	1	0
		4	64	0	1	0	1	0
		5	48	0	1	0	1	0
		6	34	0	1	0	1	0
1	3	1	62	1	0	0	0	1
		2	72	1	0	0	0	1
		3	61	1	0	0	0	1
		4	91	1	0	0	0	1
2	3	1	56	0	1	0	0	1
		2	62	0	1	0	0	1
		3	57	0	1	0	0	1
		4	72	0	1	0	0	1
		5	73	0	1	0	0	1
		6	72	0	1	0	0	1
		7	81	0	1	0	0	1
		8	60	0	1	0	0	1

As a third example,

$$\sum' y_{ijv} X_{1ijv} = \sum y_{ijv} X_{1ijv} - \frac{\sum y_{ijv} \sum X_{1ijv}}{n}$$
$$= (17 \times 1 + \cdots + 54 \times 1 + 64 \times 1 + \cdots + 63 \times 1 + 62 \times 1 + \cdots + 91 \times 1) - \frac{1644 \times 12}{33} = \frac{1260}{33}.$$

The complete set of sums of squares and products of deviations is given in Table 18.8.

Table 18.8

	y	X_1	X_2	Z_1	Z_2	Z_3
y	12,980.909	1260/33	−1260/33	−7161/33	−138/33	7299/33
X_1		252/33	−252/33	0	12/33	−12/33
X_2			252/33	0	−12/33	12/33
Z_1				242/33	−110/33	−132/33
Z_2					230/33	−120/33
Z_3						252/33

The normal equations, when all multiplied throughout by the constant 33, are:

$$\begin{aligned}
252x_1 - 252x_2 + 0z_1 + 12z_2 - 12z_3 &= 1260, \\
-252x_1 + 252x_2 + 0z_1 - 12z_2 + 12z_3 &= -1260, \\
0x_1 + 0x_2 + 242z_1 - 110z_2 - 132z_3 &= -7161, \\
12x_1 - 12x_2 - 110z_1 + 230z_2 - 120z_3 &= -138, \\
-12x_1 + 12x_2 - 132z_1 - 120z_2 + 252z_3 &= 7299.
\end{aligned} \tag{6.1}$$

In addition, we have the side conditions, from (2.3) and (3.3):

$$x_1 + x_2 = 0, \tag{6.2}$$

$$z_1 + z_2 + z_3 = 0. \tag{6.3}$$

Using these to eliminate x_2 and z_1, the equations (6.1) reduce to

$$504x_1 + 12z_2 - 12z_3 = 1260, \tag{6.4}$$
$$-504x_1 - 12z_2 + 12z_3 = -1260, \tag{6.5}$$
$$0x_1 - 352z_2 - 374z_3 = -7161, \tag{6.6}$$
$$24x_1 + 340z_2 - 10z_3 = -138, \tag{6.7}$$
$$-24x_1 + 12z_2 + 384z_3 = 7299. \tag{6.8}$$

These five equations contain only three unknowns, but in point of fact there are only three independent equations, as (6.4) is identical except for sign with (6.5), and (6.6) can be obtained as the sum of (6.7) and (6.8). In this simple example the solution of these equations is easy and leads to

$$x_1 = 2.958201, \qquad x_2 = -2.958201,$$
$$z_1 = -19.144108, \qquad z_2 = -0.050159, \qquad z_3 = 19.195268.$$

The sum of squares due to regression on these variables, by (17.9.7), is

$$x_1{\sum}'yX_1 + x_2{\sum}'yX_2 + z_1{\sum}'yZ_1 + z_2{\sum}'yZ_2 + z_3{\sum}'yZ_3 \tag{6.9}$$
$$= 2.958201 \times 1260/33 + (-2.958201)(-1260/33)$$
$$+ (-19.144108)(-7161/33) + (-0.050159)(-138/33)$$
$$+ 19.195268 \times 7299/33$$
$$= 8625.803.$$

This sum of squares has degrees of freedom $(r-1) + (t-1) = (2-1) + (3-1) = 3$, since it involves in effect three constants, x_1 [with x_2 dependent on x_1 through (6.2)] and z_1 and z_2 [with z_3 dependent on z_1 and z_2 through (6.3)].

We also can in effect fit five constants to these data by regarding them as a one-way classification with six groups. The two additional constants correspond to the 2 degrees of freedom that would be attributed to interaction between the two rows and three columns. Such an analysis yields Table 18.9. We can combine Table 18.9 and (6.9) to get Table 18.10.

Table 18.9

Source of variance	Degrees of freedom	Sums of squares
Between six groups	5	8,644.177
Within groups	27	4,336.732
Total	32	12,980.909

If there were a significant interaction, the mean square for the difference due to adding the interaction to the row and column effects X_i and Z_j would be significantly larger than the remainder mean square. Here it is actually smaller, though not significantly so, and so we must accept the null hypothesis of no interaction.

Table 18.10

Source of variance	Degrees of freedom	Sums of squares	Mean squares
Regression on X_i, Z_j and their interaction	5	8,644.177	
Regression on X_i and Z_j	3	8,625.803	
Difference due to adding interaction to X_i and Z_j	2	18.374	9.187
Remainder when using regression on X_i, Z_j, and their interaction	27	4,336.732	160.616
Total	32	12,980.909	

We may now proceed to test the null hypothesis that the row effect is zero by regressing on the columns only. If we ignore the rows completely, we will have (see Table 18.6) a one-way classification with three groups, the sum of squares for which is

$$\frac{(331)^2}{11} + \frac{(494)^2}{10} + \frac{(819)^2}{12} - \frac{(1644)^2}{33} = 8359.350.$$

This can be combined with (6.9) to give Table 18.11.

Table 18.11

Source of variance	Degrees of freedom	Sums of squares	Mean squares
Regression on X_i and Z_j	3	8,625.803	
Regression on Z_j only	2	8,359.350	
Difference due to adding X_i to Z_j	1	266.452	266.452
Remainder when using regression on X_i and Z_j	29	4.355.107	150.176
Total	32	12,980.909	

The variance ratio 266.452/150.176 = 1.77 does not reach the 0.05 level of significance, and so the null hypothesis that the row effect is zero can be accepted.

18.7. Missing-Value Techniques

Suppose that we have a two-way classification, say r treatments in t blocks, with one observation in every cell except for one cell for which the observation is missing. In principle we can proceed by the methods of Section 18.6 to construct Table 18.12, the same as Table 18.5 for the case

Table 18.12

Source of variance	Degrees of freedom	Sums of squares
Treatments and blocks	$(r-1)+(t-1)$	J
Blocks alone	$t-1$	K
Difference due to adding treatments to blocks	$r-1$	$L = J - K$
Remainder using treatment and blocks	$(r-1)(t-1)-1$	$G = H' - J$
Total	$rt-2$	H'

of $N = rt - 1$, from which the test of the null hypothesis that the effect of the treatments is zero is given by the ratio of the mean squares

$$\frac{L/(r-1)}{G/[(r-1)(t-1)-1]}.$$

However, an alternative technique, which is fundamentally identical though superficially different, is traditional. Briefly, this technique is to estimate the missing value and then to carry out the standard analysis, followed by some adjustments [3].

Suppose that the missing observation is on the rth treatment in the tth block. Let the observed total for the rth treatment be T_r, the observed totals for the blocks be $B_1, B_2, \ldots, B_{t-1}, B_t$, all the blocks containing r observations except the tth which contains $(r-1)$. Let the observed grand total, $\sum_j^t B_j$, be denoted by M.

The regression method of Section 18.6 rests essentially upon the principle of least squares, i.e., on minimizing $\sum_i^r \sum_j^t (Y_{ij} - y_{ij})^2$, where the y_{ij} are the observed values and the Y_{ij} are given by the estimated regression equation

$$Y_{ij} = a + t_1 X_{1ij} + \cdots + t_r X_{rij} + b_1 Z_{1ij} + \cdots + b_t Z_{tij}. \qquad (7.1)$$

Suppose that the above procedure has been carried out and estimates a, t_i, b_j obtained. Then we can use their numerical values in (7.1) to give us an estimated value Y_{ij} for the missing cell, traditionally represented by the symbol x. If we use this estimate x in an ordinary analysis of variance, then for this cell the "observed" value x (not really observed) will be identical with the predicted value Y_{ij}, so that this cell will contribute zero to $\sum_i^r \sum_j^t (Y_{ij} - y_{ij})^2$. We will thus get the same result if we sum $(Y_{ij} - y_{ij})^2$. over the observed cells omitting the cell which has the missing observation replaced by x. Thus

$$\sum_{\substack{i \quad j \\ \text{excl. } i=r, \\ j=t}}^{r \quad t} (Y_{ij} - y_{ij})^2 = \sum_i^r \sum_j^t (Y_{ij} - y_{ij})^2. \tag{7.2}$$

It is apparent that to minimize the right-hand side is the same as to minimize the left-hand side. We use this fact to obtain x.

From Table 13.9 the remainder sum of squares, say R, is

$$R = \sum_i^r \sum_j^t x_{ij}^2 - \frac{1}{t}\sum_i^r \left(\sum_j^t x_{ij}\right)^2 - \frac{1}{r}\sum_j^t \left(\sum_i^r x_{ij}\right)^2 + \frac{1}{rt}\left(\sum_i^r \sum_j^t x_{ij}\right)^2. \tag{7.3}$$

To find the value of x which makes R a minimum, we are going to differentiate R with respect to x and equate to zero. Upon this differentiation all terms made up of constants, including the observed numbers, vanish. Therefore it is sufficient to consider R', defined as those parts of R containing x:

$$R' = x^2 - \frac{1}{t}(T_r + x)^2 - \frac{1}{r}(B_t + x)^2 + \frac{1}{rt}(M + x)^2. \tag{7.4}$$

For example, in (7.3) $\sum_i^r \sum_j^t x_{ij}^2$ is made up of the squares of the numerical values of the observations x_{ij} plus x. All the numbers squared yield zero on differentiation with respect to x, and the only part of $\sum_i^r \sum_j^t x_{ij}^2$ which does not yield zero on such differentiation is x^2, whose derivative with respect to x is of course $2x$.

Multiplying R' by rt and differentiating with respect to x and equating to zero gives

$$rt\frac{dR'}{dx} = 2rtx - 2r(T_r + x) - 2t(B_t + x) + 2(M + x) = 0,$$

whence, solving for x,

$$x = \frac{tB_t + rT_r - M}{(r-1)(t-1)} . \tag{7.5}$$

The conventional missing-value procedure, introduced by Yates [3], is to make the usual analysis of variance, using the estimate of the missing value in the vacant cell, and reducing the total degrees of freedom and the degrees of freedom for remainder each by one. This gives Table 18.13.

Table 18.13

Source of variance	Degrees of freedom	Sums of squares
Treatments	$r-1$	E
Blocks	$t-1$	F
Remainder	$(r-1)(t-1)-1$	G
Total	$rt-2$	H

We have seen that the correct sum of squares for the numerator for the variance ratio test for treatments is L in Table 18.12. Now L is obtained as $(J-K)$, and J is equal to $(H'-G)$. Thus

$$L = J - K = H' - G - K. \tag{7.6}$$

This G, the remainder sum of squares, is identical with the G of Table 18.13, where it is equal to $(H-E-F)$. Thus

$$L = H' - H + E + F - K = E - (H - H' - F + K), \tag{7.7}$$

where the quantity $(H - H' - F + K)$ is known as the *adjustment for bias*, say Q, in the treatment sum of squares.

For the missing-value analysis, the total sum of squares, H in Table 18.13, includes the missing-value estimate x which replaces the missing observation x_{rt}. The total sum of squares can be calculated from the usual identity

$$H = [x_{11}^2 + x_{12}^2 + \cdots + x_{r(t-1)}^2 + x^2] - \frac{[x_{11} + x_{12} + \cdots + x_{r(t-1)} + x]^2}{rt} .$$

The second term here is the grand sum of all observations, including x, which we can express as the sum of the block sums:

$$B_1 + B_2 + \cdots + B_{t-1} + (B_t + x) = x + \sum_j^t B_j .$$

Thus
$$H = x^2 + \sum_i^r \sum_j^t x_{ij}^2 - (x + \sum_j^t B_j)^2/rt, \tag{7.8}$$
where $\sum_i^r \sum_j^t x_{ij}^2$ excludes the rtth cell.

For the regression analysis, the total sum of squares, H' in Table 18.12, is computed from the $(rt - 1)$ actual observations:
$$H' = \sum_i^r \sum_j^t x_{ij}^2 - (\sum_j^t B_j)^2/(rt - 1), \tag{7.9}$$
where again $\sum_i^r \sum_j^t x_{ij}^2$ excludes the vacant rtth cell, and where $\sum_j^t B_j$ is a convenient way of writing the grand sum of all observations.

In the missing-value analysis the block sums are $B_1, \ldots, B_{t-1}, B_t + x$; so the sum of squares for blocks, F in Table 18.13, is
$$F = \frac{1}{r}[B_1^2 + \cdots + B_{t-1}^2 + (B_t + x)^2] - \frac{[B_1 + \cdots + B_{t-1} + (B_t + x)]^2}{rt}$$
$$= \frac{1}{r}\sum_j^{t-1} B_j^2 + \frac{1}{r}(x + B_t)^2 - (x + \sum_j^t B_j)^2/rt. \tag{7.10}$$

In the regression analysis (Table 18.12), the quantity K is the sum of squares for blocks in a simple one-way analysis of variance on blocks, ignoring treatments, based on the observed block totals $B_1, \ldots, B_{t-1}, B_t$: These blocks will contain $r, \ldots, r, r - 1$ observations, and so the total number of observations is $(t - 1)r + (r - 1) = rt - 1$, and the sum of squares for blocks is
$$K = \frac{B_1^2}{r} + \cdots + \frac{B_{t-1}^2}{r} + \frac{B_t^2}{r-1} - \frac{(B_1 + \cdots + B_{t-1} + B_t)^2}{rt - 1},$$
$$= \frac{1}{r}\sum_j^{t-1} B_j^2 + \frac{B_t^2}{r-1} - (\sum_j^t B_j)^2/(rt - 1). \tag{7.11}$$

Substituting (7.8) for H, (7.9) for H', (7.10) for F, and (7.11) for K in the expression for the adjustment for bias, we get
$$Q = H - H' - F + K = x^2 - \frac{1}{r}(x + B_t)^2 + \frac{B_t^2}{r-1} = \frac{[B_t - (r-1)x]^2}{r(r-1)}. \tag{7.12}$$

Thus, if we estimate the missing value x with (7.5), carry out a standard analysis of variance leading to Table 18.13, and subtract the adjustment for bias Q from the treatment sum of squares E, the resultant treatment mean square $(E - Q)/(r - 1)$ is identical with the mean square in

Table 18.12 for testing the significance of treatments $L/(r-1)$. The two remainder mean squares are also identical, and so the two F tests are identical. The missing-value technique is thus a convenient arithmetical method of carrying out the test that is more explicitly given by the regression analysis of Table 18.12.

18.8. The Variance between Two Treatment Means in a Randomized-Block Experiment When One Mean Contains a Missing Value

Suppose that the missing observation is on the rth treatment in the tth block. We will use the notation of Table 18.14.

Table 18.14

$x_{11} + x_{12} + \cdots + x_{1(t-1)} = \sum_{j}^{t-1} x_{1j} = A$	$x_{1t} = B$
$x_{21} + x_{22} + \cdots + x_{2(t-1)}$ $\vdots$ $x_{(r-1)1} + x_{(r-1)2} + \cdots + x_{(r-1)(t-1)} = \sum_{i=2}^{r-1} \sum_{j=1}^{t-1} x_{ij} = C$	x_{2t} $\vdots$ $+ x_{(r-1)t} = \sum_{i=2}^{r-1} x_{it} = D$
$x_{r1} + x_{r2} + \cdots + x_{r(t-1)} = \sum_{j=1}^{t-1} x_{rj} = E$	x_{rt}, missing, estimated as x

Suppose that we want $V[\bar{x}_{1\cdot} - \bar{x}_{r\cdot}]$. The observed total for the rth treatment T_r is equal to E, and the observed total for the tth block B_t is equal to $(B + D)$. The observed grand total M equals $(A + B + C + D + E)$. Substituting these quantities in (7.5), the missing value x is estimated as

$$x = \frac{t(B + D) + rE - (A + B + C + D + E)}{(r-1)(t-1)}.$$

The mean of the rth treatment will be

$$\bar{x}_{r.} = \frac{E + x}{t} = \frac{(r-1)(t-1)E + t(B + D) + rE - (A + B + C + D + E)}{t(r-1)(t-1)}, \tag{8.1}$$

and the mean of the first treatment is

$$\bar{x}_{1.} = \frac{A + B}{t} = \frac{(r-1)(t-1)(A + B)}{t(r-1)(t-1)}, \tag{8.2}$$

and so the difference between the two means is

$$\bar{x}_{r.} - \bar{x}_{1.} = \frac{1}{t(r-1)(t-1)}[-(rt - r - t + 2)A - (t-1)(r-2)B - C + (t-1)D + t(r-1)E]. \quad (8.3)$$

When we take the variance of this, the various coefficients become squared; each part, A, B, etc., is independent of the others, and so there are no covariance terms. Also

$$V[A] = V[\sum_j^{t-1} x_{1j}] = \sum_j^{t-1} V[x_{1j}] = (t-1)\sigma^2,$$

etc. Hence

$$\begin{aligned} V[\bar{x}_{r.} - \bar{x}_{1.}] &= \frac{\sigma^2}{t^2(r-1)^2(t-1)^2}[(rt - r - t + 2)^2(t-1) \\ &\quad + (t-1)^2(r-2)^2 \cdot 1 + 1^2 \cdot (r-2)(t-1) \\ &\quad + (t-1)^2(r-2) + t^2(r-1)^2(t-1)] \\ &= \frac{\sigma^2}{t}\left[2 + \frac{r}{(r-1)(t-1)}\right] \end{aligned} \quad (8.4)$$

18.9. Balanced Incomplete Blocks

We may have r treatments which we wish to compare in randomized blocks, but the natural block size k may be less than r. A certain class of incomplete-block designs, introduced by Yates [1], known as balanced incomplete blocks, have the properties

1. Each treatment occurs equally frequently, say n times.
2. Each pair of treatments occurs together in a block the same number of times, say λ.

These designs, though lacking the symmetry of the randomized-block designs whose analysis was discussed in Section 18.3, can be analyzed relatively easily. The theory of their construction has been dealt with comprehensively by Bose [5]. Tables of solutions are available in Fisher and Yates [6] and in Cochran and Cox [7]. We suppose that there are t blocks. The total number of observations, say N, is equal to $kt = rn$.

To determine λ, we note that a given treatment, say the ith, occurs in n blocks. These n blocks will contain a total of $n(k-1)$ other plots occupied by the other treatments. There are a total of $(r-1)$ treatments other than the ith. By the symmetry of the situation, they will occur equally frequently on these $n(k-1)$ plots, and so

$$\lambda = \frac{n(k-1)}{r-1}. \quad (9.1)$$

Balanced incomplete-block designs with $\lambda = 1$, 2, and 3 and $k = 3$ are given in Tables 18.15, 16, and 17, respectively, to illustrate the general nature of these designs.

Table 18.15

	Block						
Treatment	1	2	3	4	5	6	7
1	X	X	X				
2	X			X	X		
3	X					X	X
4		X		X		X	
5		X			X		X
6			X	X			X
7			X		X	X	

$r = 7, t = 7, k = 3, n = 3, \lambda = 1$

Table 18.16

	Block			
Treatment	1	2	3	4
1	X	X	X	
2		X	X	X
3	X		X	X
4	X	X		X

$r = 4, t = 4, k = 3, n = 3, \lambda = 2$

Table 18.17

	Block									
Treatment	1	2	3	4	5	6	7	8	9	10
1	X	X	X	X	X	X				
2	X	X	X				X	X	X	
3	X			X		X	X	X		X
4		X			X	X	X		X	X
5			X	X	X			X	X	X

$r = 5, t = 10, k = 3, n = 6, \lambda = 3$

For the normal equations we need the sums of squares and products:

$$\begin{aligned}
\sum{}' X_{i'ij}^2 &= n - \frac{n^2}{nr} = \frac{n}{r}(r-1), \\
\sum{}' Z_{j'ij}^2 &= k - \frac{k^2}{kt} = \frac{k}{t}(t-1), \\
\sum{}' X_{i'ij} X_{i''ij} &= 0 - \frac{n^2}{nr} = -\frac{n}{r}, \\
\sum{}' Z_{j'ij} Z_{j''ij} &= 0 - \frac{k^2}{kt} = -\frac{k}{t}.
\end{aligned} \tag{9.2}$$

The cross product for $X_{i'}$ and $Z_{j'}$ depends on whether the i'th treatment does or does not occur in the j'th block. If it does,

$$\sum{}' X_{i'ij} Z_{j'ij} = 1 - \frac{nk}{tk} = \frac{t-n}{t}, \tag{9.3}$$

but, if it does not,

$$\sum{}' X_{i'ij} Z_{j'ij} = 0 - \frac{nk}{tk} = -\frac{n}{t}. \tag{9.4}$$

The cross products with y are

$$\begin{aligned}
\sum{}' y_{ij} X_{i'ij} &= \sum_i \sum_j y_{ij} X_{i'ij} - \sum_i \sum_j y_{ij} \sum_i \sum_j X_{i'ij}/rn \\
&= \sum_j^n y_{i'j} - \sum_i \sum_j y_{ij}/r \equiv T_{i'},
\end{aligned} \tag{9.5}$$

$$\begin{aligned}
\sum{}' y_{ij} Z_{j'ij} &= \sum_i \sum_j y_{ij} Z_{j'ij} - \sum_i \sum_j y_{ij} \sum_i \sum_j Z_{j'ij}/kt \\
&= \sum_i^k y_{ij'} - \sum_i \sum_j y_{ij}/t \equiv B_{j'}.
\end{aligned} \tag{9.6}$$

We can now write down the first normal equation:

$$t_1 \cdot \frac{n}{r}(r-1) + t_2\left(-\frac{n}{r}\right) + \cdots + t_r\left(-\frac{n}{r}\right)$$

$$\underbrace{+ b_1\left(\frac{t-n}{t}\right) + \cdots}_{\text{for the } n \text{ blocks which contain the first treatment}} \quad \underbrace{+ b_{n+1}\left(-\frac{n}{t}\right) + \cdots}_{\text{for the } (t-n) \text{ blocks which do not contain the first treatment}} = T_1. \tag{9.7}$$

To this equation we add

$$\frac{n}{r}\sum_i^r t_i + \frac{n}{t}\sum_j^t b_j = 0 + 0 \tag{9.8}$$

and get

$$\underbrace{nt_1 + b_1 + \cdots}_{\substack{\text{for the } n \text{ blocks which} \\ \text{contain the first} \\ \text{treatment}}} = T_1. \tag{9.9}$$

The first r equations will be similar to this: We can write them as

$$nt_i + \sum_j^{(t_i)} b_j = T_i \tag{9.10}$$

where $\sum_j^{(t_i)} b_j$ means: Sum those b_j that correspond to blocks containing the ith treatment. There are, of course, n such blocks.

The $(r + 1)$th normal equation is

$$\underbrace{t_1\left(\frac{t-n}{t}\right) + \cdots}_{\substack{\text{for the } k \text{ treatments which} \\ \text{occur in the first block}}} \quad \underbrace{+ \, t_{k+1}\left(-\frac{n}{t}\right) + \cdots}_{\substack{\text{for the } (r-k) \text{ treatments which} \\ \text{do not occur in the first block}}}$$

$$+ \, b_1 \frac{k}{t}(t-1) + b_2\left(-\frac{k}{t}\right) + b_3\left(-\frac{k}{t}\right) + \cdots = B_1 . \tag{9.11}$$

Adding

$$\frac{n}{t}\sum_i^r t_i + \frac{k}{t}\sum_j^t b_j = 0 + 0 \tag{9.12}$$

to this gives

$$\underbrace{t_1 + \cdots}_{\substack{\text{for the } k \text{ treatments which} \\ \text{occur in the first block}}} + \, kb_1 = B_1 \tag{9.13}$$

and the following equations are similar: We can write them as

$$\sum_i^{(b_j)} t_i + kb_j = B_j \tag{9.14}$$

where $\sum_i^{(b_j)} t_i$ means: Sum those t_i that correspond to treatments occurring in the jth block. There are, of course, k treatments in each block.

The $(r + t)$ equations (9.10) and (9.14) constitute the normal equations, and we shall see that reasonably simple solutions for the t_i can be obtained as a consequence of the balanced nature of the design. We multiply (9.14) by $1/k$, to give

$$\frac{1}{k}\sum_i^{(b_j)} t_i + b_j = \frac{B_j}{k} . \tag{9.15}$$

Now sum this for the j corresponding to the blocks containing the ith treatment:

$$\frac{1}{k}\sum_{j}^{(t_i)}\sum_{i}^{(b_j)} t_i + \sum_{j}^{(t_i)} b_j = \frac{1}{k}\sum_{j}^{(t_i)} B_j . \tag{9.16}$$

The nature of the sum $\sum_{j}^{(t_i)}\sum_{i}^{(b_j)} t_i$ needs examination. For a particular i in (t_i), $\sum_{j}^{(t_i)}$ means: Sum over those blocks that contain the specified treatment; there will be n such blocks, each containing $(k - 1)$ plots occupied by other treatments. By the definition of a balanced incomplete block design, each of the other $(r - 1)$ treatments occurs with the ith treatment $\lambda = n(k - 1)/(r - 1)$ times. $\sum_{i}^{(b_j)} t_i$ means: Sum those t_i (where here the i is a variable index) that correspond to the treatments that occur in the jth block. But we have just seen that, in the set of blocks determined by specifying the i in $\sum_{j}^{(t_i)}$, the particular t_i occurs n times and each of the other t_i occurs $n(k - 1)/(r - 1)$ times, so the sum is

$$\begin{aligned}\sum_{j}^{(t_i)}\sum_{i}^{(b_j)} t_i &= nt_i + \frac{n(k-1)}{r-1}\sum_{i'\neq i} t_{i'} \\ &= t_i\left[n - \frac{n(k-1)}{r-1}\right] + \frac{n(k-1)}{r-1}\sum_{i}^{r} t_i \\ &= t_i\frac{n(r-k)}{r-1} .\end{aligned} \tag{9.17}$$

Substitute this in (9.16):

$$\frac{n(r-k)}{k(r-1)} t_i + \sum_{j}^{(t_i)} b_j = \frac{1}{k}\sum_{j}^{(t_i)} B_j . \tag{9.18}$$

Subtract this from (9.10):

$$t_i\left[n - \frac{n(r-k)}{k(r-1)}\right] = T_i - \frac{1}{k}\sum_{j}^{(t_i)} B_j ,$$

whence

$$t_i = \frac{r-1}{nr(k-1)}\left(kT_i - \sum_{j}^{(t_i)} B_j\right) = \frac{r-1}{nr(k-1)} Q_i , \tag{9.19}$$

if we define

$$Q_i = kT_i - \sum_{j}^{(t_i)} B_j . \tag{9.20}$$

Reference to the definitions of T_i (9.5) and B_j (9.6) shows that

$$Q_i = \Big(k\sum_j^n y_{ij} - k\sum_i\sum_j y_{ij}/r\Big) - \Big(\sum_j^{(t_i)}\sum_i^k y_{ij} - n\sum_i\sum_j y_{ij}/t\Big)$$

$$= k\sum_j^n y_{ij} - \sum_j^{(t_i)}\sum_i^k y_{ij} \tag{9.21}$$

$= k \times$ sum for ith treatment $-$ sum of block sums for blocks containing ith treatment.

In the above, the coefficient of the grand sum $\sum_i\sum_j y_{ij}$ is zero since $k/r = n/t$ since $kt = rn = N$. The form (9.21) is usually easier for computation than (9.20).

Usually there is no particular interest in the block constants b_j. However, if they are needed, they can be obtained by first obtaining the t_i and then substituting in (9.15).

The standard procedure for an unbalanced analysis of variance was given in Table 18.5. The customary procedure is to compute A, B, and T in that table, and obtain C as $(A - B)$ and D as $(T - A)$. In the case of balanced incomplete blocks it is possible to derive an algebraic form for C, and the remainder D is found as $(T - B - C)$.

The sum of squares due to regression on treatments and blocks is

$$A = \sum_j^t b_j B_j + \sum_i^r t_i T_i \tag{9.22}$$

and the sum of squares due to regression on blocks alone is

$$B = \frac{1}{k}\sum_j^t\left(\sum_i^k y_{ij}\right)^2 - \frac{1}{kt}\left(\sum_i^r\sum_j^t y_{ij}\right)^2 = \frac{1}{k}\sum_j^t B_j^2. \tag{9.23}$$

Hence the sum of squares due to adding regression on treatments to regression on blocks is

$$C = A - B = \sum_i^r t_i T_i + \sum_j^t\left(b_j - \frac{B_j}{k}\right)B_j. \tag{9.24}$$

Into this we substitute

$$t_i = \frac{r-1}{nr(k-1)}\,Q_i$$

from (9.19) and

$$T_i = \frac{Q_i}{k} + \frac{1}{k}\sum_j^{(t_i)} B_j$$

from (9.20): Thus

$$C = \sum_i^r \frac{r-1}{nr(k-1)} Q_i\left(\frac{Q_i}{k} + \frac{1}{k}\sum_j^{(t_i)} B_j\right) + \sum_j^t \left(b_j - \frac{B_j}{k}\right)B_j$$
$$= \frac{r-1}{nrk(k-1)}\sum_i^r Q_i^2 + \frac{1}{k}\sum_i^r \frac{r-1}{nr(k-1)} Q_i \sum_j^{(t_i)} B_j + \sum_j^t \left(b_j - \frac{B_j}{k}\right) B_j$$
$$= \frac{r-1}{nrk(k-1)}\sum_i^r Q_i^2 + \frac{1}{k}\sum_i^r t_i \sum_j^{(t_i)} B_j + \sum_j^t \left(b_j - \frac{B_j}{k}\right)B_j \,. \tag{9.25}$$

Now (9.15) gives

$$b_j - \frac{B_j}{k} = -\sum_i^{(b_j)} t_i/k \;;$$

so

$$\sum_j^t \left(b_j - \frac{B_j}{k}\right)B_j = -\frac{1}{k}\sum_j^t B_j \sum_i^{(b_j)} t_i \,. \tag{9.26}$$

We now wish to make use of the fact that

$$\sum_j^t B_j \sum_i^{(b_j)} t_i = \sum_i^r t_i \sum_j^{(t_i)} B_j \,. \tag{9.27}$$

To see that this identity is true, we recall that $t_i \sum_j^{(t_i)} B_j$ means sum the B_j, as defined in (9.6), for those blocks containing the ith treatment, and multiply this sum by t_i. When this is summed over all treatments we get $\sum_i^r t_i \sum_j^{(t_i)} B_j$. Thus this quantity contains every B_j multiplied by the t_i corresponding to the treatments in those blocks. But this is precisely $\sum_j^t B_j \sum_i^{(b_j)} t_i$, which proves (9.27). Using this result in (9.26), it then follows that

$$\sum_j^t \left(b_j - \frac{B_j}{k}\right) B_j = -\frac{1}{k}\sum_i^r t_i \sum_j^{(t_i)} B_j \;;$$

so the second and third terms on the right-hand side of (9.25) cancel each other, and we are left with

$$C = \frac{r-1}{nrk(k-1)}\sum_i^r Q_i^2 \,. \tag{9.28}$$

This is entered in Table 18.18.

To construct confidence limits for $(\tau_i - \tau_{i'})$ we need $V[t_i - t_{i'}]$, where, from (9.19),

$$t_i - t_{i'} = \frac{r-1}{nr(k-1)}\left[k(T_i - T_{i'}) - \left(\sum_j^{(t_i)} B_j - \sum_j^{(t_{i'})} B_j\right)\right]. \tag{9.29}$$

Define P as

$$P = k(T_i - T_{i'}) - \left(\sum_j^{(t_i)} B_j - \sum_j^{(t_{i'})} B_j\right). \tag{9.30}$$

Table 18.18

Source of variance	Sums of squares	Degrees of freedom
Treatments (adjusted for block effects)	$\frac{r-1}{nrk(k-1)} \sum_i^r Q_i^2 = C$	$r-1$
Blocks (unadjusted for treatments)	$\frac{1}{k}\sum_j^t\left(\sum_i^k y_{ij}\right) - \frac{1}{kt}\left(\sum_i\sum_j y_{ij}\right)^2 = B$	$t-1$
Remainder	$T - C - B$	$N - r - t + 1$
Total	$\sum_i\sum_j y_{ij}^2 - (\sum_i\sum_j y_{ij})^2/kt = T$	$N-1$

Then

$$V[t_i - t_{i'}] = \frac{(r-1)^2}{n^2r^2(k-1)^2} V[P]. \tag{9.31}$$

We now have to compute $V[P]$. We note first, using the definition of T_i, (9.5), that

$$\begin{aligned} T_i - T_{i'} &= \sum_j^n y_{ij} - \sum_i\sum_j y_{ij}/r - \sum_j^n y_{i'j} + \sum_i\sum_j y_{ij}/r \\ &= \sum_j^n y_{ij} - \sum_j^n y_{i'j}\,; \end{aligned} \tag{9.32}$$

Similarly, using (9.6),

$$\sum_j^{(t_i)} B_j - \sum_j^{(t_{i'})} B_j = \sum_j^{(t_i)}\sum_i^k y_{ij} - \sum_j^{(t_{i'})}\sum_i^k y_{ij}\,. \tag{9.33}$$

Thus

$$P = k\sum_j^n y_{ij} - k\sum_j^n y_{i'j} - \sum_j^{(t_i)}\sum_i^k y_{ij} + \sum_j^{(t_{i'})}\sum_i^k y_{ij}\,. \tag{9.34}$$

In finding the variance of this, it will be helpful to visualize the relevant features of a typical design (Table 18.9). The blocks can be regarded as falling into groups of the following types:

(H): These blocks, λ in number, contain both the ith and i'th treatments. B represents the sum of the observations from the λ plots in these blocks with the ith treatment, C the sum of the observations from the λ plots with the i'th treatment, and F the sum of the observations from the $\lambda(k-2)$ plots with treatments other than the ith and i'th.

Table 18.19

Treatment i	A	B			$\sum_j^n y_{ij}$
Treatment i'		C	D		$\sum_j^n y_{i'j}$
Other treatments	E	F	G		
Blocks	I	H	J	K	

(I): In these blocks, $(n-\lambda)$ in number, A represents the sum of the observations from the $(n-\lambda)$ plots with the ith treatment, and E the sum of the observations from the $(n-\lambda)(k-1)$ plots with treatments other than the ith and i'th.

(J): In these blocks, $(n-\lambda)$ in number, D represents the sum of the observations from the $(n-\lambda)$ plots with the i'th treatment, and G the sum of the observations from the $(n-\lambda)(k-1)$ plots with treatments other than the ith and the i'th.

(K): In these blocks, neither the ith nor the i'th treatments occur.

Referring to (9.34), we see that

$$\sum_j^n y_{ij} = A + B, \quad \sum_j^{(t_i)} \sum_i^k y_{ij} = (A + E) + (B + C + F)$$

$$\sum_j^n y_{i'j} = C + D, \quad \sum_j^{(t_{i'})} \sum_i^k y_{ij} = (B + C + F) + (D + G).$$

Substituting in (9.34),

$$\begin{aligned} P &= k(A + B) - k(C + D) - [(A + E) + (B + C + F)] \\ &\qquad + [(B + C + F) + (D + G)] \\ &= (k-1)(A - D) + k(B - C) - (E - G). \end{aligned}$$

Each plot has a variance σ^2, and so, for example,

$$V[A - D] = 2(n - \lambda)\sigma^2,$$

since A and D each contain $(n - \lambda)$ plots. Thus

$$V[P] = 2\sigma^2 [(k - 1)^2 (n - \lambda) + k^2\lambda + (n - \lambda)(k - 1)]. \quad (9.35)$$

Substituting in (9.31) and reducing, we get

$$V[t_i - t_{i'}] = \frac{2(r - 1)}{t(k - 1)} \sigma^2. \quad (9.36)$$

If a randomized complete-block design had been used, there would have been n replicates of each treatment, and, if the variance of the plots in the randomized complete-block design had been σ_c^2, then the variance of the difference between two treatment means would have been $2\sigma_c^2/n$. The ratio of this variance to the corresponding variance in the balanced incomplete-block design, (9.36), is

$$\frac{2\sigma_c^2}{n} \cdot \frac{t(k - 1)}{2(r - 1)\sigma^2} = \frac{r(k - 1)\sigma_c^2}{k(r - 1)\sigma^2} = \frac{1 - 1/k}{1 - 1/r} \cdot \frac{\sigma_c^2}{\sigma^2}. \quad (9.37)$$

The factor

$$\frac{r(k - 1)}{k(r - 1)} = \frac{1 - 1/k}{1 - 1/r} \quad (9.38)$$

is known as the efficiency factor E. In the case of the design in Table 18.20, for example, $k = 4$, $r = 7$, and $E = 21/24 = 0.875$; so, unless the variance in blocks of size 4 is less than in blocks of size 7 by this ratio, an actual loss in accuracy will have resulted.

The data of Table 18.20 give the measurements on seven modifications of a material whose preparation involved heat treatment in an oven. The oven would only hold four batches at a time and constituted the natural block. For this design the number of treatments is $r = 7$, the number of blocks $t = 7$, the block size $k = 4$, and the number of replicates of each treatment $n = 4$. To obtain the Q_i we use (9.21), e.g.,

$$Q_1 = 4 \times 317.3 - 313.9 - 310.8 - 318.4 - 316.2 = 9.9 .$$

The t_i are derived from the Q_i with (9.19), e.g.,

$$t_1 = \frac{7 - 1}{4 \times 7 \times (4 - 1)} \times 9.9 = 0.707.$$

We might wish to add a column of corrected treatment means, made up of the grand mean plus the t_i. From (9.23), the sum of squares for blocks, unadjusted for treatments, is

$$\tfrac{1}{4}(306.2^2 + \cdots + 322.7)^2 - \frac{(2203.3)^2}{28} = 42.0872.$$

From (9.28), the sum of squares for treatments, adjusted for blocks, is

$$\frac{7-1}{4 \times 7 \times 4(4-1)}(9.9^2 + \cdots + 9.8^2) = 11.9243.$$

Table 18.20

Treatment	$j \rightarrow$ Block A	B	C	D	E	F	G	$\sum_j^n y_{ij}$	Q_i	t_i
$i = 1$		76.8	77.3	82.0		81.2		317.3	9.9	0.707
2			77.3	78.9	77.9		80.7	314.8	−6.8	−0.486
3	77.0			79.4	79.3	79.2		314.9	4.7	0.336
4		78.9			77.8	77.4	82.1	316.2	−2.1	−0.150
5	79.2		78.6			78.4	78.8	315.0	4.1	0.293
6	74.3	76.9		78.1			81.1	310.4	−19.6	−1.400
7	75.7	81.3	77.6		79.1			313.7	9.8	0.700
$\sum_i^k y_{ij}$	306.2	313.9	310.8	318.4	314.1	316.2	322.7	2202.3	0	0

The total sum of squares is obtained in the usual way, and the remainder sum of squares found by difference. These sums of squares are assembled in Table 18.21.

Table 18.21

Source of variance	Sums of squares	Degrees of freedom	Mean squares
Treatments (adjusted for block effects)	11.9243	6	1.9874
Blocks (unadjusted for treatments)	42.0872	6	
Remainder	39.5782	15	2.6385
Total	93.5897	27	

A test of the null hypothesis $\tau_i = 0$ for all i is given by the ratio of the treatment to the remainder mean square. An individual confidence interval can be constructed from the estimated variance of the difference between t_i and $t_{i'}$ (9.36):

$$\hat{V}[t_i - t_{i'}] = \frac{2 \times (7-1)}{7 \times (4-1)} \times 2.6385 = 1.508.$$

REFERENCES

1. Yates, F., "The principles of orthogonality and confounding in replicated experiments," *Journal of Agricultural Science*, 23(1933), 108–145.
2. Menzler, F. A., *Statistical Design of Experiments*. London: London Transport Executive, 1954.
3. Yates, F., "The analysis of replicated experiments when the field results are incomplete," *Empire Journal of Experimental Agriculture*, 1(1933), 129–142.
4. ——— "Incomplete randomized blocks," *Annals of Eugenics*, 7(1936), 121–140.
5. Bose, R. C., "On the construction of balanced incomplete block designs," *Annals of Eugenics*, 9(1939) 353–400.
6. Fisher, R. A., and F. Yates, *Statistical Tables for Biological, Agricultural, and Medical Research*. 3d ed.; Edinburgh;: Oliver & Boyd, 1948.
7. Cochran, William G., and Gertrude M. Cox, *Experimental Design*. 2d ed.; New York: John Wiley & Sons, 1957.

EXERCISES

18.1. Youden ["Statistics in analytical chemistry," *Annals of the New York Academy of Sciences*, 52(1950), Art. 6, 815–819] quotes data by Baxter and Lundstedt ["A revision of the atomic weight of iodine," *Journal of the American Chemical Society*, 62(1940), 1829–1834]. Sixteen determinations of the ratio of the reacting weights of iodine and silver were made. These 16 determinations came from various combinations of two batches of iodine and five batches of silver. The number of replicate determinations for a given iodine-batch–silver-batch combination varies from zero to three.

Incidentally, silver batch C is a repurification of batch B which is a repurification of batch A.

Ratio of Iodine to Silver

Iodine	Silver	Ratio	Iodine	Silver	Ratio
I	*A*	1.176422	II	*A*	1.176399
	A	1.176425		*A*	1.176440
				A	1.176418
	B	1.176441		*B*	1.176423
	B	1.176441		*B*	1.176413
	C	1.176429			
	C	1.176420			
	C	1.176437			
	D	1.176449		*D*	1.176461
	D	1.176450			
	E	1.176455			

Make an analysis of variance of these data. Make a test of significance of the null hypothesis that there is no interaction between the batches of silver and iodine. If this null hypothesis is acceptable, make a test of significance of the null hypothesis that there is no difference between the batches of iodine. If this null hypothesis is acceptable, make a test of significance of the null hypothesis that there is no difference between the batches of silver. Construct 95 per cent confidence limits for the difference between the mean for silver batches *A*, *B*, and *C* and the mean for silver batches *D* and *E*, assuming (*a*) that this was the intention before the data were obtained, and (*b*) that this was suggested by the way the data came out.

CHAPTER 19

Topics in the Design of Experiments

19.1. Introduction

In the previous chapters, we have been laying the foundations for the topic usually known as the design and analysis of experiments. Most of the facets of this subject are elaborate extensions of the ideas introduced in Chapters 13 through 18.

Here we will merely give a brief catalog of the topics. A detailed examination would involve us in a book of the length of the present one, see, for example, [12], [21], [22], and [23]).

19.2. Randomization

It will be recalled that one of the assumptions of regression analysis is that the errors be independent. If we consider a field experiment, it is obvious that errors on adjacent plots will tend to be correlated, and the analogous phenomenon occurs in almost any sphere of experimentation. The idea of randomization, introduced by Fisher in 1926 [1] and given wider circulation with the publication of his *Design of Experiments* in 1935 [2], is a beautifully simple way to achieve this independence of errors. It is well understood that randomization is necessary to avoid bias in the estimates of the effects, but it is not so widely realized that it is also necessary to avoid bias in the estimate of error. This point was discussed in a sequence of papers by Yates [3], [4], Student [5], and Fisher [6].

A further function of randomization as a justification of the use of the F test was given by Welch [7] and Pitman [8].

For general reviews of the philosophy of experimentation, see Yates [9], Neyman et al. [10], Anscombe [11], and the books of Fisher [2] and Kempthorne [12].

19.3. Incomplete Blocks

In addition to the class of balanced incomplete blocks described in Section 18.9, other types of incomplete-block designs have been developed, in particular

1. Partially balanced incomplete blocks [13].
2. Chain blocks [14].

The balanced incomplete-block designs are quite restricted in number, and for a specified number of treatments and size of blocks we may find that the only possible design requires an unsatisfactorily large number of replicates. These further classes of designs offer greater choice in the number of replications.

A special subclass of balanced incomplete-block designs, known as Youden squares [15], [16], has the property that, if blocks are regarded as columns, then the treatments can be arranged so that each treatment occurs once and only once in each row.

19.4. Confounding

In multifactor experiments the total number of plots required is the product of the number of levels of the factors. Particularly for the cases where the numbers of levels are the same for all the factors, schemes exist for splitting up the experiment into a number of blocks, with comparatively minor loss of information. This device is known as confounding [9], [17].

19.5. Fractional Replication

In multifactor experiments, particularly of the form 2^n and 3^n, where 2 and 3 are the number of levels of the factors, all the same, and n is the number of factors, schemes exist for obtaining satisfactory information on the main effects and two-way interactions with replicating only a fraction of the whole number of plots. These designs are known as fractional replicates. Usually a fractional replicate can also be confounded in blocks [18], [19].

19.6. Response Surface Study

In multifactor experiments in which all the factors are numerical-valued variables, the results can be analyzed by the methods of Chapter 18, fitting a multiple-regression equation to the response. This immediately suggests two lines of inquiry. The first is how to interpret the resulting multiple-regression equation. This may be simplified by the device of transforming it to its so-called canonical form. The second line of inquiry is what arrangement of points in the experiment space will give maximum precision to the determination of the coefficients of the equation of the canonical form. This gives rise to a series of special experimental designs, in particular the second-order composite rotatable designs. Some of these designs can be run in incomplete blocks [20], [21].

19.7. Other Topics

A statistician who is familiar with the principles of construction, analysis, and potential sphere of application of the designs mentioned in Sections 19.2 through 19.6 is reasonably well qualified to act as a consultant on the design and analysis of experiments. To be expert, however, he should also be acquainted with a host of other topics, including

1. The analysis of covariance in complex designs.
2. Partial confounding.
3. Double confounding.
4. Split-plot confounding.
5. Dummy treatments.
6. Weighing designs.
7. Various types of lattices.
8. Experiments balanced for carry-over of effects.

For reviews, and references to these topics, see the books by Kempthorne [12] and Cochran and Cox [22].

The foregoing topics are concerned mainly with the arrangement of the treatments onto the experimental units, or plots. The complicated nature of the designs produced makes this field largely the exclusive province of the statistician. An experiment involves other questions as well, for example, the choice of factors or treatments and the number of levels of each, the choice of experimental unit, and the choice of the dependent variable. In principle these are the province of the experimenter, but frequently in practice the experienced statistician will have substantial contributions to make. Even more basis is a careful and searching examination of the objectives of the experimental program, which are often surprisingly ill-defined when the experimenter brings his problem to the statistician. An experienced statistician, perhaps through talking to many experimenters, acquires the ability to demand clarity in what the experiment is supposed to achieve.

REFERENCES

1. Fisher, R. A., "The arrangement of field experiments," *Journal of the Ministry of Agriculture*, 12(1926), 291–301.
2. ——— *The Design of Experiments.* 1st ed.; Edinburgh: Oliver & Boyd, 1935.
3. Yates, F., "The formation of Latin squares for use in field experiments," *Empire Journal of Experimental Agriculture*, 1(1933), 235–244.
4. ——— "The comparative advantages of systematic and randomized arrangements in the design of agricultural and biological experiments," *Biometrika*, 30(1939), 440–464.
5. "Student," "Comparison between balanced and random arrangements of field plots," *Biometrika*, 29(1937), 363–379.
6. Barbacki, S., and R. A. Fisher, "A test of the supposed precision of systematic arrangements," *Annals of Eugenics*, 7(1936), 189–193.
7. Welch, B. L., "On the z test in randomized blocks and Latin squares," *Biometrika*, 29(1937), 21–52.
8. Pitman, E. J. G., "Significance tests which can be applied to samples from any populations," *Biometrika*, 29(1937), 322–335.
9. Yates, F., "Complex experiments," *Supplement to the Journal of the Royal Statistical Society*, 2(1935), 181–247.
10. Neyman, J., K. Iwaskiewicz, and S. Kolodzieczyk, "Statistical problems in agricultural experimentation," *Supplement to the Journal of the Royal Statistical Society*, 2(1935), 107–154.
11. Anscombe, F. J., "On the validity of comparátive experiments," *Journal of the Royal Statistical Society*, A, 61(1948), 181–211.
12. Kempthorne, O., *The Design and Analysis of Experiments.* New York: John Wiley & Sons, 1952.
13. Bose, R. C., and K. R. Nair, "Partially balanced incomplete block designs," *Sankhya*, 4(1939), 337–372.
14. Youden, W. J., and W. S. Connor, "The chain block design," *Biometrics*, 9(1953), 127–140.
15. ——— "Use of incomplete block replications in estimating tobacco-mosaic virus," *Contributions of the Boyce Thompson Institute*, 9(1937), 41–48.
16. ——— "Experimental designs to increase accuracy of greenhouse studies," *Contributions of the Boyce Thompson Institute*, 11(1940), 219–228.
17. Yates, F., *The Design and Analysis of Factorial Experiments.* (Technical Communication no. 35. Harpenden, England: Imperial Bureau of Soil Science, 1935.
18. Finney, D. J., "The fractional replication of factorial experiments," *Annals of Eugenics*, 12(1945), 291–301.
19. Kempthorne, O., "A simple approach to confounding and fractional replication in factorial experiments," *Biometrika*, 34(1947), 255–272.
20. Box, G. E. P., and K. B. Wilson, "On the experimental attainment of optimum conditions," *Journal of the Royal Statistical Society*, B, 13(1951), 1–45.
21. Davies, O. L. (ed.), *The Design and Analysis of Industrial Experiments.* New York: Hafner Publishing Co., 1956.
22. Cochran, William G., and Gertrude M. Cox, *Experimental Designs.* 2d ed.; New York: John Wiley & Sons, 1957.
23. Cox, D. R., *Planning of Experiments.* New York: John Wiley & Sons, 1958.

Appendix

Table I. The Cumulative Standardized Normal Distribution Function*

$$\Phi(u) = \frac{1}{\sqrt{2\pi}} \int_{-\infty}^{u} e^{-\frac{x^2}{2}} dx \quad \text{FOR} \quad -4{\cdot}99 \leq u \leq 0{\cdot}00.$$

u	·00	·01	·02	·03	·04	·05	·06	·07	·08	·09
− ·0	·5000	·4960	·4920	·4880	·4840	·4801	·4761	·4721	·4681	·4641
− ·1	·4602	·4562	·4522	·4483	·4443	·4404	·4364	·4325	·4286	·4247
− ·2	·4207	·4168	·4129	·4090	·4052	·4013	·3974	·3936	·3897	·3859
− ·3	·3821	·3783	·3745	·3707	·3669	·3632	·3594	·3557	·3520	·3483
− ·4	·3446	·3409	·3372	·3336	·3300	·3264	·3228	·3192	·3156	·3121
− ·5	·3085	·3050	·3015	·2981	·2946	·2912	·2877	·2843	·2810	·2776
− ·6	·2743	·2709	·2676	·2643	·2611	·2578	·2546	·2514	·2483	·2451
− ·7	·2420	·2389	·2358	·2327	·2297	·2266	·2236	·2206	·2177	·2148
− ·8	·2119	·2090	·2061	·2033	·2005	·1977	·1949	·1922	·1894	·1867
− ·9	·1841	·1814	·1788	·1762	·1736	·1711	·1685	·1660	·1635	·1611
−1·0	·1587	·1562	·1539	·1515	·1492	·1469	·1446	·1423	·1401	·1379
−1·1	·1357	·1335	·1314	·1292	·1271	·1251	·1230	·1210	·1190	·1170
−1·2	·1151	·1131	·1112	·1093	·1075	·1056	·1038	·1020	·1003	·09853
−1·3	·09680	·09510	·09342	·09176	·09012	·08851	·08691	·08534	·08379	·08226
−1·4	·08076	·07927	·07780	·07636	·07493	·07353	·07215	·07078	·06944	·06811
−1·5	·06681	·06552	·06426	·06301	·06178	·06057	·05938	·05821	·05705	·05592
−1·6	·05480	·05370	·05262	·05155	·05050	·04947	·04846	·04746	·04648	·04551
−1·7	·04457	·04363	·04272	·04182	·04093	·04006	·03920	·03836	·03754	·03673
−1·8	·03593	·03515	·03438	·03362	·03288	·03216	·03144	·03074	·03005	·02938
−1·9	·02872	·02807	·02743	·02680	·02619	·02559	·02500	·02442	·02385	·02330
−2·0	·02275	·02222	·02169	·02118	·02068	·02018	·01970	·01923	·01876	·01831
−2·1	·01786	·01743	·01700	·01659	·01618	·01578	·01539	·01500	·01463	·01426
−2·2	·01390	·01355	·01321	·01287	·01255	·01222	·01191	·01160	·01130	·01101
−2·3	·01072	·01044	·01017	$\cdot 0^{2}9903$	$\cdot 0^{2}9642$	$\cdot 0^{2}9387$	$\cdot 0^{2}9137$	$\cdot 0^{2}8894$	$\cdot 0^{2}8656$	$\cdot 0^{2}8424$
−2·4	$\cdot 0^{2}8198$	$\cdot 0^{2}7976$	$\cdot 0^{2}7760$	$\cdot 0^{2}7549$	$\cdot 0^{2}7344$	$\cdot 0^{2}7143$	$\cdot 0^{2}6947$	$\cdot 0^{2}6756$	$\cdot 0^{2}6569$	$\cdot 0^{2}6387$
−2·5	$\cdot 0^{2}6210$	$\cdot 0^{2}6037$	$\cdot 0^{2}5868$	$\cdot 0^{2}5703$	$\cdot 0^{2}5543$	$\cdot 0^{2}5386$	$\cdot 0^{2}5234$	$\cdot 0^{2}5085$	$\cdot 0^{2}4940$	$\cdot 0^{2}4799$
−2·6	$\cdot 0^{2}4661$	$\cdot 0^{2}4527$	$\cdot 0^{2}4396$	$\cdot 0^{2}4269$	$\cdot 0^{2}4145$	$\cdot 0^{2}4025$	$\cdot 0^{2}3907$	$\cdot 0^{2}3793$	$\cdot 0^{2}3681$	$\cdot 0^{2}3573$
−2·7	$\cdot 0^{2}3467$	$\cdot 0^{2}3364$	$\cdot 0^{2}3264$	$\cdot 0^{2}3167$	$\cdot 0^{2}3072$	$\cdot 0^{2}2980$	$\cdot 0^{2}2890$	$\cdot 0^{2}2803$	$\cdot 0^{2}2718$	$\cdot 0^{2}2635$
−2·8	$\cdot 0^{2}2555$	$\cdot 0^{2}2477$	$\cdot 0^{2}2401$	$\cdot 0^{2}2327$	$\cdot 0^{2}2256$	$\cdot 0^{2}2186$	$\cdot 0^{2}2118$	$\cdot 0^{2}2052$	$\cdot 0^{2}1988$	$\cdot 0^{2}1926$
−2·9	$\cdot 0^{2}1866$	$\cdot 0^{2}1807$	$\cdot 0^{2}1750$	$\cdot 0^{2}1695$	$\cdot 0^{2}1641$	$\cdot 0^{2}1589$	$\cdot 0^{2}1538$	$\cdot 0^{2}1489$	$\cdot 0^{2}1441$	$\cdot 0^{2}1395$
−3·0	$\cdot 0^{2}1350$	$\cdot 0^{2}1306$	$\cdot 0^{2}1264$	$\cdot 0^{2}1223$	$\cdot 0^{2}1183$	$\cdot 0^{2}1144$	$\cdot 0^{2}1107$	$\cdot 0^{2}1070$	$\cdot 0^{2}1035$	$\cdot 0^{2}1001$
−3·1	$\cdot 0^{3}9676$	$\cdot 0^{3}9354$	$\cdot 0^{3}9043$	$\cdot 0^{3}8740$	$\cdot 0^{3}8447$	$\cdot 0^{3}8164$	$\cdot 0^{3}7888$	$\cdot 0^{3}7622$	$\cdot 0^{3}7364$	$\cdot 0^{3}7114$
−3·2	$\cdot 0^{3}6871$	$\cdot 0^{3}6637$	$\cdot 0^{3}6410$	$\cdot 0^{3}6190$	$\cdot 0^{3}5976$	$\cdot 0^{3}5770$	$\cdot 0^{3}5571$	$\cdot 0^{3}5377$	$\cdot 0^{3}5190$	$\cdot 0^{3}5009$
−3·3	$\cdot 0^{3}4834$	$\cdot 0^{3}4665$	$\cdot 0^{3}4501$	$\cdot 0^{3}4342$	$\cdot 0^{3}4189$	$\cdot 0^{3}4041$	$\cdot 0^{3}3897$	$\cdot 0^{3}3758$	$\cdot 0^{3}3624$	$\cdot 0^{3}3495$
−3·4	$\cdot 0^{3}3369$	$\cdot 0^{3}3248$	$\cdot 0^{3}3131$	$\cdot 0^{3}3018$	$\cdot 0^{3}2909$	$\cdot 0^{3}2803$	$\cdot 0^{3}2701$	$\cdot 0^{3}2602$	$\cdot 0^{3}2507$	$\cdot 0^{3}2415$
−3·5	$\cdot 0^{3}2326$	$\cdot 0^{3}2241$	$\cdot 0^{3}2158$	$\cdot 0^{3}2078$	$\cdot 0^{3}2001$	$\cdot 0^{3}1926$	$\cdot 0^{3}1854$	$\cdot 0^{3}1785$	$\cdot 0^{3}1718$	$\cdot 0^{3}1653$
−3·6	$\cdot 0^{3}1591$	$\cdot 0^{3}1531$	$\cdot 0^{3}1473$	$\cdot 0^{3}1417$	$\cdot 0^{3}1363$	$\cdot 0^{3}1311$	$\cdot 0^{3}1261$	$\cdot 0^{3}1213$	$\cdot 0^{3}1166$	$\cdot 0^{3}1121$
−3·7	$\cdot 0^{3}1078$	$\cdot 0^{3}1036$	$\cdot 0^{4}9961$	$\cdot 0^{4}9574$	$\cdot 0^{4}9201$	$\cdot 0^{4}8842$	$\cdot 0^{4}8496$	$\cdot 0^{4}8162$	$\cdot 0^{4}7841$	$\cdot 0^{4}7532$
−3·8	$\cdot 0^{4}7235$	$\cdot 0^{4}6948$	$\cdot 0^{4}6673$	$\cdot 0^{4}6407$	$\cdot 0^{4}6152$	$\cdot 0^{4}5906$	$\cdot 0^{4}5669$	$\cdot 0^{4}5442$	$\cdot 0^{4}5223$	$\cdot 0^{4}5012$
−3·9	$\cdot 0^{4}4810$	$\cdot 0^{4}4615$	$\cdot 0^{4}4427$	$\cdot 0^{4}4247$	$\cdot 0^{4}4074$	$\cdot 0^{4}3908$	$\cdot 0^{4}3747$	$\cdot 0^{4}3594$	$\cdot 0^{4}3446$	$\cdot 0^{4}3304$
−4·0	$\cdot 0^{4}3167$	$\cdot 0^{4}3036$	$\cdot 0^{4}2910$	$\cdot 0^{4}2789$	$\cdot 0^{4}2673$	$\cdot 0^{4}2561$	$\cdot 0^{4}2454$	$\cdot 0^{4}2351$	$\cdot 0^{4}2252$	$\cdot 0^{4}2157$
−4·1	$\cdot 0^{4}2066$	$\cdot 0^{4}1978$	$\cdot 0^{4}1894$	$\cdot 0^{4}1814$	$\cdot 0^{4}1737$	$\cdot 0^{4}1662$	$\cdot 0^{4}1591$	$\cdot 0^{4}1523$	$\cdot 0^{4}1458$	$\cdot 0^{4}1395$
−4·2	$\cdot 0^{4}1335$	$\cdot 0^{4}1277$	$\cdot 0^{4}1222$	$\cdot 0^{4}1168$	$\cdot 0^{4}1118$	$\cdot 0^{4}1069$	$\cdot 0^{4}1022$	$\cdot 0^{5}9774$	$\cdot 0^{5}9345$	$\cdot 0^{5}8934$
−4·3	$\cdot 0^{5}8540$	$\cdot 0^{5}8163$	$\cdot 0^{5}7801$	$\cdot 0^{5}7455$	$\cdot 0^{5}7124$	$\cdot 0^{5}6807$	$\cdot 0^{5}6503$	$\cdot 0^{5}6212$	$\cdot 0^{5}5934$	$\cdot 0^{5}5668$
−4·4	$\cdot 0^{5}5413$	$\cdot 0^{5}5169$	$\cdot 0^{5}4935$	$\cdot 0^{5}4712$	$\cdot 0^{5}4498$	$\cdot 0^{5}4294$	$\cdot 0^{5}4098$	$\cdot 0^{5}3911$	$\cdot 0^{5}3732$	$\cdot 0^{5}3561$
−4·5	$\cdot 0^{5}3398$	$\cdot 0^{5}3241$	$\cdot 0^{5}3092$	$\cdot 0^{5}2949$	$\cdot 0^{5}2813$	$\cdot 0^{5}2682$	$\cdot 0^{5}2558$	$\cdot 0^{5}2439$	$\cdot 0^{5}2325$	$\cdot 0^{5}2216$
−4·6	$\cdot 0^{5}2112$	$\cdot 0^{5}2013$	$\cdot 0^{5}1919$	$\cdot 0^{5}1828$	$\cdot 0^{5}1742$	$\cdot 0^{5}1660$	$\cdot 0^{5}1581$	$\cdot 0^{5}1506$	$\cdot 0^{5}1434$	$\cdot 0^{5}1366$
−4·7	$\cdot 0^{5}1301$	$\cdot 0^{5}1239$	$\cdot 0^{5}1179$	$\cdot 0^{5}1123$	$\cdot 0^{5}1069$	$\cdot 0^{5}1017$	$\cdot 0^{6}9680$	$\cdot 0^{6}9211$	$\cdot 0^{6}8765$	$\cdot 0^{6}8339$
−4·8	$\cdot 0^{6}7933$	$\cdot 0^{6}7547$	$\cdot 0^{6}7178$	$\cdot 0^{6}6827$	$\cdot 0^{6}6492$	$\cdot 0^{6}6173$	$\cdot 0^{6}5869$	$\cdot 0^{6}5580$	$\cdot 0^{6}5304$	$\cdot 0^{6}5042$
−4·9	$\cdot 0^{6}4792$	$\cdot 0^{6}4554$	$\cdot 0^{6}4327$	$\cdot 0^{6}4111$	$\cdot 0^{6}3906$	$\cdot 0^{6}3711$	$\cdot 0^{6}3525$	$\cdot 0^{6}3348$	$\cdot 0^{6}3179$	$\cdot 0^{6}3019$

Example: $\Phi(-3{\cdot}57) = \cdot 0^{3}1785 = 0{\cdot}0001785.$

Table I. The Cumulative Standardized Normal Distribution Function (*continued*)

$$\Phi(u) = \frac{1}{\sqrt{2\pi}}\int_{-\infty}^{u} e^{-\frac{x^2}{2}}dx \quad \text{FOR} \quad 0{\cdot}00 \le u \le 4{\cdot}99.$$

u	·00	·01	·02	·03	·04	·05	·06	·07	·08	·09
·0	·5000	·5040	·5080	·5120	·5160	·5199	·5239	·5279	·5319	·5359
·1	·5398	·5438	·5478	·5517	·5557	·5596	·5636	·5675	·5714	·5753
·2	·5793	·5832	·5871	·5910	·5948	·5987	·6026	·6064	·6103	·6141
·3	·6179	·6217	·6255	·6293	·6331	·6368	·6406	·6443	·6480	·6517
·4	·6554	·6591	·6628	·6664	·6700	·6736	·6772	·6808	·6844	·6879
·5	·6915	·6950	·6985	·7019	·7054	·7088	·7123	·7157	·7190	·7224
·6	·7257	·7291	·7324	·7357	·7389	·7422	·7454	·7486	·7517	·7549
·7	·7580	·7611	·7642	·7673	·7703	·7734	·7764	·7794	·7823	·7852
·8	·7881	·7910	·7939	·7967	·7995	·8023	·8051	·8078	·8106	·8133
·9	·8159	·8186	·8212	·8238	·8264	·8289	·8315	·8340	·8365	·8389
1·0	·8413	·8438	·8461	·8485	·8508	·8531	·8554	·8577	·8599	·8621
1·1	·8643	·8665	·8686	·8708	·8729	·8749	·8770	·8790	·8810	·8830
1·2	·8849	·8869	·8888	·8907	·8925	·8944	·8962	·8980	·8997	·90147
1·3	·90320	·90490	·90658	·90824	·90988	·91149	·91309	·91466	·91621	·91774
1·4	·91924	·92073	·92220	·92364	·92507	·92647	·92785	·92922	·93056	·93189
1·5	·93319	·93448	·93574	·93699	·93822	·93943	·94062	·94179	·94295	·94408
1·6	·94520	·94630	·94738	·94845	·94950	·95053	·95154	·95254	·95352	·95449
1·7	·95543	·95637	·95728	·95818	·95907	·95994	·96080	·96164	·96246	·96327
1·8	·96407	·96485	·96562	·96638	·96712	·96784	·96856	·96926	·96995	·97062
1·9	·97128	·97193	·97257	·97320	·97381	·97441	·97500	·97558	·97615	·97670
2·0	·97725	·97778	·97831	·97882	·97932	·97982	·98030	·98077	·98124	·98169
2·1	·98214	·98257	·98300	·98341	·98382	·98422	·98461	·98500	·98537	·98574
2·2	·98610	·98645	·98679	·98713	·98745	·98778	·98809	·98840	·98870	·98899
2·3	·98928	·98956	·98983	$\cdot 9^2 0097$	$\cdot 9^2 0358$	$\cdot 9^2 0613$	$\cdot 9^2 0863$	$\cdot 9^2 1106$	$\cdot 9^2 1344$	$\cdot 9^2 1576$
2·4	$\cdot 9^2 1802$	$\cdot 9^2 2024$	$\cdot 9^2 2240$	$\cdot 9^2 2451$	$\cdot 9^2 2656$	$\cdot 9^2 2857$	$\cdot 9^2 3053$	$\cdot 9^2 3244$	$\cdot 9^2 3431$	$\cdot 9^2 3613$
2·5	$\cdot 9^2 3790$	$\cdot 9^2 3963$	$\cdot 9^2 4132$	$\cdot 9^2 4297$	$\cdot 9^2 4457$	$\cdot 9^2 4614$	$\cdot 9^2 4766$	$\cdot 9^2 4915$	$\cdot 9^2 5060$	$\cdot 9^2 5201$
2·6	$\cdot 9^2 5339$	$\cdot 9^2 5473$	$\cdot 9^2 5604$	$\cdot 9^2 5731$	$\cdot 9^2 5855$	$\cdot 9^2 5975$	$\cdot 9^2 6093$	$\cdot 9^2 6207$	$\cdot 9^2 6319$	$\cdot 9^2 6427$
2·7	$\cdot 9^2 6533$	$\cdot 9^2 6636$	$\cdot 9^2 6736$	$\cdot 9^2 6833$	$\cdot 9^2 6928$	$\cdot 9^2 7020$	$\cdot 9^2 7110$	$\cdot 9^2 7197$	$\cdot 9^2 7282$	$\cdot 9^2 7365$
2·8	$\cdot 9^2 7445$	$\cdot 9^2 7523$	$\cdot 9^2 7599$	$\cdot 9^2 7673$	$\cdot 9^2 7744$	$\cdot 9^2 7814$	$\cdot 9^2 7882$	$\cdot 9^2 7948$	$\cdot 9^2 8012$	$\cdot 9^2 8074$
2·9	$\cdot 9^2 8134$	$\cdot 9^2 8193$	$\cdot 9^2 8250$	$\cdot 9^2 8305$	$\cdot 9^2 8359$	$\cdot 9^2 8411$	$\cdot 9^2 8462$	$\cdot 9^2 8511$	$\cdot 9^2 8559$	$\cdot 9^2 8605$
3·0	$\cdot 9^2 8650$	$\cdot 9^2 8694$	$\cdot 9^2 8736$	$\cdot 9^2 8777$	$\cdot 9^2 8817$	$\cdot 9^2 8856$	$\cdot 9^2 8893$	$\cdot 9^2 8930$	$\cdot 9^2 8965$	$\cdot 9^2 8999$
3·1	$\cdot 9^3 0324$	$\cdot 9^3 0646$	$\cdot 9^3 0957$	$\cdot 9^3 1260$	$\cdot 9^3 1553$	$\cdot 9^3 1836$	$\cdot 9^3 2112$	$\cdot 9^3 2378$	$\cdot 9^3 2636$	$\cdot 9^3 2886$
3·2	$\cdot 9^3 3129$	$\cdot 9^3 3363$	$\cdot 9^3 3590$	$\cdot 9^3 3810$	$\cdot 9^3 4024$	$\cdot 9^3 4230$	$\cdot 9^3 4429$	$\cdot 9^3 4623$	$\cdot 9^3 4810$	$\cdot 9^3 4991$
3·3	$\cdot 9^3 5166$	$\cdot 9^3 5335$	$\cdot 9^3 5499$	$\cdot 9^3 5658$	$\cdot 9^3 5811$	$\cdot 9^3 5959$	$\cdot 9^3 6103$	$\cdot 9^3 6242$	$\cdot 9^3 6376$	$\cdot 9^3 6505$
3·4	$\cdot 9^3 6631$	$\cdot 9^3 6752$	$\cdot 9^3 6869$	$\cdot 9^3 6982$	$\cdot 9^3 7091$	$\cdot 9^3 7197$	$\cdot 9^3 7299$	$\cdot 9^3 7398$	$\cdot 9^3 7493$	$\cdot 9^3 7585$
3·5	$\cdot 9^3 7674$	$\cdot 9^3 7759$	$\cdot 9^3 7842$	$\cdot 9^3 7922$	$\cdot 9^3 7999$	$\cdot 9^3 8074$	$\cdot 9^3 8146$	$\cdot 9^3 8215$	$\cdot 9^3 8282$	$\cdot 9^3 8347$
3·6	$\cdot 9^3 8409$	$\cdot 9^3 8469$	$\cdot 9^3 8527$	$\cdot 9^3 8583$	$\cdot 9^3 8637$	$\cdot 9^3 8689$	$\cdot 9^3 8739$	$\cdot 9^3 8787$	$\cdot 9^3 8834$	$\cdot 9^3 8879$
3·7	$\cdot 9^3 8922$	$\cdot 9^3 8964$	$\cdot 9^4 0039$	$\cdot 9^4 0426$	$\cdot 9^4 0799$	$\cdot 9^4 1158$	$\cdot 9^4 1504$	$\cdot 9^4 1838$	$\cdot 9^4 2159$	$\cdot 9^4 2468$
3·8	$\cdot 9^4 2765$	$\cdot 9^4 3052$	$\cdot 9^4 3327$	$\cdot 9^4 3593$	$\cdot 9^4 3848$	$\cdot 9^4 4094$	$\cdot 9^4 4331$	$\cdot 9^4 4558$	$\cdot 9^4 4777$	$\cdot 9^4 4988$
3·9	$\cdot 9^4 5190$	$\cdot 9^4 5385$	$\cdot 9^4 5573$	$\cdot 9^4 5753$	$\cdot 9^4 5926$	$\cdot 9^4 6092$	$\cdot 9^4 6253$	$\cdot 9^4 6406$	$\cdot 9^4 6554$	$\cdot 9^4 6696$
4·0	$\cdot 9^4 6833$	$\cdot 9^4 6964$	$\cdot 9^4 7090$	$\cdot 9^4 7211$	$\cdot 9^4 7327$	$\cdot 9^4 7439$	$\cdot 9^4 7546$	$\cdot 9^4 7649$	$\cdot 9^4 7748$	$\cdot 9^4 7843$
4·1	$\cdot 9^4 7934$	$\cdot 9^4 8022$	$\cdot 9^4 8106$	$\cdot 9^4 8186$	$\cdot 9^4 8263$	$\cdot 9^4 8338$	$\cdot 9^4 8409$	$\cdot 9^4 8477$	$\cdot 9^4 8542$	$\cdot 9^4 8605$
4·2	$\cdot 9^4 8665$	$\cdot 9^4 8723$	$\cdot 9^4 8778$	$\cdot 9^4 8832$	$\cdot 9^4 8882$	$\cdot 9^4 8931$	$\cdot 9^4 8978$	$\cdot 9^5 0226$	$\cdot 9^5 0655$	$\cdot 9^5 1066$
4·3	$\cdot 9^5 1460$	$\cdot 9^5 1837$	$\cdot 9^5 2199$	$\cdot 9^5 2545$	$\cdot 9^5 2876$	$\cdot 9^5 3193$	$\cdot 9^5 3497$	$\cdot 9^5 3788$	$\cdot 9^5 4066$	$\cdot 9^5 4332$
4·4	$\cdot 9^5 4587$	$\cdot 9^5 4831$	$\cdot 9^5 5065$	$\cdot 9^5 5288$	$\cdot 9^5 5502$	$\cdot 9^5 5706$	$\cdot 9^5 5902$	$\cdot 9^5 6089$	$\cdot 9^5 6268$	$\cdot 9^5 6439$
4·5	$\cdot 9^5 6602$	$\cdot 9^5 6759$	$\cdot 9^5 6908$	$\cdot 9^5 7051$	$\cdot 9^5 7187$	$\cdot 9^5 7318$	$\cdot 9^5 7442$	$\cdot 9^5 7561$	$\cdot 9^5 7675$	$\cdot 9^5 7784$
4·6	$\cdot 9^5 7888$	$\cdot 9^5 7987$	$\cdot 9^5 8081$	$\cdot 9^5 8172$	$\cdot 9^5 8258$	$\cdot 9^5 8340$	$\cdot 9^5 8419$	$\cdot 9^5 8494$	$\cdot 9^5 8566$	$\cdot 9^5 8634$
4·7	$\cdot 9^5 8699$	$\cdot 9^5 8761$	$\cdot 9^5 8821$	$\cdot 9^5 8877$	$\cdot 9^5 8931$	$\cdot 9^5 8983$	$\cdot 9^6 0320$	$\cdot 9^6 0789$	$\cdot 9^6 1235$	$\cdot 9^6 1661$
4·8	$\cdot 9^6 2067$	$\cdot 9^6 2453$	$\cdot 9^6 2822$	$\cdot 9^6 3173$	$\cdot 9^6 3508$	$\cdot 9^6 3827$	$\cdot 9^6 4131$	$\cdot 9^6 4420$	$\cdot 9^6 4696$	$\cdot 9^6 4958$
4·9	$\cdot 9^6 5208$	$\cdot 9^6 5446$	$\cdot 9^6 5673$	$\cdot 9^6 5889$	$\cdot 9^6 6094$	$\cdot 9^6 6289$	$\cdot 9^6 6475$	$\cdot 9^6 6652$	$\cdot 9^6 6821$	$\cdot 9^6 6981$

Example: $\Phi(3{\cdot}57) = \cdot 9^3 8215 = 0{\cdot}9998215.$

* Abridged from Table II of *Statistical Tables and Formulas* by A. Hald, John Wiley & Sons, New York, 1952.

Table II. Percentage Points of the *t* Distribution*

f \ P	0.750	0.900	0.950	0.975	0.990	0.995	0.999
1	1.000	3.078	6.314	12.706	31.821	63.657	318
2	0.816	1.886	2.920	4.303	6.965	9.925	22.3
3	0.765	1.638	2.353	3.182	4.541	5.841	10.2
4	0.741	1.533	2.132	2.776	3.747	4.604	7.173
5	0.727	1.476	2.015	2.571	3.365	4.032	5.893
6	0.718	1.440	1.943	2.447	3.143	3.707	5.208
7	0.711	1.415	1.895	2.365	2.998	3.499	4.785
8	0.706	1.397	1.860	2.306	2.896	3.355	4.501
9	0.703	1.383	1.833	2.262	2.821	3.250	4.297
10	0.700	1.372	1.812	2.228	2.764	3.169	4.144
11	0.697	1.363	1.796	2.201	2.718	3.106	4.025
12	0.695	1.356	1.782	2.179	2.681	3.055	3.930
13	0.694	1.350	1.771	2.160	2.650	3.012	3.852
14	0.692	1.345	1.761	2.145	2.624	2.977	3.787
15	0.691	1.341	1.753	2.131	2.602	2.947	3.733
16	0.690	1.337	1.746	2.120	2.583	2.921	3.686
17	0.689	1.333	1.740	2.110	2.567	2.898	3.646
18	0.688	1.330	1.734	2.101	2.552	2.878	3.610
19	0.688	1.328	1.729	2.093	2.539	2.861	3.579
20	0.687	1.325	1.725	2.086	2.528	2.845	3.552
21	0.686	1.323	1.721	2.080	2.518	2.831	3.527
22	0.686	1.321	1.717	2.074	2.508	2.819	3.505
23	0.685	1.319	1.714	2.069	2.500	2.807	3.485
24	0.685	1.318	1.711	2.064	2.492	2.797	3.467
25	0.684	1.316	1.708	2.060	2.485	2.787	3.450
26	0.684	1.315	1.706	2.056	2.479	2.779	3.435
27	0.684	1.314	1.703	2.052	2.473	2.771	3.421
28	0.683	1.313	1.701	2.048	2.467	2.763	3.408
29	0.683	1.311	1.699	2.045	2.462	2.756	3.396
30	0.683	1.310	1.697	2.042	2.457	2.750	3.385
40	0.681	1.303	1.684	2.021	2.423	2.704	3.307
60	0.679	1.296	1.671	2.000	2.390	2.660	3.232
120	0.677	1.289	1.658	1.980	2.358	2.617	3.160
∞	0.674	1.282	1.645	1.960	2.326	2.576	3.090

*Abridged from Table 12 of *Biometrika Tables for Statisticians*, vol. I, edited by E. S. Pearson and H. O. Hartley, Cambridge University Press, Cambridge (1954), and Table III of *Statistical Tables for Biological, Agricultural, and Medical Research*, R. A. Fisher and F. Yates, Oliver & Boyd, Edinburgh, 1953.

Table III. Percentage Points of the χ^2 Distribution*

f \ P	0.005	0.025	0.050	0.900	0.950	0.975	0.990	0.995	0.999
1	$.0^4393$	$.0^3982$	$.0^2393$	2.71	3.84	5.02	6.63	7.88	10.8
2	.0100	.0506	.103	4.61	5.99	7.38	9.21	10.6	13.8
3	.0717	.216	.352	6.25	7.81	9.35	11.3	12.8	16.3
4	.207	.484	.711	7.78	9.49	11.1	13.3	14.9	18.5
5	.412	.831	1.15	9.24	11.1	12.8	15.1	16.7	20.5
6	.676	1.24	1.64	10.6	12.6	14.4	16.8	18.5	22.5
7	.989	1.69	2.17	12.0	14.1	16.0	18.5	20.3	24.3
8	1.34	2.18	2.73	13.4	15.5	17.5	20.1	22.0	26.1
9	1.73	2.70	3.33	14.7	16.9	19.0	21.7	23.6	27.9
10	2.16	3.25	3.94	16.0	18.3	20.5	23.2	25.2	29.6
11	2.60	3.82	4.57	17.3	19.7	21.9	24.7	26.8	31.3
12	3.07	4.40	5.23	18.5	21.0	23.3	26.2	28.3	32.9
13	3.57	5.01	5.89	19.8	22.4	24.7	27.7	29.8	34.5
14	4.07	5.63	6.57	21.1	23.7	26.1	29.1	31.3	36.1
15	4.60	6.26	7.26	22.3	25.0	27.5	30.6	32.8	37.7
16	5.14	6.91	7.96	23.5	26.3	28.8	32.0	34.3	39.3
17	5.70	7.56	8.67	24.8	27.6	30.2	33.4	35.7	40.8
18	6.26	8.23	9.39	26.0	28.9	31.5	34.8	37.2	42.3
19	6.84	8.91	10.1	27.2	30.1	32.9	36.2	38.6	43.8
20	7.43	9.59	10.9	28.4	31.4	34.2	37.6	40.0	45.3
21	8.03	10.3	11.6	29.6	32.7	35.5	38.9	41.4	46.8
22	8.64	11.0	12.3	30.8	33.9	36.8	40.3	42.8	48.3
23	9.26	11.7	13.1	32.0	35.2	38.1	41.6	44.2	49.7
24	9.89	12.4	13.8	33.2	36.4	39.4	43.0	45.6	51.2
25	10.5	13.1	14.6	34.4	37.7	40.6	44.3	46.9	52.6
26	11.2	13.8	15.4	35.6	38.9	41.9	45.6	48.3	54.1
27	11.8	14.6	16.2	36.7	40.1	43.2	47.0	49.6	55.5
28	12.5	15.3	16.9	37.9	41.3	44.5	48.3	51.0	56.9
29	13.1	16.0	17.7	39.1	42.6	45.7	49.6	52.3	58.3
30	13.8	16.8	18.5	40.3	43.8	47.0	50.9	53.7	59.7
35	17.2	20.6	22.5	46.1	49.8	53.2	57.3	60.3	66.6
40	20.7	24.4	26.5	51.8	55.8	59.3	63.7	66.8	73.4
45	24.3	28.4	30.6	57.5	61.7	65.4	70.0	73.2	80.1
50	28.0	32.4	34.8	63.2	67.5	71.4	76.2	79.5	86.7
75	47.2	52.9	56.1	91.1	96.2	100.8	106.4	110.3	118.6
100	67.3	74.2	77.9	118.5	124.3	129.6	135.8	140.2	149.4

*Abridged from Table V of *Statistical Tables and Formulas* by A. Hald, John Wiley & Sons, New York, New York (1952).

Table IV. Percentage Points of the F Distribution*

90 per cent points

f_2 \ f_1	1	2	3	4	5	6	7	8	9	10	12	15	20	24	30	40	60	120	∞
1	39.86	49.50	53.59	55.83	57.24	58.20	58.91	59.44	59.86	60.19	60.71	61.22	61.74	62.00	62.26	62.53	62.79	63.06	63.33
2	8.53	9.00	9.16	9.24	9.29	9.33	9.35	9.37	9.38	9.39	9.41	9.42	9.44	9.45	9.46	9.47	9.47	9.48	9.49
3	5.54	5.46	5.39	5.34	5.31	5.28	5.27	5.25	5.24	5.23	5.22	5.20	5.18	5.18	5.17	5.16	5.15	5.14	5.13
4	4.54	4.32	4.19	4.11	4.05	4.01	3.98	3.95	3.94	3.92	3.90	3.87	3.84	3.83	3.82	3.80	3.79	3.78	3.76
5	4.06	3.78	3.62	3.52	3.45	3.40	3.37	3.34	3.32	3.30	3.27	3.24	3.21	3.19	3.17	3.16	3.14	3.12	3.10
6	3.78	3.46	3.29	3.18	3.11	3.05	3.01	2.98	2.96	2.94	2.90	2.87	2.84	2.82	2.80	2.78	2.76	2.74	2.72
7	3.59	3.26	3.07	2.96	2.88	2.83	2.78	2.75	2.72	2.70	2.67	2.63	2.59	2.58	2.56	2.54	2.51	2.49	2.47
8	3.46	3.11	2.92	2.81	2.73	2.67	2.62	2.59	2.56	2.54	2.50	2.46	2.42	2.40	2.38	2.36	2.34	2.32	2.29
9	3.36	3.01	2.81	2.69	2.61	2.55	2.51	2.47	2.44	2.42	2.38	2.34	2.30	2.28	2.25	2.23	2.21	2.18	2.16
10	3.29	2.92	2.73	2.61	2.52	2.46	2.41	2.38	2.35	2.32	2.28	2.24	2.20	2.18	2.16	2.13	2.11	2.08	2.06
11	3.23	2.86	2.66	2.54	2.45	2.39	2.34	2.30	2.27	2.25	2.21	2.17	2.12	2.10	2.08	2.05	2.03	2.00	1.97
12	3.18	2.81	2.61	2.48	2.39	2.33	2.28	2.24	2.21	2.19	2.15	2.10	2.06	2.04	2.01	1.99	1.96	1.93	1.90
13	3.14	2.76	2.56	2.43	2.35	2.28	2.23	2.20	2.16	2.14	2.10	2.05	2.01	1.98	1.96	1.93	1.90	1.88	1.85
14	3.10	2.73	2.52	2.39	2.31	2.24	2.19	2.15	2.12	2.10	2.05	2.01	1.96	1.94	1.91	1.89	1.86	1.83	1.80
15	3.07	2.70	2.49	2.36	2.27	2.21	2.16	2.12	2.09	2.06	2.02	1.97	1.92	1.90	1.87	1.85	1.82	1.79	1.76
16	3.05	2.67	2.46	2.33	2.24	2.18	2.13	2.09	2.06	2.03	1.99	1.94	1.89	1.87	1.84	1.81	1.78	1.75	1.72
17	3.03	2.64	2.44	2.31	2.22	2.15	2.10	2.06	2.03	2.00	1.96	1.91	1.86	1.84	1.81	1.78	1.75	1.72	1.69
18	3.01	2.62	2.42	2.29	2.20	2.13	2.08	2.04	2.00	1.98	1.93	1.89	1.84	1.81	1.78	1.75	1.72	1.69	1.66
19	2.99	2.61	2.40	2.27	2.18	2.11	2.06	2.02	1.98	1.96	1.91	1.86	1.81	1.79	1.76	1.73	1.70	1.67	1.63
20	2.97	2.59	2.38	2.25	2.16	2.09	2.04	2.00	1.96	1.94	1.89	1.84	1.79	1.77	1.74	1.71	1.68	1.64	1.61
21	2.96	2.57	2.36	2.23	2.14	2.08	2.02	1.98	1.95	1.92	1.87	1.83	1.78	1.75	1.72	1.69	1.66	1.62	1.59
22	2.95	2.56	2.35	2.22	2.13	2.06	2.01	1.97	1.93	1.90	1.86	1.81	1.76	1.73	1.70	1.67	1.64	1.60	1.57
23	2.94	2.55	2.34	2.21	2.11	2.05	1.99	1.95	1.92	1.89	1.84	1.80	1.74	1.72	1.69	1.66	1.62	1.59	1.55
24	2.93	2.54	2.33	2.19	2.10	2.04	1.98	1.94	1.91	1.88	1.83	1.78	1.73	1.70	1.67	1.64	1.61	1.57	1.53
25	2.92	2.53	2.32	2.18	2.09	2.02	1.97	1.93	1.89	1.87	1.82	1.77	1.72	1.69	1.66	1.63	1.59	1.56	1.52
26	2.91	2.52	2.31	2.17	2.08	2.01	1.96	1.92	1.88	1.86	1.81	1.76	1.71	1.68	1.65	1.61	1.58	1.54	1.50
27	2.90	2.51	2.30	2.17	2.07	2.00	1.95	1.91	1.87	1.85	1.80	1.75	1.70	1.67	1.64	1.60	1.57	1.53	1.49
28	2.89	2.50	2.29	2.16	2.06	2.00	1.94	1.90	1.87	1.84	1.79	1.74	1.69	1.66	1.63	1.59	1.56	1.52	1.48
29	2.89	2.50	2.28	2.15	2.06	1.99	1.93	1.89	1.86	1.83	1.78	1.73	1.68	1.65	1.62	1.58	1.55	1.51	1.47
30	2.88	2.49	2.28	2.14	2.05	1.98	1.93	1.88	1.85	1.82	1.77	1.72	1.67	1.64	1.61	1.57	1.54	1.50	1.46
40	2.84	2.44	2.23	2.09	2.00	1.93	1.87	1.83	1.79	1.76	1.71	1.66	1.61	1.57	1.54	1.51	1.47	1.42	1.38
60	2.79	2.39	2.18	2.04	1.95	1.87	1.82	1.77	1.74	1.71	1.66	1.60	1.54	1.51	1.48	1.44	1.40	1.35	1.29
120	2.75	2.35	2.13	1.99	1.90	1.82	1.77	1.72	1.68	1.65	1.60	1.55	1.48	1.45	1.41	1.37	1.32	1.26	1.19
∞	2.71	2.30	2.08	1.94	1.85	1.77	1.72	1.67	1.63	1.60	1.55	1.49	1.42	1.38	1.34	1.30	1.24	1.17	1.00

95 per cent points

1	161.4	199.5	215.7	224.6	230.2	234.0	236.8	238.9	240.5	241.9	243.9	245.9	248.0	249.1	250.1	251.1	252.2	253.3	254.3
2	18.51	19.00	19.16	19.25	19.30	19.33	19.35	19.37	19.38	19.40	19.41	19.43	19.45	19.45	19.46	19.47	19.48	19.49	19.50
3	10.13	9.55	9.28	9.12	9.01	8.94	8.89	8.85	8.81	8.79	8.74	8.70	8.66	8.64	8.62	8.59	8.57	8.55	8.53
4	7.71	6.94	6.59	6.39	6.26	6.16	6.09	6.04	6.00	5.96	5.91	5.86	5.80	5.77	5.75	5.72	5.69	5.66	5.63
5	6.61	5.79	5.41	5.19	5.05	4.95	4.88	4.82	4.77	4.74	4.68	4.62	4.56	4.53	4.50	4.46	4.43	4.40	4.36
6	5.99	5.14	4.76	4.53	4.39	4.28	4.21	4.15	4.10	4.06	4.00	3.94	3.87	3.84	3.81	3.77	3.74	3.70	3.67
7	5.59	4.74	4.35	4.12	3.97	3.87	3.79	3.73	3.68	3.64	3.57	3.51	3.44	3.41	3.38	3.34	3.30	3.27	3.23
8	5.32	4.46	4.07	3.84	3.69	3.58	3.50	3.44	3.39	3.35	3.28	3.22	3.15	3.12	3.08	3.04	3.01	2.97	2.93
9	5.12	4.26	3.86	3.63	3.48	3.37	3.29	3.23	3.18	3.14	3.07	3.01	2.94	2.90	2.86	2.83	2.79	2.75	2.71
10	4.96	4.10	3.71	3.48	3.33	3.22	3.14	3.07	3.02	2.98	2.91	2.85	2.77	2.74	2.70	2.66	2.62	2.58	2.54
11	4.84	3.98	3.59	3.36	3.20	3.09	3.01	2.95	2.90	2.85	2.79	2.72	2.65	2.61	2.57	2.53	2.49	2.45	2.40
12	4.75	3.89	3.49	3.26	3.11	3.00	2.91	2.85	2.80	2.75	2.69	2.62	2.54	2.51	2.47	2.43	2.38	2.34	2.30
13	4.67	3.81	3.41	3.18	3.03	2.92	2.83	2.77	2.71	2.67	2.60	2.53	2.46	2.42	2.38	2.34	2.30	2.25	2.21
14	4.60	3.74	3.34	3.11	2.96	2.85	2.76	2.70	2.65	2.60	2.53	2.46	2.39	2.35	2.31	2.27	2.22	2.18	2.13
15	4.54	3.68	3.29	3.06	2.90	2.79	2.71	2.64	2.59	2.54	2.48	2.40	2.33	2.29	2.25	2.20	2.16	2.11	2.07
16	4.49	3.63	3.24	3.01	2.85	2.74	2.66	2.59	2.54	2.49	2.42	2.35	2.28	2.24	2.19	2.15	2.11	2.06	2.01
17	4.45	3.59	3.20	2.96	2.81	2.70	2.61	2.55	2.49	2.45	2.38	2.31	2.23	2.19	2.15	2.10	2.06	2.01	1.96
18	4.41	3.55	3.16	2.93	2.77	2.66	2.58	2.51	2.46	2.41	2.34	2.27	2.19	2.15	2.11	2.06	2.02	1.97	1.92
19	4.38	3.52	3.13	2.90	2.74	2.63	2.54	2.48	2.42	2.38	2.31	2.23	2.16	2.11	2.07	2.03	1.98	1.93	1.88
20	4.35	3.49	3.10	2.87	2.71	2.60	2.51	2.45	2.39	2.35	2.28	2.20	2.12	2.08	2.04	1.99	1.95	1.90	1.84
21	4.32	3.47	3.07	2.84	2.68	2.57	2.49	2.42	2.37	2.32	2.25	2.18	2.10	2.05	2.01	1.96	1.92	1.87	1.81
22	4.30	3.44	3.05	2.82	2.66	2.55	2.46	2.40	2.34	2.30	2.23	2.15	2.07	2.03	1.98	1.94	1.89	1.84	1.78
23	4.28	3.42	3.03	2.80	2.64	2.53	2.44	2.37	2.32	2.27	2.20	2.13	2.05	2.01	1.96	1.91	1.86	1.81	1.76
24	4.26	3.40	3.01	2.78	2.62	2.51	2.42	2.36	2.30	2.25	2.18	2.11	2.03	1.98	1.94	1.89	1.84	1.79	1.73
25	4.24	3.39	2.99	2.76	2.60	2.49	2.40	2.34	2.28	2.24	2.16	2.09	2.01	1.96	1.92	1.87	1.82	1.77	1.71
26	4.23	3.37	2.98	2.74	2.59	2.47	2.39	2.32	2.27	2.22	2.15	2.07	1.99	1.95	1.90	1.85	1.80	1.75	1.69
27	4.21	3.35	2.96	2.73	2.57	2.46	2.37	2.31	2.25	2.20	2.13	2.06	1.97	1.93	1.88	1.84	1.79	1.73	1.67
28	4.20	3.34	2.95	2.71	2.56	2.45	2.36	2.29	2.24	2.19	2.12	2.04	1.96	1.91	1.87	1.82	1.77	1.71	1.65
29	4.18	3.33	2.93	2.70	2.55	2.43	2.35	2.28	2.22	2.18	2.10	2.03	1.94	1.90	1.85	1.81	1.75	1.70	1.64
30	4.17	3.32	2.92	2.69	2.53	2.42	2.33	2.27	2.21	2.16	2.09	2.01	1.93	1.89	1.84	1.79	1.74	1.68	1.62
40	4.08	3.23	2.84	2.61	2.45	2.34	2.25	2.18	2.12	2.08	2.00	1.92	1.84	1.79	1.74	1.69	1.64	1.58	1.51
60	4.00	3.15	2.76	2.53	2.37	2.25	2.17	2.10	2.04	1.99	1.92	1.84	1.75	1.70	1.65	1.59	1.53	1.47	1.39
120	3.92	3.07	2.68	2.45	2.29	2.17	2.09	2.02	1.96	1.91	1.83	1.75	1.66	1.61	1.55	1.50	1.43	1.35	1.25
∞	3.84	3.00	2.60	2.37	2.21	2.10	2.01	1.94	1.88	1.83	1.75	1.67	1.57	1.52	1.46	1.39	1.32	1.22	1.00

Table IV. Percentage Points of the F Distribution (*continued*)

97.5 per cent points

f_2 \ f_1	1	2	3	4	5	6	7	8	9	10	12	15	20	24	30	40	60	120	∞
1	647.8	799.5	864.2	899.6	921.8	937.1	948.2	956.7	963.3	968.6	976.7	984.9	993.1	997.2	1001	1006	1010	1014	1018
2	38.51	39.00	39.17	39.25	39.30	39.33	39.36	39.37	39.39	39.40	39.41	39.43	39.45	39.46	39.46	39.47	39.48	39.49	39.50
3	17.44	16.04	15.44	15.10	14.88	14.73	14.62	14.54	14.47	14.42	14.34	14.25	14.17	14.12	14.08	14.04	13.99	13.95	13.90
4	12.22	10.65	9.98	9.60	9.36	9.20	9.07	8.98	8.90	8.84	8.75	8.66	8.56	8.51	8.46	8.41	8.36	8.31	8.26
5	10.01	8.43	7.76	7.39	7.15	6.98	6.85	6.76	6.68	6.62	6.52	6.43	6.33	6.28	6.23	6.18	6.12	6.07	6.02
6	8.81	7.26	6.60	6.23	5.99	5.82	5.70	5.60	5.52	5.46	5.37	5.27	5.17	5.12	5.07	5.01	4.96	4.90	4.85
7	8.07	6.54	5.89	5.52	5.29	5.12	4.99	4.90	4.82	4.76	4.67	4.57	4.47	4.42	4.36	4.31	4.25	4.20	4.14
8	7.57	6.06	5.42	5.05	4.82	4.65	4.53	4.43	4.36	4.30	4.20	4.10	4.00	3.95	3.89	3.84	3.78	3.73	3.67
9	7.21	5.71	5.08	4.72	4.48	4.32	4.20	4.10	4.03	3.96	3.87	3.77	3.67	3.61	3.56	3.51	3.45	3.39	3.33
10	6.94	5.46	4.83	4.47	4.24	4.07	3.95	3.85	3.78	3.72	3.62	3.52	3.42	3.37	3.31	3.26	3.20	3.14	3.08
11	6.72	5.26	4.63	4.28	4.04	3.88	3.76	3.66	3.59	3.53	3.43	3.33	3.23	3.17	3.12	3.06	3.00	2.94	2.88
12	6.55	5.10	4.47	4.12	3.89	3.73	3.61	3.51	3.44	3.37	3.28	3.18	3.07	3.02	2.96	2.91	2.85	2.79	2.72
13	6.41	4.97	4.35	4.00	3.77	3.60	3.48	3.39	3.31	3.25	3.15	3.05	2.95	2.89	2.84	2.78	2.72	2.66	2.60
14	6.30	4.86	4.24	3.89	3.66	3.50	3.38	3.29	3.21	3.15	3.05	2.95	2.84	2.79	2.73	2.67	2.61	2.55	2.49
15	6.20	4.77	4.15	3.80	3.58	3.41	3.29	3.20	3.12	3.06	2.96	2.86	2.76	2.70	2.64	2.59	2.52	2.46	2.40
16	6.12	4.69	4.08	3.73	3.50	3.34	3.22	3.12	3.05	2.99	2.89	2.79	2.68	2.63	2.57	2.51	2.45	2.38	2.32
17	6.04	4.62	4.01	3.66	3.44	3.28	3.16	3.06	2.98	2.92	2.82	2.72	2.62	2.56	2.50	2.44	2.38	2.32	2.25
18	5.98	4.56	3.95	3.61	3.38	3.22	3.10	3.01	2.93	2.87	2.77	2.67	2.56	2.50	2.44	2.38	2.32	2.26	2.19
19	5.92	4.51	3.90	3.56	3.33	3.17	3.05	2.96	2.88	2.82	2.72	2.62	2.51	2.45	2.39	2.33	2.27	2.20	2.13
20	5.87	4.46	3.86	3.51	3.29	3.13	3.01	2.91	2.84	2.77	2.68	2.57	2.46	2.41	2.35	2.29	2.22	2.16	2.09
21	5.83	4.42	3.82	3.48	3.25	3.09	2.97	2.87	2.80	2.73	2.64	2.53	2.42	2.37	2.31	2.25	2.18	2.11	2.04
22	5.79	4.38	3.78	3.44	3.22	3.05	2.93	2.84	2.76	2.70	2.60	2.50	2.39	2.33	2.27	2.21	2.14	2.08	2.00
23	5.75	4.35	3.75	3.41	3.18	3.02	2.90	2.81	2.73	2.67	2.57	2.47	2.36	2.30	2.24	2.18	2.11	2.04	1.97
24	5.72	4.32	3.72	3.38	3.15	2.99	2.87	2.78	2.70	2.64	2.54	2.44	2.33	2.27	2.21	2.15	2.08	2.01	1.94
25	5.69	4.29	3.69	3.35	3.13	2.97	2.85	2.75	2.68	2.61	2.51	2.41	2.30	2.24	2.18	2.12	2.05	1.98	1.91
26	5.66	4.27	3.67	3.33	3.10	2.94	2.82	2.73	2.65	2.59	2.49	2.39	2.28	2.22	2.16	2.09	2.03	1.95	1.88
27	5.63	4.24	3.65	3.31	3.08	3.92	2.80	2.71	2.63	2.57	2.47	2.36	2.25	2.19	2.13	2.07	2.00	1.93	1.85
28	5.61	4.22	3.63	3.29	3.06	2.90	2.78	2.69	2.61	2.55	2.45	2.34	2.23	2.17	2.11	2.05	1.98	1.91	1.83
29	5.59	4.20	3.61	3.27	3.04	2.88	2.76	2.67	2.59	2.53	2.43	2.32	2.21	2.15	2.09	2.03	1.96	1.89	1.81
30	5.57	4.18	3.59	3.25	3.03	2.87	2.75	2.65	2.57	2.51	2.41	2.31	2.20	2.14	2.07	2.01	1.94	1.87	1.79
40	5.42	4.05	3.46	3.13	2.90	2.74	2.62	2.53	2.45	2.39	2.29	2.18	2.07	2.01	1.94	1.88	1.80	1.72	1.64
60	5.29	3.93	3.34	3.01	2.79	2.63	2.51	2.41	2.33	2.27	2.17	2.06	1.94	1.88	1.82	1.74	1.67	1.58	1.48
120	5.15	3.80	3.23	2.89	2.67	2.52	2.39	2.30	2.22	2.16	2.05	1.94	1.82	1.76	1.69	1.61	1.53	14.3	1.31
∞	5.02	3.69	3.12	2.79	2.57	2.41	2.29	2.19	2.11	2.05	1.94	1.83	1.71	1.64	1.57	1.48	1.39	1.27	1.00

99 per cent points

1	4052	4999.5	5403	5625	5764	5859	5928	5982	6022	6056	6106	6157	6209	6235	6261	6287	6313	6339	6366
2	98.50	99.00	99.17	99.25	99.30	99.33	99.36	99.37	99.39	99.40	99.42	99.43	99.45	99.46	99.47	99.47	99.48	99.49	99.50
3	34.12	30.82	29.46	28.71	28.24	27.91	27.67	27.49	27.35	27.23	27.05	26.87	26.69	26.60	26.50	26.41	26.32	26.22	26.13
4	21.20	18.00	16.69	15.98	15.52	15.21	14.98	14.80	14.66	14 55	14.37	14.20	14.02	13.93	13.84	13.75	13.65	13.56	13.46
5	16.26	13.27	12.06	11.39	10.97	10.67	10.46	10.29	10.16	10.05	9.89	9.72	9.55	9.47	9.38	9.29	9.20	9.11	9.02
6	13.75	10.92	9.78	9.15	8.75	8.47	8.26	8.10	7.98	7.87	7.72	7.56	7.40	7.31	7.23	7.14	7.06	6.97	6.88
7	12.25	9.55	8.45	7.85	7.46	7.19	6.99	6.84	6.72	6.62	6.47	6.31	6.16	6.07	5.99	5.91	5.82	5.74	5.65
8	11.26	8.65	7.59	7.01	6.63	6.37	6.18	6.03	5.91	5.81	5.67	5.52	5.36	5.28	5.20	5.12	5.03	4.95	4.86
9	10.56	8.02	6.99	6.42	6.06	5.80	5.61	5.47	5.35	5.26	5.11	4.96	4.81	4.73	4.65	4.57	4.48	4.40	4.31
10	10.04	7.56	6.55	5.99	5.64	5.39	5.20	5.06	4.94	4.85	4.71	4.56	4.41	4.33	4.25	4.17	4.08	4.00	3.91
11	9.65	7.21	6.22	5.67	5.32	5.07	4.89	4.74	4.63	4.54	4.40	4.25	4.10	4.02	3.94	3.86	4.78	3.69	3.60
12	9.33	6 93	5.95	5.41	5.06	4.82	4.64	4.50	4.39	4.30	4.16	4.01	3.86	3.78	3.70	3.62	3.54	3.45	3.36
13	9.07	6.70	5.74	5.21	4.86	4.62	4.44	4.30	4.19	3.10	3.96	3.82	3.66	3.59	3.51	3.43	3.34	3.25	3.17
14	8.86	6.51	5.56	5.04	4.69	4.46	4.28	4.14	4.03	3.94	3.80	3.66	3.51	3.43	3.35	3.27	3.18	3.09	3.00
15	8.68	6.36	5.42	4.89	4.56	4.32	4.14	4.00	3.89	3.80	3.67	3.52	3.37	3.29	3.21	3.13	3.05	2.96	2.87
16	8.53	6.23	5.29	4.77	4.44	4.20	4.03	3.89	3.78	3.69	3.55	3.41	3.26	3.18	3.10	3.02	2.93	2.84	2.75
17	8.40	6.11	5.18	4.67	4.34	4.10	3.93	3.79	3.68	3.59	3.46	3.31	3.16	3.08	3.00	2.92	2.83	2.75	2.65
18	8.29	6.01	5.09	4.58	4.25	4.01	3.84	3.71	3.60	3.51	3.37	3.23	3.08	3.00	2.92	2.84	2.75	2.66	2.57
19	8.18	5.93	5.01	4.50	4.17	3.94	3.77	3.63	3.52	3.43	3.30	3.15	3.00	2.92	2.84	2.76	2.67	2.58	2.49
20	8.10	5.85	4.94	4.43	4.10	3.87	3.70	3.56	3.46	3.37	3.23	3.09	2.94	2.86	2.78	2.69	2.61	2.52	2.42
21	8.02	5.78	4.87	4.37	4.04	3.81	3.64	3.51	3.40	3.31	3.17	3.03	2.88	2.80	2.72	2.64	2.55	2.46	2.36
22	7.95	5.72	4.82	4.31	3.99	3.76	3.59	3.45	3.35	3.26	3.12	2.98	2.83	2.75	2.67	2.58	2.50	2.40	2.31
23	7.88	5.66	4.76	4.26	3.94	3.71	3.54	3.41	3.30	3.21	3.07	2.93	2.78	2.70	2.62	2.54	2.45	2.35	2.26
24	7.82	5.61	4.72	4.22	3.90	3.67	3.50	3.36	3.26	3.17	3.03	2.89	2.74	2.66	2.58	2.49	2.40	2.31	2.21
25	7.77	5.57	4.68	4.18	3.85	3.63	3.46	3.32	3.22	3.13	2.99	2.85	2.70	2.62	2.54	2.45	2.36	2.27	2.17
26	7.72	5.53	4.64	4.14	3.82	3.59	3.42	3.29	3.18	3.09	2.96	2.81	2.66	2.58	2.50	2.42	2.33	2.23	2.13
27	7.68	5.49	4.60	4.11	3.78	3.56	3.39	3.26	3.15	3.06	2.93	2.78	2.63	2.55	2.47	2.38	2.29	2.20	2.10
28	7.64	5.45	4.57	4.07	3.75	3.53	3.36	3.23	3.12	3.03	2.90	2.75	2.60	2.52	2.44	2.35	2.26	2.17	2.06
29	7.60	5.42	4.54	4.04	3.73	3.50	3.33	3.20	3.09	3.00	2.87	2.73	2.57	2.49	2.41	2.33	2.23	2.14	2.03
30	7.56	5.39	4.51	4.02	3.70	3.47	3.30	3.17	3.07	2.98	2.84	2.70	2.55	2.47	2.39	2.30	2.21	2.11	2.01
40	7.31	5.18	4.31	3.83	3.51	3.29	3.12	2.99	2.89	2.80	2.66	2.52	2.37	2.29	2.20	2.11	2.02	1.92	1.80
60	7.08	4.98	4.13	3.65	3.34	3.12	2.95	2.82	2.72	2.63	2.50	2.35	2.20	2.12	2.03	1.94	1.84	1.73	1.60
120	6.85	4.79	3.95	3.48	3.17	2.96	2.79	2.66	2.56	2.47	2.34	2.19	2.03	1.95	1.86	1.76	1.66	1.53	1.38
∞	6.63	4.61	3.78	3.32	3.02	2.80	2.64	2.51	2.41	2.32	2.18	2.04	1.88	1.79	1.70	1.59	1.47	1.32	1.00

Table IV. Percentage Points of the F Distribution (*continued*)

99.5 per cent points

f_2 \ f_1	1	2	3	4	5	6	7	8	9	10	12	15	20	24	30	40	60	120	∞
1	16211	20000	21615	22500	23056	23437	23715	23925	24091	24224	24426	24630	24836	24940	25044	25148	25253	25359	25465
2	198.5	199.0	199.2	199.2	199.3	199.3	199.4	199.4	199.4	199.4	199.4	199.4	199.4	199.5	199.5	199.5	199.5	199.5	199.5
3	55.55	49.80	47.47	46.19	45.39	44.84	44.43	44.13	43.88	43.69	43.39	43.08	42.78	42.62	42.47	42.31	42.15	41.99	41.83
4	31.33	26.28	24.26	23.15	22.46	21.97	21.62	21.35	21.14	20.97	20.70	20.44	20.17	20.03	19.89	19.75	19.61	19.47	19.32
5	22.78	18.31	16.53	15.56	14.94	14.51	14.20	13.96	13.77	13.62	13.38	13.15	12.90	12.78	12.66	12.53	12.40	12.27	12.14
6	18.63	14.54	12.92	12.03	11.46	11.07	10.79	10.57	10.39	10.25	10.03	9.81	9.59	9.47	9.36	9.24	9.12	9.00	8.88
7	16.24	12.40	10.88	10.05	9.52	9.16	8.89	8.68	8.51	8.38	8.18	7.97	7.75	7.65	7.53	7.42	7.31	7.19	7.08
8	14.69	11.04	9.60	8.81	8.30	7.95	7.69	7.50	7.34	7.21	7.01	6.81	6.61	6.50	6.40	6.29	6.18	6.06	5.95
9	13.61	10.11	8.72	7.96	7.47	7.13	6.88	6.69	6.54	6.42	6.23	6.03	5.83	5.73	5.62	5.52	5.41	5.30	5.19
10	12.83	9.43	8.08	7.34	6.87	6.54	6.30	6.12	5.97	5.85	5.66	5.47	5.27	5.17	5.07	4.97	4.86	4.75	4.64
11	12.23	8.91	7.60	6.88	6.42	6.10	5.86	5.68	5.54	5.42	5.24	5.05	4.86	4.76	4.65	4.55	4.44	4.34	4.23
12	11.75	8.51	7.23	6.52	6.07	5.76	5.52	5.35	5.20	5.09	4.91	4.72	4.53	4.43	4.33	4.23	4.12	4.01	3.90
13	11.37	8.19	6.93	6.23	5.79	5.48	5.25	5.08	4.94	4.82	4.64	4.46	4.27	4.17	4.07	3.97	3.87	3.76	3.65
14	11.06	7.92	6.68	6.00	5.56	5.26	5.03	4.86	4.72	4.60	4.43	4.25	4.06	3.96	3.86	3.76	3.66	3.55	3.44
15	10.80	7.70	6.48	5.80	5.37	5.07	4.85	4.67	4.54	4.42	4.25	4.07	3.88	3.79	3.69	3.58	3.48	3.37	3.26
16	10.58	7.51	6.30	5.64	5.21	4.91	4.69	4.52	4.38	4.27	4.10	3.92	3.73	3.64	3.54	3.44	3.33	3.22	3.11
17	10.38	7.35	6.16	5.50	5.07	4.78	4.56	4.39	4.25	4.14	3.97	3.79	3.61	3.51	3.41	3.31	3.21	3.10	2.98
18	10.22	7.21	6.03	5.37	4.96	4.66	4.44	4.28	4.14	4.03	3.86	3.68	3.50	3.40	3.30	3.20	3.10	2.99	2.87
19	10.07	7.09	5.92	5.27	4.85	4.56	4.34	4.18	4.04	3.93	3.76	3.59	3.40	3.31	3.21	3.11	3.00	2.89	2.78
20	9.94	6.99	5.82	5.17	4.76	4.47	4.26	4.09	3.96	3.85	3.68	3.50	3.32	3.22	3.12	3.02	2.92	2.81	2.69
21	9.83	6.89	5.73	5.09	4.68	4.39	4.18	4.01	3.88	3.77	3.60	3.43	3.24	3.15	3.05	2.95	2.84	2.73	2.61
22	9.73	6.81	5.65	5.02	4.61	4.32	4.11	3.94	3.81	3.70	3.54	3.36	3.18	3.08	2.98	2.88	2.77	2.66	2.55
23	9.63	6.73	5.58	4.95	4.54	4.26	4.05	3.88	3.75	3.64	3.47	3.30	3.12	3.02	2.92	2.82	2.71	2.60	2.48
24	9.55	6.66	5.52	4.89	4.49	4.20	3.99	3.83	3.69	3.59	3.42	3.25	3.06	2.97	2.87	2.77	2.66	2.55	2.43
25	9.48	6.60	5.46	4.84	4.43	4.15	3.94	3.78	3.64	3.54	3.37	3.20	3.01	2.92	2.82	2.72	2.61	2.50	2.38
26	9.41	6.54	5.41	4.79	4.38	4.10	3.89	3.73	3.60	3.49	3.33	3.15	2.97	2.87	2.77	2.67	2.56	2.45	2.33
27	9.34	6.49	5.36	4.74	4.34	4.06	3.85	3.69	3.56	3.45	3.28	3.11	2.93	2.83	2.73	2.63	2.52	2.41	2.29
28	9.28	6.44	5.32	4.70	4.30	4.02	3.81	3.65	3.52	3.41	3.25	3.07	2.89	2.79	2.69	2.59	2.48	2.37	2.25
29	9.23	6.40	5.28	4.66	4.26	3.98	3.77	3.61	3.48	3.38	3.21	3.04	2.86	2.76	2.66	2.56	2.45	2.33	2.21
30	9.18	6.35	5.24	4.62	4.23	3.95	3.74	3.58	3.45	3.34	3.18	3.01	2.82	2.73	2.63	2.52	2.42	2.30	2.18
40	8.83	6.07	4.98	4.37	3.99	3.71	3.51	3.35	3.22	3.12	2.95	2.78	2.60	2.50	2.40	2.30	2.18	2.06	1.93
60	8.49	5.79	4.73	4.14	3.76	3.49	3.29	3.13	3.01	2.90	2.74	2.57	2.39	2.29	2.19	2.08	1.96	1.83	1.69
120	8.18	5.54	4.50	3.92	3.55	3.28	3.09	2.93	2.81	2.71	2.54	2.37	2.19	2.09	1.98	1.87	1.75	1.61	1.43
∞	7.88	5.30	4.28	3.72	3.35	3.09	2.90	2.74	2.62	2.52	2.36	2.19	2.00	1.90	1.79	1.67	1.53	1.36	1.00

99.9 per cent points

1	4053†	5000†	5404†	5625†	5764†	5859†	5929†	5981†	6023†	6056†	6107†	6158†	6209†	6235†	6261†	6287†	6313†	6340†	6366†
2	998.5	999.0	999.2	999.2	999.3	999.3	999.4	999.4	999.4	999.4	999.4	999.4	999.4	999.5	999.5	999.5	999.5	999.5	999.5
3	167.0	148.5	141.1	137.1	134.6	132.8	131.6	130.6	129.9	129.2	128.3	127.4	126.4	125.9	125.4	125.0	124.5	124.0	123.5
4	74.14	61.25	56.18	53.44	51.71	50.53	49.66	49.00	48.47	48.05	47.41	46.76	46.10	45.77	45.43	45.09	44.75	44.40	44.05
5	47.18	37.12	33.20	31.09	29.75	28.84	28.16	27.64	27.24	26.92	26.42	25.91	25.39	25.14	24.87	24.60	24.33	24.06	23.79
6	35.51	27.00	23.70	21.92	20.81	20.03	19.46	19.03	18.69	18.41	17.99	17.56	17.12	16.89	16.67	16.44	16.21	15.99	15.75
7	29.25	21.69	18.77	17.19	16.21	15.52	15.02	14.63	14.33	14.08	13.71	13.32	12.93	12.73	12.53	12.33	12.12	11.91	11.70
8	25.42	18.49	15.83	14.39	13.49	12.86	12.40	12.04	11.77	11.54	11.19	10.84	10.48	10.30	10.11	9.92	9.73	9.53	9.33
9	22.86	16.39	13.90	12.56	11.71	11.13	10.70	10.37	10.11	9.89	9.57	9.24	8.90	8.72	8.55	8.37	8.19	8.00	7.81
10	21.04	14.91	12.55	11.28	10.48	9.92	9.52	9.20	8.96	8.75	8.45	8.13	7.80	7.64	7.47	7.30	7.12	6.94	6.76
11	19.69	13.81	11.56	10.35	9.58	9.05	8.66	8.35	8.12	7.92	7.63	7.32	7.01	6.85	6.68	6.52	6.35	6.17	6.00
12	18.64	12.97	10.80	9.63	8.89	8.38	8.00	7.71	7.48	7.29	7.00	6.71	6.40	6.25	6.09	5.93	5.76	5.59	5.42
13	17.81	12.31	10.21	9.07	8.35	7.86	7.49	7.21	6.98	6.80	6.52	6.23	5.93	5.78	5.63	5.47	5.30	5.14	4.97
14	17.14	11.78	9.73	8.62	7.92	7.43	7.08	6.80	6.58	6.40	6.13	5.85	5.56	5.41	5.25	5.10	4.94	4.77	4.60
15	16.59	11.34	9.34	8.25	7.57	7.09	6.74	6.47	6.26	6.08	5.81	5.54	5.25	5.10	4.95	4.80	4.64	4.47	4.31
16	16.12	10.97	9.00	7.94	7.27	6.81	6.46	6.19	5.98	5.81	5.55	5.27	4.99	4.85	4.70	4.54	4.39	4.23	4.06
17	15.72	10.66	8.73	7.68	7.02	7.56	6.22	5.96	5.75	5.58	5.32	5.05	4.78	4.63	4.48	4.33	4.18	4.02	3.85
18	15.38	10.39	8.49	7.46	6.81	6.35	6.02	5.76	5.56	5.39	5.13	4.87	4.59	4.45	4.30	4 15	4.00	3.84	3.67
19	15.08	10.16	8.28	7.26	6.62	6.18	5.85	5.59	5.39	5.22	4.97	4.70	4.43	4.29	4.14	3.99	3.84	3.68	3.51
20	14.82	9.95	8.10	7.10	6.46	6.02	5.69	5.44	5.24	5.08	4.82	4.56	4.29	4.15	4.00	3.86	3.70	3.54	3.38
21	14.59	9.77	7.94	6.95	6.32	5.88	5.56	5.31	5.11	4.95	4.70	4.44	4.17	4.03	3.88	3.74	3.58	3.42	3.26
22	14.38	9.61	7.80	6.81	6.19	5.76	5.44	5.19	4.99	4.83	4.58	4.33	4.06	3.92	3.78	3.63	3.48	3.32	3.15
23	14.19	9.47	7.67	6.69	6.08	5.65	5.33	5.09	4.89	4.73	4.48	4.23	3.96	3.82	3.68	3.53	3.38	3.22	3.05
24	14.03	9.34	7.55	6.59	5.98	5.55	5.23	4.99	4.80	4.64	4.39	4.14	3.87	3.74	3.59	3.45	3.29	3.14	2.97
25	13.88	9.22	7.45	6.49	5.88	5.46	5.15	4.91	4.71	4.56	4.31	4.06	3.79	3.66	3.52	3.37	3.22	3.06	2.89
26	13.74	9.12	7.36	6.41	5.80	5.38	5.07	4.83	4.64	4.48	4.24	3.99	3.72	3.59	3.44	3.30	3.15	2.99	2.82
27	13.61	9.02	7.27	6.33	5.73	5.31	5.00	4.76	4.57	4.41	4.17	3.92	3.66	3.52	3.38	3.23	3.08	2.92	2.75
28	13.50	8.93	7.19	6.25	5.66	5.24	4.93	4.69	4.50	4.35	4.11	3.86	3.60	3.46	3.32	3.18	3.02	2.86	2.69
29	13.39	8.85	7.12	6.19	5.59	5.18	4.87	4.64	4.45	4.29	4.05	3.80	3.54	3.41	3.27	3.12	2.97	2.81	2.64
30	13.29	8.77	7.05	6.12	5.53	5.12	4.82	4.58	4.39	4.24	4.00	3.75	3.49	3.36	3.22	3.07	2.92	2.76	2.59
40	12.61	8.25	6.60	5.70	5.13	4.73	4.44	4.21	4.02	3.87	3.64	3.40	3.15	3.01	2.87	2.73	2.57	2.41	2.23
60	11.97	7.76	6.17	5.31	4.76	4.37	4.09	3.87	3.69	3.54	3.31	3.08	2.83	2.69	2.55	2.41	2.25	2.08	1.89
120	11.38	7.32	5.79	4.95	4.42	4.04	3.77	3.55	3.38	3.24	3.02	2.78	2.53	2.40	2.26	2.11	1.95	1.76	1.54
∞	10.83	6.91	5.42	4.62	4.10	3.74	3.47	3.27	3.10	2.96	2.74	2.51	2.27	2.13	1.99	1.84	1.66	1.45	1.00

*Abridged from Table 18 of *Biometrika Tables for Statisticians*, vol. I, edited by E. S. Pearson and H. O. Hartley, Cambridge University Press, Cambridge, 1954, and Table V of *Statistical Tables for Biological, Agricultural, and Medical Research*, R. A. Fisher and F. Yates, Oliver & Boyd, Edinburgh, 1953.

†Multiply these entries by 100.

Table V. $y = 2 \arcsin \sqrt{x}$ *

	·000	·001	·002	·003	·004	·005	·006	·007	·008	·009
·00	0·0000	0·0633	0·0895	0·1096	0·1266	0·1415	0·1551	0·1675	0·1791	0·1900
·01	0·2003	0·2101	0·2195	0·2285	0·2372	0·2456	0·2537	0·2615	0·2691	0·2766
·02	0·2838	0·2909	0·2977	0·3045	0·3111	0·3176	0·3239	0·3301	0·3362	0·3423
·03	0·3482	0·3540	0·3597	0·3653	0·3709	0·3764	0·3818	0·3871	0·3924	0·3976
·04	0·4027	0·4078	0·4128	0·4178	0·4227	0·4275	0·4323	0·4371	0·4418	0·4464
·05	0·4510	0·4556	0·4601	0·4646	0·4690	0·4734	0·4778	0·4822	0·4864	0·4907
·06	0·4949	0·4991	0·5033	0·5074	0·5115	0·5156	0·5196	0·5236	0·5276	0·5316
·07	0·5355	0·5394	0·5433	0·5472	0·5510	0·5548	0·5586	0·5624	0·5661	0·5698
·08	0·5735	0·5772	0·5808	0·5845	0·5881	0·5917	0·5953	0·5988	0·6024	0·6059
·09	0·6094	0·6129	0·6163	0·6198	0·6232	0·6266	0·6300	0·6334	0·6368	0·6402
·10	0·6435	0·6468	0·6501	0·6534	0·6567	0·6600	0·6632	0·6665	0·6697	0·6729
·11	0·6761	0·6793	0·6825	0·6857	0·6888	0·6920	0·6951	0·6982	0·7013	0·7044
·12	0·7075	0·7106	0·7136	0·7167	0·7197	0·7227	0·7258	0·7288	0·7318	0·7347
·13	0·7377	0·7407	0·7437	0·7466	0·7495	0·7525	0·7554	0·7583	0·7612	0·7641
·14	0·7670	0·7699	0·7727	0·7756	0·7785	0·7813	0·7841	0·7870	0·7898	0·7926
·15	0·7954	0·7982	0·8010	0·8038	0·8065	0·8093	0·8121	0·8148	0·8176	0·8203
·16	0·8230	0·8258	0·8285	0·8312	0·8339	0·8366	0·8393	0·8420	0·8446	0·8473
·17	0·8500	0·8526	0·8553	0·8579	0·8606	0·8632	0·8658	0·8685	0·8711	0·8737
·18	0·8763	0·8789	0·8815	0·8841	0·8867	0·8892	0·8918	0·8944	0·8969	0·8995
·19	0·9021	0·9046	0·9071	0·9097	0·9122	0·9147	0·9173	0·9198	0·9223	0·9248
·20	0·9273	0·9298	0·9323	0·9348	0·9373	0·9397	0·9422	0·9447	0·9471	0·9496
·21	0·9521	0·9545	0·9570	0·9594	0·9619	0·9643	0·9667	0·9692	0·9716	0·9740
·22	0·9764	0·9788	0·9812	0·9836	0·9860	0·9884	0·9908	0·9932	0·9956	0·9980
·23	1·0004	1·0027	1·0051	1·0075	1·0098	1·0122	1·0146	1·0169	1·0193	1·0216
·24	1·0239	1·0263	1·0286	1·0310	1·0333	1·0356	1·0379	1·0403	1·0426	1·0449
·25	1·0472	1·0495	1·0518	1·0541	1·0564	1·0587	1·0610	1·0633	1·0656	1·0679
·26	1·0701	1·0724	1·0747	1·0770	1·0792	1·0815	1·0838	1·0860	1·0883	1·0905
·27	1·0928	1·0951	1·0973	1·0995	1·1018	1·1040	1·1063	1·1085	1·1107	1·1130
·28	1·1152	1·1174	1·1196	1·1219	1·1241	1·1263	1·1285	1·1307	1·1329	1·1351
·29	1·1373	1·1396	1·1418	1·1440	1·1461	1·1483	1·1505	1·1527	1·1549	1·1571
·30	1·1593	1·1615	1·1636	1·1658	1·1680	1·1702	1·1723	1·1745	1·1767	1·1788
·31	1·1810	1·1832	1·1853	1·1875	1·1896	1·1918	1·1939	1·1961	1·1982	1·2004
·32	1·2025	1·2047	1·2068	1·2090	1·2111	1·2132	1·2154	1·2175	1·2196	1·2217
·33	1·2239	1·2260	1·2281	1·2303	1·2324	1·2345	1·2366	1·2387	1·2408	1·2430
·34	1·2451	1·2472	1·2493	1·2514	1·2535	1·2556	1·2577	1·2598	1·2619	1·2640
·35	1·2661	1·2682	1·2703	1·2724	1·2745	1·2766	1·2787	1·2807	1·2828	1·2849
·36	1·2870	1·2891	1·2912	1·2932	1·2953	1·2974	1·2995	1·3016	1·3036	1·3057
·37	1·3078	1·3098	1·3119	1·3140	1·3161	1·3181	1·3202	1·3222	1·3243	1·3264
·38	1·3284	1·3305	1·3325	1·3346	1·3367	1·3387	1·3408	1·3428	1·3449	1·3469
·39	1·3490	1·3510	1·3531	1·3551	1·3572	1·3592	1·3613	1·3633	1·3654	1·3674
·40	1·3694	1·3715	1·3735	1·3756	1·3776	1·3796	1·3817	1·3837	1·3857	1·3878
·41	1·3898	1·3918	1·3939	1·3959	1·3979	1·4000	1·4020	1·4040	1·4061	1·4081
·42	1·4101	1·4121	1·4142	1·4162	1·4182	1·4202	1·4222	1·4243	1·4263	1·4283
·43	1·4303	1·4324	1·4344	1·4364	1·4384	1·4404	1·4424	1·4445	1·4465	1·4485
·44	1·4505	1·4525	1·4545	1·4565	1·4586	1·4606	1·4626	1·4646	1·4666	1·4686
·45	1·4706	1·4726	1·4746	1·4767	1·4787	1·4807	1·4827	1·4847	1·4867	1·4887
·46	1·4907	1·4927	1·4947	1·4967	1·4987	1·5007	1·5027	1·5048	1·5068	1·5088
·47	1·5108	1·5128	1·5148	1·5168	1·5188	1·5208	1·5228	1·5248	1·5268	1·5288
·48	1·5308	1·5328	1·5348	1·5368	1·5388	1·5408	1·5428	1·5448	1·5468	1·5488
·49	1·5508	1·5528	1·5548	1·5568	1·5588	1·5608	1·5628	1·5648	1·5668	1·5688

Example: $2 \arcsin \sqrt{0{\cdot}296} = 1{\cdot}1505$.

Table V. $y = 2 \arcsin \sqrt{x}$ (*continued*)

	·000	·001	·002	·003	·004	·005	·006	·007	·008	·009
·50	1·5708	1·5728	1·5748	1·5768	1·5788	1·5808	1·5828	1·5848	1·5868	1·5888
·51	1·5908	1·5928	1·5948	1·5968	1·5988	1·6008	1·6028	1·6048	1·6068	1·6088
·52	1·6108	1·6128	1·6148	1·6168	1·6188	1·6208	1·6228	1·6248	1·6268	1·6288
·53	1·6308	1·6328	1·6348	1·6368	1·6388	1·6409	1·6429	1·6449	1·6469	1·6489
·54	1·6509	1·6529	1·6549	1·6569	1·6589	1·6609	1·6629	1·6649	1·6669	1·6690
·55	1·6710	1·6730	1·6750	1·6770	1·6790	1·6810	1·6830	1·6850	1·6871	1·6891
·56	1·6911	1·6931	1·6951	1·6971	1·6992	1·7012	1·7032	1·7052	1·7072	1·7092
·57	1·7113	1·7133	1·7153	1·7173	1·7193	1·7214	1·7234	1·7254	1·7274	1·7295
·58	1·7315	1·7335	1·7355	1·7376	1·7396	1·7416	1·7437	1·7457	1·7477	1·7498
·59	1·7518	1·7538	1·7559	1·7579	1·7599	1·7620	1·7640	1·7660	1·7681	1·7701
·60	1·7722	1·7742	1·7762	1·7783	1·7803	1·7824	1·7844	1·7865	1·7885	1·7906
·61	1·7926	1·7947	1·7967	1·7988	1·8008	1·8029	1·8049	1·8070	1·8090	1·8111
·62	1·8132	1·8152	1·8173	1·8193	1·8214	1·8235	1·8255	1·8276	1·8297	1·8317
·63	1·8338	1·8359	1·8380	1·8400	1·8421	1·8442	1·8463	1·8483	1·8504	1·8525
·64	1·8546	1·8567	1·8588	1·8608	1·8629	1·8650	1·8671	1·8692	1·8713	1·8734
·65	1·8755	1·8776	1·8797	1·8818	1·8839	1·8860	1·8881	1·8902	1·8923	1·8944
·66	1·8965	1·8986	1·9008	1·9029	1·9050	1·9071	1·9092	1·9113	1·9135	1·9156
·67	1·9177	1·9198	1·9220	1·9241	1·9262	1·9284	1·9305	1·9326	1·9348	1·9369
·68	1·9391	1·9412	1·9434	1·9455	1·9477	1·9498	1·9520	1·9541	1·9563	1·9584
·69	1·9606	1·9628	1·9649	1·9671	1·9693	1·9714	1·9736	1·9758	1·9780	1·9801
·70	1·9823	1·9845	1·9867	1·9889	1·9911	1·9932	1·9954	1·9976	1·9998	2·0020
·71	2·0042	2·0064	2·0087	2·0109	2·0131	2·0153	2·0175	2·0197	2·0219	2·0242
·72	2·0264	2·0286	2·0309	2·0331	2·0353	2·0376	2·0398	2·0420	2·0443	2·0465
·73	2·0488	2·0510	2·0533	2·0556	2·0578	2·0601	2·0624	2·0646	2·0669	2·0692
·74	2·0714	2·0737	2·0760	2·0783	2·0806	2·0829	2·0852	2·0875	2·0898	2·0921
·75	2·0944	2·0967	2·0990	2·1013	2·1037	2·1060	2·1083	2·1106	2·1130	2·1153
·76	2·1176	2·1200	2·1223	2·1247	2·1270	2·1294	2·1318	2·1341	2·1365	2·1389
·77	2·1412	2·1436	2·1460	2·1484	2·1508	2·1532	2·1556	2·1580	2·1604	2·1628
·78	2·1652	2·1676	2·1700	2·1724	2·1749	2·1773	2·1797	2·1822	2·1846	2·1871
·79	2·1895	2·1920	2·1944	2·1969	2·1994	2·2019	2·2043	2·2068	2·2093	2·2118
·80	2·2143	2·2168	2·2193	2·2218	2·2243	2·2269	2·2294	2·2319	2·2345	2·2370
·81	2·2395	2·2421	2·2446	2·2472	2·2498	2·2523	2·2549	2·2575	2·2601	2·2627
·82	2·2653	2·2679	2·2705	2·2731	2·2758	2·2784	2·2810	2·2837	2·2863	2·2890
·83	2·2916	2·2943	2·2970	2·2996	2·3023	2·3050	2·3077	2·3104	2·3131	2·3158
·84	2·3186	2·3213	2·3240	2·3268	2·3295	2·3323	2·3351	2·3378	2·3406	2·3434
·85	2·3462	2·3490	2·3518	2·3546	2·3575	2·3603	2·3631	2·3660	2·3689	2·3717
·86	2·3746	2·3775	2·3804	2·3833	2·3862	2·3891	2·3921	2·3950	2·3979	2·4009
·87	2·4039	2·4068	2·4098	2·4128	2·4158	2·4189	2·4219	2·4249	2·4280	2·4310
·88	2·4341	2·4372	2·4403	2·4434	2·4465	2·4496	2·4528	2·4559	2·4591	2·4623
·89	2·4655	2·4687	2·4719	2·4751	2·4783	2·4816	2·4849	2·4882	2·4915	2·4948
·90	2·4981	2·5014	2·5048	2·5082	2·5115	2·5149	2·5184	2·5218	2·5253	2·5287
·91	2·5322	2·5357	2·5392	2·5428	2·5463	2·5499	2·5535	2·5571	2·5607	2·5644
·92	2·5681	2·5718	2·5755	2·5792	2·5830	2·5868	2·5906	2·5944	2·5983	2·6022
·93	2·6061	2·6100	2·6140	2·6179	2·6220	2·6260	2·6301	2·6342	2·6383	2·6425
·94	2·6467	2·6509	2·6551	2·6594	2·6638	2·6681	2·6725	2·6770	2·6815	2·6860
·95	2·6906	2·6952	2·6998	2·7045	2·7093	2·7141	2·7189	2·7238	2·7288	2·7338
·96	2·7389	2·7440	2·7492	2·7545	2·7598	2·7652	2·7707	2·7762	2·7819	2·7876
·97	2·7934	2·7993	2·8053	2·8115	2·8177	2·8240	2·8305	2·8371	2·8438	2·8507
·98	2·8578	2·8650	2·8725	2·8801	2·8879	2·8960	2·9044	2·9131	2·9221	2·9314
·99	2·9413	2·9516	2·9625	2·9741	2·9865	3·0001	3·0150	3·0320	3·0521	3·0783
1·00	3·1416									

Example: $2 \arcsin \sqrt{0{\cdot}724} = 2{\cdot}0353$.

*Reproduced from Table XII of *Statistical Tables and Formulas* by A. Hald, John Wiley & Sons, New York, 1952.

Table VI. Values of d_n and Percentage Points of the Distribution of the Range*

n	d_n	0.001	0.005	0.025	0.050	0.95	0.975	0.995	0.999
2	1.128	0.00	0.01	0.04	0.09	2.77	3.17	3.97	4.65
3	1.693	0.06	0.13	0.30	0.43	3.31	3.68	4.42	5.06
4	2.059	0.20	0.34	0.59	0.76	3.63	3.98	4.69	5.31
5	2.326	0.37	0.55	0.85	1.03	3.86	4.20	4.89	5.48
6	2.534	0.54	0.75	1.06	1.25	4.03	4.36	5.03	5.62
7	2.704	0.69	0.92	1.25	1.44	4.17	4.49	5.15	5.73
8	2.847	0.83	1.08	1.41	1.60	4.29	4.61	5.26	5.82
9	2.970	0.96	1.21	1.55	1.74	4.39	4.70	5.34	5.90
10	3.078	1.08	1.33	1.67	1.86	4.47	4.79	5.42	5.97
11	3.173	1.20	1.45	1.78	1.97	4.55	4.86	5.49	6.04
12	3.258	1.30	1.55	1.88	2.07	4.62	4.92	5.54	6.09

*Abridged from Tables 20 and 22 of *Biometrika Tables for Statisticians*, vol. I, edited by E. S. Pearson and H. O. Hartley. Cambridge University Press, Cambridge (1954).

Table VII. Logarithms of $n!$ *

n	log $n!$	n	log $n!$	n	log $n!$	n	log $n!$	n	log $n!$
1	0·0000	51	66·1906	101	159·9743	151	264·9359	201	377·2001
2	0·3010	52	67·9066	102	161·9829	152	267·1177	202	379·5054
3	0·7782	53	69·6309	103	163·9958	153	269·3024	203	381·8129
4	1·3802	54	71·3633	104	166·0128	154	271·4899	204	384·1226
5	2·0792	55	73·1037	105	168·0340	155	273·6803	205	386·4343
6	2·8573	56	74·8519	106	170·0593	156	275·8734	206	388·7482
7	3·7024	57	76·6077	107	172·0887	157	278·0693	207	391·0642
8	4·6055	58	78·3712	108	174·1221	158	280·2679	208	393·3822
9	5·5598	59	80·1420	109	176·1595	159	282·4693	209	395·7024
10	6·5598	60	81·9202	110	178·2009	160	284·6735	210	398·0246
11	7·6012	61	83·7055	111	180·2462	161	286·8803	211	400·3489
12	8·6803	62	85·4979	112	182·2955	162	289·0898	212	402·6752
13	9·7943	63	87·2972	113	184·3485	163	291·3020	213	405·0036
14	10·9404	64	89·1034	114	186·4054	164	293·5168	214	407·3340
15	12·1165	65	90·9163	115	188·4661	165	295·7343	215	409·6664
16	13·3206	66	92·7359	116	190·5306	166	297·9544	216	412·0009
17	14·5511	67	94·5619	117	192·5988	167	300·1771	217	414·3373
18	15·8063	68	96·3945	118	194·6707	168	302·4024	218	416·6758
19	17·0851	69	98·2333	119	196·7462	169	304·6303	219	419·0162
20	18·3861	70	100·0784	120	198·8254	170	306·8608	220	421·3587
21	19·7083	71	101·9297	121	200·9082	171	309·0938	221	423·7031
22	21·0508	72	103·7870	122	202·9945	172	311·3293	222	426·0494
23	22·4125	73	105·6503	123	205·0844	173	313·5674	223	428·3977
24	23·7927	74	107·5196	124	207·1779	174	315·8079	224	430·7480
25	25·1906	75	109·3946	125	209·2748	175	318·0509	225	433·1002
26	26·6056	76	111·2754	126	211·3751	176	320·2965	226	435·4543
27	28·0370	77	113·1619	127	213·4790	177	322·5444	227	437·8103
28	29·4841	78	115·0540	128	215·5862	178	324·7948	228	440·1682
29	30·9465	79	116·9516	129	217·6967	179	327·0477	229	442·5281
30	32·4237	80	118·8547	130	219·8107	180	329·3030	230	444·8898
31	33·9150	81	120·7632	131	221·9280	181	331·5606	231	447·2534
32	35·4202	82	122·6770	132	224·0485	182	333·8207	232	449·6189
33	36·9387	83	124·5961	133	226·1724	183	336·0832	233	451·9862
34	38·4702	84	126·5204	134	228·2995	184	338·3480	234	454·3555
35	40·0142	85	128·4498	135	230·4298	185	340·6152	235	456·7265
36	41·5705	86	130·3843	136	232·5634	186	342·8847	236	459·0994
37	43·1387	87	132·3238	137	234·7001	187	345·1565	237	461·4742
38	44·7185	88	134·2683	138	236·8400	188	347·4307	238	463·8508
39	46·3096	89	136·2177	139	238·9830	189	349·7071	239	466·2292
40	47·9116	90	138·1719	140	241·1291	190	351·9859	240	468·6094
41	49·5244	91	140·1310	141	243·2783	191	354·2669	241	470·9914
42	51·1477	92	142·0948	142	245·4306	192	356·5502	242	473·3752
43	52·7811	93	144·0632	143	247·5860	193	358·8358	243	475·7608
44	54·4246	94	146·0364	144	249·7443	194	361·1236	244	478·1482
45	56·0778	95	148·0141	145	251·9057	195	363·4136	245	480·5374
46	57·7406	96	149·9964	146	254·0700	196	365·7059	246	482·9283
47	59·4127	97	151·9831	147	256·2374	197	368·0003	247	485·3210
48	61·0939	98	153·9744	148	258·4076	198	370·2970	248	487·7154
49	62·7841	99	155·9700	149	260·5808	199	372·5959	249	490·1116
50	64·4831	100	157·9700	150	262·7569	200	374·8969	250	492·5096

*Abridged from Table XIII of *Statistical Tables and Formulas* by A. Hald, John Wiley & Sons, New York, 1952.

Table VIII. Percentage Points of the Studentized Range, $q = (x_{max} - x_{min})/s$ *

$P = 0.95$

f \ n	2	3	4	5	6	7	8	9	10	11	12	13	14	15
1	18.0	27.0	32.8	37.1	40.4	43.1	45.4	47.4	49.1	50.6	52.0	53.2	54.3	55.4
2	6.09	8.3	9.8	10.9	11.7	12.4	13.0	13.5	14.0	14.4	14.7	15.1	15.4	15.7
3	4.50	5.91	6.82	7.50	8.04	8.48	8.85	9.18	9.46	9.72	9.95	10.1	10.3	10.5
4	3.93	5.04	5.76	6.29	6.71	7.05	7.35	7.60	7.83	8.03	8.21	8.37	8.52	8.66
5	3.64	4.60	5.22	5.67	6.03	6.33	6.58	6.80	6.99	7.17	7.32	7.47	7.60	7.72
6	3.46	4.34	4.90	5.31	5.63	5.89	6.12	6.32	6.49	6.65	6.79	6.92	7.03	7.14
7	3.34	4.16	4.68	5.06	5.36	5.61	5.82	6.00	6.16	6.30	6.43	6.55	6.66	6.76
8	3.26	4.04	4.53	4.89	5.17	5.40	5.60	5.77	5.92	6.05	6.18	6.29	6.39	6.48
9	3.20	3.95	4.42	4.76	5.02	5.24	5.43	5.60	5.74	5.87	5.98	6.09	6.19	6.28
10	3.15	3.88	4.33	4.65	4.91	5.12	5.30	5.46	5.60	5.72	5.83	5.93	6.03	6.11
11	3.11	3.82	4.26	4.57	4.82	5.03	5.20	5.35	5.49	5.61	5.71	5.81	5.90	5.99
12	3.08	3.77	4.20	4.51	4.75	4.95	5.12	5.27	5.40	5.51	5.62	5.71	5.80	5.88
13	3.06	3.73	4.15	4.45	4.69	4.88	5.05	5.19	5.32	5.43	5.53	5.63	5.71	5.79
14	3.03	3.70	4.11	4.41	4.64	4.83	4.99	5.13	5.25	5.36	5.46	5.55	5.64	5.72
15	3.01	3.67	4.08	4.37	4.60	4.78	4.94	5.08	5.20	5.31	5.40	5.49	5.58	5.65
16	3.00	3.65	4.05	4.33	4.56	4.74	4.90	5.03	5.15	5.26	5.35	5.44	5.52	5.59
17	2.98	3.63	4.02	4.30	4.52	4.71	4.86	4.99	5.11	5.21	5.31	5.39	5.47	5.55
18	2.97	3.61	4.00	4.28	4.49	4.67	4.82	4.96	5.07	5.17	5.27	5.35	5.43	5.50
19	2.96	3.59	3.98	4.25	4.47	4.65	4.79	4.92	5.04	5.14	5.23	5.32	5.39	5.46
20	2.95	3.58	3.96	4.23	4.45	4.62	4.77	4.90	5.01	5.11	5.20	5.28	5.36	5.43
24	2.92	3.53	3.90	4.17	4.37	4.54	4.68	4.81	4.92	5.01	5.10	5.18	5.25	5.32
30	2.89	3.49	3.84	4.10	4.30	4.46	4.60	4.72	4.83	4.92	5.00	5.08	5.15	5.21
40	2.86	3.44	3.79	4.04	4.23	4.39	4.52	4.63	4.74	4.82	4.91	4.89	5.05	5.11
60	2.83	3.40	3.74	3.98	4.16	4.31	4.44	4.55	4.65	4.73	4.81	4.88	4.94	5.00
120	2.80	3.36	3.69	3.92	4.10	4.24	4.36	4.48	4.56	4.64	4.72	4.78	4.84	4.90
∞	2.77	3.31	3.63	3.86	4.03	4.17	4.29	4.39	4.47	4.55	4.62	4.68	4.74	4.80

$P = 0.99$

1	90	135	164	186	202	216	227	237	246	253	260	266	272	277
2	14.0	19.0	22.3	24.7	26.6	28.2	29.5	30.7	31.7	32.6	33.4	34.1	34.8	35.4
3	8.26	10.6	12.2	13.3	14.2	15.0	15.6	16.2	16.7	17.1	17.5	17.9	18.2	18.5
4	6.51	8.12	9.17	9.96	10.6	11.1	11.5	11.9	12.3	12.6	12.8	13.1	13.3	13.5
5	5.70	6.97	7.80	8.42	8.91	9.32	9.67	9.97	10.2	10.5	10.7	10.9	11.1	11.2
6	5.24	6.33	7.03	7.56	7.97	8.32	8.61	8.87	9.10	9.30	9.49	9.65	9.81	9.95
7	4.95	5.92	6.54	7.01	7.37	7.68	7.94	8.17	8.37	8.55	8.71	8.86	9.00	9.12
8	4.74	5.63	6.20	6.63	6.96	7.24	7.47	7.68	7.87	8.03	8.18	8.31	8.44	8.55
9	4.60	5.43	5.96	6.35	6.66	6.91	7.13	7.32	7.49	7.65	7.78	7.91	8.03	8.13
10	4.48	5.27	5.77	6.14	6.43	6.67	6.87	7.05	7.21	7.36	7.48	7.60	7.71	7.81
11	4.39	5.14	5.62	5.97	6.25	6.48	6.67	6.84	6.99	7.13	7.25	7.36	7.46	7.56
12	4.32	5.04	5.50	5.84	6.10	6.32	6.51	6.67	6.81	6.94	7.06	7.17	7.26	7.36
13	4.26	4.96	5.40	5.73	5.98	6.19	6.37	6.53	6.67	6.79	6.90	7.01	7.10	7.19
14	4.21	4.89	5.32	5.63	5.88	6.08	6.26	6.41	6.54	6.66	6.77	6.87	6.96	7.05
15	4.17	4.83	5.25	5.56	5.80	5.99	6.16	6.31	6.44	6.55	6.66	6.76	6.84	6.93
16	4.13	4.78	5.19	5.49	5.72	5.92	6.08	6.22	6.35	6.46	6.56	6.66	6.74	6.82
17	4.10	4.74	5.14	5.43	5.66	5.85	6.01	6.15	6.27	6.38	6.48	6.57	6.66	6.73
18	4.07	4.70	5.09	5.38	5.60	5.79	5.94	6.08	6.20	6.31	6.41	6.50	6.58	6.65
19	4.05	4.67	5.05	5.33	5.55	5.73	5.89	6.02	6.14	6.25	6.34	6.43	6.51	6.58
20	4.02	4.64	5.02	5.29	5.51	5.69	5.84	5.97	6.09	6.19	6.29	6.37	6.45	6.52
24	3.96	4.54	4.91	5.17	5.37	5.54	5.69	5.81	5.92	6.02	6.11	6.19	6.26	6.33
30	3.89	4.45	4.80	5.05	5.24	5.40	5.54	5.65	5.76	5.85	5.93	6.01	6.08	6.14
40	3.82	4.37	4.70	4.93	5.11	5.27	5.39	5.50	5.60	5.69	5.77	5.84	5.90	5.96
60	3.76	4.28	4.60	4.82	4.99	5.13	5.25	5.36	5.45	5.53	5.60	5.67	5.73	5.79
120	3.70	4.20	4.50	4.71	4.87	5.01	5.12	5.21	5.30	5.38	5.44	5.51	5.56	5.61
∞	3.64	4.12	4.40	4.60	4.76	4.88	4.99	5.08	5.16	5.23	5.29	5.35	5.40	5.45

*Abridged from Table 29 of *Biometrika Tables for Statisticians*, vol. I, edited by E. S. Pearson and H. O. Hartley, Cambridge University Press, Cambridge, 1954.

Table IX. Percentage Points of the Largest of k Variance Ratios*

$P = 0.95$

f \ k	1	2	3	4	5	6	7	8	9	10
10	4.96	6.79	8.00	8.96	9.78	10.52	11.18	11.79	12.36	12.87
12	4.75	6.44	7.53	8.37	9.06	9.68	10.20	10.68	11.12	11.53
15	4.54	6.12	7.11	7.86	8.47	8.98	9.43	9.82	10.19	10.52
20	4.35	5.81	6.72	7.40	7.94	8.39	8.79	9.13	9.44	9.71
30	4.17	5.52	6.36	6.97	7.46	7.87	8.21	8.51	8.79	9.03
60	4.00	5.25	6.02	6.58	7.02	7.38	7.68	7.96	8.20	8.41
∞	3.84	5.00	5.70	6.21	6.60	6.92	7.20	7.44	7.65	7.84

$P = 0.99$

f \ k	1	2	3	4	5	6	7	8	9	10
10	10.04	13.17	15.08	16.43	17.43	18.25	18.91	19.48	19.97	20.41
12	9.33	11.88	13.52	14.73	15.69	16.47	17.12	17.68	18.16	18.60
15	8.68	10.82	12.18	13.21	14.03	14.72	15.30	15.81	16.26	16.66
20	8.10	9.93	11.08	11.93	12.61	13.19	13.67	14.09	14.49	14.83
30	7.56	9.16	10.14	10.86	11.43	11.90	12.31	12.66	12.97	13.26
60	7.08	8.49	9.34	9.95	10.43	10.82	11.15	11.45	11.72	11.95
∞	6.63	7.88	8.61	9.15	9.54	9.87	10.16	10.41	10.62	10.82

*Reproduced from Table 19 of *Biometrika Tables for Statisticians*, vol. I, edited by E. S. Pearson and H. O. Hartley. Cambridge University Press, Cambridge (1954).

Table X. Random Sampling Numbers*

15	77	01	64	69	69	58	40	81	16	60	20	00	84	22	28	26	46	66	36	86	66	17	34	49
85	40	51	40	10	15	33	94	11	65	57	62	94	04	99	05	57	22	71	77	99	68	12	11	14
47	69	35	90	95	16	17	45	86	29	16	70	48	02	00	59	33	93	28	58	34	32	24	34	07
13	26	87	40	20	40	81	46	08	09	74	99	16	92	99	85	19	01	23	11	74	00	79	41	69
10	55	33	20	47	54	16	86	11	16	59	34	71	55	84	03	48	17	60	13	38	71	23	91	83
05	06	67	26	77	14	85	40	52	68	60	41	94	98	18	62	20	94	03	71	60	26	45	17	92
65	50	89	18	74	42	07	50	15	69	86	97	40	25	88	14	17	73	92	07	93	11	93	45	15
59	68	53	31	55	73	47	16	49	79	69	80	76	16	60	58	53	07	04	53	66	94	94	18	13
31	31	05	36	48	75	16	00	21	11	42	44	84	46	84	83	20	49	17	12	21	93	34	61	16
91	59	46	44	45	49	25	36	12	07	25	90	89	55	25	83	47	17	23	93	99	56	14	39	16
63	59	73	21	67	80	00	25	58	25	72	06	12	86	74	54	79	70	85	88	71	58	21	98	48
89	72	47	46	94	78	56	10	65	97	84	79	42	31	49	94	15	31	13	09	45	43	03	82	81
70	51	21	03	18	50	21	99	49	73	06	99	19	24	96	39	43	10	14	12	94	08	55	54	70
14	15	99	60	44	62	72	38	18	36	63	92	61	55	93	77	66	82	10	91	81	51	67	01	47
92	46	90	39	99	64	08	00	97	27	54	96	63	40	54	34	70	27	48	18	68	59	91	83	32
81	23	17	13	01	37	57	92	16	34	15	80	90	25	64	67	77	29	95	84	80	84	84	87	22
87	54	42	46	56	28	89	02	06	98	59	90	74	13	38	98	66	23	20	23	90	55	31	83	48
74	73	84	98	13	11	48	25	33	39	27	36	08	99	57	60	42	88	68	25	22	89	67	83	16
94	55	14	00	97	32	51	92	47	03	92	33	73	20	21	29	77	37	06	98	64	63	34	31	43
69	21	94	26	20	73	90	70	92	76	49	14	60	34	43	90	51	72	11	07	75	94	19	49	40
82	36	36	89	29	87	70	08	71	98	49	00	89	89	99	29	08	02	72	32	68	16	29	82	19
25	06	22	30	87	87	44	48	90	91	38	53	10	60	29	40	07	58	97	84	09	04	33	56	72
82	37	97	60	92	76	39	17	84	34	67	65	52	89	90	62	97	04	33	81	91	27	56	46	35
83	71	07	22	15	17	55	56	82	62	88	83	86	38	14	63	89	39	81	90	25	62	58	68	87
73	13	79	15	12	18	34	22	24	75	56	47	45	22	81	30	82	38	34	52	57	48	30	34	17
91	28	00	57	30	92	12	38	95	21	15	70	78	50	88	01	07	90	72	77	99	53	04	34	73
33	47	55	62	57	08	21	77	31	05	64	74	04	93	42	20	19	09	71	46	37	32	69	69	89
56	66	25	32	38	64	70	26	27	67	77	40	04	34	63	98	99	89	31	16	12	90	50	28	96
88	40	52	02	29	82	69	34	50	21	74	00	91	27	52	98	72	03	45	65	30	89	71	45	91
87	63	88	23	62	51	07	69	59	02	89	49	14	98	53	41	92	36	07	76	85	37	84	37	47
32	25	21	15	08	82	34	57	57	35	22	03	33	48	84	37	37	29	38	37	89	76	25	09	69
44	61	88	23	13	01	59	47	64	04	99	59	96	20	30	87	31	33	69	45	58	48	00	83	48
94	44	08	67	79	41	61	41	15	60	11	88	83	24	82	24	07	78	61	89	42	58	88	22	16
13	24	40	09	00	65	46	38	61	12	90	62	41	11	59	85	18	42	61	29	88	76	04	21	80
78	27	84	05	99	85	75	67	80	05	57	05	71	70	21	31	99	99	06	96	53	99	25	13	63
42	39	30	02	34	99	46	68	45	15	19	74	15	50	17	44	80	13	86	38	40	45	82	13	44
04	52	43	96	38	13	83	80	72	34	20	84	56	19	49	59	14	85	42	99	71	16	34	33	79
82	85	77	30	16	69	32	46	46	30	84	20	68	72	98	94	62	63	59	44	00	89	06	15	87
38	48	84	88	24	55	46	48	60	06	90	08	83	83	98	40	90	88	25	26	85	74	55	80	85
91	19	05	68	22	58	04	63	21	16	23	38	25	43	32	98	94	65	35	35	16	91	07	12	43
54	81	87	21	31	40	46	17	62	63	99	71	14	12	64	51	68	50	60	78	22	69	51	98	37
65	43	75	12	91	20	36	25	57	92	33	65	95	48	75	00	06	65	25	90	16	29	34	14	43
49	98	71	31	80	59	57	32	43	07	85	06	64	75	27	29	17	06	11	30	68	70	97	87	21
03	98	68	89	39	71	87	32	14	99	42	10	25	37	30	08	27	75	43	97	54	20	69	93	50
56	04	21	34	92	89	81	52	15	12	84	11	12	66	87	47	21	06	86	08	35	39	52	28	09
48	09	36	95	36	20	82	53	32	89	92	68	50	88	17	37	92	02	23	43	63	24	69	80	91
23	97	10	96	57	74	07	95	26	44	93	08	43	30	41	86	45	74	33	78	84	33	38	76	73
43	97	55	45	98	35	69	45	96	80	46	26	39	96	33	60	20	73	30	79	17	19	03	47	28
40	05	08	50	79	89	58	19	86	48	27	98	99	24	08	94	19	15	81	29	82	14	35	88	03
66	97	10	69	02	25	36	43	71	76	00	67	56	12	69	07	89	55	63	31	50	72	20	33	36

Table X. Random Sampling Numbers (*continued*)

15	62	38	72	92	03	76	09	30	75	77	80	04	24	54	67	60	10	79	26	21	60	03	48	14
77	81	15	14	67	55	24	22	20	55	36	93	67	69	37	72	22	43	46	32	56	15	75	25	12
18	87	05	09	96	45	14	72	41	46	12	67	46	72	02	59	06	17	49	12	73	28	23	52	48
08	58	53	63	66	13	07	04	48	71	39	07	46	96	40	20	86	79	11	81	74	11	15	23	17
16	07	79	57	61	42	19	68	15	12	60	21	59	12	07	04	99	88	22	39	75	16	69	13	84
54	13	05	46	17	05	51	24	53	57	46	51	14	39	17	21	39	89	07	35	47	87	44	36	62
95	27	23	17	39	80	24	44	48	93	75	94	77	09	23	48	75	91	69	03	55	51	09	74	47
22	39	44	74	80	25	95	28	63	90	41	19	48	46	72	51	12	97	39	83	35	83	23	17	29
69	95	21	30	11	98	81	38	00	53	41	40	04	16	78	67	29	83	41	18	30	90	44	37	64
75	75	63	97	12	11	57	05	86	52	82	72	47	72	14	37	72	69	75	48	72	21	52	51	81
08	74	79	30	80	70	11	66	79	25	88	01	94	52	31	38	57	98	71	62	12	56	61	01	54
04	88	45	98	60	90	92	74	77	87	40	18	65	87	37	08	68	62	39	52	84	74	90	68	18
97	35	74	05	75	42	13	49	48	38	74	19	06	42	60	20	79	90	81	77	18	51	71	27	27
53	09	93	28	29	80	19	68	30	45	94	49	49	71	21	93	93	71	30	34	52	65	83	40	13
26	36	68	48	09	37	69	26	22	80	23	34	10	45	70	83	51	07	37	44	62	96	74	42	64
49	16	57	15	79	56	63	22	94	28	11	39	69	55	38	53	06	97	20	42	09	14	90	43	48
03	51	79	78	74	75	23	73	75	98	47	85	07	26	02	61	28	01	22	16	14	12	15	67	22
21	88	87	28	48	23	44	03	03	80	53	89	07	87	93	30	17	84	17	74	16	53	31	39	01
56	41	73	33	41	59	16	59	50	98	24	24	87	06	75	99	52	09	88	05	86	25	43	50	94
72	39	19	70	17	01	04	01	22	33	04	84	63	27	65	84	39	45	55	31	95	88	93	90	37
97	28	25	81	49	71	69	22	04	51	56	46	56	15	10	69	59	99	50	29	33	50	16	93	09
18	87	02	72	08	74	52	16	03	82	20	19	66	23	62	37	51	04	89	31	32	19	59	85	57
53	40	11	75	45	13	56	85	31	37	09	17	71	96	79	39	50	79	27	62	71	14	95	53	03
60	49	03	41	56	78	33	77	28	92	21	90	10	62	01	97	06	45	01	19	95	12	24	18	52
09	16	12	75	04	39	69	95	00	48	26	85	28	73	08	66	92	10	66	75	62	61	27	82	57
64	20	19	87	54	88	15	12	54	24	06	99	57	07	28	51	34	54	98	50	70	88	02	86	48
31	28	07	58	77	03	98	26	76	09	10	44	57	61	28	60	29	85	70	79	80	29	19	98	92
80	04	28	47	76	35	73	67	78	28	09	39	88	63	74	41	26	92	42	33	06	80	06	33	84
24	60	22	51	19	34	54	08	24	73	86	72	11	44	69	76	90	81	17	85	57	47	35	16	84
59	16	11	26	29	18	97	78	44	43	58	92	78	70	80	09	65	32	68	26	65	73	90	50	46
58	54	29	98	27	40	51	92	07	13	58	41	59	56	94	16	32	51	42	54	77	37	13	85	19
20	18	34	22	73	57	40	67	17	28	63	57	74	36	18	65	55	25	50	68	35	90	00	03	38
53	90	46	56	19	50	58	33	84	53	14	74	17	40	73	86	11	04	02	04	02	28	49	62	36
97	16	93	94	65	70	95	95	83	20	91	42	57	95	63	00	86	29	02	53	02	27	86	70	95
72	55	71	70	92	04	22	53	19	29	67	29	13	56	70	45	73	45	05	04	32	43	30	93	41
99	19	72	58	35	49	09	26	00	74	26	42	94	52	02	83	31	85	65	66	31	97	67	52	15
48	21	49	72	97	79	19	64	81	82	78	92	51	96	51	28	79	13	20	82	34	81	39	46	86
52	37	68	15	53	22	98	30	16	31	83	24	87	69	29	24	85	44	25	50	75	62	83	95	41
97	50	52	53	52	26	78	21	68	69	57	79	42	40	89	55	81	75	24	52	51	32	79	97	05
36	05	09	18	11	71	01	63	17	60	11	65	19	43	07	44	86	19	58	92	23	71	32	96	19
20	79	70	09	30	81	14	53	80	93	71	94	10	18	14	83	69	76	53	25	27	36	65	65	05
13	07	89	72	08	00	37	75	14	94	83	85	06	72	66	07	47	30	17	11	16	02	63	97	30
94	26	82	37	43	34	23	00	14	50	96	85	41	17	71	69	20	15	98	82	79	69	68	50	31
13	55	88	38	43	75	37	43	83	85	53	74	54	62	99	68	93	74	43	95	06	26	79	78	87
02	44	24	97	71	97	93	12	70	89	42	52	33	24	91	05	87	53	15	77	49	92	83	97	80
34	90	96	63	54	22	84	36	38	99	85	36	25	03	27	49	24	72	10	50	95	14	18	26	64
13	67	06	34	98	04	20	80	12	54	01	18	54	20	76	92	10	47	04	65	54	45	82	42	90
18	75	55	82	66	34	77	27	71	79	67	65	85	92	68	16	43	83	18	74	12	48	68	87	22
91	25	52	57	15	21	54	40	05	50	67	51	66	45	69	84	72	74	32	30	17	70	40	90	24
76	24	00	14	92	14	29	12	17	73	77	46	44	24	30	48	50	36	30	24	93	08	01	39	37

*Abridged from Table XIX of *Statistical Tables and Formulas* by A. Hald, John Wiley & Sons, New York, 1952.

Partial Answers to Selected Exercises

1.1. (*a*) $P_3^{10} = 720$, (*b*) $\binom{10}{3} = 120$.
1.3. (*a*) $\binom{12}{5} = 792$, (*b*) $\binom{4}{2}\,(_2)\,\binom{3}{1} = 180$.
1.6. 0.8076 for first strategy.
1.9. 1/20.
1.13. (*a*) $1 - (5/6)^4 = 0.517747$.
1.16. $E[x] =$ \$0.01.
1.19. (*a*) 0.15, (*b*) 0.5.
1.20. 0.0304.
1.22. 0.817.

2.1. $P = 0.0052$, confidence limits (0.006, 0.034).
2.2 (*a*) $x > 522.34$, (*b*) 0.825, (*c*) $\sqrt{n} = 8.027$, $n = 65$.
2.4. Power = 0.1251.

3.1. $P = 0.033$ with normal approx., 0.035 with angular transformation.
3.3. (*a*) 0.0218, (*b*) 0.024, (*c*) 0.019.
3.6. (*a*) (0.0011, 0.0800), (*b*) (0.00081, 0.0730).

4.1. (*a*) 0.223, (*b*) 0.192.
4.3. (0.62, 8.75).
4.5. (*a*) $\binom{4}{0}\binom{48}{13}\binom{52}{13} = 0.3038$.

5.1. $\chi^2(11) = 12.497$.

6.1. (*a*) 0.00535, (*b*) 0.0023, (*c*) 0.0028.

7.1. $P = 0.0044$ (one-sided).
7.2. (*a*) 0.211 normal approx., 0.212 exact, (*b*) 0.150.
7.5. $\chi^2(2) = 6.452$, $P < 0.05$.

9.2. (*a*) $(2.71 \times 10^{-4}, 10.6 \times 10^{-4})$, (*b*) $F(10, 8) = 5.0$, $P < 0.10$ (two-sided), (*c*) (0.75, 21.2) for ratio $s_1^2 = 94.0 \times 10^{-8}$, $s_2^2 = 18.8 \times 10^{-8}$.
9.3. 118.
9.5. (i) $t(1) = 1.283$, $(-4.95, 19.68)$, (ii) $t'(10.03) = 1.258$, $(-5.68, 20.41)$.
9.11. $\chi^2(4) = 6.08$, $P > 0.10$.

10.1. (*a*) $F(3, 65) = 2.53$, $P > 0.05$, (*b* i) (0.19, 1.87), (*b* ii) $(-0.18, 2.24)$, (*c*) $(-0.08, 1.78)$.

11.1. (*a*) $y = -9.402 + 2.8845x$, (*b*) $F(3, 7) = 0.86$, (*c*) $s^2 = 0.005235$, (*d*) 1.350, (*e*) (1.28, 1.42), (*f*) (2.39, 3.30), (*g* i) (3.703, 3.827), (3.701, 3.823).

14.1.

Source of variance	D.F.	S.S.	M.S.
Concentration: linear	1	15,051.125	15,051.125
quadratic	1	104.167	104.167
Batches	3	1,712.500	570.833
Strains	3	8,701.667	2,900.556
Batch × concentration (linear)	3	186.625	56.208
(quadratic)	3	56.250	18.750
Strain × concentration (linear)	3	140.125	46.708
(quadratic)	3	369.583	123.194
Batch × strain	9	1,001.833	111.315
Remainder	18	882.792	49.044
Total	47	28,188.667	

Confidence limits for $C - D$, using batch × strain interaction as error term, are $(-4.41, 15.08)$. A "pooler" who pooled all interactions to form an error term would obtain $(-1.43, 12.10)$.

15.2. Model might be

$$x_{ijkm} = \xi + b_i + \{p(b)\}_{j(i)} + \rho_k + (b\rho)_{ik} + \{\rho p(b)\}_{j(i)k}$$
$$\gamma_m + (b\gamma)_{im} + \{\gamma p(b)\}_{j(i)m} + (\rho\gamma)_{km} + (b\rho\gamma)_{ikm} + e_{ijkm}.$$

S.V.	S.S.	D.F.	E[M.S.]
Batches	1,030.433	2	$\sigma^2 + uv\sigma^2_{p(b)} + tuv\sigma^2_b$
Pressings within batches	1,135.833	9	$\sigma^2 + uv\sigma^2_{p(b)}$
Rows	1,335.755	4	$\sigma^2 + v\sigma^2_{\rho p(b)} + tv\sigma^2_{\rho b} + rtv\sigma^2_\rho$
Rows × batches	353.178	8	$\sigma^2 + v\sigma^2_{\rho p(b)} + tv\sigma^2_{\rho b}$
Rows × pressings within batches	2,188.000	36	$\sigma^2 + v\sigma^2_{\rho p(b)}$
Columns	697.900	2	$\sigma^2 + u\sigma^2_{\gamma p(b)} + tu\sigma^2_{\gamma b} + rtu\sigma^2_\gamma$
Columns × batches	1,514.367	4	$\sigma^2 + u\sigma^2_{\gamma p(b)} + tu\sigma^2_{\gamma b}$
Columns × pressings within batches	737.067	18	$\sigma^2 + u\sigma^2_{\gamma p(b)}$
Rows × columns	603.878	8	$\sigma^2 + t\sigma^2_{\rho\gamma b} + rt\sigma^2_{\rho\gamma}$
Rows × columns × batches	369.109	16	$\sigma^2 + t\sigma^2_{\rho\gamma b}$
Remainder	2,603.600	72	σ^2
Total	12,569.200	179	

Confidence limits for the difference in means between row 1 and row 3 are $-9.81, -2.58$).

16.2. Model might be

$$x_{ijk} = \xi + p_i + \{b(p)\}_{j(i)} + \tau_k + (p\tau)_{ik} + e_{ijk}.$$

16.3. Model might be

$$x_{ijkl} = \xi + y_l + p_i + (py)_{il} + \{b(py)\}_{j(il)} + \tau_k + (\tau y)_{kl}$$
$$(\tau p)_{ik} + (p\tau y)_{ikl} + e_{ijkl}.$$

Index